## VELOPMENT AND PRODUCTION

### gine Development in the United States
*f Excellence*



s (1900's)
68
70
72
74
76
78
80
82
84
VIETNAM WAR
GULF WAR
UNITED STATES AIR FORCE
LEGEND
Air - AiResearch
All. - Allison
GE - General Electric
He - Heinkel
IHPTET - Integrated High Performance Turbine Engine Technology
Lyc. - Lycoming
P&W - Pratt & Whitney
RR - Rolls-Royce
Tel. - Teledyne
WE - Westinghouse
WI - Williams International
Tel. J402
V F100
GE F404
GE F110
IHPTET

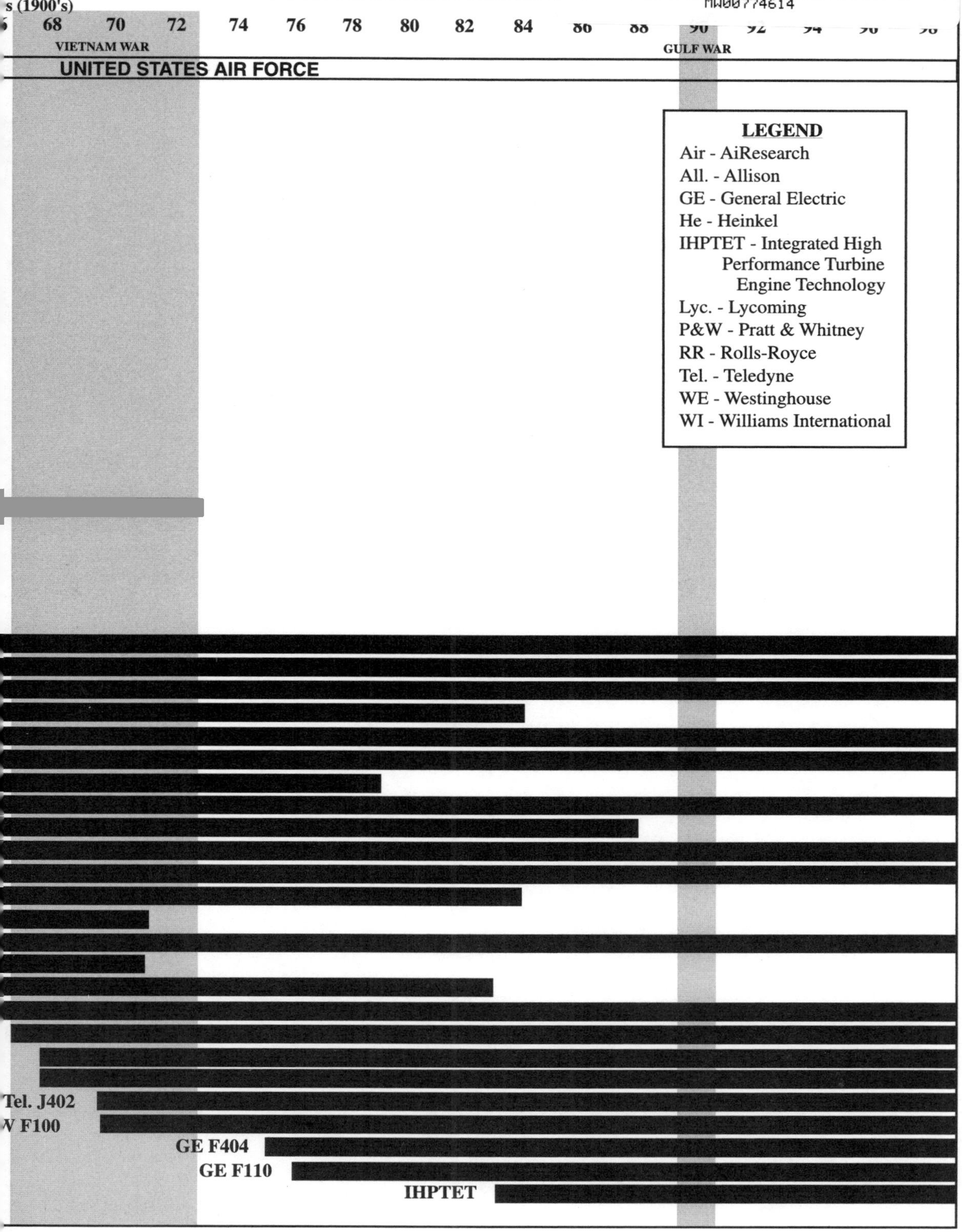

# The History of Aircraft
# Gas Turbine Engine Development
# in the United States ...
## *A Tradition of Excellence*

# The History of Aircraft
# Gas Turbine Engine Development
# in the United States ...
## *A Tradition of Excellence*

## James St. Peter

## Sponsored by ...

**U.S. Air Force**

**U.S. Army**

**U.S. Navy**

**National Aeronautics and
Space Administration**

**ASME International
Gas Turbine Institute**

**Published by the International Gas Turbine Institute of
The American Society of Mechanical Engineers
Atlanta, Georgia**

Development of this book was under contract,
funded by the sponsoring organizations and
administered by the Turbine Engine Division
of the U.S. Air Force Research Laboratory,
Propulsion Directorate.

Library of Congress Cataloging-in-Publication Data:

St. Peter, James, 1956-
    The history of aircraft gas turbine engine development in the United States : a tradition
of excellence / James St. Peter ; sponsored by U.S. Air Force ... [et al.].— 1st ed.
        p. cm.
    Includes bibliographical references and index.
    ISBN 0-7918-0097-0 (hard cover)
    1. Airplanes--United States--Turbojet engines--History. 2. Aircraft
gas-turbines--History. I. United States. Air Force. II. Title.

TL709.3.T83 S77 1999
629.134'353'0973--dc21

                                                                99-048358

This book is dedicated to the
memory of Sir Frank Whittle,
Dr. Hans von Ohain and all the
great pioneers of this technology.
To them we are indebted.

# CONTENTS

Time Line of Major Engine Development and Production . . . . . . . . . . . Inside Covers

Engine Nomenclature . . . . . . . ix

Preface . . . . . . . . . . . . . . xi

Introduction. . . . . . . . . . . xiii

Chapter 1.   Sir Frank Whittle and the First British Aircraft Gas Turbine . . . . . . . . . 3

Chapter 2.   Dr. Hans von Ohain and the First German Aircraft Gas Turbine . . . . . . . 41

Chapter 3.   Early American Gas Turbine
Engine Development . . . . . . . . . . 59

Chapter 4.   Nathan Price and the Lockheed L-1000  . 89

Supplement . . . . . . . . . . . . . 103

Chapter 5.   General Electric and the British . . . . . . . . . . . . . . . . 111

Chapter 6.   Westinghouse Innovations and Developments . . . . . . . . . . . 131

Chapter 7.   GE Applies New Ideas and
American Technology. . . . . . . . . 143

Chapter 8.   Postwar Development
Begins at Pratt &Whitney . . . . . . . 161

Chapter 9.   The Multiple-Spool Concept at Pratt &Whitney . . . . . . . . . . . . . 173

Chapter 10.  Turboshaft Development . . . . . . . . . . . . . . . . . . 197

Chapter 11.  Turboprop Development . . . . . . . . . . . . . . . . . 229

Chapter 12.  High-Mach Aircraft Gas Turbines. . . . . . . . . . . . . . . 257

Chapter 13. Variable Compressor Technology . . . . . . . 277

Chapter 14. The High Thrust-To-Weight Turbojet . . . . . 295

Chapter 15. Ducted Augmented Turbofan Engines . . . . . . . . . . . . . . . . . 309

Chapter 16. High-Bypass and Very-High-Bypass Turbofan Engines . . . . . . . . . . . 327

Chapter 17. Vertical/Short Takeoff and Landing
          Aircraft Gas Turbine Engines . . . . . . 343

Chapter 18. The Development of Cruise Missile
          Propulsion . . . . . . . . . . . . . . . 367

Chapter 19. Research and Technology Focus . . . . . . . . . . . . . . . . . . . 383

Addendum: Engine Features and Specifications for Selected Models

| Engine: | Page: | Engine: | Page: | Engine: | Page: |
|---|---|---|---|---|---|
| ATF3 | 430 | J35 | 476 | T53 | 522 |
| F100 | 432 | J40 | 478 | T55 | 524 |
| F101 | 434 | J42 | 480 | T56 | 526 |
| F102 | 436 | J47 | 482 | T58 | 528 |
| F103 | 438 | J48 | 484 | T60 | 530 |
| F106 | 440 | J52 | 486 | T63 | 532 |
| F107 | 442 | J54 | 488 | T64 | 534 |
| F108 (CFM56). | 444 | J57 | 490 | T65 | 536 |
| F109 | 446 | J58 | 492 | T67 | 538 |
| F110 | 448 | J60 | 494 | T72 | 540 |
| F117 | 450 | J65-W-20, -420 | 496 | T76 | 542 |
| F118 | 452 | J69 | 498 | T400 | 544 |
| F119 | 454 | J71 | 500 | T406 | 546 |
| F401 | 456 | J73 | 502 | T700 | 548 |
| F402 | 458 | J75 | 504 | T800 | 550 |
| F404 | 460 | J79 | 506 | TF30 | 552 |
| F405 | 462 | J85 | 508 | TF33 | 554 |
| GE4 | 464 | J93 | 510 | TF34 | 556 |
| I-A | 466 | J97 | 512 | TF35 | 558 |
| J30 | 468 | J400 | 514 | TF37 | 560 |
| J31 | 470 | J402 | 516 | TF39 | 562 |
| J33 | 472 | T31 | 518 | TF41 | 564 |
| J34 | 474 | T34 | 520 | TFE731 | 566 |

Acronyms and Abbreviations not in the Index . . . . . . . . . . . . . . . . . 568

Index . . . . . . . . . . . . . . . . . . . . . . . . . . . . . . . . . . . 571

# Engine Nomenclature

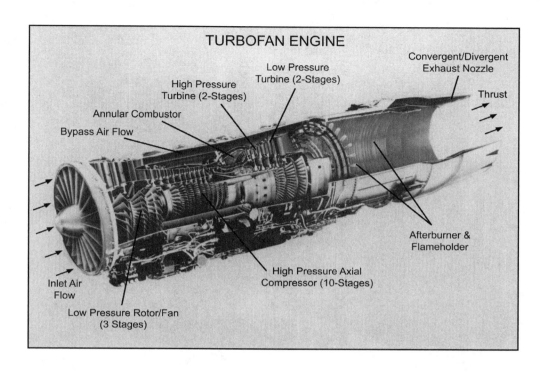

TURBOFAN ENGINE

Convergent/Divergent Exhaust Nozzle

Thrust

Low Pressure Turbine (2-Stages)

High Pressure Turbine (2-Stages)

Annular Combustor

Bypass Air Flow

Afterburner & Flameholder

Inlet Air Flow

High Pressure Axial Compressor (10-Stages)

Low Pressure Rotor/Fan (3 Stages)

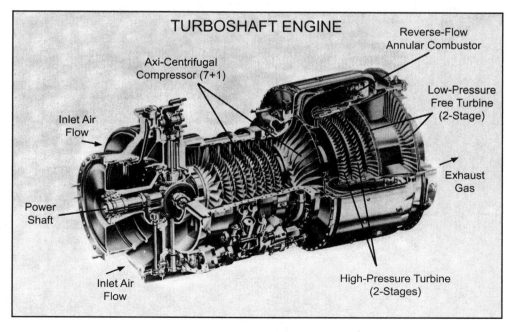

TURBOSHAFT ENGINE

Reverse-Flow Annular Combustor

Axi-Centrifugal Compressor (7+1)

Low-Pressure Free Turbine (2-Stage)

Inlet Air Flow

Exhaust Gas

Power Shaft

High-Pressure Turbine (2-Stages)

Inlet Air Flow

# Preface

In this history of aircraft gas turbine engine development in the United States, technological advancements will be traced through the evolution of specific engines. Each engine examined represents an important advance in this critical technology. Although every model of aircraft gas turbine ever developed represents some technological change, in the opinion of the author, the engines presented here demonstrate clear and significant advances over previous technologies. These American-made turbojets have had a greater impact on U.S. aircraft gas turbine usage than any other models we could examine. The four British engines described are exceptions to this all-American discussion. The Whittle engine, introduced into this country during World War II, became the model for the General Electric I-A. The other three engines are the British Derwent and Tay, which introduced Pratt & Whitney into the jet engine business, and the Pegasus. The Pegasus is the only non-U.S. engine to be "featured" as the topic of an entire chapter because it not only is representative of the finest in vectored-thrust technology, but also is the standard powerplant for U.S. Marine Corps Harrier aircraft.

Propulsion technology has always been a key to the successful advancement of aeronautics. Advancements in propulsion have been, in turn, dependent upon advancements in aerodynamics, thermodynamics, and materials technologies. All of these will be discussed as part of the technology of aircraft gas turbine engines. Note that although *aircraft gas turbine engine* is a specific term for describing the overall technology, the terms *turbojet, turboprop, turboshaft, turbofan and jet engine* have also evolved into common usage. To facilitate understanding of the subject matter, we will use all of these terms and differentiate among them where appropriate.

To reduce the potentially unwieldy scope of a technology involving a multitude of companies and a plethora of products, our field of inquiry will be limited to an examination of turbojet, turboprop, turboshaft, and turbofan engines. Furthermore, in order to capture as much of this history as possible, the description of a large number of additional turbine engines, not specifically covered in the main body of this book, are included at the end in a relatively comprehensive addendum. Although progress in ramjet technology has not been as dramatic as that in gas turbine engines, there have nevertheless been real advances in this field of propulsion. A history of ramjet technology, however, is outside the scope of this discussion.

You may be asking yourself, why publish a history now and why entitle it *A Tradition of Excellence*? The most significant systematic approach to the history of aircraft engines, the work of Robert Schlaifer, focused on prop plants and ended at 1949 when gas turbine technology was still in its infancy. The aircraft gas turbine, however, needed a base on which to build further histories. With the recent passing of Sir Frank Whittle (1907-1996) and Dr. Hans von Ohain (1911-1998), the aging of the other early innovators, the consolidation of engine development and manufacturing, and the elimination of many archives, access to vital persons and material used here may never again be possible. The host of primary and secondary research sources blended together in this manuscript include a number of personal interviews and corporate oral histories. Remembrances were verified whenever possible, but the recollections of others may vary. Hopefully, this work will serve as a touchstone upon which to develop future histories.

Why *A Tradition of Excellence*? When you look at the last 60 years of jet engine development, there have been far more outstanding successes than abject failures. The jet engine business doesn't tolerate failure very well. The ever-increasing costs of designing, developing, and building these complicated prime movers do not allow for expensive miscues. So in most cases, the engineers and builders have had to get it right, or at least close, the first time. And they have! The last 60 years of the aircraft gas turbine engine business has been a tradition of excellence. That tradition very much includes the people who helped in the research and the writing of this book.

There have been many individuals who have contributed to this work. I wish to thank in particular the following: Dr. Walter O'Brien, Donald Hill, A. Stuart "Butch" Atkinson, Hank Morrow, Donald Widehuner, Stoney MacAdams, Donald C. Berkey, William Travers, Bill Rodenbaugh, Harvey Lippincott, Robert Meyer, Richard Cour, William Brown, Eric Falk at the General Electric Archives for his invaluable help, Ray Standahar, Ivan Bush, J. Robert Hamm, Walter Moe, Robert E. Smith, Ed Horn, Peter Tramm, Richard Alpaugh, Pete Stranges, Maj. Gen. Marv Demler, Dr. Anselm Franz, Dr. Sam Williams, the kind and cooperative folks at Allison, Garrett, Pratt & Whitney, General Electric, Rolls-Royce, Lycoming, Westinghouse, Solar, and the others who contributed through their interviews to this history. I would like to thank Dr. Hans von Ohain for his guidance and inspiration. Additionally, I would like to recognize the special assistance provided by Richard Hill (Air Force Research Laboratory) and the team of Dr. Carol Russo, Dr. Arun Sehra, and Daniel Sokolowski (NASA Glenn Research Center) in the writing of the Research and Technology Focus chapter. I would also particularly like to thank Fred Oliver for his dedication in collecting the finest set of aircraft gas turbine cutaways in the world. Also of particular note are the principal sponsors of the research which went into this book, the Air Force, Navy, Army, NASA and the ASME International Gas Turbine Institute whose continued support during the development of this book made its completion possible. Additionally, my thanks to the many editors and reviewers of the various drafts and chapters of the book: Dr. Kervyn Mach, Bob Henderson, Dave Lindsay, Jay O'Leary, Dr. George Serovy, and George Opdyke Jr., just to name a few. I would especially like to thank the following Universal Technology Corporation and IGTI staff for their administrative and technical support: Pamela Kearney, Kathleen Greaney, Rose Mediratta, Maria Schohn, Kathy Otero, Angela Al-Dineh, Jessica Blackburn, William McCuddy, Toni DeLoach, Janice Mach, Leslie Schworm, and Dianne Schread, without whose help this book would never have been finished. Also I would like to recognize the special photos contributed by Dave Menard of the U.S. Air Force Museum as well as those provided by the National Air & Space Museum. And finally, a special thanks to Marvin Stibich, who got me involved in this aircraft gas turbine history in the first place, and who has seen it through all the ups and downs and right turns to the end with me. Marv, you have been incredibly patient.

James St. Peter
Author

The ASME International Gas Turbine Institute is pleased to support the publication of this gas turbine history book. We believe it is an important contribution to the documentation of gas turbine development. A best effort has been made to be as inclusive as possible given the focus of the book and the time available. We hope that this book is accepted in the spirit in which it was developed.

Board of Directors, IGTI

# INTRODUCTION

Throughout the development of military and commercial/civil aviation in the United States, the relationship between government and industry has been particularly close. The U.S. military has been the largest customer of the aircraft and aircraft engine manufacturers, and its priorities and desires have always been reflected in the products of industry. The evolutions of both the aircraft reciprocating engine and the aircraft gas turbine engine have been tied to this relationship between government and industry, and the constant give-and-take between the two has spurred on engine development. The United States government has constantly set industry development targets for its military aircraft and engine requirements. The focal points for this government and business interaction have been the military service establishments of the Air Force, Army, and Navy. In addition, the research establishment of the National Aeronautics and Space Administration (NASA, 1958-) and its predecessor, the National Advisory Committee for Aeronautics (NACA, 1915-58), have also played important roles in aircraft and engine development, but primarily for commercial applications. This has been true of initial aircraft and reciprocating engine development as well as throughout the first sixty years of the turbine engine evolution. Today the United States is well-established as the global leader in developing commercial aircraft and aircraft turbine engines. Indeed, this country's commercial manufacturers have been instrumental in precipitating the dramatic growth in the commercial air transportation industry. Some of the pioneering efforts that helped spark this growth occurred in no small part because of the military-sponsored developments about which this book elaborates.

NASA/NACA sponsored research that focused on progress in the commercial technology area generally aimed at very advanced aeronautical concepts and improvements to industry's design analysis system. In addition, the government has built and sustained a number of specialized and unique national test facilities, including wind tunnels, in support of aircraft and propulsion system technology developments/needs. Such capabilities often benefit the military as well as the commercial manufacturer.

Since the mid-60s, much progress on developing energy efficient and environmentally compatible gas turbine engines has emanated from work at the NASA Glenn Research Center (GRC), formerly NASA Lewis Research Center (LeRC) in Cleveland, Ohio. NASA-sponsored research has led to production of new turbofan engine components, materials, analytical methods, low emissions combustor technology, and noise-reduction technology.[1]

Differences in military and commercial environments begin with the fact that when the military develops aircraft, systems, and components, it is completely in control because it sets the requirements and then uses the devices it conceives. NASA, in contrast, provides research and technology in the hope that manufacturers will incorporate its developments. Likewise, other arms of the government, the Environmental Protection Agency (EPA) and the Federal Aviation Administration (FAA), set standards that it expects commercial manufacturers to attain. NASA's role is to help develop technology so manufacturers can meet the standards that these other branches of government establish.

Robert Schlaifer in 1949 effectively explored the relationship between government and industry in his book *Development of Aircraft Engines*. This was before the term "military-industrial complex" came into vogue. Schlaifer traced the history of the aircraft engine from early pre-World War I development to the advent of the turbojet engine immediately before and during World War II. His study focused on the interactions between government and industry in the United States and in Great Britain. His research into early turbojet development also covered Germany immediately before and during World War II.

Schlaifer made the point early in his book that the United States government was the single greatest factor in American aircraft engine development in the period between the two world wars. The military services were the government agencies most responsible for determining aircraft engine requirements. This advantaged position gave the government a great deal of control over industry development programs. This control, however, did not carry over into the technological development of the aircraft engines themselves.

Schlaifer points out that the military service engine establishments were unable to develop aircraft engines nearly as quickly as industry. The Army tried to design and develop an aircraft engine completely on its own; however, it took so long that the engine was obsolete before it entered production. The best development took place when the government gave industry engine design and development freedom. Because the government remained the primary market for all types of high-power engines, it retained overall control of development through the contract allocation process. The government supervised the general course of engine development, and occasionally forced companies down an unwelcome path. The government did this through the allocation of development contracts with specific provisos. The government did, however, make significant contributions to areas of propulsion technology through research into areas that companies did not, or would not, pursue. Commercial aircraft companies benefitted from these advances by often using derivatives of engines originally developed for the military.

What incentives drove industry research, design, and development? Schlaifer's research revealed that initially the only significant incentive was the prospect of profits on quantity production. There existed no development program similar to the current core development programs of the major aircraft gas turbine engine manufacturers. Only after there were sufficient procurement programs in place would companies be motivated to start investing in even modest levels of engine development.

Impatience with government technical interference and contract funding allocation delays led engine manufacturers to move toward internal funding of engine development. The government made this transition easier through two changes in the procurement system. First, it permitted companies to charge new model development as overhead. Second, it permitted companies to include this new overhead charge in the price of current models sold to the government. There was still substantial risk to the company, however. The failure of an engine development project could lead to the cessation of quantity sales and thus precipitate a corporate financial crisis.

The American system of development at private risk produced a series of piston engines, which at the outbreak of the war in 1939 were roughly equal in military utility to the engines resulting from the British system. The British system of aircraft engine development had the government paying for the full cost of development and the government, therefore, assuming all the risk.

The American government, however, would assume full responsibility for funding essential military projects in two instances. The first case would be where applications would be limited in scope. The second would be where technical obstacles would be more difficult to overcome. Where this took place, the American government usually was not as effective as the British in getting the most results for its money. This lack of effectiveness was due to the instability of American development programs resulting from often frequent changes in government personnel and funding by year, and the excessively restrictive American legal framework which prevented informal but effective agreements from being reached quickly and easily.

The major advantage of the American system was the dual system of service engine development. The American army and navy carried out separate but equal programs of aircraft engine development. This ensured that naval aviation needs were also considered, and that capabilities of little importance to one service were still available to the other.

Schlaifer also found that during the period between the two world wars most development of aircraft engines, both that done at private risk and that directly financed by the government, were refinements of well-known basic types of engines rather than genuine design innovations. Schlaifer states:

> The only radical innovation of this period, the turbojet, was backed in its early stages neither by government nor by the engine industry, but by such sources as airframe builders (in Germany) or even venture capital entirely unconnected with the aviation industry (in Britain).[2]

Aircraft engine companies gave full attention to the "progressive" development of their established products. They were unwilling to develop other types of engines even when the government was willing to pay the cost because companies would have been financially stretched to divert a large percentage of their work to studying and experimenting with every new type of engine suggested. The companies would have been unable to carry out their most important task, getting the most out of their normal technology—the reciprocating engine.[3]

The government didn't assume responsibility for studying new engine designs because it concentrated on research into solutions to current problems. The government did analyze and assess new designs. Any money spent for supporting radical innovations, however, would detract from their primary mission, the extensive development and improvement of the normal technology. Up to the late 1930s, the co-evolution of airframe and propulsion technologies had progressed rather evenly. The point of "presumptive anomaly" had not yet arrived.

Schlaifer concludes:

> The real trouble with the various unorthodox engines on which public funds were spent with no result in the United States between the wars was that, even granting that they were perfectly practical technically, they did not promise enough superiority over existing engines to make it worthwhile to spend enough money to make them work.

That conclusion does not agree with the facts. Schlaifer himself makes the case that only a relatively small amount of money is necessary for preliminary development or experimentation to prove an innovation's worth. In the case of the aircraft gas turbine engine, it differed from other radical propulsion ideas put forth between the wars. The jet engine promised improved performance based on reasonable (if untested) assumptions.

Why wasn't the turbojet revolution implemented in the United States as it was in Britain, Italy, and Germany?

Edward W. Constant II, in *Origins of the Turbojet Revolution*, points out that America concentrated on different national priorities in aviation. He attributes this to national differences in the pursuit of aerodynamic science reflecting "diverse national scientific traditions and fundamentally different political, economic, social, and geographical exigencies." [4] He reviewed American progress in aeronautics compared with the leading European air powers in nine key categories.

1. **High-speed aerodynamic phenomena:** The United States lagged behind Germany and Great Britain in exploration of this area.

2. **Axial turbo-compressor phenomena:** Germany and Switzerland led the world in this field. The United States did not undertake either empirical or theoretical investigations in this field.

3. **Subsonic flight problems:** The United States rigorously investigated these problems, along with Germany, Britain, and other countries.

4. **Commercial aviation:** The United States led the world in building commercial airliners and in developing commercial airlines. Germany and Great Britain used commercial aviation as an instrument of national policy and built mediocre airliners.

5. **Preparation for upcoming war:** The United States dawdled while Germany (after 1933) and Britain (after 1936) prepared for war.

6. **Schneider Trophy competition:** Britain and Italy competed for this seaplane race trophy; the United States did not.

7. **World absolute speed record:** Britain, Italy, and finally Germany held the world absolute speed record during the 1930s; the United States did not.

8. **Other forms of aeronautical competition:** The United States, the Soviet Union, and other countries indulged in other forms of aeronautical competition (around-the-world flights, etc.).

9. **Turbojet engines:** Germany and Great Britain produced indigenous turbojet engines before 1940; the United States did not.

Altogether, these comparisons do not paint a flattering picture of American aeronautics. But if you add several other categories of aeronautical developments that Constant omitted, then a slightly different picture emerges.

10. **Aircraft engine reliability**: Although heavier than German or British engines, American aircraft engines were much more reliable, especially for long flights over water.

11. **Turbosupercharger development:** The United States had a clear superiority in the field over both Germany and Great Britain.

12. **Turboprop development**: The United States had two turboprop designs on paper before 1940, and was working on a third. Great Britain and Germany each had one turboprop project in 1939.

13. **Development of naval aviation:** The United States led both Germany and Britain. The only other country with perhaps equal naval air capability was Japan.

14. **Long-distance or endurance flights**: The United States led all other countries in this category.

15 **Polar flight**: The United States was second only to the Soviet Union in polar flight research.

16. **Long-range or heavy bomber development**: The United States led the world in this area. Germany had no heavy bomber programs. Britain only had a limited capability.

If you consider these seven additional categories, the United States was clearly not behind any country in overall aeronautical science. It simply did not have the same national priorities as did the European countries. The United States did, however, have the national capability to master any of the first nine categories of aeronautical science and later did master each of them.

Although U.S. gas turbine engine technology developed quickly and rose to unequalled heights, a great debt of gratitude is owed to those who gave birth to the technology in Great Britain and Germany, and to those engineers and technicians who emigrated to the United States after World War II to nurture its growth and development.

## Endnotes

[1] Dawson, Virginia P., Engines and Innovation: *Lewis Laboratory and American Propulsion Technology, NASA SP-4306, 1991.*

[2] Schlaifer, Robert. *Development of Aircraft Engines*, Boston, MA: Harvard University Press, 1949, 12. [41].

[3] Ibid., 86.

[4] Constant, Edward W. II. *The Origins of the Turbojet Revolution* Baltimore: The Johns Hopkins University Press, 1980, 151.

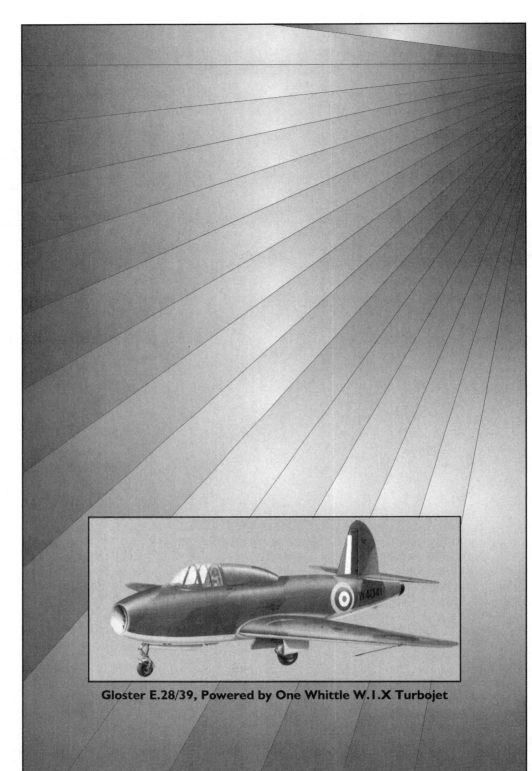

**Gloster E.28/39, Powered by One Whittle W.1.X Turbojet**

# Chapter 1

# Sir Frank Whittle and the First British Aircraft Gas Turbine

**Figure 1-1. Sir Frank Whittle**
*(Photo courtesy of Rolls-Royce)*

The common perception that the United States did not have any aircraft gas turbine engine research before 1941 is incorrect. The United States did begin to develop an aircraft gas turbine engine before the importing of the Whittle turbojet; however, the first working American aircraft gas turbine engine was a direct derivative of the pioneering work of Sir Frank Whittle (Figure 1-1) in Britain.

Sir Frank Whittle was perhaps the last of the individual innovator-inventors. An individual who combined the hands-on skill of the mechanic and pilot with the acquired knowledge of the trained engineer and aerodynamicist, Whittle conceived the idea of a jet engine and made his idea work, in spite of great difficulties.

In 1928 Flight Cadet Whittle was attending the Royal Air Force (RAF) College at Cranwell. He wrote a fourth-semester thesis entitled "Future Developments in Aircraft Design," which speculated on the possibilities of jet propulsion and gas turbines.[1] The *Royal Air Force Cadet College Magazine* published the paper in the fall of 1928 under the title "Speculation." In this thesis, Whittle discussed rocket propulsion and gas turbine driven propellers. This thesis in itself does not represent an advance in aerodynamic theory, but it does represent the beginning of an idea in the mind of a young officer candidate. Although materials technology was not sufficiently advanced and much of the theoretical groundwork had yet to be laid, Whittle had already grasped the potential of the gas turbine.

In 1930 while at the RAF Central Flying School at Whittering, Whittle continued to work on his idea, trying different theoretical solutions to the question of successful jet flight. He briefly considered a compound engine. In such a configuration, a piston engine powers a low-pressure blower. Both the blower and the engine are ducted within the plane's fuselage. Fuel may be burned in the flow-stream aft of the engine to increase thrust.[2] He soon discarded this design for what would become the design for a practical gas turbine. He did not yet have the RAF's approval to work in any official capacity on his ideas. That situation was soon to change.

In a fateful meeting, Whittle discussed his proposal with a Central Flying School instructor named W.E.P. Johnson. Johnson in turn encouraged Whittle to talk to the commandant of the school, Group Captain John "Jack" Baldwin (later Air Marshal Sir John Baldwin). Whittle impressed Baldwin with his ideas and Baldwin forwarded Whittle and his proposal up the chain of command. Whittle went to see W.L. Tweedie in the Directorate of Scientific Research of the Department of Engine Development, located at the British Air Ministry's South Kensington Laboratory. Although Tweedie was unconvinced, he sent Whittle to the laboratory's A.A. Griffith. Griffith pointed out an error in Whittle's calculations and told Whittle that his turbojet assumptions were overoptimistic.[3] As Whittle states in his autobiography, *Jet, The Story of a Pioneer:*

> In due course I received a letter from the Air Ministry to the effect that the scheme I proposed was a form of gas turbine, and that as such its successful development was considered to be impracticable, because materials did not then exist capable of withstanding the combination of high stresses and high temperatures which would be necessary if a gas turbine were to have an acceptable efficiency. In fairness to the Air Ministry, I should add that I think that what they said was true. Nevertheless, I feel that they should have foreseen the possibility of big improvements in materials and kept the proposal "on ice" for a later period. I agree that at the end of 1929 it was before its time, but only by very few years.[4]

Was Whittle right? At that time the British government assumed all the costs of new developments in aircraft engine design. Why didn't they include the Whittle design within this policy? Schlaifer, in his analysis of British aircraft engine policy, states that even if Whittle's design was technically sound, it was an extremely uncertain proposition. The Air Ministry shared the conventional wisdom that the state of metallurgy and component design would not support Whittle's design. It didn't help Whittle that he was only twenty-three years old and a student with very little advanced engineering training.

Griffith had already started his own theoretical design of an axial turbojet by the time Whittle presented his proposal. Griffith was well aware of the theoretical potential of the turbojet. In 1927 he received approval from the Air Ministry and British Aeronautical Research Council to begin experiments on his design for an axial turbine driving a propeller. One can only speculate on Griffith's reasons for dismissing Whittle's design as overoptimistic. Did he see Whittle as a potential rival for RAF funding? At any rate the Air Ministry canceled Griffith's aircraft gas turbine engine design program in 1931. The official reason cited was the Depression sweeping Britain and the need to use available funds for problem-solving research into piston engines. Whittle was undaunted by Griffith's rebuff of his proposal. Once he had corrected the error in his calculations, Whittle went ahead with his plans. The next step was to patent his concept.

The young Whittle filed a Provisional Specification on January 16, 1930, for a patent based on the principle of using a gas turbine for jet propulsion.[5] His design (Figure 1-2) called for a turbojet with two axial intake fans followed by a single-sided, single-stage centrifugal compressor. The compressor fed several straight-through combustion chambers, which exhausted through a two-stage axial turbine and then out through multiple-channel exhaust nozzles.[6] The major uncertainty regarding the patent was the position of the British Air Ministry towards the young serving officer's patent?

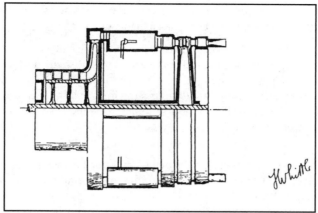

**Figure 1-2. Drawing of Whittle Gas Turbine,
British Patent No. 347206**
*(Drawing courtesy of Rolls-Royce)*

The usual British government practice toward invention by government employees (and this included serving officers) depended on the nature of the invention in question. If the particular invention or innovation was a secret, the government retained all rights. If the invention or innovation was patentable and not secret, the government retained the right of "free use" and gave the inventor the commercial and foreign rights. This grant was subject to the payment of a certain fraction of the royalties to the government.[7] Whittle formally notified the Air Ministry of his filing, but they informed him that the ministry had no official interest in the patent. The Air Ministry therefore did not place Whittle's design on the "secret list" of patents. In effect, they felt that his concept had no use in the RAF.

Whittle put the rejection by the Air Ministry behind him and decided to try to market his turbojet design commercially. He approached several investment firms and the aircraft engine manufacturer Armstrong Siddeley. Armstrong Siddeley turned him down because in the opinion of their chief engineer:

> ...the whole scheme depends upon obtaining material which will work satisfactorily at a very high temperature. Personally I doubt very much whether such material is available and this, I think, prevents the development of the internal combustion turbine. I fear therefore that I cannot hold out any hopes that this firm will take any serious interest in your proposal.[8]

Bristol Aircraft and the electrical turbine design firm of British Thomson-Houston (BTH) also turned Whittle down. He had experienced total rejection of his idea from both the government and the private sector. He had to come up with a way to get the aircraft establishment to recognize his breakthrough.

During this period (1930-31) Whittle wrote a paper published in the *Journal of the Royal Aeronautical Society*, entitled "The Turbo-Compressor and the Supercharging of Aero-Engines."[9] The purpose of this paper was to convince people of the value of his compressor proposals. If he could do that, Whittle could get the establishment to look seriously at his comprehensive scheme for a complete engine. Another object of this paper was to make a case for using an independent engine to drive the supercharger of the main power plant. This was a design for which Whittle and Flying Officer J.H. McReynolds had filed a joint patent application. Whittle estimated that the turbojet engine would require a compressor having a pressure ratio of the order of 4:1. The proposal would also require an efficiency of at least 75 percent. This would be a dramatic increase in the aircraft engine technology of the time. For example, the British Supermarine Aircraft Company's S.6 won the Schneider Trophy in 1931. Its Rolls-Royce "R" engine incorporated the best aero-engine turbosupercharger of that time. It had a pressure ratio of just under 2:1 and an efficiency of 62 percent.[10] Whittle's design would have to produce a much greater pressure ratio and a much higher efficiency.

Some time after writing the paper on supercharging, Whittle wrote a paper entitled "The Case for the Gas Turbine." Although he did not try to get it published, this paper is the earliest of his surviving documents in which he discusses the potential applications of his theory of the jet engine. The paper contained sample calculations showing the large increase in efficiency that could be achieved with the gas turbine at high altitudes. This increase was due to the beneficial effects of low air temperature. The paper also contained calculations to prove the degree to which the range of turbojet-engine aircraft would depend on altitude.[11]

Between 1930 and 1936, Whittle followed the normal advancement path of an RAF officer. His writings tell of his discouragement with trying to find a military or commercial sponsor for his turbojet research. Whittle had to let his 1930 Rover expire in 1935 because of financial difficulty. He did, however, continue his theoretical work in mechanical and aeronautical science. From 1934 to 1936 the RAF posted Whittle to Cambridge for advanced education in the mechanical sciences. Whittle responded to this opportunity for advanced training by completing three years of work in two. He advanced his knowledge of aeronautics through working with B.M. Jones of the Aeronautical Laboratory at Cambridge.[12]

## The Development of the Whittle Unit (W.U.)

Nineteen thirty-five was a crucial year for Whittle. Shortly after his original patent had expired, Whittle received a letter from a former RAF officer named R. Dudley Williams expressing interest in Whittle's design. Together with J.C.B. Tinling, another former RAF officer, Whittle and Williams drew the interest of M.L. Bramson. Bramson was a financial consultant to the investment banking firm of Falk and Partners. After brief negotiations Falk and Partners agreed to help underwrite the initial development of Whittle's engine.

Whittle, Williams, and Tinling formed a company called Power Jets Limited on January 27, 1936, to build the engine. The British Air Ministry was a party to the formation of this company, but with a caveat. The Air Ministry restricted Whittle's participation with the new company to six hours per week. This was not quite the degree of support that Whittle required, but he was grateful that the Air Ministry was participating at all. As development progressed, Whittle increasingly ignored the time restriction. He assigned all his patent rights to the new company, and 25 percent of his shares in the company to the British Air Ministry. Although Whittle and the others had formed Power Jets with working capital of only £2,000, the company did have some inherent advantages. The chief engineer, Whittle, was also a serving officer in the RAF, so Power Jets did not have to pay him a salary. Although the British government did not assume any developmental costs of the new company, their allowing Whittle to devote any time to the new company was a tacit admission that his new design had merit. The new company was officially established in March of 1936.[13]

Whittle began design of a bench test engine called the Whittle Unit, or W.U., during his work with B.M. Jones. From May 26 through mid-June of 1935, Whittle also filed three provisional patent specifications covering improvements to his original design.[14] Finally, Whittle managed to convince the British Thomson-Houston Company (BTH) to undertake construction of the engine. BTH engineers Samuelson and Collingham agreed to undertake construction on a cost-plus basis.[15]

BTH agreed to provide the shop drawings of the Whittle engine and to fabricate the compressor impeller, rotor shaft, turbine disc, and turbine. Power Jets began on-site operations in the BTH shop at Rugby. Power Jets intended to manufacture a turbojet for a fast, high-altitude transatlantic mail plane.[16] Whittle and BTH originally intended to manufacture and test components separately (Figure 1-3). The components would then be joined together and the combined engine tested again as a unit. When cost estimates for separate component testing were developed, however, the high development costs forced the company to reconsider its methodology. A 3,000-horsepower electric motor and compressor testing rig alone would cost an estimated £27,000. Faced with these cost estimates, Whittle decided to develop the complete engine at one time. He estimated that the complete engine would cost less than £5,000.[17]

**Figure 1-3. Combustion Arrangements Outside the BTH Factory Prior to the Completion of the Experimental Engine**
*(Photo courtesy of Rolls-Royce)*

Whittle realized that Power Jets could not build the engine on its own. It would need experienced help in dealing with the many practical problems associated with a new engine development. Whittle persuaded A.B.S. Laidlaw, of Laidlaw, Drew and Company of Edinburgh to aid in the development of the combustion system for the W.U. and subsequent Whittle turbojets,[18] and he contracted with the Hoffman Company for bearings and the Alfred Herbert Company for shaft machinery. His compressor design called for a:

> ...single stage centrifugal type generally similar to, but much larger than, an aero-engine supercharger... The turbine was also a single stage unit... Thus the main moving part of the engine - the rotor - was made up of the compressor impeller, the turbine wheel and the shaft connecting the two. It was designed to rotate at 17,750 rpm, which meant a top speed of nearly 1,500 feet per second for the 19-inch diameter turbine... Our target was a pressure ratio of 4.0 with an efficiency of 80%.[19]

Whittle, in "The Birth of the Jet Engine in Britain," described his engine as follows:

> It had a single stage double-sided centrifugal compressor of 19 inches diameter driven by a single stage axial flow turbine of 16.4 inches diameter. The compressed air from the compressor passed to the nozzle volute of the turbine via a single large combustion chamber of helical form. The exhaust from the turbine finally expanded through a jet nozzle.[20]

Whittle's development philosophy and methodology were very similar to those of Thomas Edison and many other entrepreneur-inventors at the turn of the century. He kept a watchful eye on every detail of his engine's design and construction, and established a pattern on March 23, 1936, when he rejected preliminary assembly drawings produced by BTH. Whittle decided after that date to specify drawings more precisely.[21] This methodological rigidity provided a background of tension throughout the development of Whittle's turbojet engines, and adversely affected his subcontractors' and Whittle's own health.

British Air Ministry support of Whittle's design, however, began to pick up. In March of 1936, Whittle met H.E. Wimperis and Henry Tizard at a Cambridge Air Squadron Dinner. Wimperis was at that time Director of Scientific Research at the Air Ministry and Tizard chaired the Air Ministry's Aeronautical Research Committee. Whittle impressed Tizard and Wimperis with his earnestness and his ideas on the future of turbojet design. In October, Tizard asked A.A. Griffith of the Royal Aircraft Establishment to evaluate Whittle's engine design.[22] In February of 1938, after considering Whittle's design again (Griffith had already seen Whittle's ideas in late 1929) Griffith concluded:

> In its present form, the proposed jet propulsion system cannot compete with a conventional power plant in any case where economical flight is demanded (e.g., the transport of the maximum percentage of useful load over a given distance). It is of value only for special purposes, such as the attainment of high speed or high altitude for a short time, in cases where takeoff requirements are not stringent.
>
> In order that the proposed system may become a competitor in the field of economical flight, a large improvement, of the order of at least 50-100%, must be made in the ratio of takeoff thrust to power plant weight.[23]

Griffith submitted his report to Tizard's committee. Notwithstanding the negative report by Griffith, Tizard's subcommittee issued a small contract to Power Jets for information on the first series of engine tests.

The subcommittee also promised some support for a second series of tests.[24] Whittle realized the significance of Tizard's moves and noted that this report marked the beginning of official government interest in his work. Whittle had overcome the first and perhaps the most important hurdle in the development process. He had convinced several highly influential people in the British aircraft establishment that his ideas were worthy of the government's financial support.

While Griffith and the Royal Aircraft Establishment considered Whittle's designs, Whittle pushed ahead in his development program. In April of 1936, BTH began work on detailed drawings for the Whittle turbojet.[25] W.A. Randles was put in charge of the design drawing effort. Whittle enlisted the assistance of A.A. Hall in his compressor design. BTH also began the initial stages of manufacturing the W.U. in April.

From October to December 1936 Whittle and Laidlaw, Drew and Company started combustion experiments. By the end of 1936, most of the detailed design work on Whittle's turbojet was completed, and manufacture of the engine was well underway. Whittle estimated that £3,000 had been spent on the engine up to that point.[26]

Whittle chose Stayblade steel, made by Firth Vickers, for the wheel and blades of the turbine. BTH and Whittle decided to construct the compressor impeller and casing of an aluminum alloy known as RR.56, made by High Duty Alloys Limited.[27]

In 1937 Whittle was placed on the RAF special duty list and posted to Power Jets. This development meant that the Air Ministry and the RAF thought Whittle's turbojet development was important enough to warrant his assignment on a full-time basis. The government's faith and the private development funding for Power Jets paid off on April 12, 1937, when Whittle first test-ran his turbojet engine (Figure 1-4). Whittle recorded the event in his diary as follows:

> Pilot jet successfully ignited at 1,000 rpm. Speed raised to 2,000 rpm by motor. I requested a further raising of speed to 2,500 rpm and during this process I opened valve 'B' and the unit suddenly ran away. Probably started at about 2,300 and using only about 5 horsepower starting power...noted that return pipe from jet was overheating badly. Flame tube red hot at inner radius; combustion very bad.[28]

Fuel system problems caused runaways of the engine the first five times that they (the Whittle team) started it. This was largely due to inexperience in fuel system design. For example, they ran the first tests with upstream fuel injection, a design in which the fuel injector was immersed in the burner flame. The next design incorporated downstream fuel injection, but much of the fuel burned in the exhaust pipe after the turbine, not in the combustion chamber. Whittle then switched again to upstream fuel injection, but this time used a boiler which vaporized the kerosene fuel. The vapor was then injected into the combustion chamber. This didn't work, however, because the kerosene boiler lacked sufficient heating surface, and injected liquid kerosene instead of vaporized kerosene into the chamber. Following Laidlaw's advice, Whittle's team tried downstream fuel injection yet again, with some improvement. The engine, however, never achieved more than 12,000 rpm.[29]

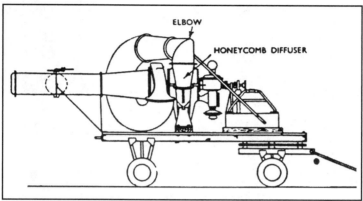

**Figure 1-4. Test Assembly of the
First model of the Experimental Engine**
*(Drawing courtesy of Rolls-Royce)*

Negotiations opened between Power Jets and the Air Ministry in June of 1937. Power Jets sought to find ways by which the ministry could defray some of the cost of Whittle's work. On July 9, the Air Ministry proposed a contract worth £10,000 to Whittle and Power Jets,[30] offering £1,000 for a report on the first series of test runs, followed by an additional £2,000 for research running up to 14,000 rpm, £2,000 for further research running up to full speed, and finally, £5,000 for the purchase of the engine. In September, the Air Ministry decided not to buy the Whittle engine and reduced their offer to £5,000. This reduction in funding meant a financial crisis for Power Jets. They did not have the capital to continue development on their own. It looked as if the project would stall or even die from lack of capital.

At that point BTH agreed to put company funds into the program, and Falk and Partners provided additional private funding as well. Thus Power Jets could continue its development program, though not at the speed nor scale that Whittle desired. Although Power Jets had not realized the level of government funding that they desired, they had succeeded in obtaining direct government support for the program for the first time. It was not to be the last.

On August 23, Whittle and Power Jets suspended testing on the W.U. They moved the site of their turbojet development to the BTH Ladywood Works at Lutterworth. New combustion tests began there on October 22. Throughout the rest of 1937, Whittle and his team worked on combustion testing and constructed the first rebuild of the Whittle engine.[31]

During the design, construction, and testing of his first engine, Whittle continued to increase his understanding of aerodynamics and thermodynamics. In November, he attended a lecture on high-speed flight and compressibility phenomena by C.N.H. Lock, the outstanding ballistician from the National Physical Laboratory. Whittle continued to theorize and then incorporate these new ideas into his designs. Sometimes the new designs met resistance. In December, Whittle began a new turbine design using "vortex theory." Vortex theory used a change of angle or twist from root to tip of the turbine blades which was twice that of conventional blading.

Whittle met resistance to his new design at British Thomson-Houston, who were unwilling to depart from the conventional method of constructing turbine blades. After all, the company had been manufacturing ground power turbines for quite some time. The fact that Whittle and Power Jets had already patented the vortex theory design also did nothing to ameliorate the hard feelings between the two companies. BTH's resistance to this new design, along with Whittle's too-close monitoring of all aspects of design and construction, led to the deterioration of relations between the two companies.[32]

On December 6, the RAF promoted Whittle to squadron leader without requiring him to take the promotional examination. This unusual waiving of an RAF regulation is another example of the government's support for Whittle's work, even at a time when they weren't supporting him very much financially.[33]

The year 1938 was not an easy one for Frank Whittle and Power Jets. Whittle reports that during the first part of the year, Power Jets continued to suffer from a "precarious financial position."[34] He attributed it to personal distrust of himself by the new Director of Scientific Research (Dr. Pye) and his deputy, W.S. Farren. This is an excerpt of a March 28 discussion with Farren taken from Jet, The Story of a Pioneer:

> He says that my general policy has been such that they have not felt that they could give me their confidence. He seems to have several erroneous impressions. He thinks I was connected with the delay in signing the contract. I told him I had refused to take part in discussions on the subject. I left still in the dark as to why there should be a misinterpretation of my motives and feeling rather depressed that this should have happened. I gave him as strong an assurance as I could that I put my duty as a Serving Officer before any commercial interests.[35]

What influence could this attitude on the part of the Air Ministry have had in hampering the development of Whittle's turbojet? Whittle was not an insider in the engine development community. In his case, espousing a new approach to high-speed flight meant a two-front battle...one to gain professional acceptance of his theory and subsequent technology, the other to win approval of his management style.

As both a serving officer in the RAF and an inventor interacting with the government, Whittle was unable to control all aspects of his invention. He was acting as both an agent of the government and as a protagonist in a struggle for recognition and funding from that government. In addition, Whittle claimed that the Director of Scientific Research was hesitant to support Power Jets' work because of work the Royal Aircraft Establishment had recently started on a propeller gas turbine project.

During this wrangling with the Air Ministry and British Thomson-Houston, Whittle and the engineers from BTH were busy with the design of the new variant of the W.U. (Figure 1-5). On April 16, testing began on the modified turbojet at British Thomson-Houston in Rugby.[36] Whittle's rebuilt engine incorporated a vaned diffuser with separate passages, a redesigned combustion chamber, a new turbine inlet, and a redesigned turbine. A 10-horsepower BSA automobile engine on a truck mount provided starting power. The engine was built by three fitters from BTH named Bentley, Berry, and Bailey.[37]

Until the government gave Whittle a contract to build a flight engine prototype, Power Jets had to keep reconstructing the experimental engine so that new design changes could be tested. The experimental engine was to undergo three rebuilds before a new engine was constructed. With a lack of resources, limited facilities, and only one experimental engine, it is surprising that Whittle and his small team made the progress they did. If an established aircraft engine manufacturer had developed the engine, four or five prototype experimental engines would have been produced in the first stage so that development could follow multiple paths. Whittle and his colleagues did not have that luxury.

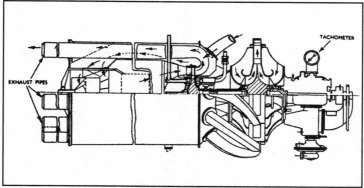

**Figure 1-5. General Arrangement of
First Rebuild of the W.U. (1937)**
*(Drawing courtesy of Rolls-Royce)*

With the first rebuild complete, Whittle's group resumed testing the new components. The engine achieved a major goal of running over one hour at 8,200 rpm on April 29, before ingesting an oily shop rag, causing minor damage. On May 6, however, the turbine second stage disintegrated, extensively damaging the turbine. The engine ran for 1 hour 45 minutes before the failure occurred, attaining a thrust of 480 pounds at 13,000 rpm. Whittle attributed his engine failure to rubbing of the turbine nozzle assembly with the turbine wheel at high speed, causing severe overheating and failure of the turbine blades.[38]

This engine failure, as with other developmental setbacks, resulted in emotional distress for Whittle which contributed to feelings of depression and anxiety. These anxieties also manifested themselves through severe headaches and stomach disorders.[39]

In this second rebuild, Whittle decided to abandon the single-combustion-chamber design for a series of ten small combustion chambers (Figure 1-6). The small chambers would be lit in series from two ignition points through a series of "inter-connecting tubes." British Thomson-Houston, Hayne Constant of the Royal Aircraft Establishment, and the Director of Scientific Research approved the change as well. Whittle felt that Constant approved of his work and thought it deserved increased support from the Air Ministry.[40] On May 30, Whittle and the directors of Power Jets decided to reconstruct the experimental engine for a second time. [41]

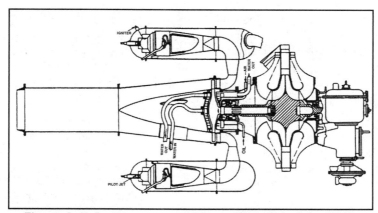

**Figure 1-6. Arrangement of Second Rebuild of the W.U.**
*(Drawing courtesy of Rolls-Royce)*

On July 19, Bramson, a director of Power Jets, summarized the technical position as follows:

1. The work done to date constitutes a quantitative experimental verification of the principle underlying the Whittle system of jet propulsion.

2. At 73.3% of the design speed, quantitative verification of the jet engine has been obtained and there is a strong probability of obtaining it shortly at full speed.

3. Experimental evidence already makes it practically certain that the thermal efficiency of the unit (which it has not yet been possible to measure) cannot be so far below estimate as to nullify the positive results.

4. The feasibility of jet propulsion for aircraft has been, for the first time, experimentally established.[42]

On October 26, 1938, testing began on the third rebuild of the experimental engine. The new rebuild included ten can-annular combustion chambers and a new turbine inlet and turbine. Whittle also added individual vaporizers in each combustion chamber (Figure 1-7).

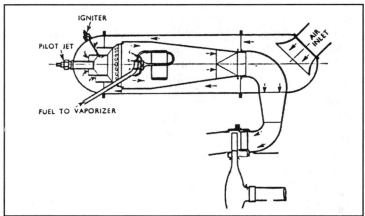

**Figure 1-7. Typical Combustion Chamber with Vaporizer and Turbine Arrangement**
*(Drawing courtesy of Rolls-Royce)*

The British Air Ministry agreed to assume the full development cost of this new engine, which ended the old contract after a payment of £1,900 for a report on the first series of tests and £900 for the engine run that had taken place in the second series of tests. Under the new contract, the Air Ministry agreed to pay for the greater part of the cost of the second reconstruction, and for twenty hours' experimental engine testing at £200 per hour. The total sum involved was about £6,000. Testing on this new engine continued until February 1941.[43]

Reproductions of the Whittle patents of 1930 and 1935 appeared in the German publication *Flugsport* in 1939, which caused considerable consternation at Power Jets.[44] The British Official Secrets Act did not protect Whittle's own work until 1938, so German patent research could not have failed to come up with Whittle's patent. Whittle did, however, keep current with foreign gas turbine developments. In February of 1939 Whittle attended a lecture by Dr. Adolph Meyer of the Swiss Brown-Boveri Company to the British Institution of Mechanical Engineers in London.[45]

Whittle and his team made some real progress during the first part of 1939. While integrating new component designs into a rebuilt engine, Whittle and Power Jets were able to attain some degree of the performance expected from the new components. On February 20, they raised the speed of their third engine to over 8,000 rpm.[46] This advance apparently wasn't enough, for on February 29, 1939, the Ministry of Aircraft Production pressed Whittle for more results. They informed him of this in a letter from Deputy Director for Scientific Development W.S. Farren. Whittle writes:

> [I was informed] that my position would come up for review in a comparatively short time, and that he would have some difficulty in making a case to the other Service departments to secure the retention of my appointment. He said that it was most important, both from my point of view and his own, that we should produce much more in the way of results than we had done up till then. He pointed out that if I were a civilian there would be no particular problem, but because I was a serving officer he found himself in a difficulty because he had made promises to the other Service departments based, in turn, on our promises which, in effect, were not being kept.[47]

Was this an attempt to get Whittle out of the RAF? Whittle felt that although Farren did not intend for this to put increased pressure on him, in fact it did. Whittle considered this the most critical point in the entire development of his turbojet.

> Had the Air Ministry lost interest in the job, it would almost certainly have meant closing down altogether. Fortunately, our improvisations began to produce results and the intensity and speed of running increased.[48]

In March, Whittle was able to increase the maximum speed of his engine to about 14,000 rpm, an accomplishment he credited with saving his program from termination. A turbine blade failure, however, caused a two-month delay.[49] In an attempt to deal with this new problem, Whittle and Power Jets ordered from Firth Vickers a quantity of Rex 78 to replace the Stayblade turbine blades in their engine. Rex 78 was high nickel-chrome alloy steel, and proved to be much more durable. Constant of the Royal Aircraft Establishment told Whittle in April that he was coming to believe that Whittle actually had a practical engine in sight.[50]

On June 17, testing resumed at Power Jets Ltd. with the installation of a new impeller. The new impeller had 29 blades instead of 30 to avoid resonant coupling with the 10-blade diffuser system. On June 23, Whittle and his team attained a speed of 14,700 rpm with the third rebuild experimental engine. On June 24, they attained a speed of 15,700 rpm, and two days later they reached a speed of 16,000 rpm.[51] At this point, although combustion problems (bad temperature distribution, among others) continued to plague the team, Whittle felt that he had solved the major design problems. He invited Director of Scientific Research Pye to visit Ladywood for a demonstration.

During that visit Pye saw a test run of the engine at 16,000 rpm for twenty minutes. Afterward Pye accepted the new, radical technology that the turbojet represented. Although a great deal of work had yet to be done, Whittle believed he had convinced the government that his engine was worth full-scale development.[52]

## The Development of the Whittle W.1 Turbojet

In July of 1939 the Air Ministry awarded contracts to Power Jets for the Whittle flight engine designated the W.1 (Figure 1-8). BTH was to build the engine. Gloster Aircraft was to build an accompanying experimental jet-powered aircraft to be designated the E.28/39.[53] Actually, Whittle had expected that Power Jets would get the authority and responsibility to determine the airframe manufacturer. Power Jets had already prepared tentative layouts and shown them to Pye.[54] Although one familiar with current practice might consider this expectation unrealistic, Whittle's development philosophy called for retaining total design and development responsibility for all aspects of the development process, including integration of the engine with an airframe. Whittle was never able to achieve such control. Power Jets proved unable to retain authority even over subsequent production prototypes of engines built by subcontractors such as BTH and, later, Rover and Rolls-Royce.

Whittle was already at work in early July on the design of the flight engine. At the request of the Director of Scientific Research, the W.1's design was to be very close to that of the third experimental engine rebuild, except for changes to achieve a very considerable weight saving.[55] By the middle of the month, engine revolutions per minute increased to 16,650, or 94 percent of full design speed.[56]

**Figure 1-8. Whittle W.1 Engine**
*(Photo courtesy of Rolls-Royce)*

While disappointed with the Air Ministry's decision to contract directly with an aircraft manufacturer, Whittle was nevertheless happy with the choice of Gloster. On April 28, Whittle had visited the Gloster Aircraft works, where he met Chief Designer George Carter, Chief Test Pilot Gerry Sayer, and Test Pilot Michael Daunt.[57] What made the choice of airframe developer even more palatable to Whittle was that his good friend Wing Commander J.H. McC. Reynolds was the Air Ministry liaison at Gloster. In July, Wing Commander Reynolds visited Power Jets and brought with him Gloster's initial aircraft design proposals. Chief Aircraft Designer George Carter suggested a tail-first canard fighter, but this radical approach was later modified to a more conservative design (Figures 1-9 and 1-10).[58]

Power Jets reached another important developmental milestone at the end of August. Director of Scientific Research Pye told Whittle and Power Jets that Whittle's special appointment with Power Jets was to continue and that the Air Ministry would wish the work to go on if war broke out.[59] Germany invaded Poland on September 1. France and Britain stood by their mutual-assistance treaty with Poland, and war did break out in Europe.

In October 1939, the Air Ministry directed Dr. Hayne Constant to prepare an advisory report on wartime development of gas turbines. Constant was in favor of having Power Jets and Gloster go ahead with eight engines and four aircraft, but the Air Ministry did not agree.[60]

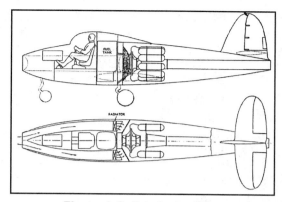

**Figure 1-9. Fuselage of the Experimental E.28/39**
*(Drawing courtesy of Rolls-Royce)*

**Figure 1-10. Views of the Gloster E.28/39**
*(Illustration courtesy of Rolls-Royce)*

After war broke out, Whittle felt that although the government had agreed to continue funding his work, they exhibited no particular urgency in doing so. Power Jets was at this time completely funded by the government. He realized that this placed Power Jets at the mercies of changes in government procurement priorities. Whittle ascribes this lack of enthusiasm to four points:

1.  Perhaps it was because certain officials who had an influence on policy did not yet believe in the soundness of our proposals.

2.  Perhaps it was because those who did believe that the development was important felt that Power Jets were the wrong people to handle it, and that it would be better to hand it over to a long-established engineering firm.

3.  Others may have felt that the work which had been started by the Royal Aircraft Establishment in co-operation with Metro-Vickers was more likely to yield fruitful results.

4.  There were also indications that personal antagonisms towards Whyte and myself were affecting the situation.[61]

Whyte was Chief Executive Officer of Power Jets at this time. This statement is important as it reflects Whittle's feelings about what happened to him later in his work:

> The feeling spread from one official to another that Whyte was difficult to deal with. As happened with me later, influential individuals, who had as yet had no opportunity to judge for themselves, became prejudiced against him before meeting him.

By the end of January 1940, the design of the W.1 flight engine was well along and Power Jets was working on the preliminary design of the W.2 turbojet. The W.2 had a design target of 1,600 pounds maximum thrust, compared with 1,240 pounds for the W.1. Its general arrangement was similar to that of the W.1 but incorporated several significant changes, one being the change from water cooling to air cooling for the turbine wheel. Combustor problems still plagued Whittle and his team. Power Jets experimented with 31 different types of vaporizers. They still, however, encountered "coking up" of vaporizer tubes, local overheating and distortion, and bad temperature distribution at the outlets from the combustion chambers.[62]

Whittle later cited three difficulties that he faced in introducing this new technology. The first problem was the engineering background of the BTH engineers. They were trained to think in terms of manufacturing large stationary electric power generators for power stations and the like. Low manufacturing costs were far more important to them than low weight. Whittle on the other hand was an aeronautical engineer, trained to think in terms of low weight and great precision. Many of these engineers had worked twenty or more years in their discipline and had little or no familiarity with modern aerodynamic theory.

The second difficulty Whittle noted was that the machine tools in the BTH turbine factory were unsuitable for building aircraft engines. For example, the design called for fabrication of the W.1 combustion chambers from Staybrite[63] stainless steel only 1/64-inch thick. BTH told Whittle that they could not weld these pieces, so Whittle challenged one of their welders to do it, and he eventually did.[64]

As for the third difficulty, Whittle confessed that his own impatience and intolerance with mistakes caused a great deal of friction with the BTH engineering staff. This was limited, however, to those engineers not working directly with Power Jets Ltd.[65] The friction between Whittle and the management and top engineers at BTH would soon come to the point where Whittle would replace the company with another subcontractor. At the end of January 1940, Whittle started meeting with Maurice Wilks, Chief Engineer of the Rover Company. Whittle suggested that Power Jets should place contracts with Rover. The suggestion met with hostility at the Air Ministry. Major G.P. Bulman, Director of Engine Development, told Rover to back off.[66] The Air Ministry soon reversed this decision, however, and Whittle and Power Jets began negotiations for Rover to assume the subcontracting role that BTH held.

In February, Whittle and Power Jets began design of the W.1.A, a compromise between the W.1 and W.2 turbojets. Its purpose was to test out such special features of the W.2 as the air cooling of the turbine wheel and the novel compressor intake arrangement.[67] This W.1.A was to go into the second E.28 prototype. This second prototype was designed to test a new high-speed wing section.

Also in February, Rolls-Royce's Stanley Hooker saw the Whittle engine for the first time. The development program impressed Hooker and he convinced the director of Rolls-Royce, E.W. Hives, to go down to Lutterworth to look at the Whittle engine.[68] This interest by Rolls-Royce was to prove crucial to the Whittle program after the relationship between Rover and Whittle also soured.

Whittle always remained very conscious of his professional relationships with both the Air Ministry and with his subcontractors. He kept detailed notes of his interactions with them and did not hesitate to let them know what he thought of his interactions with them. The following letter sheds light on his interactions with the Air Ministry. On February 15, Whittle had lunch with W.S. Farren at the Royal Aircraft Establishment. During the discussion, Farren's remarks disturbed Whittle, who referred to these remarks in a letter to Farren on February 16, 1940:

> During our conversation at lunch yesterday you made various remarks, some of which were to the following effect:
>
> 1. People who had put their money in Power Jets were an unselfish crowd of people who had done a very good job of work, and that there was no hope of them ever getting any return of their money, and that in fact they would be very lucky indeed if they ever made good their loss.
>
> 2. The Air Ministry would not allow Power Jets to become a manufacturing organization and intended to keep it as a small organization, and that for manufacture some existing firm would be used.

3. That nobody would make anything out of this engine because it belonged wholly to the Air Ministry and the Department would see that nobody made anything out of it. There would only be the normal legitimate manufacturing profit (from which Power Jets was excluded).

4. That the Air Ministry did not like Mr. Whyte's suggestion of an organization to handle manufacture in which Power Jets would be part owners.

5. That it was not healthy for an organization such as ours to depend so much on Air Ministry money: that it should get private money as well, but that it was of little use anybody putting money into Power Jets because if they did so they would lose it, there being no way by which they would get a normal return, Power Jets having no patent position by virtue of the fact that the Air Ministry controlled the situation in this respect, and no manufacturing rights.

6. That the Air Ministry would not place orders with Power Jets for other than experimental engines, and definitely would not place orders for other engines through Power Jets.

It is fortunate that I regard the above as expressions of your own opinion, and not those of the Department, as otherwise I would be most upset, since it would seem to me grossly unfair that the Air Ministry should allow Power Jets to ripen the fruit and others to pluck it. I am not after big dividends myself, but at the same time it would weigh heavily on me if I thought that many individuals who had put their money in largely because of their faith in me were not to see a just return on that money in the future. In any case I regard Power Jets' organization as almost as much my creation as the engine itself, and for that reason I want to see it expand. It is in a sense my only 'command' and I believe that Power Jets as such could handle this job in its future stages better than some existing aero-engine firm, who would probably rather kill it than get on with it.

We have plenty of evidence that the wolves are gathering round the door, and I have a very depressing feeling that your sympathies lie with the wolves.[69]

On February 22, after an angry meeting between Whittle and Whyte and British Thomson-Houston's H.N. Sporborg, Sporborg announced that BTH would do no more work on the W.2.[70] In the meantime, Whittle's attempts to work out a similar subcontracting relationship with the Rover Company were not getting anywhere. In fact, on March 31 commercial negotiations between Rover and Power Jets broke down, in Whittle's view, "in circumstances which had thoroughly poisoned the relationship between the two firms."[71] Meanwhile, Rover began negotiating with the Air Ministry to contract directly with them to produce the Whittle engine.

On March 25 the Air Ministry held a major development policy meeting at Harrowgate regarding the future of the Whittle engine. Air Marshal Tedder presided, with Pye, Tweedie and an official of the Contracts Directorate representing the government. Whyte and Whittle represented Power Jets and the Wilks Brothers represented Rover. Sporborg of BTH was not there. Whittle recalls the meeting:

Tedder said the purpose of the meeting was to reach conclusions which would enable development work to proceed as fast as possible. He was not expecting a production plant to be laid down yet, but development and design work should be done with production in view. To the great dismay of Whyte and myself, he went on to say that the Ministry proposed to give direct contracts to the Rover Company. Power Jets would be maintained as a research and development organization and would be expected to co-operate intimately with the Rover Co.[72]

The Air Ministry also made clear that they would not allow Power Jets to contemplate engine manufacture.[73] Although Tedder later reiterated in a meeting with BTH and Rover that Power Jets was to play a central role in the development of the Whittle turbojet, the two companies, henceforth, felt free to proceed as they wished.

Rover began quantity production of the Power Jets W.2 engine under subcontract in April. This would lead to the engine models W.B23, the prototype of the Rolls-Royce Welland (Figure 1-11), and the W.B26, the prototype of the Derwent I (see Figure 1-15).[74] Personal and design differences, however, were to plague the relationship among Rover, Power Jets, and the new British Ministry of Aircraft Production.[75]

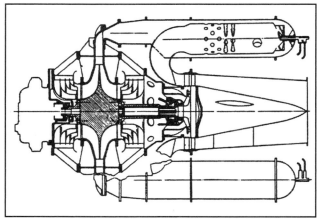

**Figure 1-11. W.B23, Prototype for the
Rolls-Royce Welland**
*(Drawing courtesy of Rolls-Royce)*

This troubled relationship had a great deal to do with the desire by Whittle and Power Jets to become a manufacturer of turbojets as well as a research, design, and test firm. Before deciding on Rover, Whittle had turned down a suggestion by W.L. Tweedie that Armstrong Siddeley take up production and further design work.[76] Whittle had a definite idea where he wanted Power Jets to go as a company, but he did not realize that the British Air Ministry had other plans.

The Ministry of Aircraft Production dealt Whittle another blow on April 12, 1940, with the news that the Air Ministry decided to split production of the Whittle W.1 engine between BTH and Rover. BTH agreed to resume development work on the W.2 engine. The Ministry of Aircraft Production placed direct contracts with both firms and retained Power Jets as a research firm only.[77]

Faced with this decision, Whittle mended his fences with Rover, and the development program got back on track. On the airframe side, Gloster was given authorization by the Air Ministry to proceed with development of the E.28/39 and F.9/40 (Meteor) prototypes.[78]

In London, Winston Churchill formed a new government in May 1940 and began a reorganization of British war production.[79] Whittle wanted the position of chief engineer of the whole turbojet development project, but Tedder and Freeman were noncommittal on this point.[80] On May 20 another blow fell on Power Jets. Whittle and Power Jets received a telegram from the Air Ministry "removing all priority from their work because it had been decided to concentrate the maximum possible effort on urgent short-term requirements, particularly fighters ... Aircraft in production were given absolute priority..."[81] Work virtually ceased as Whittle, Whyte, Bramson and others at Power Jets scrambled to obtain a commitment from the Ministry of Aircraft Production to reinstate the turbojet program as a war priority. They were able to accomplish this on June 11, after the reorganization of the Air Ministry as the Ministry of Aircraft Production.

Churchill named Lord Beaverbrook head of the Ministry of Aircraft Production and the Air Ministry transferred their technical departments to the new ministry. Lord Beaverbrook in turn appointed Roxbee Cox as Deputy Director of Scientific Research, giving him the special responsibility for jet engine research and development. Cox had formerly been Superintendent of Scientific Research at the Royal Aircraft Establishment. He named D.G. Tobin as his assistant, who became the channel for Power Jets communication with the ministry.[82]

In July, Whittle and Power Jets began work on a new combustion chamber utilizing atomized fuel injection developed by I. Lubbock of the Shell Petroleum Company. Whittle made it clear in *Jet* that at this point combustion ceased to be a significant obstacle to turbojet development. By September Power Jets had developed the capability to build enough internal components of combustion chambers to supply their own needs and those of BTH and Rover.[83]

Whittle also decided to construct an experimental version of the W.1, using a spare rotor and certain other components. The new version, designated the W.1X, was sent to the Gloster Company for use as a mockup for the E.28. The mockup worked fine and Gloster installed the engine in the E.28 without any difficulty.[84] Whittle's program was still progressing in spite of major development problems, one of which was in engine testing. Whittle and Power Jets could not test components separately due to their lack of component test facilities. Although he repeatedly asked the Air Ministry for component testing apparatus, Whittle was always turned down.[85] Was this part of a coordinated policy designed to keep Power Jets Ltd. "in its place" and therefore not a threat to the engine establishment, or was it a matter of ignorance and the "not invented here" syndrome? From the following events, it appears the former was the case.

In September 1940, Rolls-Royce's Hooker and Rolls-Royce President E.W. Hives visited the Rover plant to view the Whittle engine.[86] They were undoubtedly aware that the Ministry of Aircraft Production had decided that the turbojet was a potential war-winner. Although Rolls-Royce had major contracts with the Ministry of Aircraft Production for reciprocating aircraft engines, the company was, as later events were to prove, willing and able to expand facilities and expertise to produce turbojets as well. The British Air Ministry decided on a production target of 80 jet airframes and 160 jet engines per month from British industry.[87] This was no doubt a spur to Rolls-Royce's interest, as well as that of other British companies. Major British companies involved at this time included:

- Power Jets Research and Development
- Gloster Airframes
- BTH Engines
- Rover Engines
- Vauxhall Engines
- Lucas Combustion Development
- Shell Petroleum Combustion Development
- Ransome and Marles Bearings
- National Physical Laboratory Bearings
- Ricardo Engineering Company with Power Jets on "special problems"
- Mond Nickel Materials
- Metropolitan-Vickers with Royal Aircraft Establishment on engines
- Fraser & Chalmers with Royal Aircraft Establishment
- Armstrong Siddeley with Royal Aircraft Establishment on engines[88]

Not all interactions between Whittle and the Ministry of Aircraft Production resulted in setbacks. On October 18, Air Chief Marshal Sir Wilfred Freeman and Roxbee Cox visited Power Jets. Freeman and Cox told Whittle that Rover Company's first W.2.B would be made to Power Jets' design, a victory for Whittle and his team.[89] The Air Ministry also decided at this time to bring Vauxhall in to make turbojets strictly to Power Jets' design. On November 19 a delegation from Vauxhall visited Whittle and Power Jets. A week later, at a meeting at Vauxhall's works at Luton, Vauxhall contracted to build six W.2.Bs to Power Jets' design.[90]

On December 11 Power Jets received, assembled, and tested the first W.1.X engine. Gloster used this engine for taxiing runs in the Gloster E.28/39 in April 1941.[91] The W.1.X differed from the experimental engine in that the turbine had a greater number of blades (72 compared to the experimental engine's 66) and its new turbine incorporated "fir-tree" attachment of blade roots, whereas the first engine had incorporated the DeLaval type blade attachment (Figures 1-12 and 1-13). The W.1.X delivered 16,450 rpm. With this engine, Power Jets Ltd. now had two engines to test and work with. They had had only one engine, the W.1, to work with since April 1937.

**Figure 1-12. Fir Tree Blade Roots
for W.U. and W.I.X.**

*(Photo courtesy of Rolls-Royce)*

**Figure 1-13. 'DeLaval' Blade Roots
of W. U. After Failure**

*(Photo courtesy of Rolls-Royce)*

At this point Whittle devoted almost the whole of his design effort to the W.2.B turbojet engine. The design target for this engine was 1,800 pounds of thrust. This engine was to be the power plant of the Gloster F9/40 Meteor twin-engined interceptor fighter. This engine incorporated a very simple engine mounting. (The time to change an engine in the Meteor was about 30 minutes). This maintenance approach reflected Whittle's strong military background. BTH made the W.2 on Power Jets' contract. Another W.2 was under construction by Rover. This model differed slightly from the original Power Jets design.[92]

On January 2, 1941, Sir Henry Tizard announced at a meeting with BTH, Rover, Vauxhall and Power Jets, that the Air Ministry had decided to give the production contract for the W.2.B engine to Rover because that company already had two shadow factories capable of short-term conversion to jet engine production. As a result of this meeting, Vauxhall decided not to pursue development of turbojets. In order to help the production of engines, the Air Ministry ordered BTH to convert one of their W.2 engines to a W.2.B by stages. This conversion eventually became known as the W.2 Mark IV. The Ministry of Aircraft Production gave Rover a pre-production order for thirty engines and Gloster a preproduction order for twelve aircraft. The ministry also instructed Gloster to plan jigging and tooling for a rate of 20 aircraft per week.[93]

Power Jets received a W.1 turbojet from BTH for test running in February. The engine was not run right away; Power Jets dispatched it to Gloster to complete installation procedures in the E.28 airframe.[94]

On February 22, however, the third rebuild of the Whittle experimental engine was destroyed by a turbine failure after running a total of 170 hours since October 1938.[95] After receiving the W.1.X, Whittle had decided to subject the first engine, the W.1, to a series of endurance runs at cruising speed. The two most noteworthy of these were one of a little over 8 hours at 14,500 rpm, and one of just over 10 hours at 14,000 rpm.[96] Both tests made a statement about the durability of the engine.

On March 5, the Air Ministry decided that Rover was to be entirely responsible for the general mechanical and structural design and for the production of drawings of the W.2.B.[97] Rover was required to consult with Whittle on the entire design and to follow his requirements on turbine and compressor design, and on the general aerodynamic characteristics of the engine. The key clause in the agreement was:

... that the Ministry does not contemplate that the Rover Company will depart from the basic W.2.B drawings supplied by Power Jets Limited, other than is dictated by production reasons or their relevant mechanical experience.[98]

At that point, Whittle had lost the control that he desired on the general mechanical and structural design of the W.2.B.

On March 11, Power Jets handed over a complete set of drawings for the W.2.B engine to Rover.[99] A few days later, at a meeting of the ministry with Sir Henry Tizard presiding, Whittle and Power Jets were given equipment to make their own development engines, largely independent of sub-contractors.[100] It was a mixed victory. Power Jets had completed 40 hours of running on the W.1.X engine by the end of March,[101] but was still encountering bearing failures. The Power Jets team also began testing of the Rover-built W.2 (now nearly complete) over the strenuous objections of Rover.

Gloster completed the E.28 at the beginning of April and began taxiing trials on grass with the W.1.X engine on April 7. The engine throttle stop was set at 13,000 rpm, and as the grass was a little wet, the plane required 12,000 rpm to move at all and therefore would go only about 20 mph at 13,000 rpm. Whittle reported that P.E.G. Sayer, the Gloster test pilot, wasn't very happy about that.[102]

On April 8, the Gloster E.28 with the Whittle W.1.X reached a maximum speed of 60 mph in initial taxiing runs, with an engine speed of 15,000 rpm. In the afternoon Gloster Test Pilot Sayer took the E.28 airborne three times for a distance of 200 to 300 yards each time. Power Jets then removed the engine from the plane and took it back to their facility at Lutterworth to continue bench development work.[103] On April 12, the Whittle W.1 engine underwent a 25-hour bench test to clear it for a flight test.[104] Whittle called this 25-hour test a "special category" test. The maximum speed for the test was 16,500 rpm, which produced 860 pounds of thrust, except for one run up to 17,000 rpm and 1,000 pounds of thrust.[105]

At the beginning of May, Power Jets shipped the W.1 turbojet to Gloster for installation in the E.28.[106] On May 15, 1941, the E.28/39 took flight for the first time (Figure 1-14), with Flight Lt. P.E.G. Sayer at the controls. With its W.1 engine, the aircraft attained an altitude of 25,000 feet and a speed of 370 mph, and the jet age was born in Britain.[107] Whittle tells of that first flight:

**Figure 1-14. Gloster E.28/39**
*(Photo courtesy of Rolls-Royce)*

> Sayer was in position at about 7:40 p.m. He ran the engine up to 16,500 rpm against the brakes. He then released the brakes and the aeroplane quickly gathered speed and lifted smoothly from the runway after a run of about 600 yards. It continued to the west in a flat climb for several miles and disappeared from view behind cloud banks. For several minutes we could only hear the smooth roar of the engine. Then it came into sight again as it made a wide circuit preparatory to landing. As Sayer came in it was obvious that he had complete confidence in the aeroplane. He approached in a series of gliding turns as though he had flown the machine for hundreds of hours. Those of us who were pilots knew that he felt completely at home. He made a perfect landing at the far end of the runway and came to a stop somewhere short of where we were standing - the flight had lasted 17 minutes. He taxied towards us, stopped, and gave us a "thumbs up" sign.[108]

Flight trials continued for the next twelve days, during which time Gloster got in 10 hours flying time on the engine. After the first flight the Gloster crew was surprised when the Power Jets crew did not break the engine down for an immediate inspection, as was usual in test flights. Whittle states that the crew knew by the "smooth note" of the engine sound that everything was okay. Unlike the taxiing trials (which were on grass), the first official test flight took place at Royal Air Force Cranwell, on a concrete runway. No one from the Ministry of Aircraft Production was there on that historic occasion. The official demonstration flight for the dignitaries from the Ministry of Aircraft Production and officials from companies took place on May 21.[109]

By the end of May the total engine test time for Power Jets engines was at 292 hours. Of this, 108 hours had been distributed between the W.1.X and the W.1, including the flying time of 10½ hours. Testing time for the W.1.A was 7 hours, and for the W.2 was 2 hours. The W.2 engine, built by Rover, proved to be a disappointment on the test stand, suffering from compressor surges at 75 percent of full design speed. Power Jets also had surging trouble with the W.1.A, but they quickly found the cause of the trouble and corrected it.[110]

At a meeting in May 1941 the Ministry of Aircraft Production decided on a production target of 1,200 engines and 500 aircraft. These new aircraft and engines were scheduled to begin to appear in June and July of 1942 with production rising to 80 aircraft a month by November 1942. The Ministry estimated there was a chance of completing the first 500 jets by spring of 1943. Whittle considered that projection wildly optimistic: "The Ministry's optimism on this point may be gauged by the fact that one prototype only had flown by the end of March 1943."[111]

Whittle wrote to Tizard expressing concern that development efforts for the W.2.B were not being properly concentrated at Power Jets in Lutterworth so that the engine could be placed into production quickly. His goal was to concentrate efforts on those areas in doubt, rather than see BTH or Rover start from scratch with new designs. In his letter to Tizard, Whittle pointed out the areas in the W.2.B that did not need immediate concentration of efforts, and those areas that he believed did need such efforts:

> We know the gear box works, we know the fuel system works, we can feel fairly confident of the combustion chambers and blower, but there is grave doubt about the turbine end at present, and by far the greater part of the total effort should be directed to solving that problem.

He later admitted that he was over-confident about the blower and combustion chambers and unduly pessimistic about the turbine.[112]

Whittle was also having more problems interacting with Wilks and Rover. At this point he became upset that Rover was beginning to undertake basic design modifications to the W.2.B, while fighting the modifications proposed by Power Jets.[113] With his renewed difficulties with Rover, Whittle began to think of Rolls-Royce as a development partner. This was the opening that Rolls-Royce had been looking for. They had already been helping Power Jets in compressor development, having lent them the use of a compressor test rig. Rolls-Royce wanted to produce turbojets as well. They realized that the turbojet was going to be the high-speed aircraft engine of choice immediately after the war, when time and circumstances would be right for its development, and they had no turbojet development program of their own. A developmental re lationship with Power Jets would go a long way to helping Rolls-Royce develop turbojet engine-building expertise for future use. In June, the first in a series of meetings between Power Jets and Rolls-Royce took place at Rolls-Royce Derby. E.W. Hives promised to help Power Jets.[114]

In *Jet*, Whittle talks about a whispering campaign directed against Power Jets after the flight trials of the E.28. How much of this did Whittle imagine and how much was true? It obviously disturbed Whittle enough to write a letter about it to Bulman at the Ministry of Aircraft Production (dated June 22, 1941). Whittle felt that this campaign had been going on against him and Power Jets for some time. He also cited a phone call from Roxbee Cox on July 4, 1941, in which Cox expressed anxiety about fuel consumption. He said that he allayed Cox's anxiety by quoting some new fuel figures from tests of the W.1.A. It is possible that Whittle construed the concerns for fuel consumption— the turbojet is poor at low speed and low altitude—as a personal attack. Power Jets was reluctant to give out fuel consumption figures "when we had reason to believe that they were wanted solely to support propaganda against the jet engine as such."[115]

In July of 1941, BTH delivered the W.2 Mark IV to Power Jets for testing. This was the original Power Jets W.2 engine which BTH had modified in stages to bring it near to the W.2.B design. Whittle found during his tests of this engine that its speed was, like that of the W.2, limited by surging of the compressor. When airflow through the engine was increased until the surging stopped,

> … the resulting drop in efficiency was such that the speed was limited by a rise in the exhaust temperature above that permissible for the material of the turbine blades ... Observations made on the W.2.Mk.IV suggested that the turbine efficiency could be raised by a small change to the turbine blades, namely altering their setting by about five degrees.[116]

Although he also recommended this change to Rover, its relationship with Whittle and Power Jets had deteriorated to the point that Rover ignored Whittle's recommendation.

At the end of August 1941, D.N. Walker and G.B.R. Fielding of Power Jets developed an automatic starter for the W.1.X. Whittle gives the Ricardo Engineering Company substantial credit for fuel system development. Ricardo produced a speed limit governor and a barostat relief valve which automatically reduced the pressure in the fuel line as the airplane climbed, thus relieving the pilot from continuous adjustment of the throttle control.[117]

During September, Power Jets ran more than 24 hours of tests on the W.2 Mark IV.[118] The group was still concerned with the surging problem. Also during this month, Power Jets tried to have its relationship with the Ministry of Aircraft Production clarified. This was in line with Whittle's desire to have developmental control and a viable aircraft gas turbine engine-producing company as well. On September 10, Tinling of Power Jets wrote to Ministry of Aircraft Production of the difficulties of the company's position as a result of Ministry policy. He also requested that the Ministry of Aircraft Production recognize certain broad principles of policy concerning Power Jets Limited:

1.  that Power Jets Limited ought not to be prejudiced, or placed in financial jeopardy by the Ministry's policy, but, on the contrary, had a special claim to security;

2.  that the Company was entitled to be regarded as the main seat of the development of the Whittle and ancillary inventions both during the war and after;

3.  that Whittle's services should continue to be at the disposal of Power Jets Limited as long as was required to fulfill the objects of the Company;

4.  that the Company was entitled to protection against the competition of other organizations to whom its technology had been divulged;

5.  that if and when a similar situation arose in respect of developments in the United States, the company's American rights should not be prejudiced.[119]

Whittle claimed that Tinling was seeking something more specific than Tedder's assurance of a 'moral obligation' to protect the Company, but this was asking more than the Company could expect. Clause 3 was unusual, considering that Whittle had always, during the course of his turbojet work, been a serving officer in the RAF. If he was so committed to Power Jets Ltd., why didn't he resign his commission and "go private?" It would have been a difficult choice, but Whittle would have had a much stronger position to advocate what was in essence a corporate development philosophy.

In October 1941, Rover delivered the first of its W.2.Bs to Power Jets, which ran it for the first time on October 31. Whittle reported that they had trouble with this engine, like others, surging at low speeds. However, by fitting a W.2.B impeller (the first tests were done with a W.2 impeller, since the two impellers supplied were defective), they managed to get to 15,750 rpm before surging.[120]

## The British Gas Turbine Collaboration Committee

On August 23, 1941, Roxbee Cox talked to Whittle about having regular meetings among all the parties concerned in jet engine development.[121] On October 3, Cox created the Gas Turbine Collaboration Committee; all British organizations engaged in turbojet work were members.[122] The Ministry of Aircraft Production invited Power Jets, British Thomson-Houston, the Royal Aircraft Establishment, Metropolitan-Vickers Electrical, Major H. Halford, Messrs. Ricardo & Company, and Rolls-Royce. Whittle and Power Jets received a letter from Air Marshal Linnell, Controller of Research and Development, to the following effect:

> ... to encourage and guide collaboration, it has been decided to form a committee under the chairmanship of Dr. Roxbee Cox on which all the firms engaged on gas turbine projects will be represented with the object of:
>
> 1. avoiding duplication of effort;
>
> 2. pooling ideas;
>
> 3. pooling testing facilities;
>
> 4. pooling experience;
>
> 5. relating power units to the most appropriate airframes.

The first meeting of the Gas Turbine Collaboration Committee took place on November 1.[123] Cox summed up the purpose of the committee as follows:

> Each organization would provide, through the Committee, all the others with information on the layouts and performances of the engines they were designing.[124]

The Ministry of Aircraft Production also formed a High Temperature Materials Research Committee, which held frequent meetings during the war.

On October 10, Power Jets had a W.2 Mark IV compressor impeller burst, slightly injuring two of the crew.[125] Whittle estimated that the disaster cost the program six months. He attributed it to replacement of the W.2 Mark IV's compressor rotor with a compressor rotor of a W.2.B design. This rotor impeller shattered at 9,000 rpm.

> The impeller, weighing about 56 pounds had burst into two pieces which had hurtled round the test cell several times before coming to rest. The shaft linking the compressor impeller to the turbine wheel had fractured within half an inch of the turbine and remained attached to one of the two portions of the impeller.[126]

Inspection of the impeller showed that an extensive crack had existed in the impeller for some time, evidently escaping a BTH inspection. On October 14 the Air Ministry held a meeting to ascertain the cause of the incident. The Ministry of Aircraft Production immediately authorized Power Jets to provide an overspeed rig in which it would be possible to spin new rotor components up to a speed well above the design full speed before fitting them to engines.[127]

On November 18th the Air Ministry decided to clear twelve Rover/Whittle W.2.B turbojets at a reduced rating. Four of the turbojets were to be at 1,000 pounds of thrust, and the other eight at 1,200 pounds of thrust. By November 23 Power Jets was getting results from the W.2.B of 1,000 pounds at 14,750 rpm with a jet pipe temperature of 590°C and 1,190 pounds at 15,500 rpm with a jet pipe temperature of 620°C.[128] Surging occurred at 15,800 rpm at which the thrust and temperature were 1,270 pounds and 640°C, respectively. Whittle regarded 600°C as the maximum acceptable temperature at that time.[129]

In late November, the Ministry of Aircraft Production replied without commitment to Tinling's letter from Power Jets seeking assurances of the company's position.[130] The ministry said that it was impossible for the government to commit to anything beyond the current contract. They did, however, state "that the Department would not be an assenting party to the exploitation for commercial purposes by third parties of information obtained by the Company for military purposes and not otherwise procurable. The Minister considers that this problem must be left for consideration in the light of the circumstances prevailing, if and when it arises."[131]

Power Jets and Gloster cleared the W.1.A for flight in December.[132] Power Jets had not, however, solved all the problems. Not only was surging still a problem, but turbine blades began to fail as well. The availability of Nimonic 80, a product of the Mond Nickel Company and tested by the National Physical Laboratory at the end of 1941, was to prove very important in the subsequent history of the development of the turbojet. Nimonic 80 replaced Rex 78 in all subsequent Power Jets designs.[133] Power Jets also helped solve manufacturing problems for Rover and British Thomson-Houston. Whittle came up with a novel solution to turbine blade manufacture. He assigned two engineers attached to Power Jets Ltd. from the United Shoe Manufacturing Company of Leicester — J.A. Kestell and B. Barton — to the design of special machines for manufacturing turbine blades.[134]

On December 23, 1941, the Ministry of Aircraft Production, at a meeting at the Lucas Works in Birmingham under the chairmanship of Bulman's Deputy, Major A.A. Ross, redefined the relationship between Rover and Power Jets.[135] The Ministry made Rover directly responsible to it for the production development and design of the Rover Whittle W.2.B. This responsibility included all the major components for the accessory services and control systems. The Ministry also permitted Rover to experiment with changes in the basic Power Jets design and to make any changes that would assist production or enhance reliability, simplicity, and operation or performance. All former restrictions on the latitude of design for Rover vis-à-vis Power Jets were removed. Rover was clearly in control.[136]

Air Marshal Linnell then placed Power Jets under Bulman's authority as Director of Engine Research and Development (ER&D) instead of the company's normal position under the Director of Scientific Research. Bulman and Ross could thus direct Power Jets through ER&D's rulings.[137]

By the end of the year, Whittle's two existing turbojets had accumulated over 500 hours testing time.[138] Power Jets had also won from the Ministry of Aircraft Production the right to make experimental engines and spares up to an equivalent of twelve complete engines per year.[139]

In a letter to Air Marshal Linnell of the Ministry of Aircraft Production, Whittle reported that Power Jets had attained a thrust of 1,560 pounds with their W.2.B:[140]

> … though the results might seem a little disappointing when compared with expectations, the circumstances were such that we regard them as highly satisfactory and constituting an important landmark in the development - I will go so far as to say that the most serious aerodynamic and thermodynamic troubles which were limiting the development have now been overcome, and the main purpose of this letter is to put this opinion on record.[141]

Whittle probably did not realize at the time that this letter effectively ended all chances that Power Jets would become an independent producer of aircraft gas turbine engines. The government did not need Power Jets Ltd. to develop basic turbojet technology when Whittle had just stated that this technology was past the prototype development stage, where a company like Power Jets had the advantage. Now the technology was in the preproduction stage, where the engine companies who already had personnel and facilities available could take the engine technology to a fully mature condition and who could produce the engines in quantity. The government needed an establishment through which it could monitor the technology and work on advancing that technology in key areas, and it converted Power Jets into that establishment.

## Rolls-Royce Enters the Turbojet Field

On January 12, 1942, a new period in British aircraft gas turbine engine development began when Hives of Rolls-Royce invited Whittle to Derby to discuss a proposal. Hives wanted to build a version of the Whittle engine.[142] On January 21 Johnson, Whittle, and Walker of Power Jets met with Hives and Sidgreaves of Rolls-Royce at Derby. Rolls-Royce outlined their proposal for a larger engine similar to the W.2.B but with a thrust of 2,000 pounds. This marked the beginning of the Derwent turbojet (Figure 1-15).[143]

**Figure 1-15. Rolls-Royce Derwent I**
*(Photo courtesy of Rolls-Royce)*

Whittle felt that the Rolls-Royce design was "based on very conservative design assumptions..." He relates that Hives and Rolls-Royce considered the Griffith engine a long-term project. Rolls-Royce and Power Jets agreed to develop an engine together, with Power Jets the main contractor and Rolls-Royce a subcontractor. When the Ministry of Aircraft Production approved the deal several months later, Power Jets received contracts for the design and development of six engines, and immediately placed the requisite subcontracts with Rolls-Royce.[144]

On January 30 Hives and Sidgreaves visited the Power Jets facilities at Lutterworth and Brownsover. Rolls-Royce and Power Jets confirmed their informal agreement to cooperate. The next day, Whittle visited Derby and discussed Rolls-Royce's future activities with Hives.[145] Hives' concern centered on the end of the war, and Rolls-Royce's position in the aircraft engine market. Whittle relates how Hives predicted an "absolute glut of Merlin engines, which threatened stagnation in the aero-engine business unless they had something on the go which rendered the Merlin obsolete."[146]

By this time, Rover had introduced their version of the Whittle W.2.B, designated the B.26. Whittle asserted that the chief difference between the B.26 and the W.2.B was that the B.26 had straight-through combustion chambers instead of Power Jets' counterflow arrangement.

Whittle also stated that Power Jets in fact had a through-flow design in an engine he designated the W.3.X, but that Power Jets could not get this engine design built due to lack of facilities. Power Jets was quite indignant over this new development, calling it a "rearrangement" of the W.2.B.[147] Power Jets felt that Rover had not maintained a "full and frank interchange of information" between Rover and Power Jets. Whittle wanted Rover to share all engine development information with Power Jets, which would in effect keep Power Jets in the lead in development. What Whittle and Power Jets did not realize at this time was that Rover and Power Jets were in fact competitors. It was later learned that in April 1942, Major Ross of the Directorate of Engine Development had authorized the secret development of the B.26 by Rover, without notifying the Controller of Research and Development, the Director of Scientific Research, or Roxbee Cox, among others.[148]

Whittle and Power Jets had three engines of the W.2.B type to work with by the end of January. Two were Rover-built B.26 engines, and the third was manufactured by subcontractors. Flight trials of the E.28 powered by the W.1.A began at Edgehill in February, during which the test pilot reached a speed of 430 miles per hour at an altitude of 15,000 feet.[149] In the latter part of the month, Whittle and Power Jets committed to increasing the W.R.1 thrust target to 3,000 pounds.[150]

On March 13, 1942, Power Jets started a complete redesign of the W.2.B, which they designated the W.2/500.[151] While pursuing this additional line of development, Power Jets' Johnson pressed for flight-testing of the W.2.B turbojet in a Wellington bomber flying test-bed. Power Jets wanted the installation and testing conducted by Rolls-Royce. Air Marshal Linnell approved the plan.[152] Whittle felt that the Ministry of Aircraft Production's agreement to flying test-bed testing of the W.2.B. reflected their uneasiness with the project as a whole and was a response to previous industry over-optimism. Frequency of turbine blade failures was becoming the latest technological barrier to overcome. At this point Power Jets accepted a recommendation by the Royal Aircraft Establishment to adopt fewer (therefore larger) and stiffer turbine blades. Whittle credits this decision, along with Nimonic 80, as crucial to important turbine advances later.[153]

In May the Air Ministry finally provided Power Jets with the capability to test components separately. Power Jets installed this new test facility at Whetstone.[154] Also in May, Rover initiated a move to have the B.26 variant of the W.2.B made the authorized production engine, instead of the W.2.B. On May 21, at a Ministry of Aircraft Production meeting at Clitheroe, the ministry decided to permit Rover to develop the B.26. The W.2.B production development was, however, to take priority.[155] It is significant that at this meeting Dr. Constant of the Royal Aircraft Establishment made points against adoption of the B.26 as the production engine. These points agreed with arguments set forth by Power Jets.

During May 1942 Whittle sat down and laid out Power Jets' research and development mission. In his words:

> We ought to be required and to be equipped to carry out the following duties:
>
> 1. To design and develop up to the production stage such types of aircraft gas turbines as might be considered by the Ministry of Aircraft Production to be likely to be required in quantity, including the manufacture of the prototype engines necessary for this work, and if necessary to produce for this purpose (say) fifty prototypes in nine months from the initiation of design.
>
> 2. To do all forms of work directed towards development of the "species", and for this purpose to design and manufacture experimental engines, experimental compressors, turbines, etc.
>
> 3. To design, make and try out tools and production equipment suitable for quantity production of any type of engine developed by Power Jets, and to obtain the complete data required to plan a factory for large-scale production, and generally to perform the functions of a "production nursery."

4.  To undertake a certain amount of research and development on production methods and technique, such work to include:

    a)  extension of applications of (the then) existing processes to meet the needs of gas turbine production;

    b)  to devise and develop new processes and tools.

Gloster used two Rover B23s (prototype of the Welland) for taxiing trials in the prototype Meteor (Figure 1-16) in July.[156] Also in July, the Gas Turbine Collaboration Committee established a Combustion Panel devoted to combustor research under the chairmanship of Professor Lander of the Imperial College of Science and Technology. The panel was composed of representatives from Asiatic Petroleum, Lucas, Power Jets, Royal Aircraft Establishment, universities and other research groups.[157] In August, the Ministry of Aircraft Production formed a technical committee to advance the development of the W.2.B for the F.9/40 Meteor and to bring Power Jets and Rover together to discuss problems.[158]

**Figure 1-16. Britain's First Jet Fighter, the Gloster Meteor**
*(Photo courtesy of Rolls-Royce)*

Power Jets test-ran the 835-pound W.2/500 turbojet on September 13, 1942.[159] After a preliminary run of thirty minutes to adjust it, Whittle's team ran the engine up to full speed and made full sets of readings. They recorded a thrust of 1,750 pounds at full speed and 1,800 pounds at a slight overspeed. The engine ran an official acceptance test at full speed for five minutes. The W.2/500 had a problem with the compressor impeller of the same kind as was occurring on W.2.B engines — a risk of failure through resonant vibration. Power Jets continued to test, but with interim modifications to make the impeller safe enough to test the rest of the W.2/500 for reliability. These modifications reduced the engine thrust to 1,600 pounds.[160] Power Jets had tried injecting water at the compressor intake with the W.1.A and got a thrust increase of about 10 percent.[161] Ammonia injection on the W.2.B resulted in about a 33 percent increase in thrust, but Power Jets dropped the experiments when they found that the ammonia was corroding copper alloys in the engine.[162]

Power Jets had a total of three compressor impeller failures during the months of September and October. General Electric (GE) in America and Rover were having similar troubles. These failures usually caused extensive damage and thus slowed development. Modifications suggested by GE and the Royal Aircraft Establishment eventually eliminated the trouble.[163]

Hives and Sidgreaves of Rolls-Royce visited Power Jets on October 8. Whittle invited them to consider quantity production of the W.2/500 turbojet.[164] Whittle followed this up on November 16 with a letter formally requesting Rolls-Royce to consider quantity production of the W.2/500 turbojet. This was due to the proposal by Air Marshal Linnell of the Ministry of Aircraft Production on October 18 to introduce the W.2/500 as a replacement for the W.2.B. This substitution would be subject to the completion of a 100-hour type test of the engine. If the test was successful, Linnell promised to authorize Power Jets to manufacture an additional 12

W.2/500 engines plus spares at Whetstone.[165] However, on October 16, Tinling of Power Jets wrote to Linnell that Power Jets was far from able to fill a proposed production order of twelve W.2/500s.[166] Power Jets had capacity to build only four engines per year at Whetstone. He attributed this to lack of manpower. Hence the decision by Power Jets to approach Rolls-Royce.

Hives again visited Power Jets on December 4. He briefed them on a series of discussions that had taken place with Sir Wilfred Freeman, chief executive of the Ministry of Aircraft Production, on the production of jet engines.[167] A week later Freeman summoned Whittle to the Ministry of Aircraft Production. With Linnell present, Freeman told Whittle that he was transferring the Rover factories at Barnoldswick and Clitheroe to Rolls-Royce management. Although he at first proposed to place Power Jets under Rolls-Royce as well, Whittle convinced him to wait. Freeman had in addition made some important changes at the Ministry of Aircraft Production. He had placed Roxbee Cox directly in charge of all gas turbine development, reporting directly to Linnell.[168]

On December 12, a meeting of the Gas Turbine Collaboration Committee took place at Rolls-Royce's Derby facility. Roxbee Cox, Rolls-Royce's Chief Engineer A.G. Elliot, and Whittle agreed to the terms of the new development and production relationship between Rolls-Royce and Power Jets Limited. Whittle recorded the terms of the agreement:

1.  Machine tools and labor at Rolls-Royce Barnoldswick must continue to be used to the full.

2.  Rolls-Royce should undertake the production of the W.2/500 at Barnoldswick.

3.  Production of the W.2/500 would be to a design agreed between Rolls-Royce and Whittle.

4.  That in relation to the W.2/500 and future engines of the same series, Power Jets' engineering policy would be one agreed between Whittle and Rolls-Royce - this engineering liaison to be so close that any blame or credit was carried jointly.

5.  That research and development especially in relation to new designs should remain the function of Power Jets Limited, and that it should continue to take place at Whetstone.

6.  Rolls-Royce to undertake such manufacture of experimental parts as was necessary.

7.  Rolls-Royce would do all they could to increase the efficiency of Whetstone.[169]

Roxbee Cox placed this agreement on record on December 15 in a letter to Power Jets. To cap this important event, Rolls-Royce's Hives called Whittle on December 19. Hives told Whittle that, in a meeting the day before, Hives and Wilks of Rover had met and agreed to trade Rolls Royce's tank engine production for Rover's aircraft gas turbine engine work.[170] This marked a historic moment for Britain and Rolls-Royce. In the last forty years, Rolls-Royce has come to stand for the best in British aircraft gas turbine technology. They largely have Sir Frank Whittle and E.W. Hives to thank for their start in the new technology. Meanwhile, at Power Jets, Whittle's team completed a 25-hour special category test on the W.2/500 of five 5-hour cycles, each cycle including 40 minutes at full speed.[171] The total running time during 1942 at Power Jets was just over 709 hours.[172] Rover had about twenty engines in development at the end of 1942, with a total running time of over 578 hours.[173]

Whittle relates that 1943 was to bring some labor unrest to Power Jets' facilities. He attributed this unrest to the poor quality and quantity of workers at Whetstone, poor morale stemming from workers' perception of Power Jets' future, and the presence of Communist agitators.[174] The Ministry of Aircraft Production put pressure on Power Jets to complete a 100-hour type test as soon as possible, because such a test was a prerequisite to production.[175] At this time the production schedule for the W.2.B had been cut back from an anticipated eighty a month to thirty a month. Later the Meteor I program would be cut back to a total of fifty, pending a decision whether or not the H.1 would power the Meteor II.[176]

On January 5, 1943, Whittle and Rolls-Royce's Hives agreed that Rolls-Royce would henceforth be responsible for all engineering work at Barnoldswick and Clitheroe. Hives placed Rolls-Royce's Stanley Hooker in charge at the two new Rolls-Royce facilities. Power Jets agreed to forward all W.2/500 drawings to Rolls-Royce at once.

Power Jets began testing a second W.2/500 in February, and a third went on test in March. This third engine, however, was damaged beyond repair later that month.[177]

On April 19 a key discussion of the Rolls-Royce/Power Jets relationship took place at Derby between Hives of Rolls-Royce and Whittle of Power Jets.[178] Rolls-Royce had begun initial development of a variant of the W.2/500 called the RB.37. Rolls-Royce claimed, naturally, that this design was an improvement over Whittle's. Whittle should have expected this from Rolls-Royce. This was what engine companies did, improve engine designs. This of course was not what Whittle had in mind when he wanted to work with Rolls-Royce. Whittle believed that development of the RB.37 marked the beginning of Power Jets' difficulties with Rolls-Royce. Again the point of contention was the frame of reference between Power Jets and an engine company, with the company (Rolls-Royce) claiming difficulty dealing with Power Jets. The root cause of disagreement proved, however, to have been an abortive attempt at agreement between Rolls-Royce and Power Jets in January 1942. At that time both companies had allowed a potential collaborative agreement to lapse because each side thought the other should act first.[179] Whittle also stated that it became clear that Rolls-Royce linked cooperation with Power Jets with Whittle remaining part of the Power Jets organization. This was an issue because Whittle had recently been ordered by the RAF to attend the War Course at the Staff College at Bulstrode Park, Gerrard's Cross, at the time, and he was uncertain whether or not the RAF would let him return to Power Jets.[180] Rolls-Royce's Sidgreaves told Whittle that Rolls-Royce considered him to be Power Jets Limited's major asset.

On April 23, during a visit to Power Jets, Rolls-Royce announced that with its influence, Rolls-Royce had been able to change the Ministry of Aircraft Production's production program once again to boost quotas to over 300 Meteors. However, Rolls-Royce's Dr. Stanley G. Hooker informed Whittle that the B.37 engine combined what Rolls-Royce regarded as the best features of the B.26 and the W.2/500.[181] Whittle relates in *Jet* that in a separate discussion between Rolls-Royce's Hives and Power Jets' Johnson, Hives informed Johnson that Rolls-Royce intended to be the center of the entire jet engine business. Therefore, Rolls-Royce was not accepting the Ministry of Aircraft Production's proposed agreement for collaboration with Power Jets Limited. Rolls-Royce did not intend to remain in an inferior position vis-à-vis Power Jets. In fact the proposed commercial collaboration between Rolls-Royce and Power Jets never did take place. The technical collaboration, however, remained unaffected and cordial.

In late April 1943, Whittle wrote to Sir Stafford Cripps, the Minister of Aircraft Production, advocating the nationalization of the aircraft gas turbine engine industry. He also recommended that the Ministry of Aircraft Production take specific steps to accomplish this.[182] Whittle advocated this course for several reasons. First, Whittle estimated that 99 percent of the total expenditure to that point had been government funds. The remaining one percent represented £23,000 from Power Jets. Second, government institutions such as the Royal Aircraft Establishment and the National Physical Laboratory had provided to industry a great deal of the necessary information required for design of aircraft gas turbine engines. Thirdly, two of the three leading engineers in the field, Dr. Constant and Whittle, were currently State servants. The third engineer, Dr. Griffith, now worked for Rolls-Royce. The fourth reason was that the State was logically going to be the principal user of the new technology (Whittle clearly did not foresee the commercial passenger-carrier market after the war). Finally, Whittle believed that the interchange of technology between the government and the companies, and between the companies themselves, that had taken place would make it "virtually impossible" to sort out patent rights and competing claims after the war. On May 11 Whittle and Sir Stafford Cripps met to discuss nationalization of the aircraft gas turbine engine industry. Whittle came away from that meeting with the uneasy feeling that the Ministry of Aircraft Production intended to nationalize only Power Jets Limited.[183]

Gloster Aircraft flew the Meteor with the W.2.B turbojet in June 1943 (Figure 1-17). Power Jets devoted the last six months of 1943 to transferring development efforts from the W.2/500 to the W.2/700, a 2,000-pound-thrust variant of the W.2/500 (Figure 1-18).[184] By August, Power Jets had four W.2/500s and one W.2/700 on test. In November, Gloster test-flew two W.2/500 turbojet engines in a Meteor prototype.[185] By the end of 1943 Power Jets had succeeded in getting over 2,000 pounds of thrust from a W.2/500 engine. This was accomplished under overspeed conditions with an experimental compressor casing and employing a "Type 16" diffuser.[186]

**Figure 1-17. The Meteor I in Flight**
*(Photo courtesy of Rolls-Royce)*

Power Jets Ltd. was beginning to have failures of impellers that had accumulated many hours of running time. Whittle, after considering the problem, theorized that the impeller failures were due to a resonant vibration occurring at relatively low speeds.

> On investigation I found that the test-house personnel were in the habit of running quickly through the speed at which there was a pronounced "howl" from the engine, which probably accounted for the apparent safety of some impellers. After running an engine for an hour at "howling speed" to test this hypothesis we found every impeller blade cracked.

This was probably high-cycle fatigue caused by either a rotating stall or flutter. Whittle relates that Rolls-Royce dealt with the problem by stiffening the impeller blades.[187] During this period, research on the W.2.B at Power Jets also diminished. Whittle attributed this to Rolls-Royce's intensive work on the W.2.B at Barnoldswick.[188] Was Power Jets Limited putting too much of their effort into their W.2/700 design, which was competing with the RB.37? Was

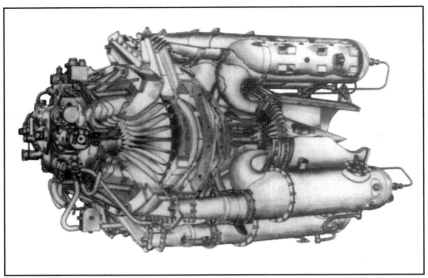

**Figure 1-18. Cutaway of the W.2/700**
*(Illustration courtesy of Rolls-Royce)*

Power Jets maintaining their objectivity, or were they becoming a competitor with Rolls-Royce? Whittle stated that the Ministry of Aircraft Production was in a quandary as to which engine to put into production to replace the W.2.B.[189] Ultimately, the Ministry of Aircraft Production chose the RB.37.

In January of 1944, a Power Jets W.2/700 engine completed a 100-hour test at a thrust rating of 1,800 pounds. A second W.2/700 achieved a thrust rating of 2,130 pounds, with a specific fuel consumption of 1.042 pounds per hour per pound of thrust.[190] Power Jets could claim with some justification that in the three years since the flight trials of the E.28, they had achieved a reduction of about 30 percent in specific fuel consumption.[191] In April, Power Jets and Gloster installed and flight tested two W.2/700 turbojets in one of the prototype Meteors. They conducted test flights of the W.2/700 as well in the Gloster E.28 and the Wellington flying test-bed.[192]

In December, Power Jets Limited Research & Development (R&D) fitted a W.2/700 engine with lengthened turbine blades and achieved a thrust of 2,290 pounds.[193] They had accomplished a substantial amount of development on the W.2/500, but it was secondary development. They had achieved a speed of 476 mph with an E.28 powered by a W.2/500. An altitude of 43,000 feet was the limit, as the E.28 did not have a pressurized cockpit. Nevertheless, by the end of 1944, work on the W.2/500 had ceased. Power Jets Ltd., and later Power Jets Ltd. (R&D), concentrated on two subsequent areas: running the engines with petrol instead of kerosene and the development of thrust augmentation by burning additional fuel in the exhaust after the turbine (afterburning).[194]

In March of 1945, Power Jets Ltd. (R&D) had reached a level of production of 30 complete W.2/700 engines per year, with additional parts equivalent to 15 engines per year.[195] In April, a Power Jets Ltd. (R&D) W.2/700 completed a 100-hour test at a rating of 2,200 pounds. This represented the peak of the main line of engine development at Power Jets.

## The Transfer of the Whittle Engine to the United States

This chapter would not be complete without a brief summary of the transfer of the Whittle engine technology to the United States. In May of 1941, U.S. General Henry H. "Hap" Arnold observed the Whittle engine during a test run. He went on to observe the Gloster airframe and other British developments in aircraft gas turbines.[196] Arnold was convinced that the United States needed a similar capability. He told his staff to find a way to transfer this knowledge to America.

Meetings between an Army Air Force (AAF) Liaison Committee and the British began on July 22. The American members were Colonel A.J. Lyon and Major Carl Brandt of the Army Air Force and D. Roy Shoults of the General Electric Company's Gas Turbine Division senior staff. The British representatives were Air Marshal Linnell of the Ministry of Aircraft Production, a representative from Power Jets, and Roxbee Cox. The Army Air Force's Lyon and his deputy, Major Donald J. Keirn, concentrated on the transfer of the Whittle engine to the United States. Major Brandt focused on liaison with Gloster on the Meteor airframe, consulting with George Carter, designer of the Gloster E.28/39 and the Meteor.[197] The British RAF officers appointed as liaisons to the Americans were Wing Commander G.E. Watt at the Ministry of Aircraft Production and Major J. Heenan at the British Air Commission in Washington.[198]

On October 1, upon completion of test facilities in the United States, Major Keirn returned to the United States from England with the W.1.X jet engine, drawings of the W.2.B, and a team of Power Jets engineers.[199] The members of the Power Jets team were Chief Test Engineer D. Walker, Experimental Fitter G.B. Bozzoni, and RAF Flight Sergeant J.A. King.[200] Whittle reports that Power Jets did not send a copy of the W.2.B plans with their W.1.X engine. The British Ministry of Aircraft Production must have provided the W.2.B design.[201] Whittle later related that the British Air Commission informed him that the GE Company was going to build engines in accordance with the W.2.B design, instead of the W.1.X. GE also informed Whittle that the GE work was to be known as the "exhaust turbo-blower Type I" for security purposes.[202]

On October 1, 1941, the drive to construct and perfect the Whittle turbojet had gone international. On that date, the U.S. Army Air Corps delivered a W.1.X engine and drawings of the W.2.B engine, along with a team of Power Jets engineers to the GE Company at Lynn, Massachusetts. This event culminated efforts begun in July 1941 by the U.S. Army Air Corps to transfer British turbojet technology to the United States for further development.

On April 22, 1942, the first GE W.2.B engine (designated the GE I-A) went onto the test bench in the United States, beating the target date of May 1.[203] Whittle arrived in Boston in May with drawings of the W.2/500 turbojet engine.[204] Whittle places his arrival in New York as taking place on June 4, and he says nothing about having the plans for the W.2/500 with him.[205] However, after Whittle returned home on August 14, he learned that GE had decided to proceed with a new engine based on the W.2/500, which they called the Type I-16. How else would they have gotten the design for the W.2/500 if Whittle had not brought the plans with him?

Whittle related that his schedule for this trip included stops in Washington D.C.; Buffalo and Schenectady, New York; Dayton, Ohio; and Los Angeles, California. Whittle worked most closely with Donald F. Warner, GE's chief engineer responsible for the work, and his staff of engineers and draftsmen. The GE engine was chiefly based on the Rover drawings, but as Whittle remembered:

> They had preferred Power Jets' practice in certain features of the mechanical design, especially bearings, and in some ways they had modified from the British drawings as a result of their own experience...

At the time of his visit, GE had only one engine running (Figure 1-19), but they had almost finished another and a few others were nearing completion.[206]

**Figure 1-19. GE 1-A on Test**
*(Photo courtesy of GE)*

While on his trip, Whittle visited the GE TG180 project in Schenectady. This was an axial turbojet effort independent of British technology that had been started by GE in 1939. Whittle observed:

> This engine was well beyond the preliminary design phase. Indeed, manufacture was then well advanced, but nevertheless by comparison with our work it was still very much in the embryo stage.[207]

Whittle also reports that the Bell Aircraft Corporation had nearly completed construction of the first P-59A prototype. While in Los Angeles, he visited "another propeller gas turbine project in a very preliminary stage." This was the axial turbojet designed by Nathan Price starting in 1939, again independent of British technology.

Whittle heard about the Navy aircraft gas turbine engine developments while in Washington. He relates that the Navy was "sponsoring about four schemes altogether, of which the most important was a turbo-jet engine project at Westinghouse, similar to the Royal Aircraft Establishment/Metropolitan Vickers F2. ... None of them had reached the test bench." Whittle also learned that a new facility for high-altitude testing of jet engines was already under construction.[208]

## The Nationalization of Power Jets

On October 25, 1943, Whittle's worst fears came to pass. Sir Stafford Cripps told Whittle that the Ministry of Aircraft Production intended to nationalize Power Jets Ltd.[209] Whittle related the conversation:

> He told me that he had decided that Power Jets was to be taken over by the State on the ground that it was essential to have a State-owned gas turbine experimental establishment, and that it would be wasteful to start building another while an organization which had already absorbed a large amount of public money was already in existence.

The following day Whittle wrote to the Ministry of Aircraft Production protesting the takeover. On November 2, Sir Stafford Cripps and Sir Harold Scott of the Ministry of Aircraft Production met with Whittle, Williams and Tinling of Power Jets. At this meeting, Cripps threatened to assume control over the government-owned assets of Power Jets Ltd., unless the company agreed to a government buyout of those assets.[210]

On January 6, 1944, a letter from Sam Browne of the Ministry of Aircraft Production to Power Jets' Tinling arrived. In it the Ministry of Aircraft Production went on record as offering to delay repossession of Power Jets' facilities at Whetstone in return for a decision by Power Jets to arrive at a "mutually negotiable price" for the company.[211] The Ministry invited Whittle to become a member of the Board of the new company, to be called Power Jets Limited (R&D).[212]

In February, Rolls-Royce arrived at an agreement with the Ministry of Aircraft Production. They agreed that the new government gas turbine establishment to be set up from Power Jets Ltd. would not be competitive with industry.[213] It appeared that Rolls-Royce had come away from the fray with all the battle honors. They had established themselves in the new technology with three distinct advantages. First, they had taken over the largest aircraft gas turbine engine manufacturer's facilities (Rover) while sacrificing a facility that would require large amounts of capital to retool (their tank manufacturing facility). Second, they had incorporated the latest and best turbojet design available (Power Jets' W.2/500) with little effort on their own part. Finally, they had eliminated from the field one of their biggest potential new design competitors (Power Jets) while ensuring their support for future work.

On April 27, in a letter from the Ministry of Aircraft Production to Power Jets Limited, the Ministry laid out the terms of reference for the new Power Jets Limited (R&D).[214] Whittle recorded the full text of the letter:

> Now that Power Jets (R&D), has been formed and is ready to operate, I think it would be useful to you and your colleagues on the Board if I were to set out shortly the primary objective which I would like the Board to pursue in managing this undertaking. This objective may be summarized as follows:
>
> To act as the recognized national establishment for furthering, in collaboration with industry and the Services, the advancement of knowledge on the subject of gas turbine engines and their use in aircraft, and for this purpose:
>
> 1. to conduct research on such engines and their components, accessories and materials of construction;
>
> 2. to design, construct and develop prototype engines, components and accessories, and to develop materials for their construction;
>
> 3. to devise methods of manufacture appropriate to such engines, and to manufacture small batches of such engines so as to carry development up to the production stage;
>
> 4. to test such engines, their components, accessories and materials of construction, on the test bed, in the laboratory and in the air, and to design, develop and construct apparatus for this purpose;
>
> 5. to make available to those concerned by reports and otherwise the knowledge obtained by such work;
>
> 6. to train Service and civilian personnel for the various countries of the British Commonwealth in the technique of the gas turbine engine and the other work carried on at the Establishment; and
>
> 7. to do such other work or things as the responsible Minister may direct on behalf of His Majesty's Government.
>
> As you are aware, it is my wish that on questions of technical policy, you and your colleagues should seek the advice and assistance of, and work in the closest collaboration with, the Gas Turbine Technical Advisory and Co-Ordinating Committee, which I am establishing under your Chairmanship.[215]

On April 28, 1944, Power Jets formally accepted the purchase of the company by the government for £135,563 and 10s. Dr. Hayne Constant, formerly the head of Pyestock, became Power Jets Limited (R&D) engineering chief. Whittle became the Chief Technical Advisor to the Board. When the Power Jets Limited shareholders met to accept the government offer, the government circulated a letter summing up the sums spent in support of the company's programs. Plant and equipment support costs had come to £350,000 and development costs had come to £950,000.[216]

Whittle's thoughts on the end of Power Jets Limited as a private company:

> So ended Power Jets Limited, the private Company which had founded an industry. Rarely, I imagine, have a Ministry's powers been used so ruthlessly, and I still do not understand why even arbitration was refused.[217]

The Ministry of Aircraft Production appointed an advisory committee, the Gas Turbine Technical Advisory and Co-Ordinating Committee (GTTACC), whose function was to advise the Power Jets Limited (R&D) Board. Roxbee Cox was the chair. The aircraft industry was well represented in the persons of Hives of Rolls-Royce, Halford of de Havilland, Rowbotham of Bristol, Sporborg of British Thomson-Houston, and K. Baumann of Metropolitan Vickers. Whittle was also a member, but was not present at the first two meetings as he was convalescing in a hospital. The GTTACC also formed an internal subgroup, called the Technical Policy Committee. Whittle was also a member of this subgroup for a short time. Disenchanted with the government's maneuverings, Whittle resigned from the Board of Power Jets Limited (R&D) on January 26, 1946.

On May 26 the British government divested Power Jets Limited (R&D) of its facilities, which they then assigned to a newly formed National Gas Turbine Establishment.[218] The companies had won, and Power Jets was no longer a rival to their interests.

The Whittle Era of British aircraft gas turbine engine development was over. King George VI knighted Frank Whittle in 1948. Although he ultimately failed in his quest to make Power Jets a full-fledged turbojet manufacturer, his contributions to British aircraft gas turbine technology proved to be invaluable.

Whittle lost his campaign to save Power Jets as an independent corporate entity because he strove to retain total control over his invention and subsequent innovations. He sought to develop his technology in the traditions of Edison, Bell, and others. That tradition, although a successful model of development up to that time, was inapplicable to the British aircraft engine community shortly before, during, and after World War II. Whittle strove to maintain total design, construction, component development, and production control over his engines, while struggling with both limited resources and the demands of a military career. At the same time, the British government, intent on both maintaining its own control over the development process and channeling the young officer's creative ability, sought to produce engines in a time of war.

Given his limited ability to shape decisions in the British Air Ministry from the start, Whittle could not hope to beat the system. In the end, the aircraft engine community sought to eliminate what they felt to be a potential rival. This goal coincided with the British government's desire for an easily acquired, established focus of expertise to use as the nucleus for a national aircraft gas turbine research and development center. Looking back with the perspective of forty-five years, it is amazing how Sir Frank was able to maintain his organization's independence and focus for so long in the face of such determined efforts by the British aircraft establishment to absorb it.

## Endnotes

[1] Whittle, Frank, *Jet: The Story of a Pioneer*, London: Frederick Muller, 1953, 20-21.

[2] Whittle, Frank, "The Birth of the Jet Engine in Britain," from *The Jet Age: Forty Years of Jet Aviation,* Walter J. Boyne and Donald S. Lopez, editors, Washington, D.C.: Smithsonian Institution, 1979, 3-4.

3   Whittle, *Jet*, 25-26.

4   Whittle, *Jet*, 26.

5   Ibid.

6   Constant, Edward W. II, *The Origins of the Turbojet Revolution*, Baltimore: The Johns Hopkins University Press, 1980, 184-185.

7   Schlaifer, Robert, *Development of Aircraft Engines*, Boston, MA: Harvard University Press, 1949, 339.

8   Whittle, *Jet*, 38.

9   Constant, *Origins*, 296.

10  Whittle, *Jet*, 39-40.

11  Ibid, 40.

12  Ibid, 42.

13  Ibid, 50-51.

14  Ibid, 47.

15  Ibid, 49.

16  Constant, *Origins*, 188.

17  Whittle, *Jet*, 51.

18  Ibid, 53, and Golley, John, in association with Sir Frank Whittle, *Whittle: The True Story*, Washington, D.C.: Smithsonian Institution Press, 1987, 74.

19  Whittle, *Jet*, 52-53.

20  Whittle, "Birth of the Jet," 7.

21  Whittle, *Jet*, 54.

22  Constant, *Origins*, 190, and Golley and Whittle, *Whittle*, 76.

23  Whittle, *Jet*, 59.

24  Constant, *Origins*, 190-191.

25  Whittle, *Jet*, 54, and Golley and Whittle, *Whittle*, 76.

26  Whittle, *Jet*, 56.

27  Ibid, 57, and Golley and Whittle, *Whittle*, 81, and Whittle, *Jet*, 60.

28  Whittle, *Jet*, 60-65.

29  Ibid, 67.

30  Ibid, 65.

31  Constant, *Origins*, 194.

32  Whittle, *Jet*, 71-75.

33  Golley and Whittle, *Whittle*, 98-99.

34  Whittle, *Jet*, 75.

35  Ibid, 75-76.

36  Golley and Whittle, *Whittle*, 106.

37  Whittle, *Jet*, 76-77.

38  Ibid, 77.

39  Ibid, 78.

40  Ibid, 77.

41  Golley and Whittle, *Whittle*, 109.

42  Whittle, *Jet*, 82.

43  Ibid, and Golley and Whittle, *Whittle*, 114.

44  Constant, *Origins*, 194.

45  Golley and Whittle, *Whittle*, 122.

46  Whittle, *Jet*, 82.

47  Ibid, 84.

48  Ibid, 84.

49  Ibid, 84.

50  Ibid, 86-87, and Golley and Whittle, *Whittle*, 118.

51  Whittle, *Jet*, 85.

52  Ibid, 89

53  Neville, Leslie E. and Silsbee, Nathaniel F., "The AAF and American Industry Pull a Miracle," from *Jet Propulsion Progress*, New York: McGraw-Hill Book Company, 1948, 42, and Whittle, *Jet*, 89.

54  Ibid.

55  Ibid.

56  Golley and Whittle, *Whittle*, 122.

57  Ibid, 120.

58  Ibid, 127.

59  Whittle, *Jet*, 90.

60  Golley and Whittle, *Whittle*, 124.

61  Whittle, *Jet*, 91.

62  Ibid, 97-98.

63  Golley and Whittle, *Whittle*, 134.

64  Whittle, *Jet*, 99.

65  Golley and Whittle, *Whittle*, 133-134.

66  Whittle, *Jet*, 100-101.

67  Ibid, 123-124.

68  Johnson, Brian, *The Secret War*, New York: Methuen Inc., 1978, 291.

69  Whittle, *Jet*, 102-103.

70  Ibid, 107.

71  Ibid, 106, and Golley and Whittle, *Whittle*, 141.

72  Whittle, *Jet*, 104.

73  Ibid, 104-105, and Golley and Whittle, *Whittle*, 139.

74  Neville and Silsbee, *Jet Propulsion Progress,* 43.

75  Constant, *Origins*, 193.

76  Whittle, *Jet*, 100.

77  Ibid, 105, and Golley and Whittle, *Whittle*, 141.

78  Ibid, 143.

79  Morgan, Kenneth O., editor, *The Oxford Illustrated History of Britain*, Oxford: Oxford University Press, 1984, 556, and Parrish, Thomas, ed., *The Simon and Schuster Encyclopedia of World War II*, S.L.A. Marshall, Chief Consultant Editor, New York: Simon and Schuster, 1978, 112.

80  Golley and Whittle, *Whittle*, 144.

81  Ibid, 146.

82  Whittle, *Jet*, 111.

83  Ibid, 122.

84  Ibid, 123.

85  Ibid, 120.

86  Johnson, *The Secret War,* 291.

87  Whittle, *Jet*, 135.

88  Ibid.

89  Ibid, 125.

90  Ibid, 129.

91  Neville and Silsbee, *Jet Propulsion Progress*, 43.

92  Whittle, *Jet*, 124-125.

93  Ibid, 138-139.

94  Ibid, 137.

95  Constant, *Origins*, 192.

[96] Whittle, *Jet*, 137.

[97] Ibid, 144.

[98] Ibid.

[99] Ibid, 145.

[100] Ibid, 146.

[101] Ibid.

[102] Ibid, 147-148.

[103] Ibid, 148-149.

[104] Neville and Silsbee, *Jet Propulsion Progress*, 44, and Johnson, *The Secret War*, 290.

[105] Whittle, *Jet*, 149.

[106] Ibid, 150.

[107] Ibid, 153, Johnson, *The Secret War,* 290, and Neville and Silsbee, *Jet Propulsion Progress*, 44.

[108] Whittle, *Jet*, 152.

[109] Ibid, 151-154.

[110] Ibid, 156-157.

[111] Ibid, 157.

[112] Ibid, 158.

[113] Ibid, 159-161.

[114] Ibid, 172.

[115] Ibid, 161-162.

[116] Ibid, 166-167.

[117] Ibid, 165-166.

[118] Ibid, 170.

[119] Ibid, 181.

[120] Ibid, 176.

[121] Ibid, 174.

[122] Constant, *Origins*, 194.

[123] Whittle, *Jet*, 175.

[124] Cox, H. Roxbee, "British Aircraft Gas Turbines," Ninth Wright Brothers Lecture. *Journal of the Aeronautical Sciences* Vol. 13 (February 1946), 72.

[125] Whittle, *Jet*, 171.

[126] Ibid.

[127] Ibid, 172.

[128] Ibid, 177.

[129] Ibid.

[130] Ibid, 182.

[131] Ibid.

[132] Ibid, 190.

[133] Ibid, 179.

[134] Ibid, 179.

[135] Ibid, 185.

[136] Ibid.

[137] Ibid, 186.

[138] Constant, *Origins*, 193.

[139] Whittle, *Jet*, 183.

[140] Ibid, 189.

[141] Ibid.

[142] Ibid, 191.

[143] Ibid, 192.

[144] Ibid.

[145] Ibid, 193.

[146] Ibid.

[147] Ibid, 198.

[148] Ibid, 206.

[149] Ibid, 195.

[150] Ibid, 192.

[151] Ibid, 197.

[152] Ibid.

[153] Ibid.

[154] Ibid, 170 and 216.

[155] Ibid, 215.

[156] Neville and Silsbee, *Jet Propulsion Progress*, 45.

[157] Cox, *Journal of Aeronautical Sciences*, 76.

[158] Whittle, *Jet*, 232-233.

[159] Neville and Silsbee, *Jet Propulsion Progress*, 45, and Whittle, *Jet*, 226.

[160] Ibid, 227.

[161] Ibid, 228.

[162] Ibid, 119.

[163] Ibid, 229.

[164] Ibid, 236.

[165] Ibid, 235.

[166] Ibid.

[167] Ibid, 236.

[168] Ibid, 240.

[169] Ibid, 241.

[170] Ibid.

[171] Ibid, 227.

[172] Ibid, 230.

[173] Ibid.

[174] Ibid, 251-252.

[175] Ibid, 235.

[176] Ibid.

[177] Ibid, 245-246.

[178] Ibid, 246-249.

[179] Ibid, 248-249.

[180] Ibid, 249.

[181] Ibid.

[182] Ibid, 262-263.

[183] Ibid, 264.

[184] Whittle, *Jet*, 257.

[185] Ibid, 275.

[186] Ibid.

[187] Ibid, 258.

[188] Ibid.

[189] Ibid.

[190] Ibid, 275.

[191] Ibid.

[192] Ibid, 276.

[193] Ibid.

[194] Ibid.

195    Ibid, 285.

196    Neville and Silsbee, *Jet Propulsion Progress*, 44.

197    Ibid, 7, Cox, *Journal of the Aeronautical Sciences*, 72, and Whittle, *Jet*, 217-218.

198    Ibid, 218.

199    Neville and Silsbee, *Jet Propulsion Progress*, 9 and 44, and Whittle, *Jet*, 217.

200    Cox, *Journal of the Aeronautical Sciences*, 72.

201    Whittle, *Jet*, 218.

202    Ibid, 219.

203    Ibid.

204    Neville and Silsbee, *Jet Propulsion Progress*, 45.

205    Whittle, *Jet*, 219.

206    Ibid, 219-220.

207    Ibid, 221.

208    Ibid, 221-222.

209    Ibid, 264.

210    Ibid, 265.

211    Ibid, 267.

212    Ibid, 281.

213    Ibid, 268.

214    Ibid, 268-269.

215    Ibid, 269.

216    Ibid, 268.

217    Ibid.

218    Ibid, 304.

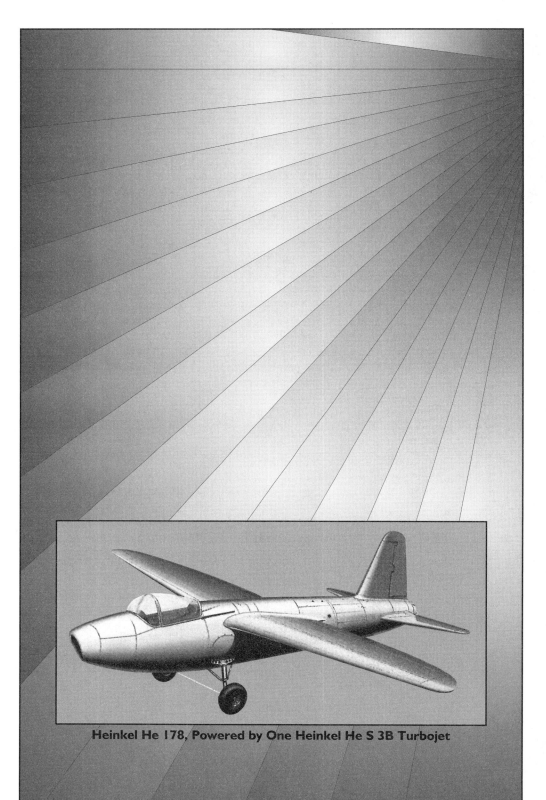

**Heinkel He 178, Powered by One Heinkel He S 3B Turbojet**

# Chapter 2

# Dr. Hans von Ohain and the First German Aircraft Gas Turbine

The turbojet revolution occurred in two countries in Europe, Britain and Germany, almost simultaneously. Of the four men who recognized the opportunity posed by the turbojet engine, three were Germans. Two of them, Herbert Wagner and Helmut Schelp, played significant roles in German turbojet development. This chapter, however, will focus on the work of Dr. Hans Pabst Joachim von Ohain (Figure 2-1). His pioneering developments had an impact upon the history of the aircraft gas turbine engine in the United States in two ways. He invented the first turbojet to power an aircraft in flight (the Heinkel 178). He also contributed greatly to the aircraft engine communities of both Germany (during the war) and the United States (after the war).

**Figure 2-1. Dr. Hans von Ohain**
*(Photo courtesy of Dr. Hans von Ohain)*

Dr. von Ohain, like Whittle, was an outsider to the aircraft engine technical community. His sole connection with aviation before 1933 was his limited participation in a gliding club while attending the University of Goettingen. Dr. von Ohain first considered the idea of a nonreciprocating engine while working in a doctoral program at Goettingen in physics.

Dr. von Ohain credits two professors in Germany for generating his interest in aircraft propulsion. He was partially motivated by the applied science methodology of his advisor at Goettingen, Professor Robert W. Pohl. Pohl constantly urged von Ohain to generate practical applications from the physics theory he was learning. Although the pure physics of Einstein captivated von Ohain, he also found that he enjoyed things mechanical and working with his hands. This appreciation of machinery stood him in good stead in the future, when he was to show an ability to communicate with and understand mechanics and machinists as well as scientists and engineers. The lectures of aerodynamicist Dr. Ludwig Prandtl also heavily influenced the young von Ohain.[1] Prandtl's lectures on aerodynamic theory spurred von Ohain to join the university gliding club. He also loved to drive fast sports cars. Speed and the elegance of flying that he learned in the gliding club combined to produce an interest in 1933 in developing a new and more efficient means of propelling an airplane. In "The First Turbojet Flights and Other German Developments," von Ohain wrote:

> My interest in Jet Propulsion was triggered by the great noise and vibrations of the propeller piston engines which seemed to destroy the inherent smoothness and elegance of flying. It appeared to me that a steady thermodynamic flow process was needed. Such a process would not produce vibrations and probably could result in machinery much lighter than a propeller-piston engine. This would be important for high-speed aircraft.[2]

Hans von Ohain undertook preliminary design studies for such a turbojet in 1934, embarking on it as another project in applied physics and thermodynamics. He considered several design approaches and came up with the following:

> For such a process, many possibilities seemed to exist. I finally decided to work on a gas turbine process which could be called a "modified Nernst turbine" having a back-to-back radial outflow compressor rotor and a radial inflow turbine rotor. This configuration also promised correct matching simply by providing equal outer diameters for the straight radial outflow compressor rotor and the straight radial inflow turbine rotor.[3]

He was aware of the possibility of employing an axial compressor and turbine, but rejected them as too complex and expensive for beginning research. This was the first example of von Ohain's development method. His approach stressed the "here and now" and the best use of available technology. He also avoided another potential problem with his decision to use a centrifugal compressor. This was the stage-matching difficulty attending with multiple axial stage machines.

Dr. von Ohain, like Whittle, had a firm idea of what he wanted to build.

> During 1934, I conducted rudimentary design and weight studies and made some performance calculations based on a pressure ratio of 3:1. This appeared attainable with a single-stage compressor and a turbine inlet temperature of about 1200-1400°F. It appeared that at a high flight speed of about 500 mph, an overall efficiency could be obtained which was about 60% of that of an equivalent propeller piston engine. The corresponding high fuel consumption was somewhat discouraging. However, the weight of such a propulsion system promised to be only a fraction (quarter or less) of that of an equivalent propeller-piston engine system. At that time the propulsion system of a fighter aircraft constituted a much greater weight portion than the fuel. Consequently, the above trade between fuel weight and propulsion system weight seemed to be a very favorable one.[4]

While studying for his final exams and writing his physics thesis, von Ohain decided in 1935 to undertake construction of a working model of his turbojet design. He felt that such a model was necessary to sell the idea of turbojet development. The naive graduate student set out to build this design with his own money. He chose the Bartels & Becker auto repair shop in Goettingen (Figure 2-2) to construct the engine because he saw that the head machinist there, Max Hahn, had a natural talent for engineering despite little formal training in the subject. Hahn would prove invaluable to von Ohain, complementing the pure science background of von Ohain with a pragmatic, mechanical point of view.

Although Hahn estimated that the total cost of constructing von Ohain's engine would be 1,000 marks, they decided to begin construction. The actual price turned out to be somewhat greater. Despite having a sizable allowance from his father, who operated a successful electrical supply business, Dr. von Ohain realized that he would soon run out of funds.[5]

In early 1936, von Ohain showed his theories and designs to Professor Pohl, who reacted positively and granted von Ohain permission to use university equipment and instruments to conduct the experiments necessary to his engine. It was during these experiments that von Ohain encountered the problem of combustion, the first of the obstacles to limit further aircraft gas turbine engine development.

> It appeared that the combustion did not take place within the combustor, but rather inside the radial turbine rotor extending into the exhaust jet. Long yellow flames leaped out of the turbine, and the apparatus resembled a flamethrower more than a turbine.[6]

**Figure 2-2. Engine in the Bartels
& Becker Repair Shop**
*(Photo courtesy of Dr. Hans von Ohain)*

The young von Ohain's experiments also convinced him that he needed to spend time and funds on basic combustor experiments. His combustor design was flawed and needed systematic development, which would require more time and more money than he had.[7] Professor Pohl came to von Ohain's rescue. Pohl was well known in the aeronautical technology community in Germany and had many contacts, among them his good friend, aircraft engineer and manufacturer Ernst Heinkel. Pohl provided an introduction to Heinkel for von Ohain. Heinkel proved to be very receptive to Pohl's letter.[8]

In 1935, Heinkel had written a paper entitled "An Inquiry into Engine Development." In it, he argued that 500 mph was the maximum speed one could expect a propeller-driven aircraft to fly. Heinkel was renowned throughout Europe as a devotee of fast aircraft. The Ernst Heinkel Aktiengesellschaft had built and raced some of the fastest aircraft of the era. In his aircraft development philosophy, Heinkel combined the entrepreneurial spirit of an Edison with the obsessive desire for secrecy of a Howard Hughes. The mercurial Heinkel had a well-deserved reputation for getting the utmost out of his personnel and for producing new aircraft designs quickly.[9]

On March 17, 1936, Heinkel and the twenty-two-year-old von Ohain met at Heinkel's home at Warnemuende in Germany. After listening to von Ohain's theories and design proposals, Heinkel told von Ohain what he was going to do. First, he wanted the turbojet development to be separate from his airframe organization. For this purpose Heinkel would construct a small building close to the Warnow River in Marienehe. There von Ohain and his team would conduct the turbojet development and testing. Second, Heinkel wanted to finance the development cost himself. He did not want the Reichsluftfahrtministerium (or RLM, the German Air Ministry) informed of his private enterprise.[10] Heinkel arranged for a conference between his top engineers,

Siegfried and Walter Guenther, and von Ohain for the next day, March 18. Dr. von Ohain remembered that the conference:

> …was stimulating, critical, but not negative. The fuel consumption of the jet engine seemed to the group extremely high, but the power-to-weight ratio of a turbojet was considered as potentially better than that of the propeller-piston engine. Heinkel's two top aerodynamic designers, Siegfried and Walter Guenther, emphasized the need for high power output per frontal area (more than 2,000 equivalent horsepower per square meter of frontal area). They also acknowledged the importance of abolishing the propeller in view of future high-speed aircraft. They saw difficulties in the development of the combustor and recommended conducting combustion tests first. This was in full agreement with my views.[11]

## Development of the He S I Turbojet

In April 1936, von Ohain began work on his aircraft gas turbine engine. Heinkel designated the engine the He S (the S stood for Strahl, or jet).[12] Initial work began at the Heinkel facility at Warnemuende, north of Berlin. On April 3, Heinkel signed von Ohain to a preliminary consulting contract, in which von Ohain agreed not to work for any other company and agreed to the level of success and conditions under which Heinkel would issue a license and employment contract to him. On April 15, Max Hahn joined von Ohain.[13]

Heinkel realized that von Ohain did not have any engineering background. He therefore assigned Dipl-Ing. (Diplom-Ingenieur, equivalent to a Master's Degree) Wilhelm Gundermann to the von Ohain team. Gundermann had studied aircraft engineering at the Technical University of Berlin and turbo machinery engineering under Professor Hermann Fottinger.[14] As usual in a Heinkel development program, Ernst Heinkel personally assigned the program goals. He gave von Ohain a technical target thrust equivalent to 600 horsepower and insisted as well that von Ohain immediately begin design of a flight engine. Heinkel also wanted ground testing to begin after one year, about June 1937.[15] This was the directive of an owner wanting results. Heinkel set the development schedule, not von Ohain. Compare this with the developmental program established by Whittle and Power Jets. Whittle (and von Ohain as well) was a developmental amateur. Ernst Heinkel was a professional aircraft developer, used to working in an established time frame. Whereas Whittle had to enter into a developmental relationship with a subcontractor (first British Thomson-Houston, then Rover, and then Rolls-Royce), Heinkel was the sole source for development funds. Whittle had to solicit funds from private sources and the government, while Heinkel gave von Ohain all the financial support necessary. This last point is perhaps the most important one to consider when starting the development of a new and unproven technology.

Dr. von Ohain focused initially on building a turbojet engine of minimum risk to demonstrate his concept, then, later, on developing a flight engine. His development philosophy was characterized by two themes. First, von Ohain stressed new solutions to overcoming obstacles that presented themselves. When he couldn't get the combustion results he wanted with gasoline, von Ohain switched to hydrogen. He knew that combustor technology would "catch up" with his design and development.[16]

The second major characteristic of von Ohain's aircraft gas turbine engine development was the relationship he formed with Heinkel from the beginning of his work. Heinkel and von Ohain were the first turbojet pioneers to develop the close-knit working relationship between science and industry that has become the standard for technological progress in the aircraft gas turbine engine field today. Dr. von Ohain and Ernst Heinkel established a model of what could be accomplished in a short time by teaming a hard-driving design and development team with industry entrepreneurship and financing.

All was not as easy at it first appears, however. The young von Ohain was under pressure to produce results quickly. This led to a major development decision for von Ohain:

> It became quite clear to me that my original plan to develop first a well-functioning combustor and then begin with an engine design was impossible. This was due to the political climate, my rather tenuous position in the Heinkel Corporation, and most of all, the great impatience of Ernst Heinkel. On the other hand, it was also clear to me that a poorly functioning combustor could result in a non-functioning engine. This would mean the end of the turbojet project. In this situation I decided to follow a twofold approach. First, I would quickly build a simple jet engine of minimum risk, which would demonstrate the jet principle in a very convincing and impressive manner. Next I would immediately begin a systematic gasoline combustor development program. I was convinced that after a successful demonstration of a jet engine I could win the necessary time for the development of combustor and flight engine.[17]

The "rather tenuous position in the Heinkel Corporation" occupied by von Ohain shows one of the potential problems faced by outsiders trying to impact a given technical community. Here was the twenty-three year old von Ohain, fresh out of the university, given carte-blanche by a major corporation to pursue his dream. Dr. von Ohain reported directly to Ernst Heinkel, and could take the best fitters and mechanics from other workshops for his team. This made several more-experienced people in the Heinkel organization very nervous. The organizational current of uncertainty and suspicion undoubtedly contributed to von Ohain's apprehension and fear of failure.

These circumstances led von Ohain to choose hydrogen as the fuel for his demonstrator engine, rather than gasoline or kerosene. Hydrogen has a very high flame speed and wide fuel-air stability range in which combustion is possible. He designed a hydrogen combustor which he was certain would function well without elaborate pretesting, which would take too much time.[18]

> Now I was faced with the difficult task of convincing Heinkel and obtaining his consent to build the hydrogen demonstrator engine. In a meeting with Heinkel I gave my assurance that the hydrogen engine would be a full success, and that the development time for the flying engine with liquid fuel would greatly be reduced by the experience gained from the hydrogen demonstrator.[19]

Heinkel told von Ohain to proceed.

Wilhelm Gundermann made some key contributions which directly shortened the development time for the first engine. He made fullest use of Heinkel's ability to produce large metal spinnings very quickly. This avoided time-consuming castings. He also demanded that the team strengthen spin parts by using ring flanges, which could be manufactured quickly at a nearby shipyard. He did all the necessary stress analyses for the rotating parts. Gundermann headed a design office that initially had twelve designers, but grew as the team's design activities increased. Gundermann's designs incorporated sound machine-construction principles with lightweight structures. His work contributed a great deal to the success of the von Ohain team. Hahn also played a key role in the design of the engine, particularly the combustion system.[20]

In February of 1937, the team completed the He S 1 turbojet engine (Figure 2-3). Test runs began in March and were completed by April.[21] Dr. von Ohain was pleased:

> The apparatus fully met expectations. It reached the anticipated performance, it handled very well in acceleration and deceleration, probably because of the relatively small moment of inertia of the compressor and turbine rotor, and the great stability of the hydrogen combustor over the wide operational range.[22]

This successful test was a major milestone in von Ohain's development program. It convinced Heinkel that von Ohain's turbojet design could result in a successful flight engine and Heinkel took immediate steps to be sure von Ohain would continue to work for him. He signed von Ohain to three separate contracts on May 13, 1937. The first was to reimburse von Ohain for all his expenditures before he joined Heinkel, including model development costs, patent expenses, etc. The second was a regular Heinkel employment contract. One of its stipulations was that von Ohain was to hold the position of division manager reporting directly to Heinkel. The third contract was a licensing agreement giving von Ohain a 4 percent royalty.[23]

After these successful tests, Heinkel pushed for development of a flight engine with a target thrust equivalent to 500 horsepower. The team designated the engine the He S 2A. In September, it ran on a test stand for the first time, developing 176 pounds of thrust.[24]

In the last months of 1937, Heinkel's airframe engineers, Siegfried and Walter Guenther, began predesign studies for the first jet-propelled aircraft. Early in 1938 came the detailed design of the aircraft, designated the He 178. Gundermann also made essential contributions to the shape of the air inlet and the inlet and exhaust ducts.[25]

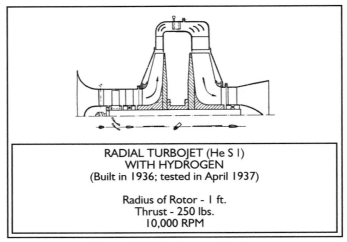

RADIAL TURBOJET (He S I)
WITH HYDROGEN
(Built in 1936; tested in April 1937)

Radius of Rotor - I ft.
Thrust - 250 lbs.
10,000 RPM

**Figure 2-3. Hydrogen Engine**
*(Drawing courtesy of Dr. Hans von Ohain)*

The He S 2A design called for liquid fuel combustion. Max Hahn was in charge of this aspect of the design. He approached the problem in two steps: First, he emphasized use of vaporized, and later atomized, liquid fuel; second, he built an electrically heated pressure boiler with the necessary safety measures for producing high-pressure gasoline vapor. After the team had designed and built combustors with excellent operational characteristics and a low total pressure drop, they combined the boiler elements into the combustors. They used this internal fuel gasification process in all initial flight engines. Despite this ultimately successful approach, von Ohain reported that the experiment with atomized liquid fuel still exhibited some difficulties during starting and low-speed operations which they had to overcome later.[26] Dr. von Ohain also incorporated Max Hahn's suggestion for arranging the combustor in the large unused space in front of the radial-flow compressor. This resulted in a new design and international patent.[27]

Development of the combustion system took eighteen months from April 1936, almost the same time as the turbine. The team designed a combustion system made up of sixteen chambers arranged in a ring around and in front of the compressor diffuser. Each chamber had a small tubular vaporizer heated by hydrogen during starting and subsequently by one burner flame. The burner tubes were of 36 percent nickel alloy, welded together.[28] The combustion development of von Ohain's team showed a steady evolution from reverse-flow combustion to a straight-through-flow design.

Apart from the combustor problems, the second major focus of the development effort was on achieving high mass flow and high component efficiencies. The team obtained the high mass flow by designing an unconventionally large ratio of compressor rotor inlet diameter to rotor exit diameter. They achieved high component efficiencies by adding an axial inducer stage which gave the inlet flow both a precompression and a prerotation. This substantially reduced the flow-relative Mach number, and curvature of the rotor inlet blading.[29]

The year 1938 also brought to Heinkel the interest of RLM's Engine Development Section. Hans Mauch, chief of the section, visited Heinkel in the summer, at which time they briefed him on the company's progress. Before this, Heinkel had succeeded in keeping his turbojet development secret from the RLM. Dr. von Ohain remembered the visit:

> Mauch soon became convinced that the turbojet was the key to high speed flight. He came, however, to the conclusion that Heinkel, as an airframe company, would never be capable of developing a production engine because the company lacked engine test and manufacturing facilities. Most of all, it lacked engineers experienced in engine development and testing techniques. He wanted the Heinkel team to join an aircraft engine company (Daimler-Benz) and serve as a nucleus for turbojet propulsion development. Furthermore, he stated that Ernst Heinkel should receive full reimbursement and recognition for his great pioneering achievements. Heinkel refused. In the summer of 1938, Mauch met with Helmut Schelp, who was in charge of jet propulsion in the Research Division of the RLM. Mauch invited Schelp to join him in the Engine Development Division, because he saw in this Division far greater opportunities for action than in his Research Division. In contrast to Mauch, Schelp was very well aware of turbojet propulsion and was convinced about its feasibility.[30]

The RLM was very much aware at this time of the potential of the jet engine.[31] During the war the Allies produced one operational jet aircraft, the Gloster Meteor. The Germans, in the same time period, got twenty-five jet or rocket aircraft into flight test status and five aircraft, the Arado AR 234, the Bachem Ba 349, the Heinkel He 162, the Messerschmitt Me 163, and the Messerschmitt Me 262, into the field with the Luftwaffe.[32]

Again, it is illustrative to contrast this government pressure on Ernst Heinkel and von Ohain with the government pressure on Whittle and Power Jets. Both governments wanted the same end result, to bring the new technology under their control as the nucleus of future turbojet development. Heinkel could protect the von Ohain team and maintain his independence because Heinkel had a strong development organization. Whittle's Power Jets had no such patron to protect it, and the British government nationalized the company in 1944.

In the summer of 1938, von Ohain advised Heinkel to begin development of axial-flow multistage compressors for future turbojet engines. This was a result of von Ohain's having attended presentations on free-vortex-flow single-stage, axial compressor stages by Walter Encke of the Ludwig Prandtl Institute (AVA). Encke subsequently invited von Ohain to visit him at his lab in the AVA Goettingen.[33]

## The Influence of Helmut Schelp in German Aircraft Gas Turbine Development

In August the RLM gained strength with the addition of a powerful new advocate for centralized turbojet development. Hans Mauch persuaded Helmut Schelp to come to work for him. Schelp became head of the Sondertriebwerke (Special Propulsion Systems) section of the Power Plant Group of the Development Division of the Technical Office of the RLM.[34]

Schelp had received his master's degree in aeronautical engineering at the Stevens Institute of Technology in Hoboken, New Jersey, in 1936. He returned to Germany shortly thereafter to the RLM. During his work at the RLM and the Deutsche Versuchsanstalt für Luftfahrt (DVL), Schelp studied the effects of the introduction of new airframe technology on current aircraft engine technology. The Heinkel He 111 midrange bomber and the Messerschmitt Bf 109 fighter exemplified this new airframe technology. Schelp studied the effects of compressibility, which according to his research, set in at Mach 0.82. Schelp also carried out a systematic analysis of reaction propulsion theory, thereby coming to the same conclusions as Whittle, von Ohain, and the group led by Dr. Herbert Wagner at Junkers Aircraft. Unlike the first three, however, Schelp was an influential government official, usually able to put his belief in the turbojet into effect with dramatic results.

The German RLM was very interested in high-speed aircraft and aircraft engines. The quest for higher speeds at higher altitudes was given the highest priority. Although a relatively young and low-ranking official in the RLM, Schelp knew all the Luftwaffe generals wanted new designs for engines and aircraft quickly. Through use of the RLM's funding power, Schelp coerced the aircraft engine and airframe companies in Germany to accept turbojet, turboprop, and new high-speed high-altitude aircraft development contracts. He had the power to shape the German aircraft engine industry, and he did so. It was largely Schelp's determination to aggressively pursue the development and production of the turbojet that led to Germany's turbojet superiority throughout the war.[35]

In the summer of 1938 Schelp learned of the theoretical work of Albert Betz and Walter Encke on axial compressors. With Schelp's encouragement, Walter Encke visited Heinkel in November to discuss axial-flow compressors. Heinkel's Siegfried Guenther was a proponent of small-frontal-area turbojet engines, and it was on Guenther's and von Ohain's recommendation that Heinkel hired Encke as a consultant.[36]

In January of 1939 Max Adolph Mueller of Junkers visited Heinkel. Mueller and a team of scientists had begun work on jet propulsion at the Aviation Institute in Berlin in 1935, and Junkers Aircraft Chief Scientist Herbert Wagner had hired Mueller in late 1935 to launch an axial turbojet development program at Junkers. Mueller briefed Heinkel on axial aircraft gas turbine engine development at Junkers and suggested that Heinkel take him and his team on. In the summer of 1939 Max Adolph Mueller and his team came to Heinkel from Junkers. They brought with them an axial turbojet development program which would be designated the He S 30.[37]

Another event that was to be significant for the future of aircraft gas turbine engine development in Germany also occurred in 1939. In the latter part of the year the Technical Office of the RLM, with Schelp's recommendation, laid down the requirements for German aircraft gas turbine engine development.[38] They called for a jet aircraft with a speed of 575 mph and a thrust of 13,200 pounds at an altitude of 30,000 feet.

The RLM followed this development with even stronger measures. In May, the RLM took control of German aircraft gas turbine engine development by decreeing that, henceforth, aircraft gas turbine engine design and development work would be government-funded. Thus, the aircraft and engine companies had lost control of the design and development process for gas turbine engines.[39]

## Development of the He S 3 Turbojet

Work proceeded on the development of the He S 3 turbojet throughout 1938, resulting in a complete redesign of the engine. Allied intelligence teams described the engine after the war as follows:

> The He S 3 turbojet was built around a compressor/turbine set comprising an axial flow inducer, a radial flow impeller, and a radial inflow turbine. Air from the impeller was divided aft of the diffuser, a portion passing forward through the annular reverse flow combustion chamber and the balance mixing with the products of combustion prior to entry into the turbine.[40]

The engine, now designated the He S 3A, weighed 795 pounds, had a frontal area of 7.3 square feet, and ran at a speed of 13,000 rpm. Flight tests of this engine were carried out with it mounted beneath an He 118. This engine was test flown many times until the turbine burned out. By this time, development of the He 178 airframe had advanced to the point where it could be designed around an improved He S 3A, now designated the He S 3B (Figures 2-4 and 2-5).[41]

The He S 3B was test-run successfully at Marienehe in March. In early summer von Ohain and his team froze the design of the first flight engine. The culmination of the first phase of von Ohain's work came on August 27, 1939, when Heinkel test pilot Erich Warsitz piloted the He 178 experimental jet aircraft (Figures 2-6 and 2-7) on the first flight of an all-turbojet-powered aircraft. The He S 3B turbojet gave 1,100 pounds of static thrust at 13,000 rpm, weighed 925 pounds, and had a specific fuel consumption of 1.6. The He 178 was a very small high-wing monoplane with a metal semimonocoque fuselage incorporating a circular air intake in the nose. It had plywood wings and a retractable tailwheel type undercarriage. The He 178 attained a maximum speed of only 250 mph.[42]

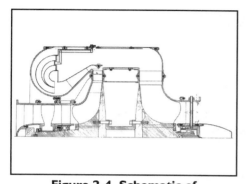

**Figure 2-4. Schematic of He S 3B Engine**
*(Drawing courtesy of Dr. Hans von Ohain)*

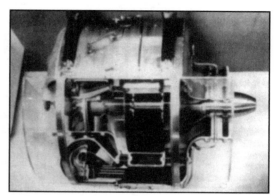

**Figure 2-5. Cutaway of He S 3B Engine**
*(Photo courtesy of Dr. Hans von Ohain)*

This historic first flight of a jet-powered aircraft had very little immediate impact on the German RLM, as RLM officials weren't present. Heinkel sponsored an official demonstration for the ministry at the Rechlin proving grounds in the fall, but again the response was that of indifference.[43] It must, however, have made some difference, because shortly thereafter the RLM accepted a Heinkel proposal for a jet fighter, the He 280.

In any event, the outbreak of war in Europe four days after the first flight, on September 1, had already distracted RLM officials. Pressing the development of the turbojet soon took a back seat at the Ministry to supporting the German blitzkrieg offensives in Europe.

**Figure 2-6. He 178**
*(Photo courtesy of Deutsches Museum, Munich)*

**Figure 2-7. He 178**
*(Photo courtesy of Deutsches Museum, Munich)*

## Development of the He S 8 Turbojet

In October of 1939, von Ohain and his team began development of the He S 8 turbojet for the He 280 experimental twin jet fighter. The design team included Gundermann and Hahn. Heinkel chose at that time to reorganize the turbojet development programs at his company. In *Stormy Life*, Heinkel recalls his decision:

> When they (the Mueller team) came to Marienehe in October 1939, the He 178 had already made its first successful flights, and I organized a large, compact development branch for jet units and jet planes, which by November employed more than 120 engineers, technicians and scientists of the most varied attainments.

> While the group under Ohain devoted its main attention to an engine with a centrifugal compressor similar to the He S 3, I decided to form a new group partly composed of the new technicians but under the general direction of Ohain, to undertake the construction of an engine with an axial compressor. I meant to pursue two parallel lines of development in order to determine which one produced the best results.[44]

Heinkel formed the following special divisions:

1. TL: Turbine-Luftstrahl, or turbojet

2. STL: Staurohr-Turbine-Luftstrahl, or ramjet-turbojet

3. ML: Motor-Luftstrahl, or reciprocating engine and jet

At the end of the year Heinkel convinced Ernst Udet, head of the RLM's newly created Office of Air Armament, to support his turbojet research with official funding.[45] Heinkel also secured Udet's agreement to guarantee the availability of raw materials. This did not endear Heinkel to the middle-level officials in the RLM, however.[46]

In early 1940, Heinkel and von Ohain began development of two turbojets: the He S 8 (a radial turbojet similar to the He S 3B) for the He 280 and the He S 30 (a very advanced axial turbojet based on Mueller's work).[47] The He S 8 (Figures 2-8 and 2-9) had a radial rotor very similar to that of the He S 3B, but had an axial diffuser and a straight through-flow combustor to accomplish a very substantial diameter reduction of 6 inches relative to the He S 3B engine. The weight of the He S 8 was 836 pounds; the He S 3B weighed 925 pounds. The diameter of the He S 8 was 30.5 inches; the He S 3B was 36.5 inches. The speed of the He S 8 was 13,500 rpm, and the frontal area was 5.16 square feet. An Allied Intelligence team described the He S 8 in May 1945 as follows:

> The He S 8 is designed around a compressor/turbine set comprising a 14-blade axial flow inducer, having airfoil type blades… which are made from aluminum alloy forgings. This inducer is followed by a 19-vane radial flow impeller of composite construction, consisting of aluminum alloy blades retained in a steel hub and rear shrouding plate. After combustion the working fluid passes through a 14-blade radial inflow turbine also being built up of steel blades retained in a steel hub. The compressor/turbine set…is mounted on two bearing sets, one between the inducer and impeller and the second aft of the turbine.

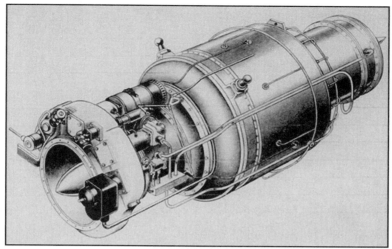

**Figure 2-8. He S 8**
*(Illustration courtesy of Dr. Hans von Ohain)*

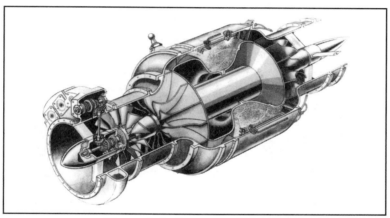

**Figure 2-9. Cutaway of He S 8**
*(Illustration courtesy of Dr. Hans von Ohain)*

Combustion is carried out in a straight through annular chamber, the compressor discharge passing through two sets of diffuser vanes before entering the chamber. The fuel system is a vaporizing system functioning in the following manner: Fuel is injected into the chamber through 16 sets of eight nozzles, giving a total of 128 individual nozzles. Each nozzle is a tube approximately 1/16 inch in diameter. Alternate nozzles differ in length by about 1/2 inch and spray into two passages ... The fuel from the nozzle impinges upon the two surfaces formed by steel rings, having their outer surface grooved, from which it is vaporized and burned.

The exhaust nozzle is of fixed area and a tailpipe was used on the He 280.[48]

In August 1940, the RLM decreed a ban on all aircraft design for which development would take more than six months. Although this ban also applied to jet aircraft, the Heinkel, Arado, and Messerschmitt companies carried on with their development programs. The first glider flight of the He 280 jet prototype was on September 11.[49] After 1940, the RLM began a series of abrupt changes in development focus. Schelp managed to keep the important turbojet development programs funded, but the crisis in management at the Ministry was not resolved until the start of 1942.

In January of 1941, Heinkel began test runs of He S 8 engines. The von Ohain team installed the engines in the He 280 jet fighter (Figures 2-10 and 2-11) prototype in mid-March. On March 30, Heinkel test pilot Dipl-Ing. Fritz Schafer made the first flight, forty days before the flight of the E.28/39 in England, and about eighteen months before the first American jet flight, on October 1, 1942.[50] It was quite an achievement.[51]

**Figure 2-10. Heinkel He 280, the First Prototype Jet Fighter**
*(Photo courtesy of Deutsches Museum, Munich)*

**Figure 2-11. Engine Installation in the He 280**
*(Illustration courtesy of Deutsches Museum, Munich)*

On April 5, RLM test pilot Paul Bader test-flew the He 280, achieving an altitude of 20,000 feet and a top speed of 485 mph. RLM Minister Udet was there and the performance of the jet fighter impressed him.[52] Udet then permitted Heinkel on April 7 to fulfill a long-term goal of buying the Hirth aviation engine company at Zuffenhausen, near Stuttgart, as well as the Hirth works in Berlin. Heinkel was now able to integrate his turbojet development with his airframe development. Heinkel's exhilaration was short-lived, however. Although the Heinkel-Hirth Corporation made repeated test flights, the Ministry never allowed them to put the He 280 into production.

The RLM gave the He S 8A designation He S 001, but it soon met the same fate as the He 280, when the RLM gave the as the RLM curtailed further development of the 001 program in mid-1942 in favor of the Junkers Jumo 004 and the BMW 003. The RLM officially turned down the He 280 as a fighter on March 27, 1943.[53]

The RLM did, however, compensate the Heinkel-Hirth Corporation with a program for a new turbojet engine, the 011. Development of this engine was slow and the engine didn't reach the bench for testing until 1944. The 011 design wasn't flight-tested before the end of hostilities, though several were brought to the United States and tested after the war.

## Development of the He S 30 Turbojet

During the summer of 1941 von Ohain and his team completed the first build of the He S 30 axial turbojet engine (designated the He S 006 by the RLM). This engine represented a new departure for von Ohain. Although von Ohain supervised the He S 30 program, the engine was based on the work of Max Adolph Mueller who was responsible for the technical details, meanwhile von Ohain concentrated on the He S 8.[54]

The He S 30 program started out with performance problems. The engine, as designed, could not reach the required RPM. It appeared that the turbine was not properly matched with the compressor. Consequently, the engine was taken to Heinkel's newly acquired Hirth Company for redesign of the turbine. In the spring of 1942, the team installed the redesigned turbine in the engine and the He S 30's performance exceeded all expectations and design targets. The frontal area of the engine was 3.23 square feet, the speed was 10,500 rpm, and the weight was 857 pounds.[55]

The He S 30 incorporated a five-stage axial-flow compressor and a single-stage axial-flow turbine, with adjustable nozzle guide vanes. Designed by Dr. Rudolph Friedrich, the compressor was a radical development. Friedrich managed to get a pressure ratio of 3:1 out of only five stages by using 50 percent reaction blading. The combustion system consisted of ten individual combustion chambers, varying from a circular section at the entry to a heart-shaped section at the nozzle vane chamber. Dr. von Ohain characterized the He S 30 turbojet as having "the most outstanding performance characteristics in comparison with all other engines of that time."[56] In spite of this performance, the Air Ministry canceled the preparations for the engine's flight testing and production, because the Jumo 004 and the BMW 003 were closer to production. Although not as good in terms of performance, the two engines were simpler and therefore easier to produce. Wartime expediency had won out over superior design and performance. If the United States or Britain had designed and built the same engine, it likely would have been produced in quantity.

In the fall of 1942, Helmut Schelp and the RLM made an important decision for future German aircraft gas turbine engine development. Friedrich's 50 percent reaction degree compressor principle impressed Schelp who then announced his intention to have all subsequent aircraft gas turbine engine designs in Germany incorporate the principle. Dr. von Ohain remarks on Schelp's plan:

> Schelp had the idea that a second generation of turbojet engines was needed with specific performance characteristics.

> The first characteristic had to be reduction of fuel consumption by a greatly increased compressor pressure ratio.

> The second characteristic was reduction of engine weight per thrust. Schelp thought that for a given thrust the 50% reaction degree compressor principle would be a major contributing factor to a reduction of frontal area, length, number of compressor stages, and weight.

> The third characteristic was greater thrust output, preferably above 1,000 horsepower. This second generation of engines was vital to Schelp's plan to develop the improved Me 262, the Arado Ar 234, the Ju 287, and the He 343.[57]

In May, personality conflicts between Ernst Heinkel and Max Adolph Mueller resulted in Mueller's abruptly leaving the Heinkel Company, so Heinkel dropped the ducted-fan project and other peripheral turbojet design programs on which Mueller had worked. At the same time,

Helmut Schelp persuaded Heinkel to stop work on the Heinkel 001 and 006 turbojet programs and concentrate effort on the more advanced 011 turbojet.

On March 25, 1943, Harold Wolff was named Commissioner for Jet Propulsion in the RLM. This was a disaster for Ernst Heinkel, who did not like Wolff. The former manager of all Heinkel operations, Wolff felt the same dislike for Heinkel. Shortly thereafter, Wolff, with the concurrence of Helmut Schelp, ordered all development of the He S 30 turbojet stopped. Wolff canceled the He 280 program as well.[58] Heinkel's fighter was at this time one full development year ahead of the Messerschmitt Me 262. Wolff and Schelp instructed Heinkel to concentrate the work of von Ohain's group on the development of a unit with 2,870 pounds of thrust, the He S 011 turbojet (Figure 2-12).

**Figure 2-12. He S 011 Axial-flow Engine Built
at the Heinkel-Hirth Corporation**
*(Photo courtesy of Dr. Hans von Ohain)*

## Development of the He 011 Turbojet

Dr. von Ohain was placed in charge of the 011 development. Heinkel placed Kurt Schiff, the Heinkel plant manager, in charge of 011 production and assigned Dr. Max Bentele, the Chief Scientist of the Hirth Company, to be in charge of engine component development and testing, including the exhaust nozzle. Helmut Schelp not only determined the performance requirements for the 011, but he also participated in establishing the design concept. The initial continuous-thrust rating requirement was for 2,900 pounds, with an eventual target of 3,500 pounds. Schelp set the initial pressure ratio requirement at 5:1, with growth to 6:1 and higher with an added stage. Schelp also favored a two-stage, air-cooled turbine to permit adding an additional axial compressor stage later. This additional stage would result in a pressure ratio of 8:1 in a later 011 version.[59]

Dr. von Ohain credits Dr. Bentele with inventing a new type of air-cooled blading for the 011 design (Figure 2-13). Dr. von Ohain described this blading:

> This type of blading in the United States is called "boot-strap blading." These hollow blades had internal vibration dampers which also served as distributors and internal guides for the cooling air. Thereby the cooling-effectiveness of the internal cooling air was increased substantially. The method of mass-producing the blades was developed by the Wuertembergische-Metall Fabrik Company. The manufacturing price was quite low.[60]

The first test-runs of the Heinkel 011 were in the fall of 1943, and the first full-scale bench test of the engine was in February 1944.[61] The engine did not reach its design potential in the first

**Figure 2-13. Air-cooled Axial Turbine
by Max Bentele**
*(Photo courtesy of Dr. Hans von Ohain)*

test runs, achieving a thrust equivalent to only 600 horsepower, and the ring combustor had numerous severely overheated regions. Bentele, however, corrected all the shortcomings of the combustor as well as the matching problems with the compressor in less than a year. In April 1944, the RLM issued the Emergency Fighter Requirement, specifying use of the Heinkel 011 as the single power plant, to Blohm und Voss, Focke-Wulf, Heinkel, Junkers, and Messerschmitt. On September 8, the basic specification for what was to become the Volksjaeger (people's fighter) was drawn up by the RLM and issued to Arado, Blohm und Voss, Fieseler, Focke-Wulf, Heinkel, Junkers, and Messerschmitt. The Volksjaeger specification called for an aircraft with a weight of no more than 4,410 pounds and over 30 minutes endurance. A minimum of strategic materials was to be used, and the design was to be ready for mass production by semi-skilled labor on January 1, 1945. Armament was to consist of two 30-millimeter cannons, and the aircraft was to be able to take off within a distance of 1,640 feet.[62] On September 23 Heinkel was declared the winner with the P.1073 design. This aircraft designation was changed first to the He 500 and later to the He 162 (Figure 2-14).

**Figure 2-14. Heinkel He 162 Salamander**
*(Photo courtesy of Daimler-Benz Aerospace)*

Incredibly, the first flight of the He 162 Salamander, piloted by Peter Gotthold, took place on December 6, 1944. This first flight, however, was not with the He S 011, but rather with a BMW 003A turbojet. By the end of 1944, the Heinkel 011A turbojet achieved 1300 horsepower in tests. Heinkel had scheduled flight testing and mass production of the He S 011 for the He 162C and D versions to start in June 1945, but was overtaken by the end of the war. The first He 162s were delivered to an operational Luftwaffe unit on February 6, 1945. The first operational use of the He 162 was in April 1945.[63]

On April 1, 1945, the Heinkel-Hirth Corporation curtailed plans to move their turbojet operations to Vienna, due to the advancing Russians. As operations in Stuttgart were scheduled to end due to the advancing Americans, Heinkel was forced to end all turbojet aircraft and engine development for the Third Reich.[64] From June onwards, however, Heinkel did build their last eight He S 011A-O pre-production turbojets in Bavaria, but these were built under American orders. The U.S. Navy shipped these engines to the United States, for bench tests.

What lessons can be drawn from the aircraft gas turbine engine development experiences of Hans von Ohain and Ernst Heinkel? Although one can contrast the experiences of Sir Frank Whittle with those of von Ohain and Heinkel, the end result of both of their confrontations with the system and the aviation technical community was the same. Heinkel's company lasted until the end of the war, but he saw his programs canceled or co-opted from him by a government with which he eventually could not get along.

Both Sir Frank Whittle and Dr. Hans von Ohain wanted to develop a new jet engine and make money in the process. The war partially defined the circumstances of both Whittle's and von Ohain's operations and departures from the engine development scene. What makes their work different, however, is the way that they proceeded to accomplish their programs. Whittle, throughout his career in aircraft engines, insisted on having all aspects of development under his direct control following the pattern of Edison in the United States (in his development of electricity). Whittle never succeeded in this goal, and his attempts to do so undermined his working relationships with all the companies he came into contact with. On the other hand, Hans von Ohain's cordial relationship with Ernst Heinkel proved to be not only beneficial throughout the war years, but also was essential in getting his engine developed in the first place. Sadly, one can only imagine what important contributions Sir Frank Whittle could have made to postwar turbojet and turboprop development in Britain had he worked hand-in-hand with the engine companies.

Dr. Hans von Ohain's contributions to aircraft gas turbine engine development did not end with the fall of Germany in 1945. Dr. von Ohain, along with other key turbojet developers, came to the United States as part of an overall American program to exploit German technology after the war. He joined Helmut Schelp, Bruno Bruckmann, Anselm Franz, Heinz Schmidt, and other important German scientists and engineers who helped the United States enhance its technological base. In the specific case of Hans von Ohain, he was hired by the U.S. Army Air Corps to carry on work in jet engine development and became famous for his ideas, energy and leadership.

## Endnotes

[1] Von Ohain, Hans P, "The First Turbojet Flights and Other German Developments," From *Celebration of the Golden Anniversary of Jet Powered Flight, 1939 - 1989*, James St. Peter, editor. Dayton, Ohio: University of Dayton Press, 1989, 19.

[2] Ibid.

[3] Ibid.

[4] Ibid.

[5] Ibid, 20.

[6] Ibid, 19.

[7] Ibid.

[8] Edward Constant claims that Heinkel had met Werner von Braun before receiving the letter from Pohl, and that this meeting with von Braun had already left him "favorably disposed" towards "radical, high-performance propulsion systems that dispensed with the propeller. Constant, Edward W. III, *The Origins of the Turbojet Revolution*, Baltimore: The Johns Hopkins University Press, 1980.

[9] Constant, *Origins.*, 198, and Masters, David, *German Jet Genesis*, London, UK: Jane's Publishing Company Limited, 1982, 9.

[10] Immediately after Hitler was named Chancellor of Germany in 1933, the Nazis set out, with the active collaboration of the military, to rebuild the German air forces. The new *Luftwaffe* was immediately placed under a totally independent Air Ministry or *Reichsluftfahrtministerium* (or RLM). This ministry controlled all funding to all German aircraft engine and airframe manufacturers, therefore giving the Nazis total control over all aircraft development. The RLM, under State Secretary (eventually Field Marshal) Erhard Milch, did not hesitate to exercise this control. Irving, David, *The Rise and Fall of the Luftwaffe: The Life*

of *Field Marshal Erhard Milch*, Boston, MA: Little, Brown and Company, 1973, 29.

[11] Von Ohain, "The First Turbojet Flights...", 20.

[12] Ibid.

[13] Ibid.

[14] Gundermann, Wilhelm, "He 178: The Development of the First German Jet Aircraft," *Air BP*, 1953, 21.

[15] Ibid.

[16] Von Ohain, "The First Turbojet Flights...", 21.

[17] Ibid.

[18] Ibid.

[19] Ibid.

[20] Ibid.

[21] Ibid.

[22] Ibid.

[23] Ibid.

[24] Johnson, Brian, *The Secret War*, New York: Methuen Inc., 1978, 275, and Heinkel, Ernst, *Stormy Life*, New York: E.P. Dutton, 1956, 213.

[25] Von Ohain, "The First Turbojet Flights...", 22-23.

[26] Ibid, 23.

[27] Ibid, 21.

[28] Gundermann, "He 178:...", 22.

[29] Von Ohain, "The First Turbojet Flights...", 22.

[30] Ibid, 26.

[31] In autumn of 1938, the RLM ordered a jet fighter from Messerschmitt to be powered by two projected BMW turbojets. This design was designated the 262 by the RLM upon its approval on March 1, 1940. A development contract was then awarded to Messerschmitt. Masters, *German Jet Genesis*, 13.

[32] "Of the lesser types, a half dozen or so were in the process of being built when the war ended, while some two dozen other had achieved an advanced stage of design before they were overtaken by events." Masters, *German Jet Genesis*, 9.

[33] Von Ohain, "The First Turbojet Flights...", 24.

[34] Ibid, 26.

[35] Constant, *Origins*, 204-205, and Von Ohain, "The First Turbojet Flights...", 24.

[36] Constant, *Origins*, 205, and Von Ohain, "The First Turbojet Flights...", 24.

[37] Ibid, 25.

[38] On January 4, the RLM circulated a top-secret discussion paper entitled "Preliminary technical guidelines for high-speed fighters with turbojet propulsion". Masters, *German Jet Genesis*, 14.

[39] Baumbach, Werner, *The Life and Death of the Luftwaffe*, New York: Coward-McCann, Inc., 1949, 165.

[40] Taylor, Michael, *Jet Fighters*, Greenwich, CT: Bison Books Ltd.,1982, 10.

[41] Masters, *German Jet Genesis*, 77.

[42] Heinkel, *Stormy Life*, 227, Von Ohain, "The First Turbojet Flights...", 23, and Masters, *German Jet Genesis*, 14.

[43] Heinkel, *Stormy Life*, 225-227.

[44] Heinkel, *Stormy Life*, 226-227.

[45] Ernst Udet, famous W.W.I ace and holder of the German Pour Le Merite, was a brilliant and troubled figure in the development of the Luftwaffe. His inability to organize and control German aircraft development and production during the crucial period of 1939 to November 1941 was a major factor in Germany's weaknesses in the air during World War II. Udet committed suicide on November 17, 1941. Irving, *Rise and Fall of the Luftwaffe*, 69 and 140.

[46] Heinkel, *Stormy Life*, 231.

[47] Von Ohain, "The First Turbojet Flights...", 23.

[48] Taylor, *Jet Fighters*, 15-20.

[49] Masters, *German Jet Genesis*, 14.

[50] The first flight of the Me 262 prototype was not until April 18. The competition between Ernst Heinkel and Willi Messerschmitt was fierce, with no quarter given or taken. Ibid, 14.

[51] Gunston, Bill, *World Encyclopedia of Aero Engines*, Second Edition, England: Patrick Stephens Limited, 1989, 76, Walker, Bryce, *Fighting Jets*, Time/Life Epic of Flight, Alexandria, VA: Time/Life Books Inc., 1983, 24, and Constant, *Origins*, 209.

[52] Von Ohain, "The First Turbojet Flights...", 23.

[53] Masters, German Jet Genesis, 14.

[54] Ibid, 25.

[55] Ibid.

[56] Ibid, 23.

[57] Ibid, 25.

[58] The development of the BMW 002 and the DB 007 turbojets was curtailed as well. Masters, *German Jet Genesis*, 14.

[59] Ibid.

[60] Ibid, and Heinkel, *Stormy Life*, 234.

[61] Ibid, 15.

[62] Ibid, 72.

[63] Von Ohain, "The First Turbojet Flights...", 26, and Masters, *German Jet Genesis*, 15.

[64] Heinkel, *Stormy Life*, 234, and Von Ohain, "The First Turbojet Flights...", 25.

"... even considering the improvements possible ... the gas turbine could hardly be considered a feasible application to airplanes mainly because of the difficulty in complying with the stringent weight requirements ..."

Gas Turbine Committee
U.S. National Academy of Sciences
1940

# Chapter Three

# Early American Gas Turbine Engine Development

## Why the United States Lagged in Jet Engine Development

The development of the aircraft gas turbine in the United States lagged behind that in Great Britain and Germany. Robert Schlaifer, in *Development of Aircraft Engines*, points out that there were "no fundamental technical obstacles to prevent the development of turbojets from being begun in the United States as soon as it was begun abroad..."[1] Yet the United States was five years behind Britain and Germany at the start of World War II.

Edward Constant II, in *Origins of the Turbojet Revolution*, asserts that differences in the national patterns of pursuit of aerodynamic science were a cause of this five-year lag in the United States.[2] Constant attributed this to "marked national differences that would seem to reflect diverse national scientific traditions and fundamentally different political, economic, social, and geographical exigencies." The United States had a preoccupation with the empirical and practical aspects of aviation development, rather than systematic scientific investigation. While Britain and Germany concentrated on investigating high-speed aerodynamic phenomena and axial turbo-compressor phenomena, the United States did not. While the United States built the world's best commercial airline system, Britain and Germany used their airline systems as instruments of national policy. In some areas, such as investigation of flight problems, Germany, Britain, and the United States devoted similar levels of effort. Constant points out that in the application of prior technology and fundamental science, different national priorities and approaches resulted in "different national patterns in the pursuit of aerodynamic science, in the development of commercial aviation, and in participation in international competition."

Schlaifer also examines the question of the time lag in U.S. turbojet development. He postulated four possible answers: technical obstacles to turbojet development, perceived lack of tactical utility of the turbojet, nonavailability of funds for turbojet development, and lack of government responsibility.

Schlaifer asserts that there were two major obstacles facing an engineer who wanted to design and build a turbojet in the 1930s: obtaining the proper high-temperature materials and getting sufficient compressor efficiency. We will examine both of those problem areas, but for now suffice it to say that Schlaifer feels the United States could have overcome both of these technical obstacles if someone had seen the advantages (superior utility at high altitude and high speed) in doing so.[3]

Schlaifer points out that America failed to evaluate what was probably the chief competitive advantage of the gas turbine engine, its lower weight. American aircraft engine designers tended to accept the airplane as given, in both its design and speed, and to discuss the power plant in terms of its performance at this given speed.[4] This overlooks the systems analysis approach, so effectively used by von Ohain.

Another argument used to explain away the American lag is that the U.S. did not perceive enough tactical utility in the turbojet. Because of the geography of the United States, there was not the need for high-performance interceptors, whose performance comes at the expense of very short range. On the other hand, in Britain and Germany the much shorter distances placed a premium on interceptor performance.[5] Schlaifer responds to this argument by recalling that the instant he learned of the development of turbojets in Britain, the Chief of the U.S. Army Air Corps (General Henry H. Arnold) immediately set about having turbojets developed and produced in the U.S.[6] Schlaifer continues:

> At no time in the 1930s was anyone in the Air Corps sure enough of the nature of a future war to say that a 300-mph long-range aircraft would always and under all circumstances be superior to a 500-mph short-range airplane.[7]

Another argument used to explain the American developmental lag was that much less money was available for military aircraft during this period in the United States than in Britain in the 1930s or in Germany after 1933. Schlaifer points out that this lack of funding "was to some extent offset by the strength of the commercial aviation market and the availability of capital on a much larger scale than abroad."[8] Schlaifer also points out that the funds necessary to build, test, and prove a bench engine similar to Whittle's was about $100,000. Heinkel spent about that much to develop the He S 3 turbojet sufficiently for first flight.[9]

As Figure 3-1 illustrates, Schlaifer is correct about U.S. government support of aviation during the period from 1931 to 1933. Net U.S. government appropriations for aircraft declined. However, the figures for later years reveal the rising government expenditures for aviation development in response to the growing tension in Europe and the Far East.[10] From 1934 through the war, net government appropriations for aviation increased dramatically.

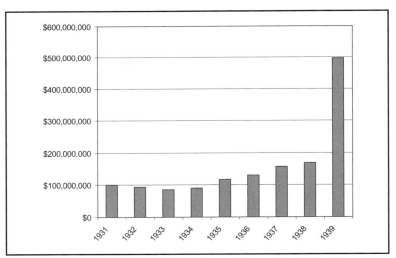

**Figure 3-1. Government Expenditures for Aviation
in the United States, 1931-1939**
*(Data courtesy of Airbook 1941)*

Was U.S. governmental policy responsible for the U.S. lag in turbojet development? Schlaifer doesn't think so.[11] In Germany, government support did not come until late in 1938 on a small scale, and during 1940 on a practical scale, until Heinkel and Junkers Aircraft informed the Reichsluftministerium (RLM) of the results of the work they were doing at their own expense and initiative. While it is true that Schelp was already an enthusiastic supporter of jet propulsion, official governmental support and funding came only after Hans Mauch (Schelp's immediate superior) was also convinced of the success of the turbojet.[12]

In Britain, the aid given by the Air Ministry to Power Jets up until the middle of 1939 amounted to only 16 percent of the total expenses of the company. Significant funding from the government came only after Whittle's work had demonstrated the promise of the engine.

In the United States the military services were at least as quick as the British and German governments to support the development of turbojets once they had an indication that the British were already making progress on the technology. In fact, the Durand Special Committee on Jet Propulsion began work in 1941 with even less knowledge of previous work than the British and Germans had before they decided to support such development.

Schlaifer asserts that the real reason the development of turbojets in the United States did not begin sooner was that no one realized how the turbojet made possible a tremendous increase in speed.[13] The logical application of turbine engines at the time seemed to be to drive propellers. No one asked the Air Corps at Wright Field whether it would accept short range in exchange for speeds of 500 mph or faster. No one asked the National Advisory Committee for Aeronautics (NACA) or the Navy's Bureau of Aeronautics whether they could find $100,000 for the development of such an engine. Schlaifer believes "subsequent history has fully justified the opinion held by the services in the 1930s, that it was not yet time to begin development of turboprops."[14] Schlaifer claims:

> Every one of the early turbojet developments was begun, on the other hand, not to obtain a better engine for existing aircraft (at) existing airspeeds, but as a means of obtaining vastly higher speeds and was connected with the design or at least a notion of a new and suitable airframe.[15]

Schlaifer finally concluded that the major reason for its lag in turbojet was the U.S. failure to realize the utility of the turbojets as an aircraft prime mover. In Britain and Germany, this recognition came from individuals outside the aircraft engine community: from a serving Royal Air Force (RAF) officer in Britain and from a recent university graduate in Germany. Thus, Schlaifer concludes, the "...relatively late date at which work began in the United States is simply the result of a historical accident: Whittle, von Ohain and (Herbert) Wagner were not Americans."[16]

Did the U.S. aircraft engine industry really lag that of Britain and Germany? Schlaifer asserts that it did not: "...the aircraft engine builders in the United States were really not behind their foreign colleagues at all..."[17] The first work done in Germany was done by an airframe manufacturer, Heinkel. Another German airframe company, Junkers, initiated the next turbojet program under Herbert Wagner. The regular aircraft engine manufacturers entered the new field in Germany in 1939 only as the result of very considerable pressure from the government.

The only turbojet development started in Britain before 1939 was the result of the efforts of an RAF officer, backed by two other RAF officers and by venture capital from sources having nothing to do with the aviation industry. The regular aircraft engine manufacturers became interested only after the first flight of a jet-propelled airplane in that country, in 1941. In the United States, Wright Aero was the first company to discover the extent of the work being done in Britain. Wright began negotiations for a license for the Whittle engine in the first half of 1941. That was just as early as any British manufacturer had become interested in the turbojet. Only the action of the U.S. military services prevented the entire U.S. aircraft engine industry from becoming intensely interested in the new field as soon as it became known that jet-propelled aircraft had been flown.[18]

Why weren't those whom one would expect to be the most interested in aircraft engine development, the power plant engineers, in the forefront of turbojet developments? Schlaifer thinks that they occupied themselves too much with incrementally developing the reciprocating engine as such to consider the possibility of the enormous increase in airplane speed inherent in the turbojet. When these engineers looked at the turbojet, they thought in terms of how it would work in the airframes of their time. They did not grasp that the turbojet would fundamentally alter the way they would have to look at considerations of weight-versus-power-versus performance at high speed (500 mph and over) in aircraft.

They looked at the turbojet in terms of how it would perform in existing aircraft, if substituted directly for existing reciprocating engines and used to produce performance about equal to that of existing aircraft. Increases in speed in the past had not come in very high increments. Wright Aero was the first U.S. company to discover the conundrum as Schlaifer describes it:

> ... with a given type of engine and propulsion system, even doubling the power at no increase in weight or size of the engine would only increase the speed of the airplane by about 25 percent
>
> ... doubling the power of the engine at the cost of nearly doubling the weight, the way in which power had always been gained in the past, would of course have brought a still smaller increase in speed.
>
> It had taken from 1927 until about 1936 for the power of the largest American aircraft engine to be (raised) from 500 horsepower to 1,000 horsepower.[19]

Schlaifer hypothesizes that had U.S. aircraft engine engineers been faced with the challenge of coming up with a power plant for a 500-600 mph fighter, they would have come up with a turbojet as the best solution to the problem. This is in fact why the Lockheed L-1000 turbojet and the L-133 jet fighter (Chapter 4) were designed in 1940.[20] Instead, American aircraft engine manufacturers took the airplane and its performance as given. Those engine manufacturers who became interested in the aircraft gas turbine at all were interested in its prop-driving form, which they considered at the time best suited to the anticipated needs of American commercial aviation.

American aircraft engine companies were not alone in their reasoning. When Rolls-Royce began work on turbines, the company started with the counterrotating counterflow ducted fan from the Royal Aircraft Establishment. When P&W started work on turbines, they took up the Swedish Gotaverken system in its PT-1 design for its advantages in fuel economy.

American historians of technology have overemphasized this question of the U.S. lag in turbojet development. How important is the fact that the United States did not have a turbojet engine in 1939? It is true that if the Germans had emphasized development of the Me 262 (Figure 3-2) a year earlier, the Allies would have had considerable trouble with it. However, even if they

**Figure 3-2. Messerschmitt Me 262**
*(Photo courtesy of U.S. Air Force Museum)*

had developed the Me 262 a year earlier, the Luftwaffe would still have had the same problems with supply, production and a lack of pilots. As it turned out, the Allied piston-engine fighters dealt successfully with the vastly superior Me 262 by attacking the jet as it came in to land.[21]

The United States came out of World War II with the strongest air force in the world, especially in heavy bombers. It had several turbojets in production and several more in the latter stages of development. Several F-80 Shooting Stars were stationed in Europe, and several more in the United States. Britain still had a slight lead in centrifugal turbojet development, but U.S. programs soon caught up.

The United States also lagged behind Germany in the development of operational axial-flow turbojets, although Westinghouse had one on test in 1942. When hostilities ended, the United States rapidly corrected that deficiency with the help of "Operation Paperclip." "Paperclip" was the code name for an intelligence operation in which the U.S. military scoured Western and Central Europe for German rocket and turbojet aircraft and engines, as well as for scientists and engineers in the aircraft and aircraft engine industry, bringing back important information that soon enabled them to catch up in axial turbojet development. Indeed, the United States found that in some areas of axial compressor development its engineers had surpassed the Germans.

## The Position of U.S. Aviation from 1936 to 1941

Other than aircraft gas turbine engine development, how did the United States rate in terms of overall aeronautical development in comparison with other countries? To get a picture of overall U.S. aeronautical development from 1934 to 1939, let us look at military aircraft, total aeronautical exports, and aeronautical production in the United States.

Two measures of a nation's aviation strength are the type and performance of the military aircraft it builds. Schlaifer points out that the United States did not know what kind of fighter it would need to fight in the next war. It was as unprepared as Europe for German Blitzkrieg warfare. The quickness of the German victories in Poland, Norway, Denmark, and the Low Countries did change the way that the U.S. Army Air Corps thought about tactical air warfare. The overall military aviation development thrust of the U.S. Army, however, did not change. The Army Air Corps of the pre-war period emphasized offensive warfare, especially strategic bombing, along with achieving local air superiority over the battlefield, as the key to successful war.

U.S. fighter/interceptor aircraft at the beginning of 1940 were not at the level of the German premier fighter aircraft, the Me 109 (Figure 3-3) or the Me 110. Our best pre-war fighter, the Curtiss P-40 Warhawk, was no match for the German fighters or the Japanese Mitsubishi

**Figure 3-3. Messerschmitt Me 109**
*(Photo coutesy of U.S. Air Force Museum)*

A6M2 Zero. The United States, however, had several outstanding fighters either in the final stages of development, well along in the development process, or about to enter service in 1940. These included the Lockheed P-38 Lightning, which entered production in 1940; the Vought F4U Corsair, which had its first flight in May 1940; the North American P-51 Mustang (Figure 3-4), which first flew on 26 October 1940 and entered service in April, 1942; and the Republic P-47 Thunderbolt, which first flew on 6 May 1941 and entered service in March, 1942.

**Figure 3-4. North American P-51 Mustang**
*(Photo courtesy of U.S. Air Force Museum)*

When the numbers and performance of U.S. long-range and medium-range bombers are considered, the Air Corps was the best in the world. In 1940 the United States already had the world's best medium-range bombers: the North American B-25 Mitchell, the Lockheed A-28 Hudson, the Martin B-26 Marauder, and the Douglas A-20 Havoc in production or in the final stages of development. While the United States lacked a good fighter-bomber until the advent of the Republic P-47 Thunderbolt, it did have the premier long-range bombers in the world, the Boeing B-17 Flying Fortress (Figure 3-5) and the Consolidated B-24 Liberator. The B-17 was later replaced by the Boeing B-29 Superfortress, an even more powerful long-range heavy bomber.

**Figure 3-5. Boeing B-17**
*(Photo courtesy of U.S. Air Force Museum)*

If one takes the value of a nation's aeronautical exports as a measure of its strength, then the United States was one of the strongest in the world. Figure 3-6 shows the totals for American aeronautical exports for the years 1929-1940. The total increase in American exports is dramatic from 1929 to 1940. The increased capital from these export sales was a big factor in the increase in research and development by U.S. aircraft and aircraft engine manufacturers and by manufacturers of turbosuperchargers. The companies had the capital in some cases to fund initial aircraft gas turbine research on their own while looking for long-term government support.[22]

As Figure 3-1 showed, U.S. government expenditures for aviation increased in the period from 1934 to 1940. The U.S. aviation industry also dramatically increased production of aircraft, aircraft engines, and aircraft parts during this same period. Figure 3-7 shows totals by category for aeronautical production in the United States from 1934 to 1939. After 1938 the government withheld total figures for aircraft and aircraft engine production from the public for security reasons.

## AERONAUTICAL EXPORTS FROM THE U.S. 1929-1940

| | *PARTS* | *ENGINES* | *AIRPLANES* | *TOTAL* |
|---|---|---|---|---|
| 1929 | $ 2,257,548 | $ 1,383,197 | $ 5,484,600 | $ 9,125,345 |
| 1930 | 2,363,456 | 1,634,197 | 4,819,669 | 8,818,110 |
| 1931 | 1,622,649 | 1,432,229 | 1,812,809 | 4,867,687 |
| 1932 | 2,069,884 | 1,517,682 | 4,358,967 | 7,946,533 |
| 1933 | 2,335,356 | 1,430,787 | 5,389,739 | 9,155,882 |
| 1934 | 4,906,596 | 4,383,101 | 8,258,484 | 17,548,181 |
| 1935 | 5,233,011 | 2,459,317 | 6,638,515 | 14,330,843 |
| 1936 | 6,060,483 | 5,397,469 | 11,299,451 | 23,055,761 |
| 1937 | 12,157,337 | 5,944,004 | 21,037,361 | 39,405,473 |
| 1938 | 21,930,343 | 7,899,844 | 37,977,924 | 68,209,050 |
| 1939 | 35,798,922 | 14,120,035 | 66,386,866 | 117,000,000 |
| 1940 | 64,462,409 | 49,873,823 | 196,352,315 | 311,757,326 |

**Figure 3-6. Aeronautical Exports from the United States, 1929-1940**
*(Data courtesy of Airbook 1941)*

## AERONAUTICAL PRODUCTION
## IN THE UNITED STATES 1934-1938
### (Dollars in millions)

| | *Mil A/C* | *Mil $$* | *Comm A/C* | *Comm $$* | *Mil Eng* | *Mil $$* | *Comm Eng* | *Comm $$* |
|---|---|---|---|---|---|---|---|---|
| 1934 | 437 | $ 9.0 | 772 | $ 10.0 | 688 | | 2,048 | $ 10.00 |
| 1935 | 459 | 11.5 | 1,109 | 10.5 | 991 | | 1,947 | 6.50 |
| 1936 | 1,141 | 27.0 | 1,559 | 12.5 | 1,794 | $ 5.9 | 2,527 | 7.94 |
| 1937 | 949 | 37.0 | 2,281 | 19.1 | 1,949 | 14.6 | 4,095 | 15.30 |
| 1938 | | 42.6 | 1,612 | 12.3 | | 14.8 | 3,088 | 12.2 |
| | | | | | | 15.3 | | |

A/C = aircraft, Eng = engine, Comm = commercial, Mil = military

**Figure 3-7. Aeronautical Production the United States, 1934-1938**
*(Data courtesy of Airbook 1940)*

There were two reasons behind this increase: rising exports to the Allies in the years preceding World War II and the increasing preparedness for America's own defense from 1934 to 1941. As the statistics show, the American aviation industry in the period 1934 to 1940 was in the midst of the biggest boom in its history. This boom and the immense capital it produced, coupled with the American recognition of outside threats to its interests in Europe and the Pacific, had a tremendous positive impact on the research and development of the aeronautical sciences in the United States.

## American High-Temperature Materials Development

The two technical areas that affected American turbojet development were high-temperature materials development and compressor development.[23] Until turbojets came along, high-temperature materials in aircraft engines were only needed for exhaust valves and in the turbine blades, or buckets, of turbosuperchargers. Aircraft engine developers could not apply valve technology to turbine blades and buckets because valve material requirements called for different properties.

Manufacturers made buckets from a steel called SAE 6150 from 1918 to 1922, then switched to a steel known as Silchrome No. 1 until 1928. Silchrome was slightly more resistant to oxidation gases and did not scale off and lose strength, as did SAE 6150. The standard material for steam turbine buckets was a type of stainless steel known as "12 percent chrome." This alloy operated at blade temperatures up to 1,000°F.

In 1928 the Army Air Corps adopted British Kayser and Steel 965 (KE-965) for use in turbosupercharger buckets. This was the first material developed to have strength at high temperatures, permitting blade temperatures from 1,100°F to 1,400°F. The Army, being unwilling to rely on foreign material, decided to substitute an American alloy. The subsequent search led to an alloy produced by Universal Cyclops Corporation called 17W, an American modification of KE-965. Manufacturers adopted the new alloy for turbosupercharger buckets in 1933. Also in that year, the Army tried out a set of buckets made of Stellite No. 6 alloy, which had a hot strength superior to that of 17W. It soon achieved temperatures as high as 1,832°F in these buckets.[24] Stellite No. 6 was developed by Ellwood Haynes of the Haynes Stellite Company, a division of Union Carbide and Carbon Corporation. Although it was very durable, Stellite No. 6 proved too hard to forge into turbosupercharger buckets; the dies wore out quickly. Austenal Laboratories, however, soon managed to fabricate a set of Stellite No. 6 buckets by using a lost-wax casting process. Machining the castings soon proved to be too impractical for mass production and the Army resumed its search for a castable, easily machined alloy.[25]

In 1936 the Army became interested in a new alloy by the Haynes Stellite Company called "Hastelloy." There were four derivatives of this alloy, designated A, B, C, and D. Haynes Stellite originally developed Hastelloy in 1926 for high resistance to corrosion by acids and chlorides at ordinary temperatures, first marketing it in 1929. In 1931, Haynes Stellite published data showing Hastelloy's advantages at high temperatures, but turbosupercharger engineers did not take advantage of this new material until 1936. In that year, Army turbosupercharger engineers realized Hastelloy's potential when Haynes Stellite published studies of wrought Hastelloy B. Wright Field engineers then asked Haynes Stellite to investigate the alloy's suitability for turbosupercharger buckets.

General Electric (GE) joined Haynes Stellite in cooperative research into the use of Hastelloy A, B, or C for turbosupercharger buckets in 1937. GE soon succeeded in drop-forging a Hastelloy alloy into a finished shape and in 1941 decided to forge all their turbosupercharger buckets from Hastelloy B.

When the United States entered the war in 1941, the services realized that they would need a mass-production process better than drop-forging of Hastelloy B (which quickly wore out dies). Austenal Corporation produced good castings using a Haynes Stellite alloy closely related to Stellite No. 6, called Vitallium. GE quickly took advantage of this new development and switched to Vitallium for turbosupercharger buckets.[26] Austenal further refined the alloy to contain less carbon, making it less brittle and better suited for turbine buckets. After the Austenal development, the Army called on Haynes Stellite to help in working out mass production methods for the new alloy. Haynes Stellite in turn improved the product even more and designated the alloy Stellite No. 21. In October 1941, GE adopted Stellite No. 21 in forged buckets for use in the Whittle engine.[27]

Hastelloy B proved vastly superior to the British Rex 78 alloy, which Whittle had used in his engines. The maximum blade temperatures — 1,200°F to 1,250°F — on the Whittle engine very much suited the properties of Hastelloy B. GE also used forged Hastelloy B on the first experimental I-40 engines starting in 1943 but soon realized that a lack of forging capacity would limit their use. In 1945 casting technology had developed to the point where manufacturers could cast Stellite No. 21 into buckets. The GE Schenectady TG-100, described later in this chapter, originally used cast buckets of Stellite No. 21.

Westinghouse developed the W19 series turbojets with the Westinghouse alloy K-42-B, but a portion of the quantity production of the turbine buckets was done with cast Stellite Alloy No. 23, a derivative of Stellite No. 21. Schlaifer asserts:

> There is no question that either the Stellite or the Hastelloy alloys were greatly superior to any material available to the Germans for use in their gas turbine buckets, the reason being that Germany suffered from severe shortages of critical constituents, particularly cobalt and nickel.[28]

Schlaifer also maintains that American alloys were unquestionably superior to the British alloys Rex 78 and Stayblade. Schlaifer doesn't know whether the American alloys were superior to Nimonic 80, but states that American engineers preferred the American materials. The British Rex 78 and Nimonic 80, the German Tinidur, and the American Westinghouse K-42-B alloys required heat treating to assure adequate hot strength, while Hastelloy and Stellite did not. Having thus examined the progress in American metallurgy in the 1930s, Schlaifer rejects the theory "that inadequate progress in metallurgy was in any degree responsible for delaying the development of aircraft gas turbines in the U.S."[29]

## American Compressor Development

The second area that Schlaifer scrutinized was compressor development. He states "second only to metallurgy as an obstacle believed in the 1930s to preclude the building of successful gas turbines was the low pressure ratio and efficiency then achieved by rotary compressors."[30]

Schlaifer calculates that turbojet development called for compressor pressure ratios of about 3:1 at about 80 percent efficiency (the early German turbojets) or 4:1 at 75 percent efficiency (the early British turbojets). A successful turboprop would require a pressure ratio of at least 5:1 with an efficiency of at least 80 percent. Gear-driven superchargers of the 1930's era were limited to pressure ratios of 1.2:1 at efficiencies not over 70 percent. By 1935, at a 1.5:1 pressure ratio, turbosuperchargers could maintain efficiencies of 70 percent, but the efficiency fell off to 65 percent at 2:1. By the late 1930s, however, engineers were beginning to understand the aerodynamics of the turbosupercharger. In 1941 U.S. Army Air Corps General Henry H. Arnold chose the GE Company to develop the Whittle turbojet because of their long-standing experience in aircraft turbosuperchargers.

## Turbosupercharger Development

Many of the aircraft engine manufacturers in the 1920s elected to pursue development of air-cooled engines, with gear-driven superchargers, eliminating the extra weight of the hot exhause pipes needed for turbosuperchargers, but incurring some weight penalty for the gear drive. GE survived this period by working with the engine companies and studying, designing, and producing impellers and diffuser plates used in the air-cooled engines. These superchargers worked well at low altitude, but as aircraft achieved higher and higher altitudes the geared supercharger became increasingly complex. The new requirements laid on the geared supercharger added unwanted weight and penalized takeoff power by increasing specific fuel consumption. The 1930s brought a new emphasis on turbosupercharger development and GE was ready (Figure 3-8).

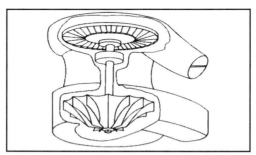

**Figure 3-8. Turbosupercharger**
*(Illustration courtesy of GE)*

## General Electric (GE)

In the early 1930s, the engineers at the U.S. Army Air Corps Power Plant Laboratory at Wright Field near Dayton, Ohio started new research aimed at continuing the turbosupercharger advances begun in the 1920s. In September 1931, the Army awarded a contract for the testing of high-temperature turbine nozzle and blade combinations to GE who continued work throughout the 1930s, gaining important data on turbocharger performance as well as their first high-temperature test stand.[31] The Army renewed this research contract in 1935 and 1939.

In the mid-1930s an alliance of the Army, Trans World Airlines, Northrop, and GE was created to test a turbosupercharger at high altitude. The airplane selected was a Trans World Airlines Northrop Gamma. With a GE turbosupercharger installed on the Gamma's reciprocating engine, the aircraft achieved the first 'over the weather' long distance flight between the cities of Kansas City and Dayton, reaching 37,000 feet in altitude. This achievement provided dramatic proof of the potential of the turbo, and resulted in a production contract for GE to build 230 units of the improved "Type B" turbosupercharger (Figure 3-9), a new design that would enable a 1,000 horsepower engine to maintain full power up to 25,000 feet.

In late 1937 GE established a Supercharger Department in Lynn, Massachusetts, to manufacture the new turbosupercharger. The Air Corps ordered the new turbo superchargers for the B-17 Flying Fortress heavy bomber and for later developments including the Lockheed P-38 Lightning, the Consolidated B-24 Liberator bomber, the Republic P-47 Thunderbolt fighter, and the Boeing B-29 Superfortress heavy bomber. Of more significance was that GE's development of the turbosupercharger, along with their excellent working relationship with the Army, made them the Army's first choice in 1941 to develop the new technology represented by the Whittle turbojet. It was this turbosupercharger development expertise that enabled GE to develop the American I-A turbojet and its derivatives, the I-14, I-16, I-18, and the I-20 quickly.

**Figure 3-9. GE Type B Turbosupercharger**
*(Photo courtesy of GE)*

## Wright Aeronautical Corporation

In 1934-35, Wright Aeronautical Corporation became the first engine manufacturer to undertake the study and development of its own superchargers. Wright did not get satisfactory performance from a GE supercharger matched to their new Cyclone two-speed supercharger drive and assigned Kenneth Campbell the job of designing an in-house supercharger. In 1935, Wright also began testing superchargers on a test stand consisting of a 150-horsepower dynamometer with the rear end of a Cyclone engine used for the gearing. Until 1941 Wright ran only complete superchargers on test and tested only existing superchargers, believing it would be too expensive to build radically different designs. Both the designing of superchargers and the rigorous testing of existing superchargers gave Wright an understanding of the design principles of the vaned diffuser.[32] All American diffusers were of the vaneless type until 1935. That year manufacturers introduced the vaned diffuser to improve the performance of the supercharger. The vaned diffusers, however, had to be more closely matched to the rest of the supercharger than the vaneless ones.

The Wright work from 1935 to 1937 resulted in considerable modifications in supercharger design. The company had adopted a considerable decrease in air passage width at the tip and had altered the contours of the wall, creating a more nearly constant cross section in the inducer or entrance portion of the impeller. In 1937, Wright set out to design completely new superchargers for the new R-2600 and R-3350 engines.

In March 1938 Wright decided to use its own superchargers rather than GE superchargers in the R-3350, and from this point on, the Wright staff designed all Wright superchargers.[33] GE, however, continued to manufacture the Wright designs. This head start in supercharger development meant that Wright was the only American firm to have an engine in production early in the war with a supercharger as good as the supercharger on the Rolls-Royce Merlin XX (put into production in 1940).[34] The Wright G-200 Cyclone supercharger had an efficiency of 70 percent at a pressure ratio of 2.3:1. The Merlin XX supercharger (as tested by Wright Field) had an efficiency of 68 percent at the same pressure ratio. German production superchargers at the end of the 1930s had somewhat lower efficiencies than that of the Merlin. Improved inducer design, narrower impeller tips, and a smaller number of vanes in the diffuser were the chief features which distinguished the Wright supercharger from other American designs.

After 1937, Wright made two important development decisions. First, the company directed its staff to further refine the supercharger inlet, impeller, diffuser, and collector. Wright engineers began studying the effects of the inlet and carburetor on the performance of the supercharger. Second, in 1939 Wright built a new 500-horsepower test rig. Increased engine production in 1941 enabled Wright to further increase their supercharger research and development. They bought a 1,000-horsepower test rig and increased testing to two shifts, with correspondingly increased test staff. These efforts paid off in 1943 with a new axial-inlet supercharger having a peak efficiency of 81 percent at a pressure ratio of 2:1, about 80 percent at 2.5:1, and 75 percent at 3:1.

## Other Developers

The Turbo Engineering Corporation designed a two-stage compressor into its first turbosupercharger in 1937. The compressor showed an efficiency of 76 percent at 3.4:1 corresponding to approximately 78 percent at 2:1 in each stage.[35]

Like Wright, Pratt & Whitney (P&W) was forced into the supercharger field. In P&W's case it was to solve the problem of surging at high altitude in the first two-stage supercharger for the R-1830.[36] In September 1939, P&W decided that they could only make progress in supercharger development if they developed instruments to observe and measure airflow at various points within the supercharger. They could then isolate the effects of design changes at various points in the interior. P&W gave contracts for the development of instrumentation and test procedures to Harvard and Massachusetts Institute of Technology. These were ready in 1943.

Work on superchargers by NACA began in June of 1940 with the establishment of a special committee composed of representatives from NACA, Wright, P&W, and Allison. The committee convinced all the manufacturers to adopt a single test technique, thereby standardizing results for their mutual benefit. NACA also began its own supercharger test and development programs, achieving pressure ratios of 3.5:1 at efficiencies up to 74 percent by 1944. Another change in compressor design resulted in the mixed-flow impeller, which discharged air partly to the rear. In a centrifugal gas turbine design this change would obviate a right-angle turn after the impeller.

One of the notable differences between American and European compressor design was that the Europeans began development on the basis of what they hoped to achieve in compressor performance, not on what they had already obtained. Whittle thought he could get 80 percent efficiency at a pressure ratio of 4:1 from a centrifugal compressor, and while he overestimated his engine's capability to meet that goal, the Rolls-Royce Derwent V attained it in 1945. The Rolls-Royce Welland achieved 75 percent efficiency at 4:1 pressure ratio in late 1941 or early 1942.[37]

## Prewar American Aircraft Gas Turbine Research

Though development of the aircraft gas turbine in the United States was not as advanced as that in Europe prior to 1945, the groundwork was being laid and a number of development efforts were underway. In an interesting parallel with the European work, all but one of these efforts were conducted outside the aircraft engine community. The one exception, as we shall see, turned out to be a blind alley.

## Lasley Turbine Motor Company

An interesting development in aircraft power plants in the mid- and late 1930s was the Lasley turbojet. This seminal work by R.E. Lasley perhaps could have resulted in a practical turbojet, given funding by the services. Lasley received several patents for gas turbines beginning in 1925, while a steam-turbine engineer for Allis-Chalmers.[38] Early in the 1930s Lasley formed the Lasley Turbine Motor Company in Waukegan, Illinois. His goal was to develop a gas turbine for aircraft.

In July 1934, Lasley showed film of his engine running on a test stand, and he claimed at that time that his engine operated with an efficiency of 11.6 percent.[39] His resources soon proved insufficient to develop his design. Later in 1934 Lasley approached the Navy for financial support, but negotiations collapsed when Lasley was unwilling to grant the Navy the usual rights expected under their development contracts. Lasley then turned to the Army.

In August 1934, representatives of the Army's Wright Field establishment visited Lasley in his shop. After reviewing his design and hardware, the Army consulted with GE's Sanford Moss. They issued a memorandum stating that Lasley's engine was too inefficient, and that the only way to improve the engine's efficiency was to run the turbine at metal temperatures of at least 2,500°F. This was in 1934 and the Army's Wright Field engineers did not discover Haynes Stellite's Hastelloy until 1936, although it had been available since 1929. Hastelloy buckets could run up to turbine inlet temperatures of 1,832°F in 1933. It still would have required both material development and cooling technology to attain the 2,500°F metal temperatures required by Lasley. No blade metal temperatures of 2,500°F are found even today, more than sixty-four years later; and it took forty years of metallurgical development plus new blade-cooling technology to achieve gas temperatures of 2,500°F.

Why did Lasley fail? Schlaifer asserts that Lasley's basic development goals were the root cause:

> Lasley was working toward the same unsound objective toward which other engineers were convinced that work should be directed: efficiency fully competitive with the reciprocating engine, with no regard for the possibility and utility of a less efficient but much lighter engine. As a result, to judge from Lasley's patents, he had made his engine very complex in order to raise the over-all efficiency in spite of low component efficiencies. In the light of hindsight, it is clear that the only course which could lead to success was to keep the engine as simple as possible, and to improve efficiency by refinement of the design of simple elements, not by gadgetry.[40]

## General Electric (GE)

Although a more thorough discussion of GE's involvement in aircraft gas turbine engine development follows in Chapter Seven, the company's pre-war development should be mentioned here. Members of the turbosupercharger design team had discussed the value of turbojets before the mid-1930s. In 1939 GE made a careful analysis of aircraft gas turbines and decided that a turbojet would be more useful than a turboprop.[41]

The GE Steam Turbine Division at Schenectady participated on the Durand Special Committee on Jet Propulsion in 1941. In response to that committee's request for research and a subsequent aircraft gas turbine design, GE/Schenectady responded with a design for a turboprop. When NACA requested that the services assume the responsibility for continuing the research started by the committee, GE/Schenectady received a research contract from the Army in late 1941 (possibly December). GE designated its design the TG-100; the Army later designated it the T-31. GE/Schenectady succeeded in getting the engine to run on a test stand without a propeller in May 1943. Also, in mid-1943, GE began design of the TG-180 axial-flow turbojet with an eleven-stage compressor. The TG-180 was 37.5 inches in diameter and weighed 2,300 pounds. It ran on April 13, 1944, only three months after the first run of the I-40, yielding a specific fuel consumption of 1.075 due to its high-efficiency, 4:1 pressure ratio, axial compressor. In February 1946, the Army first flew the TG-180 in a Republic XP-84. At this time, the TG-180 had an average rating of 4,000 pounds thrust (with a guarantee of 3,750 pounds), roughly equal to the I-40 twenty months earlier.

In October 1941, GE's Turbosupercharger Division at Lynn, Massachusetts, began development of the Whittle turbojet, designated the I-A by GE. In mid-1943 GE/Lynn began designing the I-40 turbojet.[42] The first run of the I-40 turbojet was in January 1944.

## Northrop

Two aircraft manufacturers, Lockheed Aircraft Corporation and Northrop Aircraft Inc., proposed to build aircraft gas turbine engines before the introduction of the Whittle turbojet into the United States in October 1941. Let us take a brief look at Northrop and the engine they called the Turbodyne. Lockheed will be discussed in the next chapter.

Northrop Aircraft Corporation was founded in March 1939 by John K. Northrop and La Motte T. Cohu. Northrop had recently left the Douglas Aircraft Corporation, of which his Northrop company had been a subsidiary, where he had been chief engine designer. He had established his reputation as a gifted aircraft designer with his S-1, the famous Vega, and the subsequent Northrop Alpha and Gabranna. He also had a reputation as an aviation innovator willing to take a gamble with his "Flying Wing." He formed the Northrop Aircraft Corporation in 1939 to develop advanced design aircraft with a small, dedicated staff of engineers. Among those engineers was a Czech engineer named Vladimir Pavlecka. Convinced of the practicality of an aircraft gas turbine engine, Pavlecka joined Jack Northrop because he felt that Northrop's small new company was the best place to develop that engine.

Soon after the organization of the company, Pavlecka convinced Northrop of the desirability of starting a small, conceptual research project to design a turboprop as a replacement for the reciprocating engine.[43] The company designated the new aircraft gas turbine engine the Turbodyne (Figure 3-10). Although convinced of the gas turbine's utility as an aircraft power plant, Pavlecka saw the best use of this new technology in driving a propeller.[44]

**Figure 3-10. Northrop Turbodyne**
*(Photo courtesy of Northrop)*

Pavlecka felt that a turboprop would offer an advantage over a reciprocating engine for several reasons. First, it would be simpler than a reciprocating engine, requiring less complicated accessories. Second, it would be freer of vibration and somewhat lighter than a reciprocating engine.

His design targets were a specific fuel consumption of 0.55 pounds per horsepower per hour, a very high pressure ratio of 10.5:1, and development of a compressor and turbine with efficiencies of 85 percent. He intended to obtain these compressor efficiencies through an axial compressor.

Northrop assigned six engineers to work on preliminary design and analysis. The company provided about $25,000 for initial development, but they sought government funding for the remainder of the Turbodyne's development, estimating the total development cost at about $1 million.[45] This estimate, as events unfolded, proved extremely low. However, considering that the entire Northrop Corporation was worth $3 million to $4 million at this time, this was a big step for the company. They approached both the Army and Navy, and in 1940, were able to interest the Navy in funding cycle studies to determine whether an axial or radial design would be best for the compressor and turbine.[46] On June 30, 1941, both services decided to join in funding the Turbodyne project on a limited basis. They awarded Northrop $483,600 to "design a complete compressor-turbine engine, but confining the fabrication, development, and testing to the compressor".[47] The contract was a cost-plus-fixed-fee type.[48] After the Northrop team had designed and constructed the compressor it became apparent there were no facilities available for separate testing of such a compressor, other than the complete engine itself. After extensive discussion with the services, the Navy issued a new contract on July 1, 1943. This new contract, for $1.5 million, covered the costs of building two Turbodyne engines, one a ground test model and the other a prototype aircraft engine with starter and reduction gear driving an aircraft propeller.[49] The Navy agreed to supervise the contract.[50] Northrop designated the engine the Turbodyne Alpha 1500. Pavlecka and his small team set out to design an engine with an eighteen-stage, axial-flow compressor to develop 2,400 horsepower at 18,000 feet and 375 mph.

Pavlecka resigned from the Turbodyne development team in late 1943. Northrop replaced him with Art Phelan as Chief of Development. Phelan, a forty-three-year-old British engineer, came to Northrop from Chrysler Motors, where he had headed the engine research division. Northrop also got valuable advice from another Englishman during this early period. RAF Captain Frank Whittle reviewed the Northrop design concept and made recommendations.[51]

At this time Northrop came to the conclusion that the Turbodyne project was beyond the capabilities of Northrop alone. Lockheed would reach this same conclusion a year later with their L-1000 turbojet. Northrop began searching for outside expertise to help them develop the Turbodyne, offering a 50-percent share in the project. Northrop found a willing participant in the Joshua Hendy Iron Works of Sunnyvale, California. Hendy had experience in steam turbine design and construction, and they joined Northrop to form Northrop-Hendy, Inc.

Northrop-Hendy completed the Turbodyne engines early in 1944. During test runs both engines failed in the 10,000-rpm range, although the team came out with valuable performance information. After this failure, the Navy dropped out of the development partnership with the Army, who assumed sole funding responsibility for the Turbodyne. During the latter part of 1943 and the early part of 1944, the Army's Air Materiel Command at Wright Field contracted with Northrop-Hendy to design and develop a substantially more powerful version of the Turbodyne, designated the XT37, for use in a heavy bomber. The development contract called for 4,000 horsepower at 35,000 feet and 500 mph.[52] To meet this specification, the engine would have to develop about 10,000 horsepower at sea-level static conditions.

The development of the Turbodyne and the XT37 proved to take a great deal longer than either the Army or Northrop-Hendy expected. In 1945 the Northrop program augmented their development and design team with several former GE engineers who had opted to move back to California after the war. Bill Crater, a combustion expert from GE's I-16 program; Gene Hunsaker, principal designer of GE's axial-flow compressor; Albert Craft, and Charles Dibble all joined the Northrop group. By late 1947, Northrop finally completed three XT37 turboprop engines. Testing on one of the engines achieved 5,150 horsepower with a turbine inlet temperature of 1,350°F. Six months later this same engine turned out 8,000 horsepower. Another engine passed a preflight qualification test program and achieved 10,000 shaft horsepower. Encouraged by this success, the Air Materiel Command in mid-1948 issued a letter of intent to continue the test program and fund the construction of four new flight-type engines, at a projected cost of $12 million.[53]

In 1949 the Air Force negotiated a contract to modify an existing Northrop YB-49 Flying Wing bomber (Figure 3-11) for installation of the Turbodyne XT37. The Flying Wing, powered by six J35 turbojets, was to be a flying test-bed for two Turbodyne turboprops, one on each side of the centerline. General Motors Aeroproducts Division was to provide large counterrotating pusher propellers for each Turbodyne engine.

**Figure 3-11. Northrop YB-49 Flying Wing**
*(Photo courtesy of Northrop)*

Northrop organized a subsidiary to take over development of the Turbodyne. The Turbodyne Corporation succeeded the Northrop-Hendy partnership as the development management structure in late 1949. Gene Hunsaker became president of the new company. They were confident of the Turbodyne's future success at this point. The engine had been chosen as the alternate engine for the Boeing B-52 and the Turbodyne had already developed substantially higher power than the primary engine, the Wright T35 (a turboprop version of the Lockheed/Menasco L-1000). Northrop expected the B-52 turboprop-powered high-altitude, heavy bomber to be a high-production aircraft. These hopes were dashed, however, when the Air Force decided to change the B-52's configuration from turboprops to turbojets. Both the Wright and the Northrop engines were suddenly eliminated from the competition.[54] This was the beginning of the end of the Turbodyne program. The flight test program for the Turbodyne died when the Air Force canceled the EB-35B Flying Wing test bed.

With the cancellation of the Flying Wing test bed, the Turbodyne Corporation tried hard to find substitute funding for the program. When the Air Force declined to maintain the program, the corporation approached the Navy, but without success. The Secretary of the Air Force finally terminated the program in 1950 and Northrop disbanded the Turbodyne Corporation. The Air Force ordered Turbodyne Corporation to turn over all patents, name, and technical data to GE's Gas Turbine Division in Schenectady, New York.

Why did the Northrop Turbodyne development program fail? The Air Force was attracted to the Turbodyne by its promise of high horsepower to drive a turboprop aircraft at high altitude. The program, however, took so long that turbojet technology outdistanced the Turbodyne's utility to the aircraft designer. The high cost of the engine, coupled with its lengthy development time, eventually persuaded the Air Force to use turbojets for high-speed, high-altitude power for its heavy bombers.

## Pratt & Whitney (P&W)

Unlike any engine manufacturer in either Britain or Germany, and unlike any engine manufacturer in the United States, Pratt & Whitney proposed to build a turbine engine without first being convinced about its practicability. This engine was quite different both in design and purpose from those which were successfully developed by the end of the war.[55] About 1940, P&W engineer L.S. Hobbs had a study made of gas turbines with rotary compressors. He rejected this design as being too impractical for two reasons. First, he reasoned that the fuel consumption would be much greater than that of a conventional power plant at the airplane speeds which he was considering. Second, he assumed that the weight of the turbojet engine per pound of thrust at these speeds would be as great as that of the conventional power plant.

In early 1940, Andrew Kalitinsky of the Massachusetts Institute of Technology (MIT) proposed to P&W a more efficient type of gas turbine with which he had already had experience in Switzerland.[56] Kalitinsky derived his design from a Swedish engine system called the Gotaverken system, which he had studied. This system was essentially halfway between a compound engine and a pure turbine engine. The exhaust from a two-stroke diesel (as in a compound engine) drove a turbine wheel, but only enough power was taken from the diesel engine itself to drive the compressor. Most of the net useful power came from the turbine, and the rest from the jet exhaust. Kalitinsky's design made provision for burning additional fuel between the exhaust of the diesel and the inlet to the turbine to provide additional power for short-period use. The combined diesel engine and reciprocating compressor were of the opposed-free-piston type. This system was supposed to be more fuel efficient and smoother in operation than a conventional reciprocating engine.

In the fall of 1940, P&W's Hobbs discussed the Kalitinsky design with J.C. Hunsaker of MIT. Hobbs then asked Kalitinsky to make preliminary performance calculations on his design.[57] These calculations were favorable in that they promised reduced specific fuel consumption (0.34-0.27 pounds per horsepower per hour), compared to the best contemporary piston engine's figure of 0.42. These favorable specific fuel consumption calculations coincided with P&W interest in the Air Corps' proposal to fund a new long-range strategic bomber (which became the B-36). P&W agreed to fund initial studies of the Kalitinsky engine design. Preliminary engine and installation layout began in May 1941. These led P&W to the conclusion that, although the engine would weigh more than 50 percent more than conventional reciprocating engines, the added weight was somewhat offset by the reduced weight of the accessories. Experimental investigations of components were begun as a private venture of the company. By the end of spring in 1941, P&W engineers had completed preliminary engine layouts for a 4,000 to 5,000 horsepower turboprop engine,[58] but had by 1943 made little more than a start in solving basic problems in this novel type of engine.[59] Throughout the war the company continued small-scale experimental research and long-term component research.[60]

One of the characteristics of the Kalitinsky development is the secrecy in which P&W held the development details. Schlaifer relates that P&W refused to give information on PT-1 development even to NACA. P&W was aware of the services' desire to keep the aircraft engine manufacturers out of the turbojet development business so that they could concentrate on building reciprocating engines to win the war. P&W was not alone among companies on both sides of the Atlantic. German companies were secretive as well; they refused to reveal technical secrets to each other until Germany started losing the war.

P&W never really tried to develop hardware for the Kalitinsky design, but rather kept it going as long-term applied research, spending $3.3 million on it by the end of the war. Schlaifer relates that:

> The greatest share of the work was put on the least well-known part, the free-piston Diesel compressor, and this component proved in fact to present the most serious problems; it was eventually made to

work fairly well at part speed, but it never got up to design speed. There were serious difficulties with combustion in the afterburner. On the other hand the turbine wheel itself presented no serious problems: the first model had an efficiency of 85 percent, credit being given for exhaust thrust, and the high-temperature problems of ordinary gas turbines were largely absent because of the low temperature.[61]

P&W subsequently built a complete engine for test. Like Northrop's and Lockheed's turboprop developments, however, the difficulty and length of time in developing the engine were its downfall. By the time P&W finished the engine prototype, they realized that it would take too much longer to develop the engine sufficiently for service. The turbojet had fully burst upon the scene, and there were other turboprops developed as well that gave the same 5,000 horsepower as the PT-1, while weighing only a third as much. Adding regeneration to the cycles of these turboprops and turbojets also promised to bring the specific fuel consumption down to that of the PT-1. P&W opted to pursue more orthodox turbojets and turboprops and dropped development of the Kalitinsky PT-1.[62]

Although P&W curtailed work on this engine design in June 1945, the component work on the PT-1 laid important groundwork for the next P&W effort in the development of an aircraft gas turbine, the PT-2. The Navy issued a development contract to P&W on June 30, 1945 for this new axial-flow turboprop design, designated the T34 by the Navy. The story of the T34 is continued in Chapter Eight.

## Wright Aeronautical Company

Wright Aero learned of the Whittle engine development and opened negotiations with Whittle and Power Jets in early 1941 for an American license to manufacture the Whittle turbojet. These negotiations failed when the U.S. Army intervened and negotiated directly for the rights to the engine, which they then turned over to the General Electric Company.[63]

## National Advisory Committee for Aeronautics (NACA)

Although NACA had an impact on American development, the effect was not always constructive. Both engineers and historians of the technology have singled out the 1923 Buckingham Study for NACA as a major inhibitor of American turbojet progress.[64] They have often interpreted the famous judgment rendered on turbojet development by Buckingham to mean that Buckingham was against the turbojet. Buckingham, however, did not discuss a true turbojet in his report. In the second paragraph of his report he describes the hypothetical engine that he based his study upon:

> Air is compressed and mixed with fuel in a combustion chamber, where the mixture burns at constant pressure. The combustion products issue through a nozzle, and the reaction of the jet constitutes the thrust.[65]

There is no turbine driving the compressor in this description. This leads one to believe that Buckingham was describing a compound engine, with a form of reciprocating engine driving the compressor described. This study correctly concluded that at 250 mph the fuel consumption of the most efficient jet engine possible (with a reciprocating compressor of 85 percent efficiency driven by a reciprocating engine) would be at least four times as great as that of a reciprocating engine driving a propeller.[66] Buckingham reached the following additional conclusions from his study:

> It is sometimes supposed, by those who have not considered the matter in detail, that while jet propulsion would probably be rather wasteful of fuel, it might present considerable compensating advantages in the way of lightness and simplicity. We are now in a position to see what these possibilities are with the particular scheme which has been discussed and which is, perhaps, the obvious one.
>
> In the first place, even at the highest speeds now in sight, say 250 mph, the fuel consumption could not be reduced much below four times that required by the ordinary air screw. In the second place, the power plant would be much heavier for jet than for screw propulsion, and the high fuel load would not

be offset by any saving of machinery weight. In the third place, the power plant would not be simpler but far more complicated and delicate than the ordinary one. To say nothing about the fuel injection system, the combined compressor and engine would have about twice as many pistons, valves, and other moving parts as a simple engine, and the chances of breakdown and the difficulties of upkeep would be correspondingly increased.[67]

The important missing piece here is that Buckingham never considered the addition of a turbine to his hypothetical engine, which would naturally eliminate the need for a reciprocating engine to drive the compressor.

In 1932, NACA and the U.S. Bureau of Standards reexamined the Buckingham report and specifically focused on studies of Melot-type ejectors. The results of the study revealed that the benefit obtained from ejector augmentation was too slight to alter Buckingham's test results very much. The new tests revealed that under the most favorable conditions the thrust increased by only some 37 percent.[68]

During the late 1930s, NACA looked at developing the Campini Ducted Fan (Figure 3-12), a compound engine design begun in 1930 by Italian engineer Secondo Campini.[69] The engine consisted of an ordinary reciprocating engine driving a many-bladed propeller or fan of small diameter situated within a closed air passage or duct. At cruising power it would function in much the same way as an engine with an ordinary propeller, but the location of the fan within a duct made it possible to obtain additional thrust for combat or similar purposes by burning additional fuel within the duct behind the fan.

**Figure 3-12. Caproni-Campini
Ducted Fan Aircraft**
*(Illustration courtesy of National Air & Space Museum)*

Eastman N. Jacobs of NACA attended the Volta International Aeronautical Congress in Italy in 1936, where he became interested in the Campini development.[70] In 1939, Jacobs began a theoretical study of the Campini engine, and persuaded NACA to undertake an experimental investigation. NACA began construction of an experimental engine in 1940. The engine consisted of a 600-horsepower R-1340 Wasp driving a single-stage, axial-flow fan located within a duct. First experiments revealed that it was very difficult both to maintain combustion and keep it within the duct. The engine failed to give stable combustion in tests in 1941.

In December of that year, the NACA power plant group redesigned the burner for the engine. Instead of the original vaporizing burner, they substituted a burner which injected liquid fuel. This new burner made it possible for the first time to get a thrust with afterburning stable enough to measure.

In January 1942, early tests of the new burner showed 600 pounds thrust with afterburning of about 1 pound of fuel per second against 300 pounds thrust from the fan alone (SFC =

6.0). The successful test of the new burner made a good impression on Durand and the Special Committee on Jet Propulsion. They recommended that NACA try to develop an engine suitable for flight. NACA replaced the 600-horsepower R-1340 reciprocating engine with a more powerful 825-horsepower R-1535 and designed an improved burner, completing these changes in July 1942. The modified engine delivered 900 pounds static thrust as a pure ducted fan, or 2,110 pounds of thrust with afterburning of 2.3 pounds of fuel per second, for an SFC of 3.92. NACA published the resulting report in October 1942.

## The Army

The role of the Army differed from the Navy in that the Army saw the potential of the turbojet early and at the highest levels in the service. The Army had become interested in rocket propulsion before 1938. That same year the Army asked the National Academy of Sciences to sponsor a study of booster rockets. Later in 1938 the Army joined the Navy in sponsoring a study of booster rockets by the California Institute of Technology. Early in 1941 intelligence reports of German rocket developments spurred Army leadership to promote rocket propulsion research.

On February 25, 1941, General Arnold wrote to Dr. Vannevar Bush, Chairman of NACA, to report on the Air Corps' estimate of the German research into rocket propulsion as both boosters and primary propulsion.[71] Arnold also remarked that the Army-sponsored Cal Tech rocket program would not have any systems available for at least another year. He then requested that NACA study rockets for boosters and propulsion. In March 1941, Bush responded to Arnold's request by establishing a special committee under Professor William Durand known as the Special Committee on Jet Propulsion. Durand set up the membership of the committee to include NACA staff, Air Force staff, staff from the Bureau of Aeronautics and the Bureau of Standards, faculty from Johns Hopkins University and MIT, and representatives from American gas turbine manufacturers — Westinghouse, Allis-Chalmers, and the Steam Turbine Division of GE.

Schlaifer states the Army deliberately excluded representatives from the engine manufacturers at the request of General Arnold. Arnold feared that they might oppose any unorthodox developments in the field of power plants.[72] Later this exclusion was the result of the service's desire to prevent the diversion of any of the engine companies' resources from the development and production of the conventional engines on which the Army depended for fighting the war.[73]

At the first meeting of the committee, Kalitinsky of MIT and Jacobs of NACA made presentations. The Kalitinsky turbine engine was later dropped from the committee's agenda when P&W decided to take up development of the design. This development goes against Schlaifer's argument that the services deliberately excluded the engine companies from developing aircraft gas turbines.

The committee initially rejected gas turbines as impractical for aircraft, but at the request of Professor Durand and the turbine manufacturers the committee set up a special subcommittee to look at aircraft gas turbines.[74] This subcommittee in turn played an important role by requesting that all three of the manufacturers represented on the committee submit research studies of different aircraft gas turbine configurations. By July 1941, NACA had brought all three turbine companies under research contract. Each company was to go ahead with the design it preferred; after they had finished preliminary studies, the subcommittee would choose the one design to recommend for actual development. GE/Schenectady opted to investigate a turboprop (Figure 3-13), Westinghouse opted to research a pure turbojet (Figure 3-14), and Allis-Chalmers proposed to research a ducted-fan turbojet (Figure 3-15). All three agreed on the use of axial rather than centrifugal compressors.

NACA had begun development of axial compressors in 1938, obtaining considerably higher efficiency than centrifugal compressors typically yielded. Allis-Chalmers had experience

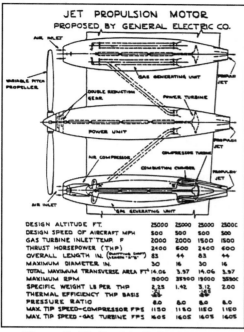

**Figure 3-13. Design Submitted by the GE Steam Turbine Division at Schenectady**

*(Illustration courtesy of GE)*

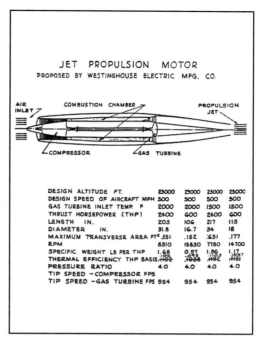

**Figure 3-14. Design Submitted by Westinghouse**

*(Illustration courtesy of Westinghouse)*

since 1938 with Houdry turbines under Brown-Boveri license; they reported their experiences to the subcommittee.

In September 1941, the committee recommended that the government give development contracts to all three companies for all three engines. NACA relinquished all supervision over these three projects in October 1941, although a smaller committee with revised membership continued to meet occasionally for about a year so that the three manufacturers and interested experts could exchange ideas and information.

Also in October 1941, the Navy invited proposals from Allis-Chalmers and awarded a contract in February 1942 for a detailed design study.[75] On December 8, 1941, the Navy gave Westinghouse a letter of intent calling for the design and construction of a small booster turbojet known as the 19A, while GE received a contract for the TG-100 turboprop (later known as the T31) from the Army.

Of the three companies initially invited to serve on the Durand committee, GE and Westinghouse went on to develop important aircraft gas turbine engines. Allis-Chalmers ultimately decided not to become involved in the aircraft gas turbine business and dropped out at the end of 1943.[76]

## The Navy

The U.S. Navy's funding of the Turbo Engineering Corporation represents the first government support for a systematic theoretical investigation of all the possibilities involved in aircraft gas turbines.[77] The principal figure in Turbo Engineering was Rudolph Birmann, an engineer of Swiss origin, trained by Professor A. Stodola in Zurich. Birmann designed and developed a turbosupercharger of novel design, incorporating a centripetal turbine and a mixed or

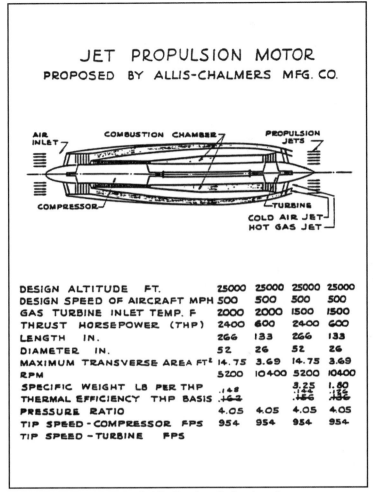

**Figure 3-15. Design Submitted
by Allis-Chalmers**
*(Illustration courtesy of U.S. Navy)*

diagonal-flow compressor. In 1937 Birmann, an independent investor, and the DeLaval Steam Turbine Company got together to form the Turbo Engineering Corporation. The purpose of the company was to exploit Birmann's turbojet and other patents. DeLaval's interest meant the company was branching out from steam applications in their research.[78]

In 1939 Turbo Engineering gained a turbosupercharger development contract with the U.S. Navy and began discussion of gas turbine research.[79] They submitted a proposal in December 1940 for a general theoretical study of all the problems involved in the design of a turboprop. The company mentioned turbojets, but high fuel consumption led to their rejection.

In January 1941, the Navy directed Turbo Engineering to proceed with the turboprop study and signed the research contract in June. Turbo Engineering delivered the results of this study in installments, the first in September 1941 and the last in June 1943. Anxious for the company to begin quantity production of turbosuperchargers and experimental work on the gas turbine, the Navy arranged for the Defense Plant Corporation to give Turbo Engineering a plant.[80]

The U.S. Navy continued to believe until 1943 that the turbojet would be useless as a primary power plant. This was undoubtedly due to the Navy's carrier-based aircraft philosophy. The early turbojets required considerably more runway for take-off than was available on the biggest Navy aircraft carrier of World War II. The high specific fuel consumption and the relatively short life of the early turbojets also mitigated against carrier use. On extended cruises away from the manufacturing centers of the United States, it would be difficult to replace worn-out turbojets. The Navy was convinced, however, that a turbojet booster engine would be a desirable means of getting short bursts of very high speed in combat, or as a means of assisting take-off from carriers. So in October 1942 it contracted with Turbo Engineering for a booster turbojet engine, aimed at 1,100 pounds of sea level static thrust.[81] Turbo Engineering moved into the new facilities in the spring of 1942, but development of the Birmann turbojet was slow. Schlaifer alleges that this was due to shortages of tooling and to the higher-priority production of Turbo's major product, turbosuperchargers.[82] By the middle of 1943, Turbo's construction of its turbojet was only beginning. By September 1944, the Turbo Engineering turbojet was not yet complete, although Turbo had shipped the compressor to NACA for tests. Because the company was still far behind schedule on production of its turbosupercharger, Turbo Engineering dropped all other work, including the turbojet, and concentrated on the turbosupercharger and the geared supercharger for the R-2800.[83]

## Government Support of Gas Turbine Research after 1941

The Army opted on or about December 1941 to pursue two research avenues, one short-range and one long-range. They funded the research on turboprops at GE's Steam Turbine Division at Schenectady, New York and assigned the Whittle turbojet imported from Britain to the GE Turbosupercharger Division at Lynn, Massachusetts. These two programs were the short-range development programs. The long-range development programs were the Lockheed/Menasco L-1000 turbojet and the Northrop-Hendy turboprop (the latter co-funded by the Navy until 1944).

By the latter part of 1942, work was proceeding in the United States on the Whittle turbojet and on the following native aircraft gas turbine engine designs:

- Northrop Turbodyne turboprop
- P&W PT-1 turboprop
- GE /Schenectady TG-100 turboprop
- Allis-Chalmers turbine-driven ducted fan
- NACA piston-driven ducted fan
- Westinghouse 19A turbojets
- Turbo Engineering booster-sized turbojet

All these companies except P&W were carrying out their programs at government expense. Preliminary designs were complete for the Lockheed engine, the L-1000, but development was awaiting government financial support.

Schlaifer asserts that by mid-1943:

> ...it was generally admitted that despite the fact that jet-powered fighters would be very much inferior in both take-off and range, there was no use in good take-off and range if the fighter possessing it was to be out-performed in combat by jet-powered enemy fighters.[84]

Also by mid-1943, according to Schlaifer, the Army and Navy had decided to either drop ducted fans and turboprops or to reclassify them as long-term projects, in the interest of proceeding further immediately with higher-powered turbojet engines.[85] Schlaifer's assertion is correct except in regard to the Army's attitude to turboprop development. The Army felt that the turboprop programs of Northrop and Lockheed (the Lockheed XT35 turboprop was a derivative of the L-1000 turbojet) were always long-term projects. The Whittle turbojet had proved, to the Army at least, that the turbojet was the immediate technology to counter the German Me 262. They didn't need the jet to win World War II, but as events turned out, they would need jet fighters to win the air war over Korea.

NACA became involved in the GE/Whittle engine program in July 1943, beginning with the construction of a special building in Cleveland, Ohio with two test cells for jet engines. By September they had begun a small program on the I-16 engine with a staff of eight people. NACA rapidly enlarged the facilities, and by the end of the war the major part of the activities of the Cleveland Laboratory was jet engine development.

In mid-1943 the Army formally invited NACA to become a participant in the Army's development program with their (NACA's) facilities that included the new engine laboratory at Cleveland as well as the aerodynamic facilities at Langley Field.[86]

The Navy took a belt and suspenders approach to aircraft turbojet development in 1943, asking the Ryan Aircraft Corporation to develop a single-seat fighter prototype using both a reciprocating engine driving a propeller in the front and a turbojet engine in the back. This contract resulted in the Ryan XFR-1 Fireball (Figure 3-16). The Fireball configuration used a Wright R-1820-72W radial piston engine in the front turning a propeller and a GE J31-GE-2 turbojet in the back. Ryan built a total of 66 Fireballs and the Navy used them for a long series of experiments to test the effectiveness of a jet engine in carrier-borne use.[87] A second version of the FR-1 called the XFR-1 flew with a T31 (GE TG100) turboprop in 1946.

**Figure 3-16. Ryan FR-1 Fireball**
*(Photo courtesy of GE)*

The first true carrier-based jet aircraft was the McDonnell FH-1 Phantom. The McDonnell Aircraft Company started this aircraft program in late 1943, and the first prototype flew in 1945. The Phantom used two Westinghouse J30-WE-20 turbojet engines.[88]

## Secrecy and Leadership

Schlaifer believes that the American military services were responsible for the fact that American turbojet development was still behind Britain at the end of World War II. He cites the deliberate choice by the services:

The services did nothing to promote, and in fact actively discouraged, collaboration among the various firms developing gas turbines.[89]

Schlaifer compares British and American industry-wide collaboration in turbojet development.[90] American policy was 'that basic differences in national laws' made collaboration between manufacturers such as the British enjoyed impossible. The American military services also believed that a policy of totally independent development by all industry actors would lead to faster development (to an overtaking of the British by American industry). The British, on the other hand, did everything possible to promote the fullest exchange of information among all private firms and public agencies in the field. The British Gas Turbine Collaboration Committee proved vital to the dissemination of information to the aircraft engine manufacturers, with the effect that British aircraft gas turbine engine work progressed rapidly after 1941 and throughout the war.

Schlaifer points out that in November 1941, General Henry H. Arnold refused a request by Major General Oliver P. Echols of Wright Field to test the intake ducts of the newly designed P-59A at the NACA Langley Field wind tunnels (the only adequate ones in the United States). However, to be fair, he also points out that Arnold refused because absolute secrecy was a condition of the technology transfer agreement made with Britain in the importation of the Whittle turbojet. Again in April 1943, Brig. General Chidlaw complained that the whole development of the I series had been slowed down by its super-secret status. Only when even the British became anxious to reduce the degree of secrecy in which the Army held the Whittle engine, did General Arnold give his permission to reduce the program's classification to confidential.[91]

NACA supported this view of collaboration in a meeting with the Army and Navy held in Washington on November 20, 1942. At this meeting Hunsaker of NACA assured Navy and Army representatives that American industry would soon overtake the British. The Navy also agreed with this conclusion. It ordered each of its gas turbine contractors to keep their work secret from all other companies and even from other government agencies. The Navy did not reveal the studies in detail by the Turbo Engineering Corporation, begun early in 1941, to anyone until at least a year later. In giving Westinghouse a contract for turbojet development on January 19, 1942, the Navy specifically instructed the company to pay no attention to work being done by others.

This secretive attitude on the part of the Army changed in mid-1943 when the Army invited NACA to assist in the Army's aircraft gas turbine development program with its facilities, which then included the new engine laboratory at Cleveland as well as the aerodynamic facilities at Langley Field.[92]

The American Army and Navy decided to fight the war with existing engine types, and absolutely forbade the engine companies to divert any of their resources to the new field until very late in the war. Why did they deliberately exclude the engine manufacturers (as Schlaifer suggests)? Schlaifer posits:

The services felt that for the short-run purpose of winning the war the most effective use would be made of the limited resources of these firms if they were not diverted from the development of the conventional engine actually in service.[93]

Was this situation justified in view of the special military defense situation facing the United States, which did not seem initially to require short-range interceptors? Maybe, but Schlaifer points out that had the Germans put their jet fighters into production a year earlier, the Allies would have had to develop a 450-500 mph jet interceptor much earlier for their European campaign.

Schlaifer also points out that the British managed their jet engine development without taking resources and personnel from their aircraft engine industry. However, were the British able to do so because American industry picked up much of the production load after December 1941? If the British had to accept a higher burden of the war production effort than they did, would they have been able to set aside facilities for turbojet development? How much did American mass production of the Merlin engine make possible Rolls-Royce's turbojet development efforts? The British not only permitted but encouraged some of their regular aircraft engine companies to undertake turbine development as early as 1942.

Was the United States behind Great Britain in aircraft gas turbine development in mid-1943? If one only matches the combined turbojet development programs of the British aircraft engine companies against the U.S. turbojet development programs of GE and Westinghouse (with the I Series and the Yankee Series turbojets), then yes, the British were ahead of the United States. If one considers, however, that the U.S. aircraft engine manufacturers were not permitted to develop turbine engines, but were instead to continue shouldering the majority of the piston engine production burden (both British and American), it then becomes unfair to match the British aircraft engine establishments of Rolls-Royce, Armstrong Siddeley, and Metropolitan Vickers against two turbosupercharger manufacturers (GE and Westinghouse). The rapid development of the Whittle design by GE and the amazing work of the Westinghouse engineers working in technological isolation are two examples of United States technological expertise to rival any aircraft gas turbine engine development program of the British.

In terms of the overall participation of the respective aircraft technology communities of Great Britain and the United States, the United States was actually well ahead of the British. The aircraft gas turbine engine development programs of Lockheed and Northrop provided much-needed insights into the aircraft gas turbine engine development process. These programs also laid the theoretical and preliminary design groundwork for future advanced turbojet and turboprop design programs at GE, Wright Aero, Westinghouse, and P&W. The advanced design of the Nathan Price L-1000 turbojet and the Pavlecka Turbodyne were visionary in terms of where the two designers believed the turbojet and turboprop could go. Again, this vision matched that of Sir Frank Whittle and Hans von Ohain.

As events transpired, U.S. aircraft engine manufacturers GE, Westinghouse, and the U.S. aircraft manufacturers soon overtook the British lead in aircraft gas turbine engines after the end of the war. Starting in Chapter Five, we will examine the American explosion of turbojet and turboprop technology that rocketed the United States into the lead in aircraft gas turbine technology— a lead which the country has not relinquished.

It is revealing to examine the fate of the British and American aircraft gas turbine establishments today. The British aircraft gas turbine establishment was essentially reduced to one company, Rolls-Royce, which eventually went bankrupt and had to be rescued by nationalization. No new manufacturers have been able to compete in the British system. In the United States, however, although two major players in the American system, Westinghouse and Wright Aero, have been eliminated, Williams International (originally Williams Research), Garrett (originally AiResearch), Continental and Lycoming have been added to the rolls of American aircraft gas turbine manufacturers. These companies began turbojet development in the post war period and have joined the Allison Division of General Motors, P&W, and GE. AlliedSignal has since merged Garrett and Lycoming and Rolls-Royce has purchased Allison from General Motors. The engine development activities of many of these companies is discussed in later chapters. Which system has ultimately proved stronger? In light of subsequent development of aircraft gas turbine engine technology, the question of the relative status and strength of the two nations' establishments in 1945 becomes something of a moot point.

## Endnotes

[1] Schlaifer, Robert, *Development of Aircraft Engines*, Boston, MA: Harvard University Press, 1949, 482.

[2] Constant, Edward W. II, *The Origins of the Turbojet Revolution*, Baltimore: The Johns Hopkins University Press, 1980, 151.

[3] Schlaifer, *Development*, 480.

[4] Ibid, 445.

[5] Ibid, 483.

[6] Ibid.

[7] Ibid.

[8] Schlaifer, *Development*, 482.

[9] Ibid, 484.

[10] Travers, William, *History Of GE*, Unpublished manuscript.

[11] Ibid, 488-489.

[12] Baumbach, Werner, *The Life and Death of the Luftwaffe*, New York: Coward-McCann, Inc., 1949, and Irving, David, *The Rise and Fall of the Luftwaffe: The Life of Field Marshal Erhard Milch*, Boston, MA: Little, Brown and Company, 1973.

[13] Schlaifer, *Development*, 484.

[14] Ibid.

[15] Ibid, 485.

[16] Ibid, 489.

[17] Ibid, 486.

[18] Ibid.

[19] Ibid, 487.

[20] Ibid, 488.

[21] Yenne, Bill, *McDonnell-Douglas: Tale of Two Giants*, Greenwich, CT: Bison Books, 1985, 288.

[22] Travers, *History*, 22, GE Company Archive file on the TG180 turbojet engine, M*ajor Innovations in the TG180 Engine Design*, 23, GE Company Archives file on the J79 turbojet engine, *J79 Engine Milestones*, 29-30, GE Company Archives file on the J79 turbojet engine, *The GE J79 Turbojet Performance and Specifications*, 40, GE Company, *J79 Achievements History*, Product Information Report, Evendale: Flight Propulsion Division, Large Jet Engine Department, June 1964, 24, and GE Company Archives file on the J79 turbojet engine, *J79 Achievements*, 572-580.

[23] Schlaifer, *Development*, 494.

[24] Ibid, 495.

[25] Ibid, 496.

[26] Ibid, 497.

[27] Ibid, 498.

[28] Ibid.

[29] Ibid, 499.

[30] Ibid, 501.

[31] Ibid.

[32] Schlaifer, *Development*, 503.

[33] Ibid, 504.

[34] Ibid, 503.

[35] Ibid, 507.

[36] Ibid, 505.

[37] Ibid, 508.

[38] Ibid, 443.

[39] Ibid, 444.

[40] Ibid.

[41] Ibid, 445 for assumptions underlying this conclusion (numbers).

[42] Ibid, 478.

[43] GE Company Archive file, TG180 *Engine Data Sheet*, 35.

[44] Schlaifer, *Development*, 446.

[45] Ibid, 447.

[46] Ibid.

[47] Ibid.

[48] Schlaifer, *Development*, 448.

[49] Ibid, 448.

[50] Ibid, 447.

[51] Ibid.

[52] Ibid.

[53] Ibid.

[54] Ibid, 449.

[55] Schlaifer, *Development*, 451.

[56] Ibid, 452.

[57] Ibid, 453.

[58] Lippencott, Harvey H, "P&W Enters the Jet Age," from "Classic Turbine Engines," edited by Robert B. Meyer, Jr. *Casting About*, Volume 85, Number 4, 6.

[59] Schlaifer, *Development*, 469.

[60] Lippencott, *Casting About*, 6.

[61] Schlaifer, *Development*, 478.

[62] Ibid, 478.

[63] Ibid, 453.

[64] Ibid, and GE Company Archive file on the TG180 turbojet engine, *Section 8: Historical Facts of the I40*.

[65]  GE Company Archive file, *I-40*, 75.

[66]  Ibid.

[67]  Ibid, 84-85.

[68]  Schlaifer, *Development*, 445.

[69]  Ibid, 450.

[70]  Ibid, 451.

[71]  Schlaifer, *Development*, 458.

[72]  Ibid.

[73]  Ibid, 459.

[74]  Ibid., 460.

[75]  Ibid, 461.

[76]  Ibid, 468.

[77]  Ibid, 454.

[78]  Ibid, 455.

[79]  Ibid, 456.

[80]  Ibid, 457.

[81]  Ibid.

[82]  Ibid, 470.

[83]  Ibid, 472.

[84]  Ibid, 471.

[85]  Ibid, 472.

[86]  Ibid, 491.

[87]  Bower, Peter M. and Swanborough, Gordon, *U.S. Navy Aircraft: Since 1911*, 402-403..

[88]  Ibid. 321.

[89]  Ibid, 489-490.

[90]  Ibid, 467.

[91]  Ibid, 491.

[92]  Ibid.

[93]  Ibid, 492.

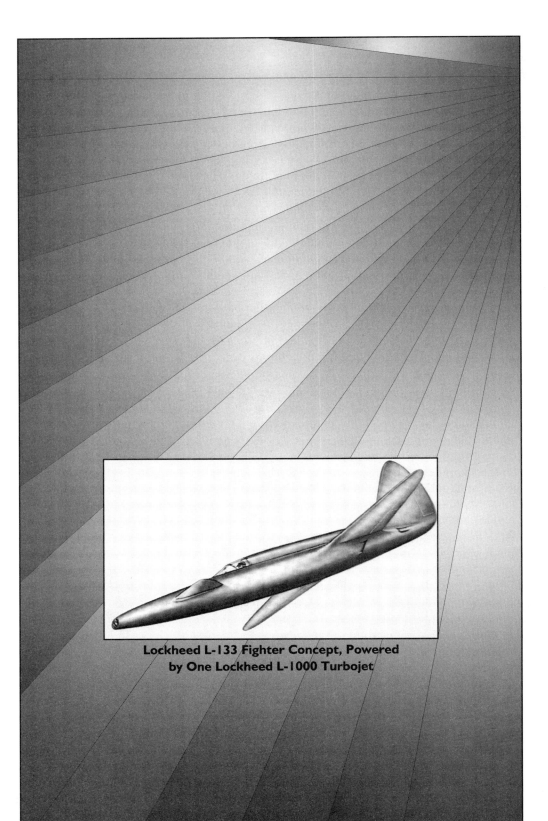

**Lockheed L-133 Fighter Concept, Powered
by One Lockheed L-1000 Turbojet**

# Chapter Four

# Nathan Price and the Lockheed L-1000

Although Britain and Germany developed the first operational turbojets, the turbojet revolution did not pass the United States by. In the previous chapter we saw how Northrop, among others, had foreseen the need for faster aircraft and planned for new propulsion systems to meet that need. In the late 1930s another aircraft manufacturer had both the same foresight and someone on hand who could make that vision into a reality. The company was the Lockheed Aircraft Corporation and the man was Nathan C. Price.

As Robert Schlaifer points out:

> Despite the fact that all the basic principles involved in the turbojet were continually being discussed in the United States in the 1930s, and that the turbojet itself was mentioned occasionally in these discussions, the first serious proposal to develop such an engine was not made until 1941, and then it was made, not by a manufacturer of aircraft engines or of turbosuperchargers, but by an airframe manufacturer, Lockheed.[1]

In late 1939 Lockheed had a solid reputation as an aircraft developer and manufacturer. The company had enjoyed a meteoric rise from its start in June 1932, building the Vega, Sirius, Altair, and Orion aircraft; and designing and developing the Electra twin-engine transport. Like many other U.S. aircraft manufacturers, Lockheed had participated in the economic boom of the late 1930s, expanding from 332 employees in 1934 to over 7,000 in 1940. By 1940 Lockheed had gained large-scale production contracts for Hudson general-reconnaissance aircraft, Lodestar transport aircraft, Harpoon naval patrol bombers, and Ventura bombers for Britain under British and Lend-Lease contracts. Lockheed also had obtained military contracts by 1942 for AT-18-LO Lodestar trainers, Ventura and Harpoon bombers, and Constellation transports; and was also building B-17F bombers under license from Boeing Aircraft Corporation. With its Model 22 twin-engine interceptor, Lockheed had also gained a reputation within the Army Air Force for developing fast fighter aircraft. More popularly known under its military designation, the P-38 Lightning, this twin-engine interceptor was capable of approaching the speed of sound in a dive.

Although Lockheed had already developed a reputation by the late 1930s as a company that thought in terms of future aircraft, its reputation alone did not give it credibility in the area of aircraft propulsion, let alone aircraft gas turbine propulsion. This credibility came to Lockheed in 1940 in the person of Nathan Price.

## Nathan C. Price Arrives at Lockheed

Nathan Price was an experienced steam turbine engineer when he came to Lockheed in 1940. He had gone to work for Doble Steam Motors in 1930, where he developed a design for atomizer burners for a combustion system for a reciprocating steam engine. During the fall of 1933 and early 1934, Price designed a steam turbine for aircraft.[2] He installed and flew the steam turbine engine in a Travel Air biplane on April 12, 1933.[3] In this engine design, the turbine which drove the propeller was also coupled to a centrifugal compressor which supplied the air for the combustion chamber. The products of combustion were expelled through a nozzle designed to produce jet thrust. Price had calculated that this engine would be as efficient at low altitude as a reciprocating engine of the same weight. Power could be maintained at higher altitudes by the use of a high blower pressure ratio without running into any of the very serious problems involved in the altitude supercharging of an internal-combustion engine.

Attempts to interest the Army or engine manufacturers failed and Doble Steam Motors dropped the project in 1936.

On his own, Price worked on a new design for a turbojet from 1938 to 1940, when he joined Lockheed. Willis Hawkins, currently senior advisor to Lockheed, describes Price's hiring by the company:

> Price was hired by Lockheed to redesign the General Electric turbosupercharger (used) with the P-38's Allison engine. Lockheed was going to make a new design of the P-38, called the P-49 (with a Continental engine). Price was brought in as a supercharger analyst to evaluate the GE supercharger for the P-49. The cockpit of the P-49 was going to be pressurized. Price designed the L-1000 in his spare time. He designed turboprop and turbojet versions.[4]

Lockheed, in its development of the P-38 and XP-49 high-altitude interceptors, had begun encountering the effects of compression when the aircraft dived. The Lockheed aircraft designers knew that new, high-altitude and high-speed aircraft were on the horizon; and they wanted to get started early. They knew that the key to the development of the next generation of aircraft lay in new and more powerful aircraft engines, and that the current generation of reciprocating engines could not deliver the necessary power at altitude without a dramatic increase in weight. Lockheed had also heard rumors of new aircraft gas turbine work in England. Schlaifer asserts that Lockheed assigned Price to the task of designing a new type of engine.[5] In reality, the idea to design the L-1000 (Figure 4-1) was Price's. What made Price's dream possible was that his design came at exactly the right time and in exactly the right place.

**Figure 4-1. Nathan C. Price (rt.)
and Hall L. Hibbard, Lockheed VP
and Chief Engineer,
with the L-1000 Turbojet**
*(Photo courtesy of Robert Smith, AEDC/Sverdrup)*

## Lockheed Proposes Complete Engine/Airframe System Design

With his turbojet design completed, Price went to see Clarence L. "Kelly" Johnson, Chief Engineer of Lockheed "The Skunk Works." Price impressed Johnson with his work and Johnson ordered the Lockheed engineers to come up with an aircraft design using the Price power plant. This was to become the L-133, a single-seat jet fighter with a canard forward of the wing (Figure 4-2). Lockheed incorporated the canard into the design to offset the effects of compressibility previously encountered with their P-38 and XP-49 fighters.

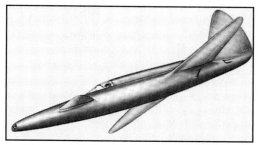

**Figure 4-2. Lockheed L-133 Fighter**
*(Illustration courtesy of Robert Smith, AEDC/Sverdrup)*

Lockheed assigned more engineers to the project and began detailed plans for the L-1000 engine and the L-133 aircraft. They designed it as a fighter-interceptor intended to fly 625 mph (0.94 Mach) at 50,000 feet. The L-133 represents the first time in the United States that a manufacturer had designed an aircraft and engine as a complete system. In many respects this engine design was novel. The jet principle provided not only propulsion, but also flight control through wing-tip jets. Figure 4-3 shows how Price planned to use bypass air to influence boundary-layer conditions in the flight regime.

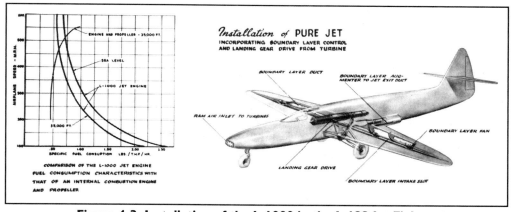

**Figure 4-3. Installation of the L-1000 in the L-133 Jet Fighter**
*(Illustration courtesy of Robert Smith, AEDC/Sverdrup)*

By 1941 the designs of the engine and plane were ready for actual development to begin. Price designed the L-1000 to have a higher efficiency than contemporary reciprocating engines. He therefore designed the L-1000 with a very high-pressure ratio, which it achieved with an axial followed by a centrifugal compressor, and a great deal of intercooling.[6] Price thus sacrificed ease and quickness of development in trying for much more general utility than that of a pure interceptor fighter.[7] Lockheed believed no regular engine company would undertake the development of the L-1000, so it decided to develop both the engine and the airframe.

Lockheed informally discussed the L-1000 and L-133 with various Army officers in 1941.[8] On March 30, 1942, Lockheed submitted a development proposal to the Army entitled "A report on the preliminary model specification of a jet propulsion engine unit for an advanced design of a single place interceptor, the L-133."

The first design of the L-1000 called for an axial-flow compressor followed by three centrifugal compressors (with intercooling between each centrifugal compressor stage). To avoid stalling at high altitudes and low compressor efficiency, Price proposed using boundary layer control in the compressor to permit use of a higher range of lift coefficients for the compressor blades. To operate the axial-flow compressor at part speed at sea level, bringing it up to full speed at 50,000 feet, Price proposed in his design a variable-speed hydraulic coupling. Lockheed Vice-President and Chief Engineer Hall L. Hibbard described this feature's purpose in a letter to Wright Field:

> It is desired to point out that due to the great atmospheric density differential between sea level and 50,000 feet, it is necessary to vary the axial blower speed considerably to maintain reasonable efficiency of compression. The fluid coupling design anticipated for this purpose is essentially similar to those now utilized in popular automobiles in great numbers except that we have rearranged the unit to allow for variation of driver vanes to minimize heat dissipation in the coupling.[9]

The engine design also called for a can-annular ("cannular") combustion chamber with walls cooled by bypass air (Figure 4-4), and a five-stage reaction turbine, with additional combustion of fuel (reheat) between turbine stages, and fuel injection in the tail pipe. Total initial design weight of the L-1000 was 1,700 pounds.

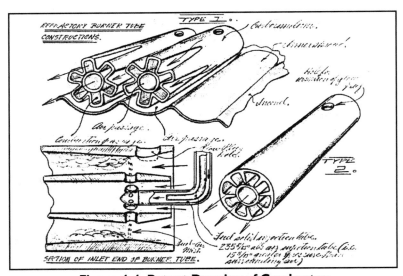

**Figure 4-4. Patent Drawing of Combustor**
*(Illustration courtesy of Robert Smith, AEDC/Sverdrup)*

The reaction to the model specification was mixed. The engineers at the Experimental Engineering Section of Wright Field believed that the engine development would take a long time. The official Air Force Case History of the L-1000/XJ37-1 describes the reaction of the Army Air Force (formerly the Air Corps) to the proposal:

> The design data are most interesting, and as plainly stated in the various reports, represents the possible goal to be achieved after a long and elaborate period of research and test. This ultimate design must always be kept in mind. However, the Material Center is of the opinion that immediate and specific plans and proposals should encompass only the first steps.[10]

The Wright Field engineers also wanted to consider the engine design (L-1000) separately from the aircraft design (the L-133):

> Insufficient data were submitted on the power plant to serve as a basis for evaluation purposes. Furthermore it is desired that the development phase of such an engine be divorced from the airplane development. Further data must be presented to the Material Center, and such data will be evaluated strictly as a power plant project.

> The airplane itself represents too many combined developments to undertake as a single project. A more conventional airplane, which can be discussed further in conference, would offer an essential first phase.[11]

It is important to place this development in time. Price began his work in September of 1940, a month before the Navy began its aircraft gas turbine research through the Bureau of Ships, and seven months before the National Advisory Committee for Aeronautics (NACA) called Dr. William Durand from retirement to head a special committee on jet-propulsion research. Finally, it wasn't until July 1941, nine months after Price began designing, that NACA's Durand Committee met with representatives of the Army, Navy, and industry to lay out an American program of turbojet development. Engineers and historians of aircraft gas turbine technology consider this the date of origination of the Westinghouse "Yankee" axial turbojet program and of the GE TG-100 axial turbojet program. The two companies, by the way, started these programs three months before the introduction of the Whittle turbojet into the United States in October of 1941.

## U.S. Army Air Force Splits the Engine and Airframe Projects

When the Lockheed model specification for the L-1000 turbojet and L-133 jet interceptor reached the Army Air Force in March of 1942, Bell had already designed and constructed the prototype XP-59A airframe. At a Lockheed/Wright Field conference on August 21, Wright Field representatives commented that in general the L-1000 power plant was too complicated, although Lockheed believed it to be a fairly simple arrangement. Lockheed, however, took these critiques back to California and went back to work on the engine design. In November 1942 Lockheed altered the design of the primary combustion chamber to use chrome-nickel steel walls. This was done in response to a Wright Field concern about carborundum refractory particles from the combustion chamber walls passing into the gas turbine buckets.[12] Lockheed also revised their overall weight estimate of the L-1000 down to 1,620 pounds.

If Lockheed felt that altering the engine design would cause Wright Field to look more favorably on their jet aircraft portion of the proposal, they were mistaken. In a letter to the chief of the Army Air Force Power Plant Laboratory at Wright Field, the engineering staff of the Army Air Force Engineering Division recommended that the Army Air Force undertake separate development of the Lockheed L-1000 and L-133. Their recommendation was based on the following rationale:

> It is the opinion of this Section that the successful completion of the proposed airplane to a point where it will approximate the performance estimated by the Lockheed Corporation, hinges almost entirely upon the successful development of the engine involved; hence, a proper and feasible power plant program is an essential first step....The Power Plant Laboratory should handle the engine development including the necessary procurement action.

> The various phases of the airplane development should be so timed and related to the engine program that in the ideal, the final, successful airplane is achieved as soon as possible, but that in the development there is a minimum of wasted engineering and cost due to unforeseen engine difficulties and changes with related changes and revisions to the airplane design....The Aircraft Projects Section will handle the airplane and intends to undertake its development in several phases.

> The first phase involving wind tunnel test and design data will be undertaken if and when the Power Plant Laboratory decides upon and initiates the engine development program.

> The remaining phases of the airplane development will be undertaken at such times as it appears to be desirable considering the program with engines.[13]

On January 9, 1943, Colonel Edward R. Page, chief of the Power Plant Laboratory, detailed the laboratory's critique of the Lockheed design in a letter to Brigadier General Carroll, chief of the Engineering Division at Wright Field.[14]

It is not believed to be good policy to encourage the aircraft manufacturers to enter the field of aircraft engine manufacture. It is felt that their facilities both for engineering and manufacture of power plants are not adequate and it becomes necessary for the Government to provide additional facilities.

Furthermore, development of power plants by aircraft manufacturers must need be slower than when that work is carried on by an engine manufacturer due to the necessity of securing the services of so many subcontractors to accomplish the work. An outstanding example is the slow progress made by Northrop on the Turbodyne.

Colonel Page suggested two possible courses of action to the Army Air Force:

1.  Initiate a development program with Lockheed for a simplified jet propulsion unit consisting of an axial compressor-turbine combination which would offer Lockheed an opportunity to prove their compressor and turbine design. If successful, then the Army Air Force would undertake the development of the additional features necessary to produce the power plant proposed.

2.  The Power Plant Laboratory could undertake development of suitable power plants through some company now engaged in similar work for the L-133 airframe.[15]

The Army Air Force decided to pursue the first recommendation by the Power Plant Laboratory. Lockheed and Nathan Price had to prove the engine concept. At any rate, Lockheed was more concerned about getting a development contract for a jet aircraft from the government than in getting into the jet engine business. The company's management seriously underestimated the commitment necessary to carry through an aircraft gas turbine engine design from initial concept to prototype.

Lockheed packaged the L-1000 and the L-133 to show the government that Lockheed had the necessary expertise to enter into the jet development arena. They knew of the Bell and GE programs to develop a jet aircraft and engine, and they were anxious that the new trend in aircraft not pass them by. They exerted a great deal of effort to bring their interest and expertise to the attention of Wright Field.

The Army Air Force opted to divorce the L-1000 turbojet from the L-133 jet fighter. Schlaifer asserts that the decision to move Lockheed towards the H-1 Goblin turbojet from de Havilland was not the only reason to separate the two projects. Schlaifer claims "the Army disapproved in principle of developing an airframe too closely tied with one specific engine..."[16] As we will see in the following chapters, that principle was to change.

Lockheed found out unofficially on January 15, 1943, that they weren't going to get a development contract for the L-133 aircraft, and that they would have to simplify the design of the L-1000 engine before the Power Plant Laboratory would give them a contract for its development.[17]

On May 17, in a conference at Wright Field, Air Materiel Command Brigadier General Carroll and his staff (Colonel E.Z. Bogert, Colonel S.H. Roth, and Colonel R.P. Swofford) requested:

Lockheed's Hibbard and Price, for the present, [to] alter its program involving the combined airframe and power plant and to submit two substitute proposals; the first to cover the design and construction of a fighter airframe to utilize the British Halford jet power plant, and the second to cover the further development and construction of the Lockheed jet power plant disclosed in the previous proposal (the informal Lockheed proposal submitted on December 21, 1942).[18]

The Halford H-1 centrifugal turbojet was a British centrifugal turbojet developed by the de Havilland Company. The Army Air Force had imported the H-1 as a backup power plant for additional airframe prototype development. The engine was ready and they wanted Lockheed to concentrate on developing an airframe for that engine. This airframe became the F-80 Shooting Star fighter.

On May 19, 1943, Lockheed's Price and the Army Air Force Materiel Command's Major Paul F. May met at Wright Field. Lockheed had made several major changes in the L-1000 engine design.[19] They had replaced the three original centrifugal compressors and the initial axial-flow compressor with two 16-stage axial compressors. Price reduced the intercooling load at altitude to 60 percent. He also dropped the last, or fifth, stage from the turbine. The new design reduced the gas temperature at the first stage of the turbine to 1,510°F. The new design also reduced the diameter of the hydraulic coupling by approximately two inches.

Price's new design offered new component efficiencies. It listed an inlet axial compressor shaft adiabatic efficiency at 85.5 percent, a central axial compressor shaft adiabatic efficiency of 90 percent, and a turbine component efficiency of 80 percent, with a new propulsive nozzle efficiency of 94 percent. Price's new design brought the weight of the unit down again to approximately 1,285 pounds. The diameter was to be 25 inches and the length 147 inches. At a speed of 550 mph, the jet plant would develop 920 pounds of thrust at 50,000 feet, with no jet augmentation (based on a 50:1 air fuel ratio). With a 33:1 air fuel ratio, Price estimated 1,090 pounds of thrust, with no jet augmentation.[20] Figure 4-5 shows the second iteration of the compressor concept.

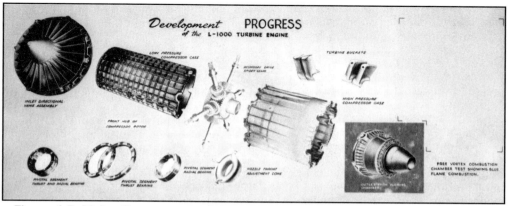

**Figure 4-5. Major Components of the L-1000, Except for the Four-Stage Turbine**
*(Photo courtesy of Robert Smith, AEDC/Sverdrup)*

Lockheed notified the Materiel Command on May 29, 1943, of their intention to submit a proposal for a jet power plant on two bases: the first a complete development proposal; and the second a phased development proposal.[21] On June 8, 1943, Lockheed prepared a preliminary specification for the development of just the L-1000 engine, along with a development program summary, to the Experimental Engine Section of the Air Materiel Command.

On June 15, 1943, Lockheed transmitted the "Lockheed Jet Power Plant Development Program Firm Proposal" to the Experimental Engineering Section. In the letter Lockheed also submitted a cost estimate and a time schedule with two options.[22] In the first option, Lockheed proposed a sequential development of four phases, and estimated the time necessary for each phase: compression, twenty-three months; combustion, eight months; expansion, nineteen months; assembly with accessories, three months. The second option was the concurrent development of all four phases of the engine. Lockheed believed they could develop all four phases in twenty-three months, projecting a total cost, including spares, of $1.3 million. This total included approximately $85,000 that Lockheed had spent in preliminary development of the engine.

In June, Kelly Johnson and Nathan Price visited Wright Field to sell the L-133/L-1000 joint program to the Army Air Force. Willis Hawkins remembers:

> The engine was a complete concept on paper before the L-133 concept was submitted to the AF. That was 6 months before the F-80 flew. Kelly Johnson took the L-133 to Wright Field. The AF gave Johnson the specs for the Halford H-1 engine in return for Johnson dropping his emphasis on the L-1000.

As Kelly Johnson tells the story:

> Independently, we developed a preliminary design for an airplane that would approach Mach 1, the speed of sound. It would be powered by a jet engine designed by a Lockheed consultant, Nathan Price, a designer of great vision and knowledge of thermodynamics, materials, and mechanical design. We proposed to the Air Corps that Lockheed be permitted to build a prototype. The response was negative. We were told to devote our energies to solving the problems with the P-38 and other immediate wartime projects. In retrospect, of course, that was short-sighted.

> But in 1941, when the British installed Frank Whittle's jet engine in one of their small fighters, the Gloster Meteor, and demonstrated the speed potential, that attitude changed. The Air Corps commissioned use of that engine in the Bell P-59, originally designed as a propeller-driven airplane. When the jet-powered version flew in 1942, the performance was hardly better than that of the piston-powered P-38 and P-51.

> Again we proposed to build an airframe and jet engine in a very short span of time. This time the Air Development Center was receptive.

> Within a week of hearing from Wright Field, I was back again in Dayton to present our design. "We'll give you a contract for the airplane, Kelly, and for Nathan's engine as well," said General Frank Carroll, commanding officer of Wright Field. "But you'll have to use the British engine in the first airplane because we need it - and all the jet fighters you can build - as soon as possible to use against the Me 262. Your new engine couldn't possibly be ready for service in time. You will have a Letter of Intent this afternoon by 1:30 p.m." He replied, "There is a plane leaving Dayton for Burbank at two o'clock. Your time starts then."

> And it did. The date was June 8, 1943. General Henry "Hap" Arnold, himself, had approved the contract.[23]

## Work Begins at Lockheed

As Lockheed started work, it soon realized that the Army Air Force had not set a very high priority on Lockheed developing a turbojet engine. Lockheed was building bombers, fighters, and transports for Britain and the United States; and facilities were tight. Lockheed had also seriously underestimated the commitment necessary in terms of money, manpower, and facilities to build a jet engine. One can judge the relative priority that the Army Air Force gave to the L-1000 engine project and the program to develop the airframe for the H-1 by the speed with which the Army Air Force encouraged Lockheed to develop the XP-80. All government-furnished equipment (GFE) arrived at Lockheed within six days of the start of the XP-80 project on June 24, 1943.[24] The L-1000 project, on the other hand, had to struggle for materials, subcontracting facilities, parts, and tools.

The Army contracted for development of the L-1000 in July 1943 as a long-range project. Its design promised a smaller diameter and much lower fuel consumption for a given thrust than any other turbojet yet under development, although the technological complexity which was to secure the good fuel economy meant that development would necessarily be slow.[25]

On June 19, 1943, Wright Field entered into Letter Contract W535-AC-40690 with Lockheed, calling for one Model L-1000 power plant at a total estimated cost of $1,275,934.80 plus a fixed fee of 4 percent.[26] The contract also called for one set of blueprints of the engine and a report, in triplicate, of performance tests. Lockheed and the Army Air Force were to negotiate type tests and endurance tests in a separate contract after Lockheed had completed satisfactory performance tests. The Army Air Force set the delivery date of the contract for August 1, 1945.[27]

On June 30, 1943, the Army Air Force approved the letter contract of June 19 with Lockheed; and the United States Reconstruction Finance Corporation assigned facilities to Lockheed to house the new program. These facilities became known as Lockheed Aircraft Corporation Unit 80, located at 813 South San Fernando Boulevard in Burbank, California.[28]

We do not know much about the progress made by Price and the Lockheed engineers between June 1943 and April 1944, when Lockheed became embroiled in a dispute over reproduction rights (a rather premature dispute, as events turned out) with the Army Air Force. We do know that Lockheed had difficulty with procuring material and parts, but we know little of how the component designs evolved.

On April 28, 1944, Lockheed terminated the letter contract of June 19, 1943, having been unable to come to an agreement with Wright Field over reproduction rights to the L-1000. We do not know if this disagreement resulted from Lockheed's inexperience with the government's policies on procurement of aircraft engines, or if some other factor was the cause. For whatever reason, in a letter to the Air Materiel Command dated June 7, 1944, Lockheed informed the Army Air Force "that further discussions of the subject had resulted in substantial agreement between the parties." Lockheed went on to propose that the Army Air Force revise the contract to reflect this agreement. Lockheed proposed a reduction in cost from $1,275,935 to $1,192,402, and a reduction in fixed fee from 4 to 2 percent. The Army Air Force revised Article 30 of the original contract. Lockheed agreed to grant the government a nonexclusive, royalty-free right and license to reproduce the power plant under any and all patent or other rights owned or controlled by Lockheed prior to June 19, 1943.

Lockheed also announced their intention to:

> ... attempt to interest some other firm or corporation in the development of this project on a joint basis mutually satisfactory to Lockheed and such other company with a view to the future production of power plant units by the other company, if the project is successful. It is believed that material assistance in the development of the project can be rendered by a firm or corporation which has had specialized experience in related fields.

Lockheed related in the letter that Army Air Force representatives had agreed to the Lockheed move to bring in outside help in developing the engine.[29]

Lockheed and the Army Air Force included these projected changes in a new, formal Contract W535-AC-40690, which the Army Air Force approved July 31, 1944. This letter represents the point where Lockheed "gave up" on developing the L-1000 by itself. The development had long since passed the stage where Lockheed thought about the development as a project "that would only require one mill and one lathe."[30]

## Lockheed Gets Some Help

On November 22, 1944, in a paper entitled "Long Range Aircraft Propulsion Development Program for the Army Air Force," Lt. Colonel C.D. Gasser summarized the developmental status of the Lockheed L-1000 turbojet:

> This is an axial flow turbojet propulsion engine that, it is anticipated, will deliver 5,100 pounds static thrust maximum and 2,500 pounds static thrust normal at sea level. It weighs 1,235 pounds and dimensions are 25 inches diameter by 127 inches long. One engine is presently on order and none have been delivered to date. No airplane application exists for this engine.

This comment reflects the relative place of the L-1000 development program in the overall Army Air Force jet propulsion development program. The Army Air Force was prepared to go the distance with the L-1000 in return for the promise inherent in the performance estimate.

On May 28, 1945, at a Wright Field conference, Lockheed representatives requested that the Army Air Force extend the delivery date under their contract with the Army Air Force from August 1, 1945, to June 1, 1946. They also informed the Army Air Force they needed $507,325 in additional funds. Army Air Force representatives agreed, if Lockheed would make the request formally to the Air Materiel Command. Colonel Wassell of the Power Plant Section expressed their opinion:

> that it is not advisable at the present time to distribute any installation information of the L-1000 engine to aircraft manufacturers until after the engine has demonstrated its performance capabilities.[31]

Lockheed representatives agreed with the Army Air Force. Clearly Lockheed had accepted the Army Air Force principle of not developing the L-1000 concurrently with any Lockheed airframe.

Lockheed had planned to contract with Menasco Manufacturing Company of Burbank, California, for the manufacture of parts and equipment for the L-1000. However, Lockheed said that because of:

> ... the demand by the Army Air Force in the fall of 1943 and spring of 1944 for increased fighter plane production, Menasco was required to use all of its available capacity for the manufacture of landing gear and other parts.[32]

Lockheed had to find other facilities, requiring additional manpower and more extensive tooling and coordination than planned. They formally requested permission to subcontract on July 2, 1945, in a letter to the Air Technical Service Command (formerly the Air Materiel Command).

Lockheed also informed Wright Field that they wanted to have the L-1000 constructed at Menasco's facilities in Burbank. Accordingly, Colonel Pearl H. Robey, chief of the Propulsion and Accessories Division, Engineering Division of the Technical Service Command, requested an amendment to Contract W535-AC-40690, dated July 19, 1945.[33]

Having convinced Wright Field of the need to extend the contract delivery date, Lockheed reported a cost overrun of $159,267 on the contract on July 24, 1945. They also repeated their request for $507,325 in additional funding because they felt they needed this additional funding to cover anticipated increases in factory cost. Lockheed presented a comparison of the original contract cost breakdown compared to the anticipated cost of the contract.[34]

The Power Plant Laboratory notified Lockheed on July 31, 1945, that their request for additional funding was under review. Lockheed then notified the Army Air Force Air Technical Service Command that the company planned to subcontract the balance of the L-1000 development work to the Menasco Manufacturing Company.[35]

Lockheed commented in the letter that fabrication of the L-1000 was about two-thirds complete. The company cited Lockheed's lack of "specialized machine tools available for fabrication of the L-1000" (something that Wright Field engineers cited in 1942 as a factor in their reluctance to give an engine development contract to an airframe manufacturer). Lockheed stated that they had already subcontracted to Menasco 37 percent of component manufacture, 20 percent of tooling, and 38 percent of test equipment. That represented the maximum capacity of Menasco during the period of the war when Menasco had had heavy war production commitments. Menasco had since then terminated most of these production contracts, freeing up capacity.[36] Lockheed would still keep control of the project, while granting to Menasco a nonexclusive license to manufacture under patents or rights owned or controlled by Lockheed. Lockheed would continue to pay the engineering team, which would move to Menasco.

On September 28, 1945, Change Order No. 2, dated July 26, 1945, to Lockheed Contract W535-AC-40690, became effective. This change order extended the delivery date from August 1, 1945, to June 1, 1946, but at no change in estimated cost.[37] On October 15, 1945, the chief of the Engineering Division at Wright Field, Brigadier General L.C. Craigie, requested the Army Air Force increase the estimated cost of the contract by $300,000, from $1,192,402 to $1,492,402.[38]

On October 22, 1945, the Army Air Force gave Lockheed approval to transfer the remaining development work on the L-1000 to Menasco Manufacturing, provided it would not result in increased cost to the government and Lockheed would retain responsibility for performance of the prime contract.[39]

On November 3 Lockheed transferred the balance of work on the L-1000 to Menasco, with Lockheed retaining contractual responsibility. The entire L-1000 engineering staff and special facilities in use were, likewise, transferred to Menasco. Menasco named Nathan Price director of power plant engineering.

On November 15, 1945, the Army Air Force, in Change Order No. 3, amended the Lockheed/Menasco contract to allocate the additional $300,000. Although this was considerably less than the $507,325 that Lockheed felt was necessary to complete development, it represented a renewed willingness on the part of Wright Field to develop the L-1000, in spite of Lockheed's inability to construct the engine as promised.[40]

On February 12, 1946, Lockheed made another request to the Air Technical Service Command to extend the contracted delivery date of the L-1000 from June 1, 1946, to February 1, 1947.[41] Three reasons were cited for the extension. The first was the mandated reduction in the workweek from 49.5 hours to 40 hours, by government order.[42] Second was Lockheed and Menasco's difficulty in working out the many production processes required in the fabrication and assembly of the engine. Specifically cited were problems in incorporating new projection welding methods for attaching turbine and compressor blading, along with other welding, furnace brazing, and induction heating processes.

The continued shortage of certain materials and facilities due to the war was the third reason cited by Lockheed and Menasco. Specifically, Lockheed cited high-alloy steel castings as "impossible to acquire," necessitating the use of parts hogged from forged billets. Lockheed and Menasco related the problems they were having in coordinating tooling. They said they knew little about the behavior of many new and specialized alloys employed in the development program. It had been necessary to redesign and rework many of the tools on a "cut-and-try" basis as knowledge of the alloys and their behavior increased. Menasco had acquired over $100,000 worth of additional machine tools for the L-1000 project.[43]

Finally, Lockheed and Menasco asked for an additional $396,800 for the project. They followed up this letter by a formal report of cost overruns, submitted by Lockheed to the Army Air Force on February 13, 1946.[44] Lockheed and Menasco submitted a new cost breakdown with the letter.

Menasco requested on February 19, 1946, that the Army Air Force transfer the lease for the Lockheed Aircraft Corporation Unit 80. This facility housed the majority of the turbojet development work.[45] Lockheed followed with a letter making the same request on February 20.[46] The Propulsion and Accessories Subdivision of the Power Plant Laboratory's Engineering Division approved this transfer of machinery and facilities on March 18, 1946.[47]

On March 5, 1946, Lockheed submitted additional information in support of their report of cost overruns of February 13, citing costs of additional component testing already accomplished or anticipated beyond that envisioned in the original program as the cause of the cost overruns.[48] Lockheed reported that they had completed the following tests (giving us a view of where the program was at that time): axial-flow blading tests, slipper-type bearing tests, intercooler 30-degree segment tests, primary combustion chamber tests, intermediate turbine combustion chamber tests, tailpipe combustion tests, and fuel pump operation tests.[49]

Lockheed sent another letter to Wright Field on March 25, 1946, describing in detail the testing mentioned in their letter of March 5. All the testing was to take place in the next one to five months. None of the tests mentioned had taken place yet (contradicting the report of March

5), and all tests required the construction of test rigs. The total funding needed for these tests was $763,392 (including the $396,800 figure cited in the report of Overrun of Costs of February 13).[50] The engineers at the Power Plant Laboratory and the Research and Engineering Division in Washington must have been getting concerned over the spiraling costs of the L-1000. They were looking at increased costs and delays with another program, the Northrop Turbodyne, as well. At this point the Army Air Force asked Lockheed to estimate the long-term development and small production costs for the L-1000.

Lockheed responded to the Army Air Force on March 27, 1946. Lockheed Aircraft Corporation President Robert E. Gross sent a telegram to Wright Field in which he estimated that preliminary work and a small production run would cost about $5 million.[51] This apparently satisfied the Army Air Force, for on April 8, 1946, the Power Plant Laboratory officially recommended revising the Lockheed/Menasco contract to include the tests suggested by Lockheed. The Power Plant Laboratory also recommended a funding increase of $449,852.[52]

On April 15, 1946, Brigadier General L.C. Craigie, chief of the Army Air Force Engineering Division in Washington, sent a teletype message to Lockheed. Craigie assured Lockheed that $2.5 million had been set aside in the Army Air Force development budget then under review in Congress.[53]

The Army Air Force Engineering Division in Washington cabled Wright Field on May 22, 1946, requesting an estimate on when the L-1000 first-run would occur.[54] Colonel R.J. Minty of the Power Plant Laboratory answered on May 24. Wright Field estimated that Lockheed would have the L-1000 sufficiently built for experimental installation approximately eighteen months after successful test, if procurement followed the test immediately.[55] The Army Air Force was clearly growing anxious about the L-1000. With a variety of successful turbojet programs available to the Army Air Force, Lockheed and Menasco faced some real pressure to move the program along. The Army Air Force Engineering Division was beginning to become skeptical about the Lockheed/Menasco predictions for the L-1000.

This pessimism was reflected in an Inter-Desk Memo on May 29, 1946, from Lt. Colonel C.D. Gasser, chief of the Propulsion Section of the Research and Engineering Division, to Brigadier General A.R. Crawford of the same division. Gasser wrote in his memo:

> While the estimates furnished by the Air Materiel Command (AMC) at Wright Field do not appear to be unduly optimistic, it is my opinion that any firm planning which is based on the successful realization of this engine should be approached with caution since there are several features incorporated in it which are highly desirable but possibly somewhat difficult to bring through. In any event, if you have not already done so, it is recommended that the next time you talk to General Craigie the question of accelerating this development by any practicable means be raised with a view toward bringing through the XJ37 engine at an earlier date than now visualized.[56]

The Engineering Division then directed the Power Plant laboratory to query Menasco regarding the procurement of four sets of unassembled detailed parts for the XJ37-1 turbojet.

The Menasco Manufacturing Company replied with a quotation for the above-mentioned four sets of parts of $1,937,000 (give or take 5 percent).[57] Menasco also asked that the Power Plant Laboratory grant a contract for the parts immediately upon receipt and approval of test reports of the experimental engine then being prepared for testing. Menasco specifically requested inclusion in the contract of the following clauses: a 90 percent partial-payment clause; authority to include in the contract the cost of work done in anticipation of the executed contract; labor and material escalation clauses; and a cancellation clause that would permit discontinuance of work under the contract should the test engine then being prepared for testing prove unsatisfactory.[58]

## L-1000 Tests Successful

Menasco was hedging their bets on the L-1000. They were undoubtedly relieved when the engine tests proved successful, as they apparently did, for on June 6, 1946, the Army Air Force issued Authority for Purchase #421288. This contract provided for the procurement from Menasco of four sets of unassembled parts necessary to build XJ37-1 turbine engines at an estimated total cost of $1,937,000, with delivery of first sets of parts estimated in twelve months.

On August 15, 1946, the Air Intelligence Division, Assistant Chief of Air Staff and the Navy's Office of Naval Intelligence published Air Intelligence Report No. 100-110-100, entitled *Synopsis of Jet Engine Development and Operating Principles*. This report summarized their knowledge of the status of the Lockheed work as follows:

> Lockheed has in development an unorthodox turbojet engine, designed for high thrust with low fuel consumption. The compressor is formed by the combination of two sixteen-stage axial flow units rotating at different speeds, driven by a three-stage gas turbine. This unit is designated as X-J-37-1 [sic] (L-1000) and is near the testing stage.
>
> The Lockheed X-J-37-1 has remarkable performance for its weight and size. This unit's static thrust is 5,100 pounds, and 7,400 equivalent horsepower is developed at sea level and 500 mph. The overall diameter of this engine is only 25 inches and the dry weight 1,235 pounds.

The Army Air Force wanted the L-1000 because its potential power surpassed anything currently under production or development. The promise of power plus reduced diameter meant that the L-1000 would be applicable to many different aircraft configurations (Figures 4-6, 4-7, and 4-8).

**Figure 4-6. Artist's Conception of a Transport Configuration
Based on the Super Constellation Aircraft,
with Counter-Rotating Pusher Propellers**
*(Illustration courtesy of Robert Smith, AEDC/Sverdrup)*

In Figure 4-8 notice the LeDuc ramjets on the wingtips and the swept-back leading edge of the wing. This drawing was rendered in 1939, before the Allied discovery of German swept-wing engineering theory after World War II.

Although the Army Air Force never officially considered any of these applications for the L-1000, the above figures illustrate the potential of the engine for future use. This promise was enough for the Army Air Force to keep funding the L-1000 in spite of the complexity of the engine, the inaccuracy of the development forecasting by Lockheed and Menasco, and the increasing cost.

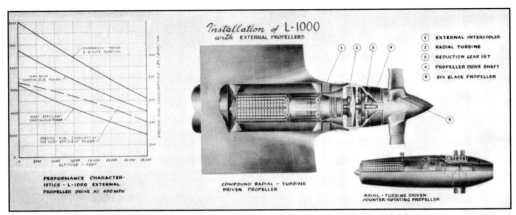

**Figured 4-7. The Turboprop Version of the L-1000**
*(Illustration courtesy of Robert Smith, AEDC/Sverdrup)*

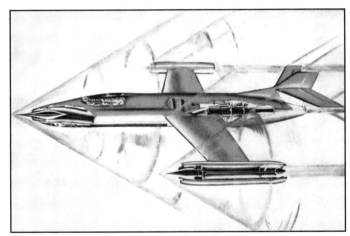

**Figure 4-8. Artist's Conception of a Supersonic Fighter
with an  L-1000 Engine Installed in the Fuselage Plus
Ramjets Installed on Each Wingtip.**
*(Illustration courtesy of Robert Smith, AEDC/Sverdrup)*

## Dissolution and Demise

On September 22, 1947, representatives from Lockheed, Menasco, the major aircraft engine manufacturers, and the Army Air Force held a conference at Wright Field. At this meeting the Army Air Force asked the major engine manufacturers to consider assuming the development and production of the L-1000 turbojet and turboprop. Menasco proposed transferring the entire development team to a major engine manufacturer. Lockheed would similarly transfer management control to the same company. Wright Aero agreed to accept the turboprop development programs and later the turbojet program as well.

It is uncertain why Wright Aero took up development of the L-1000. All mention of the XJ37 in Army Air Force engine characteristics tables ceases in 1947, leading one to believe that the Army Air Force dropped all funding for the turbojet version. It did, however,  continue funding Wright Aero for development of the XT35, the turboprop version of the L-1000.

In January of 1948 the U.S. Air Force (formerly the Army Air Force) canceled all turbo-prop development programs except the Northrop XT37, thereby killing the Wright work on the L-1000 turboprop. Wright continued work on the turbojet version with their own funds until 1952. In July 1953 Wright delivered the last three L-1000 turbojet engines to the U.S. Air Force at the Arnold Engineering Development Center in Tullahoma, Tennessee. These engines and all project files and test data were made available to all other American aircraft gas turbine engine manufacturers by the Air Force free of charge.

The figures in Supplement 4-1 show the components of the engine and illustrate some of the innovative technologies employed. These illustrations (and a lone engine at the Planes of Fame Museum in Chino, California) are all the physical evidence that remain of the L-1000 XJ37-1 turbojet engine.

## SUPPLEMENT

### Details of the L-1000

It is impossible to gauge Nathan Price's impact on American turbojet engine development; but, as we see in these figures, his engine (Figures 4-9 and 4-10) incorporated a great many innovations that have since been adopted in more successful engine designs. Price's engine was unsuccessful in that Lockheed, Menasco and Wright Aero were never able to develop the engine past an initial prototype stage. The engine could never be made to run self-sustaining. However, as shall be seen in subsequent chapters, many of the innovations attempted by Nathan Price in the L-1000 were to reach fruition in future turbojets, though in some cases more than a decade later.

**Figure 4-9. The Complete L1000 (XJ37-1) Engine**
*(Photo courtesy of Robert Smith, AEDC/Sverdrup)*

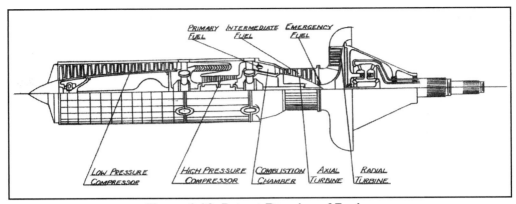

**Figure 4-10. Patent Drawing of Engine**
*(Diagram courtesy of Robert Smith, AEDC/Sverdrup)*

## The Compressor

Various views of the compressor are shown in Figures 4-11 through 4-14. The low-pressure compressor was unique in that the front four stages were independent of the aft twelve stages (Figures 4-11 and 4-12). The two sections were coupled through a hydraulic torque converter, so they could operate at different speeds, thus providing the necessary geometry for starting and acceleration. This design anticipated later two-spool engines like the J57, J75, or F100. From photographs we know that the blades on this compressor were of a lower aspect ratio design. Most axial-compressor designs of the day featured high-aspect ratio blades. (Aspect ratio is defined as the distance from blade root to tip divided by the distance from blade leading edge to trailing edge. Price's blades tended to be short and stubby, while prevailing practice favored tall, skinny blades.)

**Figure 4-11. The Aft Twelve Stages
of the Low-Pressure Compressor**
*(Photo courtesy of Robert Smith, AEDC/Sverdrup)*

**Figure 4-12. The Front Four Stages of the
Low-Pressure Compressor**
*(Photo courtesy of Robert Smith, AEDC/Sverdrup)*

Figure 4-11 shows the portion of the compressor that was driven through the hydraulic torque converter. There was basically no twist to the blades. A closer look will also reveal the circular root attachment on the blade. Price had enough insight to recognize that the design techniques of the day were not good enough to allow him to design a compressor with the proper stagger angles from scratch, so he devised this very ingenious configuration which allowed him to adjust the stagger of the blades from test to test.

This compressor used a drum rotor configuration. There is no compressor disk at all. All other U.S. engines prior to the more recent F100, F101, and F110 configurations used compressor disks. Here, the drum rotor is an innovation in aircraft gas turbine design, rediscovered some 30 years later.

Price embedded a total of six power takeoff shafts in a spider arrangement between the low-pressure and high-pressure compressors (Figure 4-13). These provided shaft power to drive the engine accessories.

**Figure 4-13.
Power Takeoff Assembly**
*(Photo courtesy of Robert Smith,
AEDC/Sverdrup)*

**Figure 4-14. The Complete 16-Stage High-Pressure Rotor**
*(Photo courtesy of Robert Smith, AEDC/Sverdrup)*

In Figure 4-14, the bevel gear on the right drove the low-pressure compressor. Both compressors were based on constant outside diameter configurations, typical of U.S. axial-flow engines.

## The Combustor

The combustion system (Figure 4-15) was annular and vortex-stabilized. It was an extremely short configuration, which may have been one of the features that proved to be the undoing of the system. So far as we know, Price designed the system for kerosene. We do know that the combustion system was the final component developed, and Wright Aero finished its development

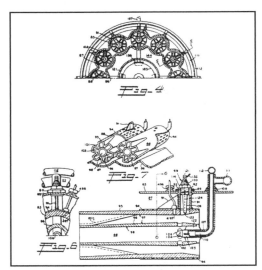

**Figure 4-15. Patent Drawing Showing
the Combustor Arrangement**
*(Diagram courtesy of Robert Smith, AEDC/Sverdrup)*

after acquiring the program. Price designed small metal blocking plates for installation at the rear of the combustor to simulate the presence of the turbine nozzle diaphragm. Component scorching in Figure 4-16 shows that high temperatures are occurring downstream of the combustor, which would indicate that the combustion process was not completed in the combustor.

## The Turbine

The patent drawing of Price's L-1000 turbine design is shown in Figure 4-17. Notice the hollow blades in Figure 4-18. This was unusual for American or British jet engine designs of the period. The first stage of the turbine (rightmost in the figure) was a purely impulse stage, while the remaining stages are the more usual combination of impulse and reaction.

**Figure 4-16. The Combustor, with Exit Blocking Plates Installed for Testing**
*(Photo courtesy of Robert Smith, AEDC/Sverdrup)*

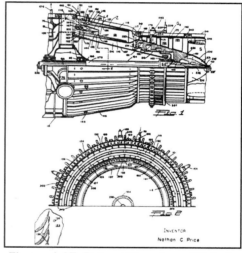

**Figure 4-17. Patent Drawing of Price's Turbine Design**
*(Diagram courtesy of Robert Smith, AEDC/Sverdrup)*

**Figure 4-18. Bladed Turbine Rotor and Stator Configuration with One Half of the Turbine Stators Removed**
*(Photo courtesy of Robert Smith, AEDC/Sverdrup)*

## Endnotes

1. Schlaifer, Robert, *Development of Aircraft Engines*, Boston, MA: Harvard University Press, 1949, 486.

2. Ibid, 448-449.

3. Gunston, Bill, *World Encyclopedia of Aero Engines*, Second Edition, England: Patrick Stephens Limited, 1989, 94.

4. Interview with Willis Hawkins, senior advisor to the Lockheed Aircraft Corporation, on April 10, 1990.

5. Schlaifer, *Development*, 449.

6. Ibid, 450.

7. Ibid.

8. Ibid.

9. Lockheed Letter No. E.S. 5100, dated September 8, 1942, from Hall L. Hibbard, Vice President and Chief Engineer, to Commanding General, AAF Materiel Center, Wright Field, Dayton, Ohio, 2.

10. AAF Letter RPS:eks:50, dated May 28, 1942 from Colonel F.O. Carroll, Chief, Experimental Engine Section, Air Materiel Center, Wright Field, Dayton, Ohio to Lockheed Aircraft Corporation, Burbank, California, 1.

11. Ibid.

12. Lockheed Letter No. E.S. 5708, dated November 24, 1942, from Hall L. Hibbard, Vice President and Chief Engineer, to Commanding General, AAF Materiel Center, Wright Field, Dayton, Ohio, 1.

13. AAF Letter RPS:MIN:50, dated January 2, 1943, from Brig. General F.O. Carroll, Chief, Engineering Division, to Chief, Power Plant Laboratory, Wright Field, Dayton, Ohio, 1.

14. AAF Letter DJK:eh:57, dated January 9, 1943, from Colonel Edward R. Page, Chief, Power Plant Laboratory, to Brig. General F.O. Carroll, Chief, Engineering Division, Wright Field, Dayton, Ohio.

15. Ibid, 3.

16. Schlaifer, *Development*, 471.

17. Transcript of telephone conversation between Mr. Hall Hibbard of Lockheed Aircraft and AAF Colonel H. Z. Bogert, Chief, Technical Staff, on January 15, 1943, 3.

18. "Lockheed Jet Power Plant Development Program Firm Proposal", dated June 15, 1943, to Commanding General, Air Materiel Center, Wright Field, Dayton, Ohio, 1.

19. AAF Memorandum PFN:eh:57, dated May 29, 1943, Subject was conference between Materiel Command and Lockheed Aircraft at Wright Field, Dayton, Ohio, 2-3.

20. Ibid, 1.

21. Ibid, 2.

22. "Lockheed Jet Power Plant Development Program Firm Proposal".

23. Johnson, Kelly and Smith, Maggie, Kelly: More Than My Share of It All, Washington, D.C.: Smithsonian Press, 1985, 95-96.

24. Francillon, Rene J., *Lockheed Aircraft Since 1913*, Annapolis, MD: Naval Institute Press, 1987, 237.

25. Schlaifer, Development, 479.

26. Contract No. 535ac 40690, dated June 19, 1943, between AAF Air Materiel Center and the Lockheed Aircraft Corporation.

27. Letter No. LAC/130551, dated July 2, 1945, from Lockheed Aircraft Corporation to Commanding General, AAF Air Technical Service Command, Wright Field, Dayton, Ohio, 1.

28. Letter from Menasco Manufacturing Company President John C. Lee, dated February 19, 1946, to Commanding General, AAF Air Technical Service Command, Attention: Colonel D. J. Keirn, TSEPL-5, Power Plant Laboratory, Wright Field, Dayton, Ohio.

29. Letter No. DYN/808, dated June 7, 1944, from Lockheed Aircraft Corporation to Commanding General, AAF Air Materiel Command, Wright Field, Dayton, Ohio.

30. Transcript of telephone conversation between Mr. Hall Hibbard of Lockheed Aircraft and AAF COL H. Z. Bogert, Chief, Technical Staff, on January 15, 1943, 1.

31. Letter No. LAC/130551 from Lockheed Aircraft Corporation to AAF Air Technical Service Command, 2.

32. Ibid, 1.

33. Air Technical Service Command Routing and Record Sheet, dated July 19, 1945, from Chief, Propulsion and Accessories Subdivision, Engineering Division, Air Technical Service Command.

34. Lockheed Letter No. LAC/132595, dated July 24, 1945, to Commanding General, Air Technical Service Command, Wright Field, Dayton, Ohio, 1.

35. Lockheed Letter No. DYF/261, dated September 26, 1945, to Commanding General AAF Air Technical Service Command, Wright Field, Dayton, Ohio, 1.

36. Ibid, 2.

37. Change Order No C-29340, dated July 26, 1945, from AAF Air Technical Service Command, Wright Field, Dayton, Ohio, to Lockheed Aircraft Corporation, Burbank, California.

38. Air Technical Service Command Routing and Record Sheet, dated October 15, 1945, from Chief, Engineering Division, Air Technical Service Command.

39. Letter to Lockheed Aircraft Corporation, dated October 27, 1945, from Chief, AAF Aeronautical Equipment Section, Procurement Division.

40. Change Order No. 30905, dated November 15, 1945, from AAF Technical Services Command, Wright Field, Dayton, Ohio, to Lockheed Aircraft Corporation, Burbank, California.

41  Lockheed Letter No. LAC/144271, dated February 12, 1946, to Commanding General, AAF Air Technical Service Command, Attention: Power Plant Laboratory TSEPL-5, Colonel R. L. Wassell, Wright Field, Dayton, Ohio, 1.

42  Ibid, 2.

43  Ibid, 3.

44  Lockheed Letter No. LAC/144272, dated February 13, 1946, to Commanding General, AAF Air Technical Service Command, Attention: Chief, Procurement Section, Wright Field, Dayton, Ohio.

45  Letter from Menasco Manufacturing Company President John C. Lee, dated February 19, 1946, to Commanding General, AAF Air Technical Service Command, Attention: Colonel D. J. Keirn, TSEPL-5, Power Plant Laboratory, Wright Field, Dayton, Ohio.

46  Lockheed Letter No. DPC/1526, dated February 20, 1946, to Commanding General, AAF Air Technical Service Command, Attention: Colonel D. J. Keirn, TSEPL-5, Power Plant Laboratory, Wright Field, Dayton, Ohio.

47  Memorandum, dated March 18, 1946, from Colonel R. J. Minty, Chief Power Plant Laboratory, Propulsion and Accessories Subdivision, Engineering Division, Wright Field, Dayton, Ohio.

48  Lockheed Letter No. LAC/145071, dated March 5, 1946, to Commanding General, AAF Air Technical Service Command, Attention: Colonel R. L. Wassell, TSEPL-5, Power Plant Laboratory, Wright Field, Dayton, Ohio, 1.

49  Ibid, 3.

50  Lockheed Letter No. LAC/145780, dated March 25, 1946, to Commanding General, AAF Air Technical Service Command, Attention: Colonel R. L. Wassell, TSEPL-5, Power Plant Laboratory, Wright Field, Dayton, Ohio.

51  Telegram, dated March 27, 1946, from Lockheed Aircraft Corporation President Robert E. Gross to BG L. C. Craigie, Air Technical Service Command, Wright Field, Dayton, Ohio.

52  Memorandum, dated April 8, 1946, from Colonel R. J. Minty, Chief Power Plant Laboratory, Propulsion and Accessories Subdivision, Engineering Division, Wright Field, Dayton, Ohio.

53  Teletype Message, dated April 15, 1946, from BG L. C. Craigie, Chief, Engineering Division, to Lockheed Aircraft Corporation, Burbank, California.

54  Telegram, dated May 22, 1946, from AAF Research and Engineering Division, Washington, D.C., to Chief, Engineering Division, Air Technical Service Command, Wright Field, Dayton, Ohio.

55  Teletype Message, dated May 24, 1946, Colonel R. J. Minty, Chief Power Plant Laboratory, Propulsion and Accessories Subdivision, Engineering Division, Wright Field, Dayton, Ohio, to Commanding General, Army Air Forces, Washington, D.C.

56  Inter-Desk Memo, dated May 29, 1946, Lt. Colonel C. D. Gasser, Chief, Propulsion Section, Research and Engineering Division, Air Technical Service Command, Wright Field, Dayton, Ohio, to Brig. General A. R. Crawford, Chief, Research and Engineering Division.

57  Menasco Manufacturing Company Letter, dated June 5, 1946, to Commanding General, AAF Air Technical Service Command, Attention: Power Plant Laboratory, Wright Field, Dayton, Ohio.

58  Ibid, 2.

**Air Force Bell XP-59, Powered by Two GE I-A Turbojets**

# Chapter Five

# General Electric and the British

## The I-A, I-14, I-16, I-20, and I-40 (J33) Engines

As pointed out in previous chapters, the United States was not ignorant of the need for increased research into aircraft gas turbine engines. The military services took the initiative in pushing for greater research into the technology. On February 25, 1941, the Army Air Forces (AAF) Deputy Chief of Staff for Air at the time, General Henry "Hap" Arnold (Figure 5-1) asked National Advisory Committee for Aeronautics (NACA) chairman Vannevar Bush to appoint a special committee on jet propulsion.[1] This committee's purpose was to coordinate U.S. jet engine research and development.

**Figure 5-1. General Henry "Hap" Arnold**
*(Photo courtesy of U.S. Air Force)*

In March 1941 General Arnold, now the chief of the U.S. Army Air Forces, called on his staff for a progress report on jet propulsion before leaving for England.[2] A month later Dr. Bush and NACA recalled Dr. William Durand from retirement to head up research projects on gas turbines and jet propulsion.[3] Durand established a special committee to coordinate an industry-wide U.S. jet propulsion program.[4] While on his British tour in May, General Arnold observed the Whittle engine and the Gloster aircraft and other British developments in aircraft gas turbines.[5] These developments instantly aroused Arnold's interest. He ordered the formation of a working group to serve as a liaison between the U.S. Army Air Forces and senior British Air

Ministry officials. The purpose of this group was to fully inform and update the U.S. Army Air Forces on British work and to serve as a conduit for the transfer of British aircraft gas turbine engine technology to the United States to complement and update U.S. turbojet development efforts.

On July 22 meetings began between the Arnold AAF Liaison Committee and senior British Air Ministry officials. The American members of the committee were originally AAF Colonel A.J. Lyon and AAF Major Carl Brandt. The British members of the committee were the British Minister for Aircraft Production, Air Marshal Linnel, and Power Jets' Dr. Roxbee Cox.

A short time later a General Electric Company representative was added to the American team. N.B. Reynolds, a senior GE engineer, interviewed the members of the GE turbojet design team in 1944 and recounted in a historical memorandum how GE was chosen to assist the Army Air Force:

> On July 16, 1941, Dr. Vannevar Bush called Mr. Roy C. Muir in Schenectady and told him that he wanted a GE engineer familiar with aviation problems to go to England and investigate a new and very secret development. Mr. Muir then telephoned Dr. A.R. Stevenson. Dr. Stevenson was riding horseback some distance from home but was called home by messenger, talked with Mr. Muir, and suggested that Mr. D. Roy Shoults, who was already in England, was the ideal person to carry out this mission. Whereupon Mr. Muir cabled Shoults and told him to report to a certain address in England where he would receive instructions.[6]

On July 25 Colonel Lyon, Shoults, Major Brandt, Dr. Pye and Dr. Cox visited Power Jets and talked with Whittle. On July 28 Cox and the three Americans visited the Gloster works, saw the E.28/39, and talked to its designer, W.G. Carter. The group also discussed the progress of the F.9/40 Meteor.[7]

Colonel Lyon and his deputy, Major Donald J. Keirn, along with Shoults, concentrated on the transfer of the Whittle engine to the United States. Major Brandt focused on obtaining details of the Gloster Meteor airframe and consulted with George Carter, designer of the Gloster E.28/39 and the Meteor.[8]

On September 4, 1941, Shoults presented the findings of the Liaison Committee to a group representing both the U.S. Army Air Force and GE. Attending for GE were Dr. A.R. Stevenson, Jr., R.C. Muir, S.R. Puffer, and Roy Shoults. Representing the government and the Army Air Force were Robert A. Lovett (Assistant Secretary of War for Air), Major General H.H. Arnold (Chief, Army Air Force), Brigadier General Oliver P. Echols (Chief, Army Air Force Materiel Division), Lt. Colonel Benjamin W. Chidlaw, Major General Spaatz, Major Irvine, and Major Brandt.[9] The Lovett group recommended setting up a jet propulsion program in the United States. The group then discussed the qualifications of several airframe companies who could work with GE in carrying out such a program. N.B. Reynolds reconstructed the meeting, based on interviews with GE personnel attending:

> General Arnold arrived, greeted the group, warned them of the utmost secrecy of the project, impressing them with the fact that it was important that no one learn that work on jet propulsion was being undertaken in the United States. He said that the papers had just arrived by Army plane from England and that he himself had not had a chance to look at them. He went to the safe, took out a package that was liberally daubed with red sealing wax, and opened the package to disclose some very incomplete drawings of the British jet propulsion power plant. As soon as the GE men had a chance to glance at these the General said that one reason he had come to GE was because of our experience in the developing of the turbosupercharger. Then he asked Mr. Muir point blank if GE was willing to undertake further development and manufacture of this type of engine in America. There was very little hesitation. Although he had no opportunity to consult the War Projects Committee or other GE policy-making groups, Mr. Muir said that GE would undertake the project. Whereupon General Arnold said that he had an appointment with the President, and he would leave them to work out further details. They were free to use his office as long as they liked, and the only thing he wanted to be sure of was that an order

was placed for fifteen engines. The only other real decision made at this meeting was the very rough estimate that something could be ready for test in about six months.[10]

General Arnold came to GE for three reasons. The first was that Pratt & Whitney and Curtiss-Wright were loaded with engine orders for military aircraft. The second was that GE had a great reputation for turbomachinery design, and the third was that the Moss supercharger work was applicable to the new type of aircraft production.

Travers cites a letter from General Arnold to Roy Shoults dated August 27, 1941. Sources close to General Arnold at the time said that he feared that the old-line firms might be opposed to the development of an unorthodox power plant.[11]

The Lovett group decided upon an initial production goal of fifteen turbojet engines and three aircraft, to be produced by the Bell Aircraft Corporation.[12] Why Bell? David Mondey, in *The Concise Guide to American Aircraft of World War II*, offers the explanation:

> Because of the Bell Aircraft Corporation's geographical location, in relation to the General Electric plant, this company was chosen to design and build a fighter aircraft to be powered by the first American-built gas turbine.[13]

The group decided to invite Lawrence D. Bell of Bell Aircraft Corporation to a conference in Washington the next morning.[14] On September 5, a secret conference was held in General Arnold's office with key representatives of the Army Air Force, GE, and Bell Aircraft. The Army Air Force signed a contract with GE for fifteen Whittle-type gas turbines and a contract with Bell for three experimental jet fighters, to be designated the XP-59A.[15]

Travers recounts that the first Army Air Force contract with GE,

> contained only one sentence specifying fifteen Type I turbosuperchargers. Later there was an Army Air Force Memo stating that GE should try to improve the engine design without jeopardizing production deliveries and that GE practices should be adapted to the Rover W2B engine. The first two engines were scheduled for delivery on April 2, 1942.[16]

GE was later authorized by the Army Air Force to also design an automatic control system for the W1X and to improve mechanical details based on the company's turbosupercharger experience.[17] They were forbidden, however, from making any changes that would have a material effect on performance.[18]

After this key meeting the Army Air Force still had to obtain permission from the British Air Ministry to bring the Whittle engine to the United States. After some quick coordination with the Royal Air Force, the Army Air Force obtained authorization from the British government that same month.[19]

## Development of the GE/Whittle I-A Turbojet Engine

GE assigned Donald F. "Truly" Warner, a top engineer from the Supercharger Department, as project engineer in charge of converting the Whittle engine; and the Army Air Force assigned Major Donald J. Keirn as project officer.[20] GE set aside Building 45 at its Lynn, Massachusetts, plant as the site of the conversion.

On October 1 Keirn returned from England with a W.1.X jet engine, drawings of the W.2.B, and a team of Power Jets engineers.[21] The members of the Power Jets team were Chief Test Engineer D.N. Walker, Experimental Fitter G.B. Bozzoni, and Royal Air Force Flight Sergeant J.A. King.[22]

On October 4, the W.1.X and the W.2.B drawings arrived at GE Lynn, and were shunted off to Building 45 under great secrecy.[23]

As recounted by Reynolds:

> After a week or so a special meeting was held by Mr. Standerwick, Mr. Thompson, and Colonel Chidlaw to discuss how the production work should be handled. It was decided that no government agency was to participate in the investigation. Moreover, the Air Corps people in charge of inspection at the works were not to be told of the work, and they were given instructions not to meddle. These plans were approved by Mr. Darling, manager of the works.[24]

Roy Shoults acted as a management coordinator between the Army Air Force, Bell, and GE. He worked with Army Air Force Colonel Ralph Swofford to plan the development of the Bell aircraft.[25]

GE found that the British drawings were incomplete, lacking a control system in particular. Other aspects of the design indicated practices that the GE team had found in their previous work to be inadequate. The Army Air Force authorized GE to design a completely new automatic control system.[26]

GE strengthened the impeller of the engine by using buttress vanes. The turbine blades were changed to Hastelloy B, a new alloy from the Haynes Stellite Company that GE had started using in 1940 on their turbosuperchargers.[27]

Travers describes other early discoveries:

> The first GE engine stalled (or surged) well below full speed. The British had run into the same problem...GE cured the problem by using thicker vanes in the diffuser, reducing the effective flow area. However, the aerodynamic design of the centrifugal impeller was considered by GE to be quite advanced since it gave good performance at a tip speed of about 1,550 feet/second, corresponding to a pressure ratio of about 4:1. Until this time, supercharger engineers had considered 3:1 a very high ratio for a single stage compressor.[28]

GE extrapolated from this design for their new series of turbosuperchargers, the BH and the CH turbos. This new series soon enabled reciprocating engines to maintain rated horsepower up to 35,000 feet. The turbos represented a substantial increase from the previous 25,000-feet altitude ceiling of the type B and C turbos.[29]

The GE design and manufacturing teams worked feverishly for six months. Retired GE engineer John Benson describes the construction of the test cells in West Lynn:

> We had set them up for turbosuperchargers, and we knew then how important it was to armor-plate the thing so that if anything blew up, it wouldn't just keep going through the walls...The type-B turbosupercharger is a little wheel...If you high-speed it and let it burst, it will take a surrounding protection cylinder two inches thick, ten inches wide (ten square inches) and split it just as clean as a whistle. So it had tremendous force. We got a real good idea of what you needed to do to protect against that. We built this test cell such that it would withstand explosive forces and the British, they kidded us about it and named it Fort Knox.
>
> It had thick walls, almost like a cube inside, maybe one dimension was greater. The air came down to a measuring funnel in the ceiling, and then the exhaust went out the rear up into a silencer. It was all reinforced concrete. It had big cell doors that you could close tightly so that no air would leak in. The instrumentation was on the outside. The cell doors, by the way, were heavy boilerplate so that if it blew up, you couldn't have any damage due to that. We ran into various problems with it and found that with the air coming down one side of the air nozzle, you get the airflow split into different directions and that caused various temperature distribution problems through the two inlets.[30]

During this time GE had some security problem with their British colleagues because of the natural curiosity of the New Englanders. The three Englishmen were put up in a small hotel outside Lynn, but as soon as they began to make friends with other guests they attracted unwanted attention. For security reasons GE had to keep moving them to other quarters. Finally the I-A unit (Figure 5-2) was ready to be tested; and on April 18, 1942, at 11:05 p.m., GE and the United States entered the jet age.[31]

**Figure 5-2. GE I-A Turbojet**
*(Photo courtesy of GE)*

The engine ran too hot; but because GE decided to use Hastelloy B instead of the British Nimonic 80, it did not suffer from the initial bucket breakage problems encountered by Frank Whittle in his first test runs. Nimonic 80 is a chromium-nickel-titanium alloy with a high rupture strength at 1,200°F, while Hastelloy B is a nickel-molybdenum alloy with a high rupture strength at 1,500°F. GE chose Hastelloy B as their bucket material because it was the strongest forging material that the company had at the time. Their method of choosing bucket alloys was to compare the various materials on the following characteristics: a) rupture strength at 100 hours at 1,500°F, and b) short-time strength at 1,500°F operation in the bucket tester, a machine for running buckets under simulated operating conditions except at higher temperatures or higher speeds than would be encountered in standard units.[32] The surge problem, well below full speed, plagued GE for two more months until Frank Whittle arrived in Lynn from Boston in June 1942.

Security continued to remain tight as Reynolds recounted:

> It was naturally a very exciting time. When the job was finished late at night, most of the men involved went home and to bed for the first time in many hours. There was one young man, however, who had a date to attend a party. Naturally excited over the success of the work, he just couldn't resist saying that big things were afoot and arousing a certain amount of curiosity among those present. The next morning, word of this indiscretion got to the Security authorities. They tracked down the young man, whose intentions were perfectly innocent, arrangements were made to transfer him to work at another plant of the Company, and that same afternoon he was on the train to the new job. He did not return to the place he had worked in Lynn even to get his tools, and no one who worked with him there has, to the best of our knowledge, seen him since. Because no explanation of any kind was made, the psychological effect of this measure was very good as far as the rest of the workmen were concerned.[33]

In June, Frank Whittle arrived in Boston with drawings of his W.2/500 turbojet engine.[34] GE and Whittle began work on redesigning the diffuser and blower casing for the I-A. The redesign inserted partitions in the existing blower casing ensuring completely separate passages through the casing to each combustion chamber. These separate passages enabled the I-A to produce 1,300 pounds of thrust.[35] In comparison, the British Rover B.23 could deliver only about 1,000 pounds of thrust without surging. It was not until November 1942 that the B.23 passed a 25-hour test at 1,250 pounds of thrust.[36]

The GE development of the I-A was not without its difficulties. John Benson, a GE engineer working on the new engine, described one problem:

> Because of the engines, the (test) cell had to be made strong, because engine after engine blew up. We tried like the dickens to find out why. We would sit for many hours sifting through bushel baskets of

broken metal, you see, and nothing would give a clue to it, because it was that much scrambled. One day I happened to be going by a rotor that was being assembled on the balancing stand, and I had one of these little fingernail clippers, and I banged on the inlet blades just for the fun of it, I was always banging things that way. Fourteen out of the sixteen on one side went "clunk", and I said 'a-ha, there is a crack in there somewhere.' I told the chief inspector 'don't let that rotor be assembled into the engine.' He said 'I inspected that rotor, it is alright, and it is going into the engine', so we see-sawed back and forth a little bit on that, then finally I said that the only one to solve that problem was Truly Warner, who was our boss, and we did. He came down, saw the fingernail clipper test, took it out and put it in the caustic etch (sodium hydroxide). That is the thing that cleans out the surface crud and helps to reveal cracks and then they put on the fluorescent fluid and put it on ultraviolet, and then you see the crack very vividly. So then there were fourteen cracks. He then assigned M.G. "Robby" Robinson, who (was) another member of the engineering team...to redesign that impeller. What Robby did was to put fillets in the inlet blades and all along the radial blades out to the tip. Instead of having an even thickness of the blades as they intersected the disk, they gradually opened out, and increased the thickness as they joined the disk. Then we tried those, and never had another engine explosion due to that reason.[37]

It is important to note here that one of the advantages of the American system of early turbojet development over the efforts of Frank Whittle is that companies like GE (and later P&W and others) could at times "test to bust" their engines. They could be assured that replacement engines could and would be fabricated for further testing. Whittle and his development team did not have the luxury of several engines with which to test.

In the late summer of 1942, Army Air Force Colonel Donald Keirn inspected the British jet engine development programs and reported to the Army Air Force that the British were ahead in four respects:

1. development of the engines themselves,

2. research on the possible application of the engines,

3. the study of the design and possible performance of turbine-driven aircraft, and

4. the coordination of the development of the planes and the engines.[38]

Keirn's report also described the operation of the British Gas Turbine Collaboration Committee. Schlaifer relates that five days after Keirn's report, Army Air Force Brig. General Benjamin W. Chidlaw wrote a memo to the authorities at Wright Field. Chidlaw described the British lead and requested that the Power Plant Laboratory present a plan for U.S. cooperative engine development similar to the British model.[39] Wright Field responded with a recommendation that such cooperation be maintained.

On November 20, representatives of the Army, Navy, and NACA met in Washington to discuss the Keirn report and the Wright Field recommendations for U.S. aircraft gas turbine engine collaboration. The representatives agreed that heretofore each of the current U.S. aircraft gas turbine engine developers knew nothing of what the others were doing. Those present at the meeting decided that "basic differences in national laws"[40] made collaboration along the British model impossible. Schlaifer states that Navy aircraft gas turbine engine development policy was particularly secretive, and cites their policy of having Westinghouse develop an aircraft gas turbine engine without knowledge of outside developments.

Taxiing tests for the XP-59A were completed on September 29 and 30. On October 1, 1942, powered by two GE I-A turbojets, the XP-59A rose in flight at Muroc Lake, California, with Bell test pilot Robert Stanley at the controls.[41] This flight was fully eight months before the British W.2.B was flown in the Meteor. Schlaifer also points out that the lighter wing loading of the XP-59A compared to other aircraft made it easier to fly at high altitude. This in turn meant that GE ran into trouble with surging at altitude and eliminated it well before the British first encountered it in mid-1943. Flight tests of the XP-59A (Figure 5-3) with the I-A lasted approximately one year. Bryce Walker notes a top speed of 415 mph,[42] while Schlaifer shows 404 mph at 35,000 feet.[43]

## The GE I-14 Turbojet

On May 15, 1942, shortly after the beginning of flight testing of the XP-59A, GE began design of the I-14B, a slightly more powerful version of the I-A designed to deliver 1,400 pounds of thrust.[44] This new design incorporated a new GE blower casing and diffuser.

> The completely separate passages from the impeller to each combustion chamber were made rectangular in cross section, and the turn from the radial to the rearward direction was made in a right angle, around which the gases were led by internal vanes.[45]

**Figure 5-3. Bell XP-59A in Flight**
*(Photo courtesy of U.S. Air Force)*

A second major innovation incorporated into the I-14B was an improved turbine wheel, copied from the Power Jets W.2/500 turbojet. This turbine featured the use of fewer, broader, and longer turbine buckets. These improved buckets both decreased breakage and increased thrust by increasing the mass flow through the engine.[46]

The third significant innovation was a new combustion liner arrangement developed by A.J. "Tony" Nerad of GE's Schenectady Research Laboratory. Whittle and the British had used finely atomized sprayed fuel with very high fuel pressure (approximately 2,000 pounds per square inch). Nerad designed combustors with a variety of holes to ensure mixing of the air with the fuel. This technique required a fuel pressure of only 200 to 300 pounds per square inch.[47]

The first test run of the I-14B was on February 12, 1943.[48] The engine delivered its projected 1,400 pounds of thrust when tested.[49] This was one month after the Rover B.23 passed a 25-hour test at this thrust. The first flight of the I-14B was on February 12, 1944. Production of the I-14 engine ended in 1945.[50]

## Design and Development of the GE I-16 (J31) Turbojet Engine

On January 19, 1943, GE began design and development of the I-16 centrifugal turbojet (Figure 5-4).[51] Again, the I-16's design incorporated a double-inlet centrifugal compressor and a single-stage turbine. J. Goldsbury, in a paper delivered at the Jet Propulsion Engine Conference of May 4-6, 1944, sponsored by GE, describes the changes incorporated in the I-16:

> A number of changes were introduced...to improve operation and simplify manufacture. The turbine nozzle area was increased to 54.5 square inches. The buckets were increased in height from 2.5

inches to 2.76 inches (blade height), keeping the inner diameter the same (11.5 inches). The bucket blade width was increased to 1.2 inches. The impeller diameter (20.69 inches) was made the same, but the diffuser was designed for the increased flow.[52]

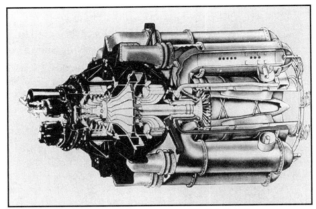

**Figure 5-4. Cutaway of I-16 Engine**
*(Illustration courtesy of GE)*

The thrust goal of the I-16 was 1,600 pounds, while maintaining the military rpm goal of 16,500.[53] The I-16 consistently gave 1,620 to 1,660 pounds static thrust with tail pipe temperature averaging about 1,180°F. Certain minor modifications caused the letter A to be added, giving the units the I-16A designation.[54]

The I-16 turbojet engine was based on Whittle's W.2B design and the GE-I-A prototypes. The compressor featured vanes strengthened on the centrifugal two-sided impeller. The combustor was developed by the GE Research Laboratory's Tony Nerad. Its refinements included implemented-air mixing and low-pressure fuel atomization. The turbine of the I-16 was manufactured from the forged turbosupercharger blade material Hastelloy B. The engine controls were entirely new designs based on D.F. Warner's patents for steam turbines.

The first test run of the I-16A occurred on April 24, 1943.[55] This was the first U.S. turbojet to deliver the thrust aimed at in the original W.2.B. It had a guaranteed thrust of 1,600 pounds and averaged about 1,650 pounds for a weight of 825 pounds, and a guaranteed fuel consumption of 1.23 pounds per hour per pound of thrust (sea-level static).[56]

The first flight of the I-16A took place in the P-59A on October 23, 1943,[57] but the overall speed of the plane was only 414 mph. The piston-engined P-51 Mustang fighter was faster. The I-16 surged at altitude when tested in the P-59A, but GE corrected this by reducing the amount of material milled from the compressor casing, thereby reducing the air passage area by approximately 5 percent. This design change meant only a small sacrifice in the sea-level thrust of the engine.[58]

As development proceeded, GE received reports from flight tests and tests in their altitude chamber that indicated excessively high bearing temperatures. To remedy this situation, larger cooling air blades were provided on the turbine wheel and a new cooling air diffuser was designed. A new cooling air inlet arrangement was worked out in an attempt to take greater advantage of ram pressure. GE engineers introduced a gas baffle to prevent hot gas from leaking in through the clearance between the nozzle diaphragm and the bucket wheel, where it could impact directly on the rear bearing support. Other changes included the use of Inconel for the flame tube material, modification of the tail cone to simplify manufacture and reduce the tendency toward warping, a change from molybdenum-bearing stainless steel to columbium-stabilized stainless steel (mostly sheet-metal parts), and a change from solid forged high-alloy turbine rotors to low-alloy shafts flash welded to high-alloy wheels. This new engine type was called the I-16A1. Production was gradually changed over from the I-16A to the I-16A1, until the development of the I-16B (Figure 5-5).[59]

The changes incorporated into the I-16B, designated the J31 by the Army Air Forces, consisted of further improvement in the bearing cooling air system and combustion system (changes which were intended to simplify and improve oil scavenging) and improvements to accessories.[60] The I-16C was developed as a modification of the I-16B to permit mounting in a Navy aircraft.

**Figure 5-5. I-16B (J31) Engine**
*(Photo courtesy of GE)*

In a series of flight tests, a fully armed P-59A was flown with modified I-16Bs at 46,700 feet. This was only one month after the Welland engine had first flown in the Meteor. The Welland, however, was still having trouble with surging at about 25,000 feet, a problem that had already been solved by the GE engineers. Two hundred and forty-one I-16B/J31s were subsequently delivered to the Army Air Force. Production of the I-16 series ended in 1945. [61]

## The GE I-18 and I-20

In between the development of the I-16 and the I-40, GE designed two development growth models of the I-16, the I-18 and the I-20. The design of the I-18 began on May 25, 1943. Although it incorporated the I-16's double-inlet centrifugal compressor and single-stage turbine, the I-18 was designed to achieve 1,800 pounds of thrust with a military specific fuel consumption of 1.17. This is in contrast to the I-16's thrust of 1,600 pounds and military specific fuel consumption of 1.23. Goldsbury describes the changes incorporated into the I-18:

> By increasing the impeller tip diameter from 20.69 to 21.37 inches, increasing the nozzle diaphragm area from 54.5 square inches to 56.5 square inches and modifying the diffuser area to correspond, an I-18 unit has been developed. Approximately 200 pounds more static thrust is expected from this type than from the I-16.[62]

The average weight of the I-18 was 850 pounds as compared to the 840 pounds of the I-16. The first testrun of the I-18 was on January 18, 1944, and the first testflight of the I-18 was on November 1, 1944.

The I-20's design began on June 9, 1943, just two weeks after GE's engines commenced the design of the I-18. It represented a growth model of the I-18, with an achieved thrust of 2,000 pounds, a military rpm of 16,500, an average weight of approximately 900 pounds, and a specific fuel consumption of 1.20 pounds of fuel per hour per pound of thrust. It too had a double-inlet centrifugal compressor and a single-stage turbine. Goldsbury describes the I-20 as follows:

> A more complete redesign has been made in the I-20 (2,000 pound static thrust). In this, the bucket height has again been increased, (to 3.025"), and a double tapered design used to keep stresses within reasonable limits. The impeller tip diameter is 21.37 as for the I-18, but the inlet annulus area is larger. The nozzle diaphragm area for the I-20 is 58 square inches. Other changes are those required by the increased capacity.[63]

The overall size of the unit was kept the same as the I-16, and the weight had been increased only by about 40 pounds. The I-20 first ran under test on April 21, 1944. It did not undergo flight testing.

The design and development of the I-14 through I-20 engines were but preludes to a more important engine design, the GE I-40. This centrifugal turbojet was to prove the penultimate pure-centrifugal turbojet engine to be designed in the United States.

## Design and Development of the GE I-40 (J33)

In early 1943 the Army Air Force asked GE to study the possibility of a turbojet that could produce 3,000 pounds of thrust.[64] GE responded with two designs: the TG-180 (later J35) axial turboprop and the I-40 (later J33) centrifugal turbojet. In May, Colonel Donald J. Keirn of the Army Air Force and GE's Development Committee of their Supercharger Engineering Division changed the thrust development target to 4,000 pounds of thrust for both new engine programs.[65] On May 3, GE initiated the design of the TG-180 axial-flow turbojet in Schenectady, N.Y. On May 23, GE proposed the I-40 (J33) to the Army Air Force Materiel Command at Wright Field. GE's I Series design team began the design of the I-40 on June 9, the same date of design start as the I-20. Dale D. Streid, I-40 project engineer, recounts the development of the design:

> Two main problems presented themselves in the early design. One was whether a large enough impeller forging could be made, and the other was whether a satisfactory turbine bucket could be designed. The first problem was finally answered by the Aluminum Company of America which indicated its willingness to try to make a forging from which an impeller 30 inches in diameter and 12 inches thick could be made. Based on this, it was decided that the rated speed would be about 11,500 rpm, which indicated that the turbine bucket should be about 4 inches long on a 22-inch-pitch diameter. Preliminary calculations showed that such a bucket could not be shrouded and would have an average stress at the root of about 32,000 pounds per square inch. Since then, this stress has been reduced to 26,000 pounds per square inch (1945) by careful design which requires that the areas vary throughout the length of the bucket according to a parabolic distribution.
>
> After various mechanical arrangements had been studied, it was finally decided to use separate rotors for the turbine and compressor, with a flexible coupling between in order to obtain advantages in line-up and assembly. Also, it was decided to use straight-through combustion chambers, in order to make the shape of the entire gas turbine more nearly a streamlined body. It was decided to use flooded lubrication for the bearings and the coupling, based on the years of successful experience with turbosupercharger bearings using this type of lubrication.[66]

Schlaifer adds the following details:

> The compressor and turbine of the I-40 were derived from the I-16 without any essential changes except in the method of manufacture. The combustion system, however, was of the straight-through type rather than the reverse-flow used in the original British W.2.B and the earlier American I-series engines. Like the right-angle blower casing first used on the I-16, this change was developed independently by GE at about the same time that a similar change was being made in Britain. GE's primary reason was to simplify assembly and service; the reverse-flow system on the I-16 was not excessively unreliable or difficult to manufacture.

The combustion system of the I-40 was made of Inconel sheet (80 percent nickel, 14 percent chromium, and 6 percent iron). The turbine nozzles were precision-cast of Stellite alloy No. 21. The turbine buckets of the first experimental engines were forged of Hastelloy B, as in the earlier I engines, and it was originally intended to make all production buckets in the same way, but as plans were made for large quantity production of the I-40 it became doubtful whether sufficient forging capacity could be created. Precision casting of Stellite alloy No. 21 had solved the production problem for turbosuperchargers, and although it was quite a different problem to cast buckets for the I-40, which were thirty-five times as large as those of the turbo supercharger, experiments were made. Half the engines built at Lynn were equipped with cast buckets of Stellite alloy No. 21, and by 1945 considerable progress had been made toward a satisfactory production technique.[67]

The design of the I-40 (J33) was entirely new. Its base thrust was two and one-half times that of the previous I-16 design. The compressor was a very large (30-inch outside diameter) forged aluminum double-sided impeller. The combustion system consisted of multiple "through-flow" can combustors. The turbine featured large unshrouded blades, and the turbine wheel was a thick forging of high-temperature steel. Cooling airflow vanes were milled on each side of the wheel. One of the I-40's special features was a flexible splined coupling between independently supported compressor and turbine rotors.

By September 1943 GE had finished the design and manufacturing drawings of the very first I-40.[68] They must have been pretty optimistic about their drawings, because Travers states that as each part was drawn up, manufacture of it was begun. GE must have been on a rush schedule.[69] In January 1944, GE first tested the I-40 turbojet. Streid remembers that first start-up:

> The fire in the combustion chambers was lighted, but actual operation was not obtained because of an unusual torching out of the exhaust jet encountered immediately after ignition. After two additional attempts to start during the next two days, the first I-40 was run up to 8,000 rpm on January 13, 1944, which was just six and a half months after the start of the project.[70]

In subsequent tests the turbine was run at various speeds up to the 8,700 rpm limit observed because the buckets had an unfavorable tilt and GE considered them unsatisfactory for higher speed operation.[71] In February, the I-40 momentarily developed a thrust of 4,200 pounds on the bench. It was soon developed to produce an average thrust of about 4,000 pounds, with a guarantee of 3,750 pounds.[72] The test was carried out in an open test stand at Lynn near the Saugus River.[73] For this test GE had designed and installed a new turbine wheel.

A total of four I-40 units were built that first year. The first three were used for performance and factory endurance tests. The fourth I-40 unit was shipped to Lockheed in California for installation in the XP-80A Shooting Star (Figure 5-6).[74]

**Figure 5-6. Lockheed XP-80A**
*(Photo courtesy of U.S. Air Force)*

Evidently the difference between the thrust/frontal area of the I-40 and that of axial-flow gas turbines, as well as the effect of that difference on aircraft design proved important because GE subsequently developed axial-flow engines rather than centrifugal-flow engines.[75]

On June 10, 1944, the GE I-40 was first flown in the XP-80As, a redesigned version of the Lockheed airframe and the first single-engine U.S. jet fighter.[76] This combination produced a speed of over 500 mph.[77] The flight lasted approximately thirty minutes and reached an altitude of 10,000 feet.[78] The I-40 delivered more performance than the British Goblin turbojet of about the same size.[79]

Due to this workable combination, the Army Air Force dropped plans to purchase the P-80 with the British Goblin turbojet engine. The GE I-40 and the Lockheed P-80A "Shooting Star" were the first jet engine and jet fighter to be produced in quantity in the United States, and the only U.S. combination to reach this stage before the end of the war.[80]

Travers describes some of the problems after the first flight:

> After the first flight of the I-40, development of the engine proceeded rapidly. As expected for an engine new in size and design, numerous problems developed in factory and flight testing. Some problems were exhaust cone buckling, sticking of automatic controls, carbon formation, and fuel pump wear. One problem developed that took considerable effort (to solve). There developed concern for consistent high quality of the quite thick turbine wheel forging. To help understand the problem, one engineer spent a year exploding (in a special new vacuum test pit which Gene Stoeckly and Marty Hemsworth designed) some 500 machined turbine disks. But, the problem was brought under control, and manufacture of the I-40 gas turbine proceeded fundamentally with the same design laid down in the summer of 1943.[81]

In June 1945, the I-40 (J33) passed a 50-hour test. Captain James L. Sparkman, at that time in the Army Air Force Power Plant Laboratory at Wright-Patterson Air Force Base, wrote of the J33 in a report published by the Air Force in 1956:

> In retrospect it is plainly evident that the J33 engine series showed signs of being a remarkably reliable engine at a very early date in its development, and it has retained that reputation up to the present.[82]

The early production engines such as the J33-GE-9, J33-A-17, and J33-A-21 were all of the same thrust rating of 3,825 pounds, which could be raised to 4,500 pounds with water injection. The development program for these engines did not concentrate on thrust increase; most of the changes in model number resulted from accessory and installation changes, although a 170-pound weight reduction was accomplished on the J33-A-21. These engines were used primarily in the F-80A, RF-80A, and F-80B aircraft.[83]

Despite their successful development of the Whittle-derived I-A, I-14, I-16, and I-40, the Army Air Force still considered GE to be a developer of turbojets, not a manufacturer. When informed in 1944 that GE could not produce more than a small number of I-40 turbojets, the Army Air Force pushed GE to license the I-40 to the Allison Division of General Motors. The Army Air Force then asked GE to take over a production plant in New Jersey. GE, in the person of GE Vice President Burrows, replied that the New Jersey plant was "in a very bad labor area".[84] The Army Air Force then suggested that GE take over a Navy D-E turbine plant in Syracuse, New York. GE agreed to produce the I-40 there. GE brought in Wilfred E. Johnson to manage the production, and the Syracuse plant delivered 271 I-40 turbojet engines before the Army Air Force closed the plant at the end of the war. In October 1945, GE passed complete responsibility for the J33 to the Allison Division of General Motors.[85] Allison went on to make J33s until 1959.[86]

## Allison's Further Development of the J33

Allison has an interesting explanation of how they came to be involved in the production and development of turbojets and turboprops. It is recounted in *Allison: Power of Excellence*:

In June 1944, Ed Newill was visiting Wright Field, home of the Air Materiel Command. Allison had just finished producing 50,000 V1710s, and government funding for new Allison test flight facilities at Plant 10 had been approved. D-Day was in the papers. Walking down the hall, Allison's general manager heard: 'Mr. Newill, will you step in here a minute?' From a desk drawer, a senior procurement man took a photo. 'Can you make this for us?' 'Aircraft engines are our business,' replied Newill looking at the photographs. 'If that's what you want, we will make them. It is a jet engine, isn't it?' 'Yes, and we would like to have your firm price and production schedule in one week.'

'That's not much time,' replied Newill. 'I know, but we need these in the worst sort of way.' 'Can we have a model and prints shipped to Allison?' 'There is no model,' interrupted the procurement man. 'A set of prints?' 'The blueprints are not complete as the design is not finished.'

'Can I have a picture? Dimensions? Weight?' 'That is about all I can give you.' With that skimpy information, Newill came home with 'one week' still in his ears. Newill called his staff together and repeated the request. With the meager information in hand, a detailed study was clearly impossible. After lengthy discussion, someone said: 'If we know how much it weighs, let's take the cost per pound of our present engine and apply that to the weight of the new engine, and give them that as the price.' No one had a better idea.

A week later Newill returned to Wright Field with a firm price quote and a delivery schedule. Allison got the order and delivered its first engine on schedule within 10 percent of the original price quotation.[87]

In May 1946, an Allison-produced J33-A-17 (Figure 5-7) passed a 100-hour test. A J33-A-21 passed the first U.S. Air Force 150-hour qualification test in April 1947. The J33-A-21 was also the first turbojet produced with water/alcohol augmentation,[88] and the first jet engine ever approved for commercial use.[89]

**Figure 5-7. Early Allison J33**
*(Photo courtesy of Allison)*

The J33-A-23 was the result of the next development step, which increased the thrust rating to 4,600 pounds dry and to 5,400 pounds with water injection. The operational altitude capability increased from 40,000 feet to 47,500 feet. The main applications of this engine were in the F-80C and T-33A. A few of the engines were also used in the XF-92A aircraft. The 150-hour test of the J33-A-23 was completed in July 1948.

To develop power for the F-94A and B aircraft (Figure 5-8), an afterburner was developed by Allison and the engine was designated the J33-A-33. The engine was basically the J33-A-35 but with numerous accessory and installation changes which resulted in a

6,000-pound-thrust engine with afterburning. A Lockheed F-94 Starfire made its first flight with an afterburning J33-A-33 engine in August 1949.[90] This engine passed its 150-hour test in January 1951.[91]

The J33-A-35 was essentially the same as the J33-A-23, but with a low-pressure fuel system. A J33-A-35 became the first engine to operate 1,000 hours without overhaul (August 1951), as well as the first turbojet engine to operate 1,400 hours without overhaul (August 1954).[92]

**Figure 5-8. Lockheed F-94 Starfire**
*(Photo courtesy of U.S. Air Force)*

The J33-A-27 and -29 engines were, in December 1952, the latest development of the J33 series engine, the J33-A-29 being an afterburner version of the J33-A-27. The J33-A-27 had a dry rating of 6,350 pounds of thrust, which could be increased to 7,000 pounds with water injection. This engine completed its 150-hour test in January 1951. The J33-A-29 had a dry rating of 5,900 pounds of thrust, 7,700 pounds with afterburner. This model completed a 50-hour test in September 1951.[93]

Allison developed the J33-A-37 for use in the B-61 missile, which required an expendable engine. This particular engine was built as easily and quickly as possible and the qualification test consisted of running three engines for five hours each in September 1951. The only rating required was a normal continuous rating of 4,600 pounds of thrust.[94]

The J33-A-41 was developed by Allison for use in the B-61B missile, which had an increased range capability. The J33-A-41 was similar to the J33-A-37 except that its thrust has been increased to 5,200 pounds with an attendant increase in rpm.[95]

In all, Allison Division of General Motors produced 15,525 J33 turbojet engines of various models for the U.S. Air Force through 1959, making the J33 one of the most mass-produced turbojet engines in history.[96]

## GE Becomes a Developer and Producer

The end of World War II in August 1945 found GE in a difficult position vis-à-vis their turbojet development plans for the future.

A struggle to determine GE's future developed. Several company officers felt that GE should get out of the turbojet development business in favor of the manufacture of commercial products. With the war's end, the Army Air Force shut down the Syracuse facility in favor of production of current models (the J33 and J35) at Allison. Although GE had been chosen for the important responsibility of developing the Whittle turbojet, and although the I-series of turbojets represented a definite series of technological advances in turbojet design, GE was not chosen to produce the J33 and J35 turbojet engines in quantity. In both cases, once the engine had been developed to the point of production, the actual production of the engine had then been allocated by the Army Air Force to the Allison Division of General Motors. No doubt GE's lack of a production facility was an important factor in the decision. There were additional pressures from within the company to curtail aircraft gas turbine development as well. C.W. "Jim" LaPierre recalls:

> After World War I, there was a great deal of concern for manufacturers as being 'Merchants of Death.' At the end of World War II, the same thought arose in the minds of many people. GE, and other large companies, did not want this image. A number of directors of GE were opposed to having GE involved in war work, except direct work for patriotic reasons.[97]

Not only was there a lack of obvious direction for GE in the turbojet business, but many executives in the company discerned the impact that the massive military cutbacks would have on this new technology. Not only were fast jet fighters no longer crucial to the war effort, but the huge production runs of high-performance piston engine manufacturers meant a surplus of aircraft engines for aircraft manufacturers to use in new aircraft. Coupled with this glut of piston engines came a concern that the turbojet was not yet ready for commercial aviation. Commercial airlines focused more development attention on the turboprop, which they believed would fit their current routes and schedules more closely and efficiently than would turbojets. The relative efficiency of the turbojet flying at speeds in excess of 500 mph at higher altitudes in a commercial application was not widely apparent in the postwar era of 1945-1950.

With these caveats in mind, any GE executive would have to think long and hard about investing additional capital in this new technology, let alone building new production facilities to manufacture jet engines. This is where Harold D. Kelsey came in.

By July 31, 1945, all aircraft gas turbine development at GE had been concentrated in Lynn, Massachusetts, in a new division. While top management discussed the future of the company, GE reorganized its jet engine development programs. The GE Turbine Division at Schenectady was given responsibility for adapting the gas turbine to railroad engines, naval ship propulsion, and ground power generation. All aircraft gas turbine work was concentrated at Lynn under Harold D. Kelsey in a new Aircraft Gas Turbine Division.[98]

In January of 1946, Kelsey was named Division Manager of the GE Aircraft Gas Turbine Division. He proposed a comprehensive postwar development plan for gas turbines in which he pushed for GE to get into the large-scale production of jet engines. GE had already established itself as a developer of turbine engines for aircraft and now it had to become a manufacturer as well. Kelsey's development plan called for new engine development, new test facilities, and new manufacturing facilities.[99]

Kelsey also recommended that GE drop development of centrifugal turbojets and concentrate on axial engines. It appears that Sam Puffer and Sir Frank Whittle advocated continued development of centrifugal-compressor turbojets, while Russ Hall, Gene Stoeckly, Glenn Warren and his team from Schenectady favored axials.[100] Kelsey took a chance and predicted in his development plan what turbojet and turboprop engines would be required in the postwar market through 1950:

- 3,000-horsepower turboprops
- double gas generator turboprops up to 6,000 horsepower
- 1,000-horsepower gas turbines
- light gas turbines of 200 horsepower
- jet engines of 6,000 pounds thrust
- turbojets of 4,000 pounds thrust
- turbosuperchargers and other related equipment[101]

In Kelsey's plan, he estimated the total aircraft gas turbine market for the five-year period after the war at $35 million. Of that market, Kelsey estimated that GE could get 25 percent.

Many executives at GE-Lynn and GE-Schenectady greeted Kelsey's plan with derision. Kelsey ended up getting about one-third of what he wanted. Most important of the items was permission to build a new compressor test facility. In his plan Kelsey asked for a facility which would have a 30,000-horsepower drive unit for testing engine compressors with flow rates up to 450 pounds per second. He was authorized to build a facility having a 12,000-horsepower drive and capacity for a 175 pound-per-second test compressor. This was well short of what Kelsey and his team required, so they looked elsewhere to get their required facility.

Elsewhere meant the Navy. Kelsey's head of technical services (and test engineering), Eugene Stoeckly, convinced the U.S. Navy to divert a new destroyer steam turbine planned for a canceled ship to Lynn for use in his proposed test facility. Stoeckly recalls:

> Well, I over-ran the appropriation by 1/2 million dollars and never came so close to getting fired in my career...(But) we did a damn good job - it has stood the test of time - made a lot of contributions - played a role in the GE Company's ability to develop compressors.[102]

The Kelsey initiatives gave GE the physical plant that would prove to be crucial to GE's next big development program, one that would establish General Electric as a permanent player in the production of aircraft gas turbine engines. The old saying "developed at General Electric, produced at General Motors" would be laid to rest forever.

## Endnotes

1   Schoneberger, William A. and Paul Sonnenburg, Allison Power of Excellence: 1915 - 1990, Indianapolis, IN: Allison Gas Turbine Division, General Motors Corporation, 1990, 91.

2   Neville, Leslie E. and Silsbee, Nathaniel F, "The Army Air Force and American Industry Pull a Miracle," from Jet Propulsion Progress, New York: McGraw-Hill Book Company, 1948, 43.

3   Ibid, and Schoneberger and Sonnenburg, Allison,91.

4   Neville and Silsbee, Jet Propulsion Progress, 44.

5   Ibid.

6   GE Memorandum from N. B. Reynolds to R. L. Gibson, dated May 19, 1944, on the history of the jet propulsion engine development at GE in 1944, 1.

7   Cox, Journal of the Aeronautical Sciences, 72.

8   Neville and Silsbee, Jet Propulsion Progress, 7, and Cox, H. Roxbee, "British Aircraft Gas Turbines," Ninth Wright Brothers Lecture, Journal of the Aeronautical Sciences, Vol. 13 (February 1946), 72.

9   Travers, William, History of GE, Unpublished manuscript, 27.

10  GE Memorandum, jet propulsion engine development at GE in 1944, 2.

11  Travers, History of GE, 27.

12  Ibid.

13  Mondey, David, The Concise Guide to American Aircraft of World War II, Feltham, Middlesex: Temple Press, 1984, 15-16.

14  Neville and Silsbee, Jet Propulsion Progress, 7-8.

15  Ibid, 44.

16  Travers, History of GE, 28.

17  Ibid, 30.

18  Schlaifer, Robert, Development of Aircraft Engines, Boston, MA: Harvard University Press, 1949, 462.

19  Ibid.

20  Travers, History of GE, 28.

21  Ibid, and Gunston, Bill, The Encyclopedia of the World's Combat Aircraft: A Technical Directory of Major Warplanes from World War I to the Present Day, New York: Chartwell Books Inc., 1976, 62.

22  Cox, Journal of the Aeronautical Sciences, 72.

23  Gunston, The Encyclopedia of the World's Combat Aircraft, 62.

24  GE Memorandum, jet propulsion engine development at GE in 1944, 5.

25  Travers, History of GE, 28.

26  Ibid, 30.

27  Ibid.

28  Ibid.

29  Ibid.

30  Interview with John Benson on April 25, 1991, in Boston, Massachusetts, 2.

31  Neville and Silsbee, Jet Propulsion Progress, 44.

32  Paulson, E., "High Temperature Materials in the Type I J. P. Engine," in GE Company, Jet Propulsion Engine Conference, Report of conference held at GE's River Works, West Lynn, Massachusetts, on May 4-6, 1944, West Lynn, MA: GE Company, 1944, 159.

33  GE Memorandum, jet propulsion engine development at GE in 1944, 6.

34  Travers, History of GE, 28.

35  Ibid, 30.

36  Schlaifer, Development, 464.

37  Interview, John Benson, 3.

38  Schlaifer, Development, 466.

39  Ibid, 466-467.

40  Ibid, 467.

41  Neville and Silsbee, Jet Propulsion Progress, 45.

42  Walker, Bryce, Fighting Jets, Time/Life Epic of Flight, Alexandria, VA: Time/Life Books Inc., 1983, 47.

43  Schlaifer, Development, 464.

44  GE Company, Aircraft Gas Turbine Engineering Conference, Report of conference held in Swampscott, Massachusetts on May 31, June 1, and June 2, 1945, West Lynn, MA: GE Company, 1945, ii.

45  Schlaifer, Development, 464.

46  Ibid, 465.

47  Travers, History of GE, 31.

48  GE Company, Aircraft Gas Turbine Engineering Conference, ii.

49  Travers, History of GE, 32, and Gunston, The Encyclopedia of the World's Combat Aircraft, 50.

50  GE Company, Aircraft Gas Turbine Engineering Conference, ii.

51  Ibid.

52  Goldsbury, J., "Type I Mechanical Design," in GE Company, Jet Propulsion Engine Conference, Report of conference held at GE's River Works, West Lynn, Massachusetts, on May 4-6, 1944, West Lynn, MA: GE Company, 1944, 2.

53  Schlaifer, Development, 465, and Gunston, The Encyclopedia of the World's Combat Aircraft, 62.

54  Goldsbury, Jet Propulsion Engine Conference, 2.

55  GE Company, Aircraft Gas Turbine Engineering Conference, ii, Neville and Silsbee, Jet Propulsion Progress, 45, Travers, History of GE, 32, and Gunston, The Encyclopedia of the World's Combat Aircraft, 62.

56  Schlaifer, Development, 465, and Travers, History of GE, 32.

57  GE Company, Aircraft Gas Turbine Engineering Conference, ii.

58  Schlaifer, Development, 465.

59  Goldsbury, Jet Propulsion Engine Conference, 7.

60  Ibid.

61  Travers, History of GE, 32.

62  Goldsbury, Jet Propulsion Engine Conference, 7.

63  Ibid, 10.

64  Schlaifer, Development, 473.

65  Streid, Dale D, "Type I-40 Jet-Propulsion Gas Turbine," in GE Company, Aircraft Gas Turbine Engineering Conference, Report of conference held in Swampscott, Massachusetts, on May 31, June 1, and June 2, 1945, West Lynn, MA: GE Company, 1945, 73.

66  Ibid.

67  Schlaifer, Development, 474.

68  Travers, History of GE, 44.

69  Ibid.

70  Streid, Aircraft Gas Turbine Engineering Conference, 73.

71  Ibid.

72  Schlaifer, Development, 474-475.

73  Travers, History of GE, 46.

74  Ibid.

75  Ibid.

76  GE Company, Aircraft Gas Turbine Engineering Conference, ii.

77  Schlaifer, Development, 475.

78  Streid, Aircraft Gas Turbine Engineering Conference, 75.

79  Travers, History of GE, 47.

80  Schlaifer, Development, 475.

81  Travers, History of GE, 47.

82  Sparkman, Capt. James L. USAF, Historical Development Study of USAF Turbojet and Turboprop Engines, Wright Air Development Center Technical Note No. 57-351, Wright-Patterson Air Force Base, OH: Wright Air Development Center, Air Research and Development Command, United States Air Force, 1957, 1.

83  Ibid.

84  Travers, History of GE, 48.

85  Gunston, The Encyclopedia of the World's Combat Aircraft, 63, and Sparkman, Historical Development Study of USAF Turbojet and Turboprop Engines, 1.

86  Ibid.

87  Schoneberger and Sonnenburg, Allison, 92-93.

88  Ibid, 200.

89  Ibid.

90  Ibid.

91  Sparkman, Historical Development Study of USAF Tur-
    bojet and Turboprop Engines, 1.

92  Ibid.

93  Ibid, 2.

94  Ibid.

95  Ibid.

96  Schoneberger and Sonnenburg, Allison, 93.

97  Travers, History of GE, 56.

98  Ibid, 57.

99  Travers, History of GE, 59.

100 Ibid.

101 Ibid.

102 Ibid, 60.

**Navy XFD-1 Phantom, Powered by
Two Westinghouse J30 Turbojets**

# Westinghouse Innovations and Developments

Chronicling the aircraft gas turbine engine development work of the Westinghouse Corporation here serves two purposes. First of all, Westinghouse successfully built, ran, and flew the first American axial-flow turbojet engine. This of itself makes this chapter worthwhile from a historical point of view. Secondly, the Westinghouse Corporation provides a significant example of some of the hazards of the jet-building business. Westinghouse built a flyable turbojet engine sixteen months after beginning its work on aircraft gas turbine engines, though it had never built an aircraft engine before. In the course of its work, the company made some significant technological strides. Westinghouse then had some success with scaling up its developments to maintain a significant share of the turbojet market. After this period of success, with its incumbent rapid growth, the company made a series of decisions that led to its subsequent decline and withdrawal from the turbojet business entirely. The history of the Westinghouse Aviation Gas Turbine Division provides some useful lessons both to those studying the history of the technology, as well as those who would design and develop this technology's products.

As first related in Chapter Three, the Westinghouse Corporation's interest in turbojet development began with the Durand Special Committee on Jet Propulsion and was fostered by a Navy letter of intent. Westinghouse's interest in turbine engines had been spurred by the research of Westinghouse engineer Winston R. New. New had designed a gas turbine power plant for naval propulsion (receiving a patent for his system in 1942). The promise of this new technology, combined with the proposal prepared by Dr. Stewart Way to the Durand Special Committee outlining an aircraft gas turbine, influenced the decision of the company to commit to developing this new technology.

## Westinghouse and the "Yankee"

Westinghouse participated in the Durand Special Committee on Jet Propulsion and indicated an interest in conducting further research on turbojets. Westinghouse's Manager of Development Engineering, Reinout P. Kroon, wrote to Westinghouse's Manager of Engineering, F.T. Hague, outlining a specific plan of approach to the Navy on October 13, 1941.[1] On December 8, the day after the Japanese attack on Pearl Harbor, representatives from Westinghouse visited the Navy Bureau of Aeronautics and asked how they could assist in the Navy's aircraft engine development program. The official Navy response to this proposal came on January 7, 1942, when the Navy gave Westinghouse a letter of intent calling for "the study and design" of a small booster turbojet to assist carrier aircraft in short takeoffs.[2] This was in keeping with the Navy's requirements for carrier aircraft. Carrier takeoffs and potential landing wave-offs required high thrust at low airspeed. The Navy required a booster turbojet capable of 600 pounds of thrust at 500 mph (basis for 500mph requirement is unclear) and an altitude of 25,000 feet—the equivalent of 1,100 pounds of thrust at sea level.[3] Schlaifer states that the initial specification called for 450 pounds of thrust at 500 mph at 25,000 feet (corresponding to approximately 1,000 pounds of thrust at sea-level static).[4]

Westinghouse was authorized on October 22, 1942, to construct two 19-inch axial-compressor turbojet engines. They designated the project the 19A. Reinout P. Kroon was named the engineering leader and Ole Rogers the head of design. The design of the 19A incorporated a six-stage axial compressor developing a pressure ratio of approximately 3.4; twenty-four conical can-type combustors arranged in groups of three around the annulus; a single-stage turbine; and a movable tail cone to adjust nozzle area for starting and maximum power. The accessories for the engine were enclosed within the compressor cone to minimize the anticipated drag on the engine as it was test-flown suspended from a Navy F4U "Corsair." The turbojet was designed to run on gasoline so that both the booster turbojet and the reciprocating engine could run on the same fuel. The engine incorporated three journal bearings, two cylindrical bearings, and a double-taper combined radial and thrust bearing. Although the original design did not include an oil sump, one was later added to help prevent oil leaking along the shaft of the engine.[5]

The 19A first ran on the test bench on March 19, 1943, developing 1,135 pounds of thrust. Former Bureau of Aeronautics engineer and Westinghouse historian Lewis Smith recalls:

> An interesting incident occurred while this engine was being tested outdoors at night at the South Philadelphia plant. Sparks came out of the tailpipe. They shut down and inspected the engine, but could find nothing wrong. After starting again, more sparks came out. They finally found that mosquitoes were being ingested and catching fire in the combustor. They were so large they were still burning out the tailpipe - which gives a good idea of the size of the mosquitoes along the Delaware River![6]

By July 1943 the 19A had passed a 100-hour endurance test, marking the successful completion of the first phase of their development contract. In a Navy memorandum dated July 10, 1943, the head of the Bureau of Aeronautics Power Plant Design Section, S.B. Spangler, rated Westinghouse's progress in completing the endurance test. Although the Navy considered that "...this test demonstrated that all of the major elements of the unit are sound, and that some of the initial troubles which were experienced have been overcome," a number of minor difficulties had shown up in the endurance test. These included overheating of the bearings, excessive oil consumption, a turbine blade failure, and trouble with operating the nozzle control of the engine. Spangler found that the Westinghouse 19B compared favorably to the then-current British jet engines, the Halford and Whittle turbojets, in terms of shape, air inlet, weight, thrust, surging and operating difficulties. In a comparison of fuel consumption the 19B showed 1.29 pounds per hour per pound of static thrust, a Metro-Vickers F-2 showed 1.11, the Whittle W.2/500 showed 1.25, and the Halford H-1 showed 1.27. Spangler summed up the work done by Westinghouse to date:

> It appears that the Westinghouse engineers have done an outstanding job in the development of their engine. Unaided by any of the British experience in this field (because of the United States Army's secrecy restrictions) they have designed a unit which appears to be fundamentally superior from almost every standpoint to the British developments. Moreover, they have accomplished this in a remarkably short time. The original conception is less than two years old. The bureau awarded a letter of intent for a study contract only seventeen months ago. The contract for the construction of the unit was let nine months ago. The first unit was completed four months ago. The time required to develop this engine to the point of passing a satisfactory type test compares most favorably with the development time of any experimental engine known to the bureau.[7]

A second 19A was test flown under an F4U Corsair in the fall of 1943. Westinghouse flew the 19A for the first time in its original function as a booster on January 21, 1944. The engine developed 1,200 pounds of thrust. A total of six of these engines was built.[8]

The initial thrilling pace of the company's design and development of the 19A was to drop off considerably as Westinghouse moved from initial design and development to ongoing incremental development and preproduction of its engines. The company was about to learn about the physical requirements of aircraft engine design and developments and the company's lack of adequate plants and facilities. Although the company received full credit for design and development of the 19A design, production of 500 subsequent 19XBs was given to P&W in January of 1944.[9]

## The Westinghouse 9.5 (J32) Turbojet Engine

By January 1944, Westinghouse had prepared three sets of designs for derivatives of the 19A. The first was for a 9.5-inch-diameter booster engine design for aircraft wing installation, jet-assisted takeoff, or missiles. This design was later designated the J32 by the Navy. The J32 had a six-stage compressor, can-annular combustors, and a single-stage turbine made of K42B alloy (although subsequent J32s used Hastelloy B and several other alloys). It incorporated two rolling-element bearings instead of three journal-type, and featured, for the first time, precision-cast turbine and compressor blading.[10] The engine control for missile use acted on the centrifugal governor to produce three different thrusts corresponding to launch, cruise, and full-out attack. The first test of the 9.5A turbojet was in June 1944, when it produced 275 pounds of thrust. The J32 missile variant never went into production due to its high cost (at $20,000) and because rocket engines were considered adequate for missile use. Of the forty-four J32s that were built, most were used in the Naval Air Factory's "Gorgon" missile and TD2N target drones.[11]

There were two reasons for the Navy's dropping the 19A booster turbojet application for its fighters. First, although the booster turbojet provided the necessary thrust, that thrust was off-center. At 400 mph, with the 19A providing approximately one-half the total thrust of the aircraft's propulsion, the gun platform was unstable. The second reason was that the pilot was too busy to control an additional engine. The booster tests, however, did point up major areas for improvement in the ignition and combustion systems.[12]

## Design and Development of the Westinghouse 19B (J30) Yankee Turbojet

The second Westinghouse turbojet derivative developed from the 19A was the 19B engine for piloted aircraft. This engine was later designated the J30 (Figure 6-1). The 19B was an improved version of the 19A, and was designed for use as a main propulsion unit in an aircraft. The accessories were now located on the outside of the unit. The engine still used a six-stage compressor and single-stage turbine with blades made from Refractalloy alloy and Stellites and discs made from 19-9-DL or Timken 16-25-6. The thrust was 1,350 pounds, the weight was now 731 pounds, and the specific fuel consumption was 1.27. The most important new feature was a single annular combustor which replaced the 24-can system and was responsible for the 200 pounds of improved thrust. This advance, the work of Dr. Stewart Way,[13] was a major step for Westinghouse.

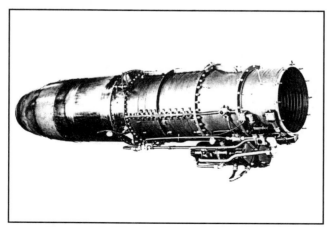

**Figure 6-1. Westinghouse 19XB-2B (J30)**
*(Photo courtesy of Westinghouse)*

By March 1944, the company was finding out that the production of turbojet engines was not an easy game to get into, even with Westinghouse's extensive background in steam turbines and their very good track record in initial development of the Yankee. The award of a production contract to P&W in January 1944 for 500 19XB turbojets (later reduced to 190) did not please Westinghouse.

The company realized that their current development facility, the "South Philadelphia Works," did not have the necessary machinery and equipment to develop and manufacture turbojet engines in addition to their main program for the design and manufacture of marine propulsion equipment to be used on destroyers, aircraft carriers, cruisers, and battleships.[14] Westinghouse had managed their to-date small amount of manufacturing work by either subcontracting or fitting it into the general shops at the Works. Realizing that the manufacture of even experimental engines was beyond their current capabilities, they asked the Navy to provide "approximately $1,000,000 worth of machinery and equipment"[15] with which to manufacture fifty experimental engines. They asked for additional Navy help in locating qualified subcontractors. Complicating things even more, the "Works" was located in what the military considered a "class two" critical labor area, which meant that the number of new workers available was going to be limited within the following six months.

An internal confidential Navy memorandum succinctly summed up the Navy's view of the company's progress in the development of turbojet aircraft engines and their current capabilities to manufacture production quantities of future engines:

> The current status of their jet-propulsion development may be summed up as follows: Of the total of six model 19A units that have been ordered, about five have been completed. There are twenty-eight model 19B units that have been ordered; the first of these is expected to be completed in March 1944 with the rate of manufacture to reach five per month starting in June. Neither of these models are believed to have sufficient performance to warrant considering their future production. Westinghouse are [sic] now proceeding with the design of a model 19XB unit with substantially improved performance; in addition, a 91/2A unit (91/2 refers to the engine's diameter) has been designed and is being constructed in small quantities for an NAF project (Gorgon).
>
> The "South Philadelphia Works" has had no experience in precision aircraft engine quality manufacture or in mass production.
>
> The record of the "South Philadelphia Works" to date in the experimental manufacture of their jet-propulsion unit design has been unsatisfactory; they are already approximately eight months late in delivery of 19A and 19B engines compared to their contract delivery schedule. This lateness was due primarily to the lack of effort put forth by the organization on their jet-propulsion project.[16]

The Navy representatives went on to state that:

> Since it is important that original production be carried on by the parent organization which develops a new piece of equipment as complex as the jet-propulsion unit, it is suggested that the problem of handling experimental manufacture and future production quantities of the Westinghouse jet-propulsion unit be presented to the top management at Westinghouse so that they may formulate a plan for meeting the bureau's requirements for experimental units, and for providing a substantial foundation on which to build up initial future production.[17]

Westinghouse ended manufacture of the J30 in 1944. Although they did not receive a production contract, Westinghouse was awarded a subcontract to assemble and test the last thirty of the 190 engines produced by P&W in October 1945. Westinghouse also got the Navy's message about facilities and corporate commitment. On February 1, 1945, Westinghouse established a separate Aviation Gas Turbine Division.

On January 2, 1945, one improved 19XB-2B (J30), developing 1,165 pounds of thrust, provided sole power for a McDonnell XFD-1 (FH-1) on a short "hop" over the runway. The second 19XB engine of the original two-engine configuration arrived late, so the first true test flight on two J30 engines took place on January 26, 1945, at Lambert Field, St. Louis, with Woodward

Burke as test pilot. He made two flights totaling 49 minutes. Originally, Westinghouse and the Navy had envisioned using six 9.5-inch-diameter turbojets to power this new all-jet fighter because the turbojet's small diameter would allow submerged installation in the wing and produce minimum drag, but two 19B engines were chosen.

The XFD-1 "Phantom" (Figure 6-2) was designed by McDonnell Aircraft Corporation as a defensive combat patrol aircraft, operating from a carrier and flying at 15,000 feet. The engineering team led by Kendall Perkins had two constraints. The first was to design the aircraft on a very conservative basis and the second was to design the aircraft to emphasize simplicity in production and maintenance. Perkins and his team found that a twin-engine configuration was superior in that it led to a lighter aircraft, simpler controls and instrumentation, and the easier manufacture of foldable wings. The two engines were installed in the fillets of the wing roots to free the fuselage for the large fuel tanks needed for patrol endurance (and because of the high fuel consumption characteristic of early turbojets). The Phantom project was first authorized in January 1943, with mockup inspection between May 31 and June 3, 1943. The final contract was signed on August 30, 1943. By April 1945 the XFD-1 had made nine flights for a total of five hours in the air. This limited program had resulted from development problems with the 19XBs, including bearing failures and one engine failing from ingestion of foreign materials.[18]

**Figure 6-2. McDonnell XFD-1 Phantom**
*(Photo courtesy of McDonnell Douglas)*

The 19B "Yankee" turbojet, soon to be redesignated the J30 by the military, was also in the second XFD-1. Piloted by Navy Lt. Commander James Davidson, this was the first U.S. takeoff and landing by a pure-jet fighter aircraft from an aircraft carrier on July 19, 1946, on the USS Franklin D. Roosevelt.

By June, 1945 Westinghouse had accumulated 2,200 hours of testing axial turbojets, of which 500 hours were on the 9.5 and 1,700 hours were on the "19" series. The compressors and turbines were proving to be relatively trouble-free, but the company was, like many other turbojet developers, having trouble with combustion problems. Reinout P. Kroon, chief engineer on the Westinghouse turbojet engine team, described their combustion problems:

> Our biggest fundamental problem is in connection with combustion. This field was an entirely new field without precedence. New concepts have developed and a great deal has been learned. Our problems can be segregated into three phases:
>
> 1. Stability of combustion. It is realized now that in any combustion chamber there exists a limit of rich mixture and one of poor fuel air mixture beyond which the flame tends to become unsta-

ble and most energy is converted into smell and ultimately blow out. In our case we are not bothered by the poor mixture limit, but we have experienced trouble at high altitude in not being able to burn a rich enough mixture. This means that under certain conditions one is unable to reach sufficiently high turbine inlet temperature. Fortunately, under these conditions increasing flight speed always improves the combustion characteristics. At this time the ceiling at which we can operate the 19XB engines at all speeds and all rpm's is somewhere around 30,000 feet.

2. A second problem in combustion is the creation of uniform temperature at the exit of the combustion chamber. If the temperature distribution at the turbine inlet is not uniform, certain parts are subjected to higher temperature and have a shorter life than desired.

3. The third subject of investigation, and a very important one, is that of obtaining suitable life of the combustor, which, of course, is subjected to high temperature. I mentioned the one 9.5A burner that ran for 150 hours during a life test. Our average basket life is not that good. We are taking a number of steps to increase basket life.

At this stage combustion appears the most important factor, as far as life of the engines and range of operation is concerned. For this reason combustion research is pursued vigorously.[19]

Westinghouse was also reportedly having metallurgical problems with soft centers in turbine discs for the 19XB in October 1945. P&W was also reported as arranging for production of the 19XB-2B engines and was expected to start making tests that fall. The production contract for the 19XB had been reduced from an original 500 engines to about 190 by the Navy after V-J Day.[20]

In the spring of 1947 Westinghouse began to press the Navy for a full production contract for 24C (Navy designation-J34) and 19XB engines. They estimated that their production capability was, starting in July 1948, seventy to seventy-five engines per month. They could produce either type of engine or any percentage combination of engines. The company stated that the decrease in marine propulsion work had freed up the capability to produce thirty to thirty-five of these engines per month at the South Philadelphia Works, with the remainder of the engines to be produced "from an outside supplier" but assembled and tested at the South Philadelphia Works. The company said that their willingness in "rendering assistance to other companies that might manufacture 24C engines was based on the large requirements of the Armed Forces over and above quantities that Westinghouse might reasonably expect to produce." Until the time came when future requirements would exceed the capacity of the company to produce, they believed "that Westinghouse should receive first consideration as the source of supply."[21]

By August 1948 Westinghouse was already beginning to plan for expansion to Kansas City, where the company was to begin manufacturing its own engines. Westinghouse estimated that it would employ 1,500 to 2,000 people at first and about 5,000 eventually. The Kansas City plant had been operated by P&W for the Navy.[22]

Westinghouse was also at this time taking the first steps in improving their combustion development capability through acquiring vaporizing combustor technology from Britain's Armstrong Siddeley Motors, Limited. After an initial visit to Armstrong Siddeley by Westinghouse's Floyd Hague that year, two Armstrong Siddeley engineers, Sidney Allen and Morris Stokes, made numerous visits to South Philadelphia. Westinghouse also dispatched E.P. Walsh and J.R. Hamm to Coventry to the Armstrong Siddeley works for a month in April 1950, and sent Hamm back for seven weeks in the fall of 1950. At the start, Armstrong Siddeley provided Westinghouse with a Mamba turbojet can combustor to test in the Westinghouse laboratory. Later, Armstrong Siddeley engineers helped design vaporizing combustors for both the J40-WE10/12 and J46 engines. The collaboration between Armstrong Siddeley and Westinghouse on vaporizing combustion ended with the cancellation of the J46 program.[23]

Westinghouse jet engine production was 50 percent greater in 1949 than in 1948, and the company expected a considerable increase in 1950 as a result of the Kansas City facility.[24]

## Design and Development of the Westinghouse J34

The third of the designs derived from the 19A design was the 24-inch-diameter 24C turbojet for piloted aircraft. The engine, designated by the Navy as the J34 (Figure 6-3), had eleven compressor stages delivering 50 pounds of air per second with a pressure ratio of 4:1. The combustion system was a double concentric annular combustor incorporating twenty-four downstream fuel injectors around the inner flame tube and thirty-six injectors around the outer flame tube. The J34 used a two-stage turbine. It weighed 1,255 pounds and delivered approximately 3,000 pounds of thrust. The first test of the 24C turbojet was in April of 1945.[25]

**Figure 6-3. Westinghouse J34**
*(Illustration courtesy of Westinghouse)*

The year 1950 proved to be important for the company. Although the year began with a series of major defense cuts by Secretary of Defense Louis Johnson, on June 25 South Korea was invaded by communist North Korea. Plans to reduce defense aviation were scrapped, new development programs were initiated, and Westinghouse shared in this upturn in defense contracts. It could show the Department of Defense some significant results in its turbojet development. The company's J34-WE-34 became the second U.S. turbojet to pass the 150-hour military qualification test. This same model was also certified for civilian use under the designation Westinghouse Model 24C-4D. Westinghouse delivered the first J34 turbojets to the military in 1950 for use in such Navy aircraft as the McDonnell Aircraft F2H Banshee, the Chance Vought F7U Cutlass, and the Douglas F3D Skyknight. J34 turbojets were also delivered to the Air Force for use in the McDonnell XF-88 Voodoo and the Lockheed XF-90 prototype aircraft.

With increased military contract requirements, Westinghouse was authorized to reopen the U.S. Navy's Naval Industrial Reserve Aircraft Plant in Kansas City, Missouri. The company hoped to begin its first jet engine assembly (of the J34) in March 1950, and expected to begin production of jet engine parts and assemblies in May of that year with a goal of 100 engines a month. The company claimed that the Kansas City plant was to be the "most complete self-contained jet engine plant in the country."[26] As events turned out, the Kansas City gas turbine plant began operation in January 1951, assembling jet engines from parts shipped in from Pittsburgh and from subcontractors. The plant began fabrication of its own parts soon thereafter. All in all, over 4,500 J34 engines were built by Westinghouse, P&W, and Ford Motor Company for the Navy.[27] In August 1951 the magazine Aviation Week reported that both Westinghouse and General Electric were working on 10,000-pound-thrust turbojet engines, with Westinghouse slightly in the lead in their development. Both programs were oriented towards late production models of military aircraft then in early phases of production. Production of the J34 ended in 1962.

## The Westinghouse J40

In June 1947, the Navy's Bureau of Aeronautics authorized Westinghouse to begin development of a 6,000-pound-thrust axial turbojet, designated the J40 (Figure 6-4). By 1951, the design thrust had grown to 10,000 pounds.

**Figure 6-4. Westinghouse J40**
*(Photo courtesy of Westinghouse)*

With the Kansas City plant up and running and the Korean War in full swing, Westinghouse was poised to introduce the 10,000-pound-thrust J40 turbojet engine into production. The J40 passed its 150-hour qualification test in January 1951. The engine had an automatic electronic control system and a stainless steel combustion chamber.[28]

Aviation Week reported on February 5, 1951, that Douglas Aircraft Corporation planned to use the Westinghouse J40 turbojet in several of its aircraft, specifically in the F4D fighter interceptor, the A3D attack plane, and a new swept-wing fighter, the F3H Demon.[29]

Riding high on Navy orders for the J40 turbojet, Westinghouse announced plans in October 1951 for an additional jet engine parts plant in Columbus, Ohio. This addition was just part of an overall $296 million expansion program planned by the company. Things were looking good for Westinghouse as they had just received military orders for several hundred million dollars worth of electronics equipment, aircraft armaments, jet pylons, jet engines, and appliances. This expansion was the largest in the company's history and would increase their manufacturing capacity by over 50 percent. The company also formed a Defense Products Group to oversee the design and development of jet engines, atomic power plant equipment, aircraft armaments, radar apparatus and other electronic gear and aircraft parts. Sales for the first nine months of 1950 were up 23 percent over the previous year for an income of $42,757,000.[30]

Westinghouse's optimism was premature, however. By August 1952 its Aviation Gas Turbine Division was in trouble. The J40 program had become a major problem for manufacturers of Naval aircraft designed around the engine. The South Philadelphia engineering team ran into development problems with the original target design, designated the J40-24, so in December 1952 the company turned to a down-rated version of the engine, designated the J40-22, to meet the contractual delivery deadlines.

In January of 1953, the Navy announced a multimillion dollar increase in the J40 development program in an effort to get the engine up to specified power. Ford's J40 backlog was listed as $154 million.

By March, however, the Navy had changed its mind. During the week of March 9, the Bureau of Aeronautics announced that it was actively considering alternate engines for several advanced aircraft types currently powered by the Westinghouse J40. The Navy also announced that it had "greatly curtailed" the J40 production program at Ford's plant in Romulus, Michigan.[31] Aircraft affected by the Navy's decision were the McDonnell F3H Demon general-purpose, all-weather interceptor, the Douglas A3D twin-jet carrier bomber, and the Douglas F4D Skyray carrier-based interceptor. In each case the aircraft manufacturer and the Navy had decided to replace the under-powered J40 engines with either Allison J71 or Pratt & Whitney J57 turbojet engines. Bureau of Aeronautics spokesmen announced that the "phasing in" of alternative engines would be governed by the relative progress of the J40 and its rivals. Westinghouse and Ford ended production of the J40 in 1953.[32] Although the J40-22 was delivered to the Navy and flew in an F3H in December, it was too late; the Navy had canceled the contract in September. The J40 wound up costing the government $137 million for 107 engines that could not meet the original design goals. The difficulties with the J40 and the subsequent Navy and congressional outcry were devastating to Westinghouse.

## The Westinghouse J46

Westinghouse was encountering similar problems with the J46 engine program. This lag was in turn retarding the development programs of Douglas Aircraft's swept-wing F3D Skyknight and Vought's F7U-3 Cutlass (Figure 6-5)[33], leading Douglas to decide in March 1952 to not use the J46 to replace the J34 in the Skyknight. This left only one application, the twin-engined Cutlass.

**Figure 6-5. Chance Vought F-7U Cutlass**
*(Photo courtesy of U.S. Navy)*

The J46 made its first flight in a Cutlass, the week of May 4, 1953. Though it was slated to be the power plant in all Cutlass aircraft, in June of that year Chance Vought announced another delay in equipping its F7U-3 Cutlass with J46 engines. Testing had shown an overspeed condition at altitude, requiring grounding of the aircraft. Chance Vought announced a target date for acceptance of the J46 engines of late July. The company had to date been flying F7U-3s with Allison J35 engines.[34]

In June 1953 Westinghouse attempted to return to a competitive position in the field with the signing of a ten-year agreement with Rolls-Royce calling for broad technical cooperation on jet engine development limited only by security restrictions imposed by their respective governments. Westinghouse announced that the initial application of the agreement would be on the ailing J46 program. The company denied that the Navy's Bureau of Aeronautics had initiated the agreement in order to bring the J46 program back on schedule.[35]

By January 1954, Chance Vought's inability to secure adequate numbers of J46 turbojets for its F7U-3 Cutlass had resulted in the forced layoff of 1,500 assembly workers, the scheduled dismissal of 1,000 more the week of January 18, and a proposal to lay off 750 more by the end of the year. Aviation Week reported that F7U-3s were sitting outside of Vought's Dallas aircraft plant awaiting J46 engines.[36]

In December 1955 the Navy canceled the rest of Vought's F7U-3 Cutlass production, having outfitted only four squadrons with the underpowered aircraft.[37] The Navy had already canceled the attack version of the aircraft, the Model A2U-1, after ordering ninety-six of them. In a speech during the week of March 21, 1955, the Assistant Secretary of the Navy for Air, James H. Smith Jr., told a propulsion meeting of the Institute for Aeronautical Sciences in Cleveland of the Navy's frustration with the Westinghouse J40 and J46 engine programs and the Allison Division of General Motors' J71 program. The development delays caused by these tardy engine programs, he said, were directly responsible for the cancellations of the Chance Vought F7U and McDonnell F3H aircraft in the fall of 1954. Smith said that the Navy had invested over $1 billion in these two aircraft and engine development programs, not counting government furnished equipment.

In 1954 Westinghouse built a new $12.5 million research and development laboratory in Kansas City to which it transferred most of the South Philadelphia personnel. In October 1955 Westinghouse became the target of a congressional investigation after several J40-powered F3H Demons crashed. Bureau of Aeronautics officials defended their selection of Westinghouse for the development contract on the basis of the company's prior record. Westinghouse officials, however, admitted to inadequate jet-engine research and development facilities at South Philadelphia. More important, Westinghouse officials also admitted to a degree of complacency arising from their earlier turbojet success.

What happened to Westinghouse and the Navy with the J40 and its development was a clear example of the inability of a company at that time to design and produce efficient and reliable high-capacity turbojets. Only the commitment of hundreds of millions of dollars by a select few companies and large military research and development programs would ultimately correct the situation.

Westinghouse used its own funds to develop and build the J54, a 6,000-pound-thrust engine. Although the engine performed up to standard in tests, the results did not lead to a production contract. A two-month strike in Kansas City further threatened the company's already precarious market position vis-à-vis GE and P&W.

The Navy tried to keep Westinghouse in the jet engine business. In 1957, they awarded Westinghouse a contract to upgrade the J34 for a North American jet trainer application, followed in 1959 by a $6.15 million production order for the engine. This, however, was not enough. In 1962 Westinghouse decided to drop out of the jet engine manufacturing business due to both an inability and unwillingness to invest the funds necessary to remain competitive. Although their J34 was an excellent engine, Westinghouse could not keep up the development pace without a major investment of facilities and capital. The company ended up surrendering their position in the Navy jet engine market to P&W.

## Endnotes

1   Letter, dated October 13, 1941, from Reinout P. Kroon, Manager, Westinghouse Development Engineering Division, to F. T. Hague, Westinghouse Manager of Engineering, Westinghouse South Philadelphia Works, 1-3.

2   Letter of Offer of Contract, dated January 7, 1942, from U.S. Navy Department, Bureau of Supplies and Accounts, Washington D. C., to Westinghouse Electric and Manufacturing Company, 159 Broadway, New York City, New York, Letter, dated October 13, 1941, from Reinout P. Kroon, Manager of Westinghouse Development Engineering Division, to F.T. Hague, Westinghouse Manager of Engineering, Philadelphia, Pennsylvania, and Smith, Lewis F. History of Westinghouse Aviation Gas Turbines, Unpublished paper, 1994, 1.

3   Smith, History of Westinghouse Aviation Gas Turbines, 1.

4   Schlaifer, Robert, Development of Aircraft Engines, Boston, MA: Harvard University Press, 1949, 470, and Woodbury, David O., Battlefronts of Industry: Westinghouse in World War II, New York: John Wiley & Sons, Incorporated, 1948, 277.

5   Smith, History of Westinghouse Aviation Gas Turbines, 2.

6   Ibid.

7   Memorandum, dated July 10, 1943, from U.S. Navy Department, Bureau of Aeronautics Power Plant Design Section, to Westinghouse Head of Engineering Branch, Experiments and Developments, VF Design, 6.

8   Kroon, Reinout P., "Engineering History," Unpublished paper, June 1945, From the Reinout P. Kroon Papers, 2, and Schlaifer, Development, 472.

9   U.S. Navy Department, "Memorandum of Conference Held in Room 2902, Bureau of Aeronautics, on October 1945, regarding Arrangements for Production of Model 19XB-2B Turbo-Jet Engines," dated October 29, 1945.

10  Kroon, Reinout P, "The Jet Engine Comes of Age," Westinghouse Engineering 10 (September, 1950), 197.

11  Kroon, "Engineering History", 2, and Smith, History of Westinghouse Aviation Gas Turbine, 5.

12  Smith, History of Westinghouse Aviation Gas Turbine, 3.

13  Ibid.

14  Internal Confidential Memorandum (now declassified), dated March 4, 1944, from Lt. (jg) F. M. van Eck, U.S. Navy Department, Bureau of Aeronautics, Washington, D.C., to Lt. Comdr. H. C. Haskell, 1.

15  Ibid.

16  Ibid, 2.

17  Ibid, 2-3.

18  Francillon, Rene J., McDonnell Douglas Aircraft Since 1920: Volume II, Annapolis, MD: Naval Institute Press, 1990, 663-665 and Smith, History of Westinghouse Aviation Gas Turbine, and Schlaifer, Development, 472.

19  Kroon, "Engineering History", 6-7.

20  "Jet Experiments Proceeding Slowly," Aviation Week 4 (October 15, 1945), 26.

21  Letter, dated May 8, 1947, from R. M. Wilson, Manager, Washington Office of Westinghouse Electric Corporation, to Chief, Bureau of Aeronautics, Navy Department, Washington, D.C., Subject: "Westinghouse Production Capacity; 24C and 19XB Turbo-Jet Engines."

22  "Briefing Production News," Aviation Week 50 (August 30, 1948), 18.

23  Hamm, R. J., Vaporizing Combustor Applications in Westinghouse Jet Engines, Unpublished paper, 1992.

24  "Industry Observer," Aviation Week 52 (March 13, 1950), 9.

25  Kroon, "Engineering History", 2, Smith, History of Westinghouse Aviation Gas Turbine, 5, and Gunston, Bill, World Encyclopedia of Aero Engines, Second Edition, England: Patrick Stephens Limited, 1989, 176.

26  "Industry Observer," Aviation Week 52 (March 27, 1950), 7.

27  "Industry Observer," Aviation Week 51 (August 22, 1949), 11, and Smith, History of Westinghouse Aviation Gas Turbines, 5.

28  "News Digest," Aviation Week 54 (January 29, 1951), 7.

29  "Industry Observer," Aviation Week 54 (February 5, 1951), 11.

30  Ibid.

31  "BuAer Considering Alternates for J40," Aviation Week 58 (March 16, 1953), 18.

32  Ibid.

33  "Industry Observer," Aviation Week 58 (May 4, 1953), 11.

34  "Industry Observer," Aviation Week 58 (June 8, 1953), 10.

35  "New Jet Pact," Aviation Week 58 (June 22, 1953), 16.

36  "News Digest: Domestic," Aviation Week 60 (January 18, 1954), 7.

37  Bowers, Peter M. and Swanborough, Gordon, United States Navy Aircraft Since 1911, Annapolis, MD: Naval Institute Press, 1990, 454.

**Air Force B-47, Powered by
Six General Electric J47 Turbojets**

# GE Applies New Ideas and American Technology

## The T31, J35, and J47 Engines

There was a reason for the U.S. Army Air Forces choosing the GE Company to build the Whittle Engine. GE's work on internal combustion gas turbines for ground power use began in 1903 and is well chronicled in Edward W. Constant II's *Origins of the Turbojet Revolution*. The work of Sanford Moss and Glenn B. Warren at GE in the 1910s, 1920s and 1930s was very important in that it gave GE a great deal of experience to draw upon.

In 1937 the Steam Turbine Division began work on locomotive gas turbines under the leadership of Glenn Warren. GE's Engineering Council approved design studies by Warren's team of a 4,000-horsepower gas turbine for railroad locomotives in February 1941. GE/Schenectady's Steam Turbine Division obtained a contract in 1940 from the Navy to build and test a combustion chamber and a single-stage turbine using shop supply air. The Steam Turbine Division also contracted to build and test a four-stage, axial-flow compressor. The gas turbine and axial compressor contracts were supposed to lead to the development of a Navy turbine-powered patrol torpedo boat. The Steam Turbine Division was in an excellent position to begin an aircraft gas turbine engine initiative led by Howard and Warren.[1]

In January 1941, the National Academy of Sciences called for the development of gas turbines for marine propulsion. This recommendation attracted the Navy, which promptly contracted with Allis-Chalmers and then with Westinghouse for marine gas turbine propulsion work. Allis-Chalmers, Westinghouse, and GE were all subsequently called by the Durand Subcommittee of the National Advisory Committee on Aeronautics (NACA) to participate in discussions that would lead to preliminary designs of whatever aircraft gas turbine type each felt was most promising. As stated in Chapter Five, General Arnold of the Army Air Corps became intensely interested in jet propulsion in March 1941.

GE's involvement with aircraft gas turbines is said to have begun in 1940, with a visit by Alan Howard of the GE Schenectady Steam Turbine Division to Cleveland to observe tests on a new axial-flow compressor which were being conducted by NACA.[2] Howard came back to GE convinced that a turboprop engine using an axial compressor was a practical possibility. The potentially lower weight of the axial compressor as compared to a centrifugal compressor, together with the much smaller frontal area (both very important to high-speed aircraft) made the axial engine an attractive proposition to Howard. His conviction was to be substantially augmented by increased Army Air Corps and NACA interest in aircraft gas turbine engine research by industry in the spring and summer of 1941.

In the summer of 1941 two engineers from GE/Schenectady, Alex Stevenson and Glenn Warren, were invited by William Durand to meet with him to discuss changing GE's research priority in gas turbine research at Schenectady from locomotive gas turbines to aircraft gas turbines. The company subsequently decided to delay their research effort on locomotives, finish up their work on gas turbines for naval propulsion, and initiate a small group to begin looking at aircraft gas turbine engines.[3]

In July 1941 a secret conference of NACA's Durand committee with Army, Navy, and industry representatives outlined an American program of turbojet development. An axial-flow turbojet design was presented by Westinghouse, a turbofan design by Allis-Chalmers, and a two-shaft, axial-flow turboprop by GE. The committee decided that each of the three companies should go ahead with a detailed study of the type of engine it preferred. GE decided to stick with the turboprop, which reflected the input of Warren and of Alan Howard.

## Design and Development of the TG-100 (T31) Axial-Flow Turboprop Engine

The GE TG-100 (Figure 7-1) was the first American turboprop engine to be designed and operated. On July 25, 1941, a GE design team began detail design of the TG-100 under Army contract at the GE Steam Turbine Division in Schenectady, New York.[4]

**Figure 7-1. GE TG-100 (T31)**
*(Photo courtesy of GE)*

Alan Howard of GE described the initial design criteria for the TG-100 in a paper presented to the 1945 Aircraft Gas Turbine Engineering Conference sponsored by GE and held in West Lynn, Massachusetts:

> With a gas-turbine power plant for propeller drive such as the TG-100 the objective is to design a plant having the optimum combination of weight, size, fuel rate, cruising power and take-off power. This optimum combination depends very materially upon the mission assumed. For long range, minimum fuel rate should be emphasized even at the expense of considerable increase in power-plant weight. The sum of fuel weight plus power-plant weight should be approximately a minimum. The proper ratio of jet power to propeller power is dependent on the speed of the airplane.[5]

The Durand Committee decided in September 1941 that all three companies working on turbine engine designs should be given development contracts, and NACA relinquished supervision of the study projects to the military services. The Navy assumed funding responsibility for the Westinghouse and Allis-Chalmers programs, and the Army Air Forces assumed funding for the GE work.

The design team at Schenectady finished the design layout of the TG-100 by December 23, 1941. The baseline of the engine design reflected GE's studies of Navy PT boat gas turbines in 1938, 1939, and 1940. The TG-100 incorporated a fourteen-stage, axial-flow compressor using a NACA database. The compressor was tested on a single spool test rig. The engine had nine cylindrical combustion chambers and a high-energy, single-stage shrouded power turbine for both compressor and propeller. The turbine blades were cast Vitallium, welded to Timken rims on ferrotic steel hubs to solve casting problems on large alloy steel forgings. The turbine nozzle, a Prandtl-Buseman C-D supersonic design with air-cooled vanes, admitted combustion gases at temperatures up to 1900°F.

The TG100 gearbox was a low-loss design (3 percent) and was very lightweight (for the era).[6] It used a double planetary reduction gear of about 10:1 ratio in series to reduce the power plant speed of 13,000 rpm to the propeller speed of 1,145 rpm. Propeller pitch was controlled as a function of engine speed and torque output. At this point the work of constructing the unit was ready to begin.[7]

In early 1942 the Army Air Forces contracted with GE for development of a specific deliverable, the TG-100 turboprop, which was given a military designation of T31. The Army Air Forces thus began a two-track approach to aircraft gas turbine development, funding the Whittle-based centrifugal-compressor turbojet at GE/Lynn, and the NACA-based axial-compressor turboprop at GE/Schenectady. From discussions with engineers at both locations, it appears that the Army's aviation engineering establishment at Wright Field controlled both development programs, while at the same time they restricted the flow of information from Lynn to Schenectady and vice versa.

Originally designed for 1,200 shaft horsepower, the TG-100 delivered 1,900 shaft horsepower in early tests. Later the engine was rated at 2,200 shaft horsepower and 630 pounds of thrust. On one test at low ambient air temperature the engine delivered 2,750 shaft horsepower.

GE engineer William R. Travers, in the GE Aircraft Engine Story, describes the engine in detail:

> The TG-100 was GE's first attempt to design and develop an axial compressor for aircraft. The single-stage large diameter power turbine was designed to handle gas temperatures of up to 1900°F. The engine weight peaked at 1,950 pounds. The turbine design was a single stage Curtiss or impulse type. The turbine had a very high load coefficient, because the turbine's single stage drove both the load and compressor. The turbine nozzle was a Prandtl-Buseman type of converging-diverging supersonic nozzle. This design made possible a large drop in gas temperature before the gas was exposed to the blades, and also provided very high velocity hot gas. The turbine buckets were made of cast Vitallium (like turbosuperchargers) and were welded to the turbine wheel, because there was no time to develop dovetail attachments.[8]

On May 15, 1943, the TG-100 was successfully test-run without the propeller, seven months after the first jet engine flight in the United States.[9] Travers relates:

> Prior to its first flight, the engine was extensively tested. Engineers tried various means of controlling the propeller pitch and speed. Because there was no facility at Schenectady to test the engine with a propeller, the engineers agreed that the engine could be run with a propeller at Wright Field in order to get flight clearance for the XP-81. They also decided to flight-test the TG-100 in the right hand nacelle of a Curtiss-Wright C-46 at the Curtiss-Wright facility in Columbus, Ohio. But the C-46 flight-testing was canceled after the attempt at a first flight failed because the direction of the aircraft could not be controlled as it rolled down the runway. Actually, it ran into a large tractor.[10]

The TG-100 did finally get into the air on December 21, 1944, as the main power plant (but without a propeller) in the nose of a Consolidated Vultee XP-81 (Figure 7-2).[11] On May 15, 1945, the TG-100 (T31) was successfully tested with a propeller for the first time.[12] Forty-seven flights took place in one year prior to December 19, 1946, and a total of 104 flights were made in the XP-81 and the Ryan XF2R-1 (a Navy aircraft) prior to June 10, 1947.[13]

With the end of the war, GE consolidated all aircraft gas turbine engine development in Lynn and the Steam Turbine Division got back to development of locomotive gas turbines. All T31 engineering and manufacturing responsibilities went to Lynn. Prior to the transfer, the team at Schenectady had delivered twelve TG-100A engines.

**Figure 7-2. Consolidated Vultee XP-81**
*(Photo courtesy of GE)*

GE engineers at Lynn started the design of the TG-100B in September 1945. The new design aimed at eliminating problems in the bearings and in turbine gas temperature distribution. Due to the fact that high turbine inlet temperatures (as high as 1900°F) resulted in relatively short and unpredictable service life of the turbines on the TG-100A, the TG-100B included turbine rim and hub cooling. The TG-100B was first run with a propeller on November 18, 1947. It passed the 50-hour Flight Qualification Test on April 5, 1949, and the 150-hour Type Test on May 16, 1949.

The TG-100 engine suffered from lack of a propeller design that could change pitch rapidly enough to prevent overspeed. High rotational inertia, however, helped keep the overspeed within tolerable limits. This was due to the configuration of the entire rotor system turbine, compressor, drive train, and propeller as one integral rotational unit. Travers describes how the GE engineers accomplished the 'fix':

> In order to overcome the problem encountered during flight tests, GE engineers incorporated into the TG-100B a new torque and fuel regulator, which controlled the pitch of the propeller directly as a function of the engine torque output. The engineers achieved very rapid power changes, using the regulator and Beta (manually) controlled pitch propellers (Hamilton Standard and Aeroproducts), which had a high rate of pitch change. The high inertia rotor served as an additional source of energy for rapid increases in engine power.[14]

The Lynn TG-100B team had overcome another serious development problem in 1948. It seemed that every engine vibrated excessively on final test.

> The compressors and turbine rotors had been balanced individually and as a unit. A metal disk (with a threaded hole in its center) was devised that screwed onto the threaded lifting lug in the center of the turbine wheel. Then a number of holes were tapped radially into that disk. Selective studs were put into these holes for rotor balance. Then the engineers devised a system to synchronize the passing of a magnetized blade with the vibration meter. It worked; the engines were shipped. Months later field engineers wondered about the purpose of this very special disk on the turbine wheel of these TG-100s.[15]

The TG-100B was developed with funding from both the Navy and the Air Force. The Navy was interested in the flight testing of this turboprop in their XFR-1 Fireball, a Ryan aircraft that incorporated a radial reciprocating engine in the nose and a turbojet engine in the fuselage, extending out the rear of the aircraft. The Navy funding was handled through Air Force procurement channels, and was to increase to the point where the Navy ultimately took over this program along with all military turboprop research and development.

On July 20, 1949, the U.S. Air Force canceled all turboprop development programs, preferring to leave turboprop development to the Navy. All Air Force development funds for the

T31 were redirected to the development of an electronic control system for an afterburner version of the J47.[16] GE opted out of the T31 development program at that point. With the strain put on GE/Lynn by the J47 development and manufacturing programs, along with all its contractual commitments, the company decided to drop the turboprop and develop turbojets exclusively.

GE/Lynn delivered an additional sixteen TG-100B (T31) turboprops, bringing the total number of TG-100s of all models to twenty-eight. The company was not to get into the turboprop business again until the design and development of the T58 and T64 turboshaft/turboprop engines. The TG-100 (T31) program, however, provided the company with necessary background work in axial-compressor development. Furthermore, their work on this engine convinced them that the axial turbojet, with its low frontal diameter, was to be the predominant military engine type in the foreseeable future. Although the company dropped their turboprop development work in 1949, they had already embarked upon the next step in their aircraft gas turbine development path, the TG-180 axial-flow turbojet.

## Design and Development of the TG-180 (J35) Axial-Flow Turbojet Engine

Although the design, development and limited production of the TG-100 gave GE a great deal of experience in axial-flow compressor and turbine design, the culmination of the first-generation work of the company was the TG-180 (Figures 7-3 and 7-4). Although the company was fated to lose the mass-production contract to the Allison Division of General Motors in 1947, the TG-180 (later designated by the Army Air Forces the J35) was a very necessary second step in GE's path to the large-scale design, development, and manufacturing of aircraft gas turbine engines.

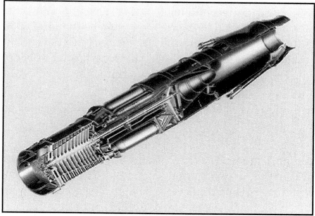

**Figure 7-3. Cutaway of TG-180 (J35) Engine**
*(Illustration courtesy of GE)*

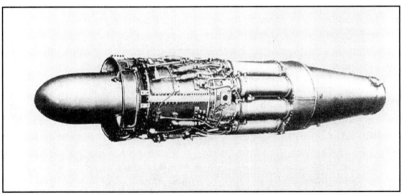

**Figure 7-4. TG-180 (J35) Engine**
*(Photo courtesy of GE)*

In early 1943 the Army Air Forces had asked GE to study the possibility of a turbojet to produce 3,000 pounds of thrust. GE responded with two designs: the TG-180 (later J35) axial and the I-40 (later J33) centrifugal turbojet. To the company's surprise, the Army Air Forces decided to fund both programs. The Army felt that the centrifugal design represented technology that could be used relatively soon on the battlefield, while the axial-turbojet design represented technology that held the most promise for applications farther down the road. On May 3, 1943, the axial-flow TG-180 (J35) project was begun at the request of the Materiel Command, at Wright Field.[17] The Army Air Forces contract with GE provided for the development of twenty-four experimental engines and one hundred development type engines for a total cost of about $16.4 million.[18]

In June 1943 GE decided after consultation with the Army Air Forces to increase their target thrust goal on the TG-180 (and, coincidentally, the I-40) from 3,000 pounds to 4,000 pounds.[19] The TG-180 design was so promising that the Army Air Forces decided to predicate a significant portion of their future heavy, high-altitude, long-range bomber program on this engine, with some ten different aircraft configurations either being designed or built with this power plant in mind.

The TG-180 represented an entirely new engine design and development program. The compressor was an axial-flow, 4:1 pressure ratio, eleven-stage unit featuring inlet screens and split casings for easier blade access. The combustor, incorporating technology from GE's Research Laboratory testing, had a straight-through air path. The turbine featured shrouded turbine blades and, as in the TG100, split casings for blade access. The engine's controls were the same as the TG100's except for a variable-displacement pump. The accessory gearbox was located in the engine air inlet. An additional new feature of the engine was the expandable oil-in-air/mist lube system for the engine bearings. The TG-180-A1 (J35) engine was tested for the first time on April 23, 1944.[20] It produced more than two and a half times the thrust of the I-16 engine.

In November 1944 GE delivered two GE-built J35 engines to Douglas Aircraft for flight tests in the XB-43. One of these engines suffered a compressor failure during ground tests and most of the rotor blades fell off.[21] The Army Air Forces felt that:

> The engine was not at all satisfactory and subsequent engines were also very poor. After ten engines had been delivered, with numerous difficulties and delays, Air Technical Service Command personnel visited the GE plant in April 1945 to eliminate the general laxness of the GE program.[22]

The early models of the J35 never passed a 150-hour test and the Army Air Forces felt that the service life of the engine was extremely low. As late as 1951, the Air Force Inspector General reported the average service life was 97 hours. From January to June 1952 the service life of the J35 increased to 102 hours.[23] Air Force records show that the J35-GE-9 did not pass the 150-hour Military Qualification Test until December 1947, although GE claims that the Military Qualification Test was passed on March 12, 1947.[24] The first Allison J35 model to pass the 150-hour test was the J35-A-17, which was rated at 4,900 pounds of thrust and was officially approved in November 1948.

In November 1944, the Army Air Forces gave the designs of the J35 to Chevrolet for production of the engine, although GE continued to develop the engine. This resulted in the J35-C-3 model, which was similar to the XJ35-GE-1, except that it was built by Chevrolet to production drawings. GE also developed a version of the J35-C-3 in which compressor stator blades were turned 5 to 7 degrees more in the axial direction. It developed 5000 pounds of thrust in both factory and wind tunnel tests in Cleveland, but for reasons unknown, GE did not produce it.[25]

After the war's end, Chevrolet decided to get out of the turbine engine production business and return to building automobiles. They turned production of the J35 over to the Allison Division of General Motors. This move did not make GE very happy, even though they did not have the capacity to undertake mass production of this or any other aircraft gas turbine engine at that time. November 8, 1945, saw the first flight of the GE TG-180 (J35) in a B-29 flying test bed.[26] On February 28, 1947, the J35-GE-7 was first flown in an XB-47 bomber.[27] It was similar to the J35-GE-1, except for a modification that caused the engine to be non-interchangeable with other J35 models.

On December 17, 1947, according to Boeing, the GE J35 was test-flown in an XP-84.[28] At this time the J35 had an average rating of 4,000 pounds of thrust, with a guarantee of 3,750 pounds. Both figures were just equal to those for the I-40 twenty months earlier. The eleven-stage axial compressor gave a smaller diameter (37.5 inches compared to 48) but greater weight (2,300 pounds versus 1,820); its higher efficiency at the same 4:1 pressure ratio gave a lower specific fuel consumption (1.075 versus 1.185 per hour).[29] The promise inherent in an axial design was there, but it would take longer and cost more to be realized. The U.S. Army Air Forces and Navy were beginning to lay down development goals that called for more thrust, lighter weight, and better specific fuel consumption. American aircraft designers were not happy with the larger diameter of the centrifugal turbojet and wanted to incorporate narrower turbojets in their new aircraft designs.

The end of World War II saw the curtailment or termination of many government contracts for aircraft and engines as the United States changed from a wartime to a peacetime economy. Coupled with the reduction in contracted production was a sudden glut of piston engines in a greatly depressed world market. Aircraft engine producers were concerned about finding use for their soon-to-be-empty manufacturing plants. They needed to either return to the products they had manufactured before the war (automobiles in the case of Chevrolet) or find new products to manufacture in their plants. One of these companies was the Allison Division of General Motors.

On September 12, 1947, when they turned over complete responsibility for the J35 to the Allison Division of GM,[30] GE was well along in the design and development of the TG-190 or J47, and the facilities at West Lynn could not really support both programs adequately. The passing of the 150-hour Military Qualification Test by the J35-GE-9 model at least cleared the way for service installation in the Republic F-84 Thunderjet (Figure 7-5) and a few B-45 aircraft, so GE would benefit from a limited amount of flight testing of the J35. GE delivered the last twelve J35 turbojets (produced prior to allocation of the J35 contract to Allison) to the U.S. Air Forces in early 1948.[31]

**Figure 7-5. Republic F-84s**
*(Photo courtesy of U.S. Air Force)*

Many GE engineers of that period expressed their opinion that GE was content to let Allison take over manufacture of the J33 and J35. They felt that this freed up GE to begin the design and development of the J47.

In retrospect it seems clear from analysis of the post-development history of both the J33 and the J35 that these engines had to undergo a lengthy period of growth in terms of durability and maintainability. From U.S. Air Forces records it is clear that in these areas, both engines left a great deal to be desired.

Development of the J35 continued at the Allison Division of General Motors in Indianapolis. The J35-A-5 was the first Allison production model of a GE designed J35. It was the same design as the Chevrolet-produced J35-C-3, except that the aft-frame flange thickness had been increased, resulting in a shortening of the aft-frame casing. This change affected the interchangeability of J35 engine parts from earlier models to this one.[32]

The J35-A-9 engine model was the same as the J35-GE-9 except for the manufacturer. Allison quickly terminated production of this model when development improvements resulted in growth models. The J35-A-11 was the same as the J35-GE-7, except for a new mid-frame with a cast firewall and a new, short exhaust cone, insulation, and island piping.[33] The J35-A-13 (the GE TG-180-D) was the same as the later J35-GE-7 except for a new mid-frame with cast firewall and the addition of a short exhaust cone. This was again a GE design manufactured by Allison. The last of these GE-designed-but-General Motors-built J35s was the J35-A-15 (the GE TG-180-A9 model). This was the same as the J35-A-5, with the exception that it had no island piping, again making it noninterchangeable with other J35 models. Allison terminated production of the model when the J35-A-17 was finished.

The J35-A-17 represented a major Allison redesign of the J35 turbojet. In November 1948 Allison succeeded in qualifying the J35-A-17 by passing the 150-hour Military Qualification Test. This engine, which delivered 4,900 pounds of thrust, represented a significant improvement over the earlier GE (J35-GE-9) and Allison (J35-A-13) models, which delivered 1,150 pounds less.[34] An Air Force Technical Note published by the Wright Air Development Center in December 1956 credited Allison as follows:

> The transition from the J35-A-13 to the J35-A-17 model was quite an important development step as indicated by the thrust improvement. This was accomplished by a slightly higher turbine inlet temperature and increased airflow...The addition of the Bendix speed density control provided automatic acceleration characteristics and better altitude performance.[35]

The development of the J35-A-17 did not prove to be painless for Allison, however, since the lubricating system was a major inadequacy. The first J35-A-17, as on all previous J35 models, had an oil spray for each main bearing and bleed air for cooling. This system had been carried over from earlier models where it also had been unsatisfactory, so the air oil mist system was continued on the J35-A-17A model. This resulted in continued bearing failures and consequently engine failures. Allison then went to the solid full scavenge oil system on the J35-A-17B with a subsequent tremendous improvement in engine service life.[36]

The first afterburning Allison engine was the J35-A-21 model, which used a Solar afterburner and the J35-A-17 model as the power section . This engine was installed in the F-89A and B (Figure 7-6) and passed the 150-hour Military Qualification Test in May 1950 with a maximum thrust rating of 6,800 pounds.

**Figure 7-6. Northrop F-89 Scorpion**
*(Photo courtesy of National Air & Space Museum)*

The next major development step in the J35 turbojet resulted in the J35-A-29 engine, which had a rating of 5,600 pounds of thrust. It completed the Military Qualification Test in October 1950 and was installed in the F-84G, the first production fighter equipped with in-flight refueling equipment.[37] The J35-A-33 was developed and produced in 1952. It was made up of a J35-A-29 power section with essentially the same afterburner unit as on the J35-A-21. The engine was rated at 7,400 pounds of thrust and was installed in the F-89C and D aircraft. Both aircraft could maintain afterburning slightly above 40,000 feet altitude. The model passed the 150-hour Military Qualification Test, but not before encountering severe trouble with turbine wheel cracking on tapered rim wheels. The last Allison model of the J35 was the J35-A-35 afterburning engine, which was able to maintain afterburning to 50,000 feet while maintaining a thrust rating of 7,400 pounds.[38]

Allison produced 14,454 J35 turbojet engines, an amazing production run. The J35 was perhaps one of the most widely used turbojets in U.S. history, with installations in bombers, fighters, transports, and experimental aircraft. It turned out to be a key learning experience for both GE and Allison, but in different ways. For GE, it was a necessary developmental step towards the J47 design. For Allison, it proved the ability of the General Motors division to develop quality turbojets and proved an important means of overcoming the "learning curve" necessary to initiating important aircraft gas turbine engine designs and developments of their own.

## Design and Development of the TG-190 (J47) Axial-Flow Turbojet Engine

On March 19, 1946, GE engineer Neil Burgess formed the TG-190 (J47) Project and began developing the engine.[39] GE submitted the original design studies of the TG-190 to the Army Air Forces on May 3, 1946.[40] Originating as a growth version of the J35 design, the J47-GE-1 (Figures 7-7 and 7-8) was first test run on June 21, 1947.[41]

**Figure 7-7. J47 Turbojet (top)**
*(Photo courtesy of GE)*

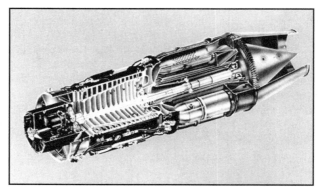

**Figure 7-8. Cutaway of J47 Engine**
*(Illustration courtesy of GE)*

The design base of the TG-190 (J47) was the J35 engine. The compressor featured an added zero stage for higher airflow and pressure ratio (5:1), a new curvic coupling rotor, and magnesium casings. The compressor inlet included low-loss inlet screens which were later made retractable and then eliminated altogether. The combustor was developed for higher pressures, higher airflow, and lower pattern factors. The turbine included a welded two-material wheel, unshrouded turbine blades, and a flash-welded turbine shaft, while the exhaust system introduced a new short exhaust cone. The controls featured an emergency fuel control system and an electrical system for the engine's afterburner. The engine also incorporated a cast magnesium front frame and an alcohol/water augmentation system.

The first model of the J47, the J47-GE-1 had a dry thrust rating of 4,850 pounds, or 5,820 pounds with water injection. According to an Army Air Forces report in December 1956, "...the early models had a variety of trouble and considerable effort was expended in development."[42]

Travers describes one of the initial design and development themes—weight control:

> The designers were urged to keep the weight down, which they did by changing to a lighter material, from aluminum to magnesium. They used the lighter material for the important large structural mid-frame casting and for several of the intermediate compressor wheel disks. Both changes were unsuccessful, however, and a return to aluminum was necessary. Later, the first fifty engines had to be retrofitted with aluminum mid-frames.[43]

Travers also relates how GE fixed an early problem with test cell failures of the turbine blades:

> (this was) caused by plate frequency modes in the outer half of the blade. The (blade) fillets were made parabolic in a new design and the problem was solved.[44]

From May 1946 until 1950, four series of the J47 were developed. The first series was the TG-190A (the J47-GE-1 and J47-GE-3). The second series was the TG-190B (the J47-GE-7 and J47-GE-9), the commercial variant, receiving Type Certificate No. 262. The third series was the TG-190C (J47-GE-11 and J47-GE-13) and the fourth series was the TG-190D (J47-GE-15 and J47-GE-17). The earlier series of J47 engines were installed in the F-86 and B-45 aircraft and four auxiliary J47s were added to the B-36.[45]

In September 1947 GE delivered the first J47s to the Army Air Forces at a cost of $39,360 each.[46] The first flight of the J47 in a B-29 flying test bed took place on April 20, 1948.[47] The first flight of the J47-GE-1 in a fighter came in an XF-86 (Figure 7-9) on May 20, 1948.

**Figure 7-9. North American XF-86**
*(Photo courtesy of U.S. Air Force)*

By the summer of 1948, J47 engines began to come off the assembly lines in GE's Building 29 in Lynn. At the suggestion of the Air Force, GE began to look at expansion of their turbojet production facilities, including a new site for turbojet manufacture.[48]

Harold Kelsey came up with several potential sites, among which were Denver, Colorado; Columbus, Ohio (the Lustron Plant); a site in San Diego; and the former Wright Aero Corporation plant in Lockland, Ohio (just north of Cincinnati). Kelsey stated in 1976 that he chose the Lockland site "because it had so many test cells."[49] The plant incorporated forty piston engine test cells used during the war. G.W. "Bill" Lawson (who was on the team to select the new site) remembers the selection of Lockland:

> the Curtiss-Wright plant near Cincinnati, according to GE lawyers, had (1) the least litigation involved, (2) the lowest price, and (3) engine test cells.[50]

GE started moving operations and J47 production to the Lockland plant in October 1948. On February 28, 1949, the GE Lockland plant was formally opened with a presentation of the first two Lockland engines to the Air Force exactly on schedule.[51] GE transferred the entire J47 operation to Lockland in November 1949.

Besides expansion of facilities, another problem to be solved by the GE development team came in the winter of 1948-49. A flight of U.S. Air Force F-84's ran into icing conditions and it became readily apparent that a de-icing "fix" had to be found. GE engineers spent the winter of 1948-49 on the top of New Hampshire's Mount Washington with -40°F winds of up to 140 mph. They tested various configurations and finally came up with a scheme to handle the problem. They developed hollow compressor inlet guide vanes with heating provided by compressor air, a technique essentially unchanged today.[52]

An important milestone for the J47 was accomplished in early 1949 when Boeing and the Air Force selected the J47 for the second prototype of the Boeing B-47 Stratojet strategic bomber (Figure 7-10). The J47-powered B-47 made its maiden flight on November 7, 1949. The J47 was a good match for the B-47, and the engine was to power many versions of the Stratojet.[53]

GE started design work on the XJ47-GE-5 afterburning engine on August 15, 1947.[54] Travers relates the development sequence for the afterburner:

**Figure 7-10. Boeing B-47 Stratojet**
*(Photo courtesy of U.S. Air Force)*

GE first developed the pilot light at the end of the inner cone (and the attending long spark plug); then the flame-holders or gutters were developed and GE designed the inner liner which helps keep the outer liner within its operating range. GE engineers encountered "screech," a phenomenon that caused large chunks of the afterburner to break off. Some thought that the inner liner controlled the combustion screech problem. Analyses of the relationships of combustion burning time and duct Mach number were conducted. GE decided early on the fully variable, i.e. a "no-boom" afterburner. The fundamentals of this design remain the same today.[55]

Although the XJ47-GE-5 was not produced, the afterburning design was carried through with the J47-GE-7. In March 1949 the J47-GE-7 and J47-GE-9 passed the Air Force 150-hour qualification test (the J47-GE-9 qualified at 5,000 pounds of thrust).[56] This was about three years after the J35 high-flow compressor version registered 5,000 pounds of thrust during factory tests.

By the end of September 1949 GE J47s were averaging eleven hours of operation between overhaul.[57] By the end of December GE had increased that average time to seventeen hours.

When the Korean War broke out in 1950, the U.S. Air Force asked GE to modify the J47 to retrofit the Republic F-84. The Air Force and Allison were having trouble with the bearing lubrication system of the J35 engine. GE developed a solid oil and scavenging system to replace the original expendable oil-mist system, and instead of replacing the Allison J35 in the F-84, the Air Force directed GE to go to Allison and put their redesign into production on the J35.[58] Development of the J47 after 1950 included the J47-GE-17, J47-GE-19, J47-GE-23, J47-GE-25, and J47-GE-27 models.

## J47-GE-17

On October 1, 1948, Neil Burgess was assigned to head up a new project called the D17 Project (TG-190-D17).[59] This engine was to be a new model incorporating a variable-thrust afterburner and an all-electric (vacuum-tube) control system designed and manufactured by a GE plant in Binghamton, New York. On June 15, 1949, GE initiated design of the J47-D17 turbojet.[60]

The J47-GE-17 was first tested on March 15, 1949,[61] and passed the 50-hour Preliminary Flight Rating Test in April of 1951. This model was installed in the F-86D fighter[62] and first flew on June 8, 1951.[63] The engine was qualified for military service on December 11, 1952.

GE had to overcome some significant production, maintainability and reliability problems in developing the J47. For instance, in 1948 the company encountered stability problems with their compressor rotor. A planning team came up with the idea of pretesting the rotors in a spin chamber built into the floor. Rotors with cracks or flaws would fail in the spin chamber and not in the assembled engine. The engineers also developed the idea of vertical assembly of J47 engines, which cut engine assembly time from twelve days to six.[64]

The reliability of the electronic control system was not very good, with over 100 F-86D fighters grounded at one time with electronic control problems. Travers describes this urgent activity:

> GE personnel felt their first priority should be to make available to crew chiefs and pilots adequate manuals on the electronic control system and its maintenance. To back up the training, GE personnel visited every F-86D base in the United States, Europe and Japan.
>
> The second step in correcting the electronic fuel controls was flight testing. GE pilot Roy Pryor had to make several 'dead-stick' landings due to failure of the electronic fuel control system. He tried several maneuvers (considered risky by some), such as shutting off the engine in flight and using the emergency fuel system, in order to develop and refine the J47-GE-17 electronic fuel control system.
>
> These controls were bulky and complex enough, but the GE-Schenectady-designed field tester for the controls was even more so. As a third step in solving the fuel control problem, engineers at the flight test center designed and built the Smithson Tester for the F-86D electronic engine controls. North American took over manufacture of these testers for the Air Force. Despite these troubles, North American concluded that the electronic fuel control system was a great success and a significant technological innovation.[65]

## J47-GE-19

The J47-GE-19 was used only on the B-36 (Figure 7-11), at the time the largest and most powerful aircraft in the world,[66] to assist in takeoff and to achieve greater over-target altitude and speed.[67]

**Figure 7-11. Convair B-36**
*(Photo courtesy of U.S. Air Force)*

## J47-GE-23 and J47-GE-25

The J47-GE-23 was similar to the J47-GE-11 except that it incorporated retractable screens, anti-icing, a thin disc turbine wheel, and a high-airflow compressor. This model included a power takeoff kit and provisions for a water injection kit.[68] It passed the 50-hour Preliminary Rating Test in February 1951 and the 150-hour Military Qualification Test on March 2, 1951. The J47-GE-23 was used in the B-47B along with the J47-GE-25 model using water injection. GE completed production of the J47-GE-23 model in January 1953. It was used in the XF-91, B-47B, RB-47B, TB-47B, and XB-47D aircraft.[69]

The J47-GE-25 passed the 150-hour test on November 28, 1952.[70] This engine was also produced by the Studebaker Corporation as the J47-ST-25 and by Packard Motors as the J47-PM-25. Production of this model was completed in March 1956.[71]

## J47-GE-27

The same as the J47-GE-23 except for the addition of an emergency fuel system, the J47-GE-27 passed the 50-hour test on October 8, 1951, and the 150-hour test in February 1953.[72] It was rated at 5,970 pounds of thrust and was subsequently installed in the F-86F.[73]

Gradually, GE worked out the production bugs and began producing quality J47 turbojet engines in earnest at Lockland. Travers describes the transition from initial production efforts to the peak of GE production of J47's:

> When the Evendale plant (Lockland) was having production problems in 1951, new management was brought in, and immediately set a new motto, 'Don't start anything until you can finish it. Don't start the assembly of an engine until you have all the parts!' Production simply had to cope with many engineering changes. In early J47 production days, GE had forty railroad carloads and forty truck-loads of engine parts coming into the plant every day. The Air Force had encouraged GE to produce and to accelerate engine deliveries for F-86 and B-47 aircraft. To solve the parts problem, GE rented warehouses in northern Kentucky for engine parts storage during a 1953 plant strike, and created a new inventory and material handling system based on first-in, first-out, so the Company could maintain strict control over the introduction of major engineering block changes. Meanwhile, engine production rose to 975 per month. For twelve consecutive months late in 1953 and early 1954, GE met the Air Force requirements and schedule. The plant strike in 1953 lasted for nine weeks but GE never held up an airframe![74]

In 1954 alone, GE delivered $343 million worth of engines. Packard Motors and Studebaker produced GE J47's under license. GE ended production of the J47 in 1956. With the development of the J47, GE had arrived as a major producer of aircraft gas turbine engines. They have remained a major player to this day.

## Endnotes

[1] Travers, William R, The GE Aircraft Engine Story, Cincinnati, OH: The GE Company, 1978, 1-3.

[2] GE Company Aircraft Gas Turbine Division, How We Grew: History of AGT, West Lynn, MA: GE Company Aircraft Gas Turbine Divisions, 1951, 18.

[3] Buckland, Bruce, Interview on January 18, 1991, in Schenectady, New York, 4.

[4] Ibid, 14.

[5] Howard, Alan, "Aircraft Gas Turbines with Axial-Flow Compressors," in GE Company, Aircraft Gas Turbine Engineering Conference, Report of conference held in Swampscott, Massachusetts on May 31, June 1, and June 2, 1945, West Lynn, MA: GE Company, 1945, 51.

[6] GE Company Turbine Engineering Department, Expected Performance Data: Type TG-100 Aircraft Gas Turbine for Propeller Drive, GE Company Data Folder No. 74714, Schenectady, NY: GE Company, 1944, 1.

[7] Buckland, Interview on January 18, 1991, 8, and Travers, The GE Aircraft Engine Story, 1-14.

[8] GE Company Aircraft Engine Business Group, Engines Produced By AEBG Through December 31, 1984, AEBG Chart No. GED-359(021985), Cincinnati, OH: GE Company Aircraft Engine Business Group, 1984, 1-14.

[9] Gunston, Bill, The Encyclopedia of the World's Combat Aircraft: A Technical Directory of Major Warplanes from World War I to the Present Day, New York: Chartwell Books Inc., 1976, 61, and GE Company, Design and Development History of the J79 Engine, GE Company presentation, dated 1960, and GE Company, Aircraft Gas Turbine Engineering Conference, ii.

[10] Travers, The GE Aircraft Engine Story, 1-17.

[11] Schlaifer, Robert, Development of Aircraft Engines. Boston, MA: Harvard University Press, 1949, 477, Gunston, The Encyclopedia of the World's Combat Aircraft, 62, and GE Company, Aircraft Gas Turbine Engineering Conference, ii.

[12] Ibid.

[13] Travers, The GE Aircraft Engine Story, 1-17.

[14] Ibid, 1-19.

[15] Ibid.

[16] Ibid, 1-12, and Wright-Patterson AFB, Ohio, U.S. Air Force Aero Propulsion and Power Laboratory Scientific and Technical Reference Files, Headquarters, USAF, "Report of the Board of Officers to Consider and Make Recommendations on the United States Air Force Engine Program," (Typewritten) July 20, 1949, 1.

[17] GE Company, Design and Development History of the J79 Engine, 14, and GE Company Archives File on the J35 turbojet engine, J35 Historical Reference Material Compilation, 1.11.

[18] Sparkman, Capt. James L. USAF, Historical Development Study of USAF Turbojet and Turboprop Engines, Wright Air Development Center Technical Note No. 57-351, Wright-Patterson Air Force Base, OH: Wright Air Development Center, Air Research and Development Command, United States Air Force, 1957, 9.

[19] Gunston, The Encyclopedia of the World's Combat Aircraft, 62.

[20] Ibid, 63, GE Company, Design and Development History of the J79 Engine, 14, Schlaifer, Development, 478, and GE Company Archives File, Historical Reference Material Compilation, 1.

[21] Sparkman, Historical Development Study of USAF Turbojet and Turboprop Engines, 9 and Hendrickson edit.

[22] Ibid.

[23] St. Peter, James J. editor, The Memoirs of Ernest C. Simpson: Aero Propulsion Pioneer, Wright-Patterson Air Force Base, OH: Aeropropulsion Laboratory, Air Force Wright Aeronautical Laboratories and Special Staff Office, Aeronautical Systems Division, United States Air Force, 1987, 34.

[24] Sparkman, Historical Development Study of USAF Turbojet and Turboprop Engines, 9, GE Company, Design and Development History of the J79 Engine, 14, and GE Company Archives File, Historical Reference Material Compilation, 1.

[25] Hendrickson edit of manuscript.

[26] GE Company, Design and Development History of the J79 Engine, 14, and GE Company Archives File, J35 Historical Reference Material Compilation, 1.11.

[27] GE Company, Design and Development History of the J79 Engine, 14.

[28] Schlaifer, Development, 478, and GE Company Archives File, J35 Historical Reference Material Compilation, 1, and Angelucci, Enzo, Rand McNally Encyclopedia of Military Aircraft: 1914-1980, New York: Military Press, 1980, 431.

[29] Schlaifer, Development, 478.

[30] Schoneberger, William A. and Paul Sonnenburg, Allison Power of Excellence: 1915 - 1990. Indianapolis, IN: Allison Gas Turbine Division, General Motors Corporation, 1990, 198.

[31] Travers, William, History of GE, Unpublished manuscript, 61. [91]

[32] Air Materiel Command, United States Air Force, Model Designations of USAF Aircraft Engines, Section 11, 5.

[33] Ibid.

[34] Sparkman, Historical Development Study of USAF Turbojet and Turboprop Engines, 9.

[35] Ibid.

[36] Ibid.

[37] Ibid.

[38] Ibid, 10.

39  Travers, History of GE, 70, and GE Company, Design and Development History of the J79 Engine, 14.

40  Sparkman, Historical Development Study of USAF Turbojet and Turboprop Engines, 42.

41  Ibid, Gunston, The Encyclopedia of the World's Combat Aircraft, 63, and GE Company, Design and Development History of the J79 Engine, 14.

42  Sparkman, Historical Development Study of USAF Turbojet and Turboprop Engines, 11.

43  Travers, The GE Aircraft Engine Story, 2-3.

44  Ibid, 2-3.

45  Sparkman, Historical Development Study of USAF Turbojet and Turboprop Engines, 11.

46  Ibid.

47  GE Company, Design and Development History of the J79 Engine, 14.

48  Travers, History of GE, 63.

49  Ibid.

50  Ibid.

51  Ibid, and Gunston, The Encyclopedia of the World's Combat Aircraft, 63.

52  Travers, The GE Aircraft Engine Story, 2-4.

53  Redding, Robert, and Bill Yenne, Boeing: Planemaker to the World, Greenwich, CT: Bison Books Corporation, 1983, 127. [304], and Travers, History of GE, 89.

54  Travers, History of GE, 73.

55  Travers, The GE Aircraft Engine Story, 2-4.

56  Sparkman, Historical Development Study of USAF Turbojet and Turboprop Engines, 11.

57  Ibid.

58  Travers, History of GE, 73, and Travers, The GE Aircraft Engine Story, 2-5.

59  Travers, History of GE, 73.

60  GE Company, Design and Development History of the J79 Engine, 14.

61  Ibid.

62  Sparkman, Historical Development Study of USAF Turbojet and Turboprop Engines, 11.

63  GE Company, Design and Development History of the J79 Engine, 14.

64  Travers, The GE Aircraft Engine Story, 2-6.

65  Ibid.

66  Sparkman, Historical Development Study of USAF Turbojet and Turboprop Engine, 11.

67  Parsons, Ian, editor, The Encyclopedia of the World's Combat Aircraft, New York, NY: Chartwell Books, Incorporated, 1976, 86. [305]

68  Air Force Propulsion Characteristics Summary, J47-GE-23 Turbojet, dated August 1955, 133. [300]

69  Air Force Propulsion Characteristics Summary, J47-GE-23 Turbojet, 133.

70  Sparkman, Historical Development Study of USAF Turbojet and Turboprop Engines, 11.

71  Air Force Propulsion Characteristics Summary, J47-GE-25 Turbojet, dated August 1955, 141. [301]

72  Air Force Propulsion Characteristics Summary, J47-GE-27 Turbojet, dated August 1955, 147. [302]

73  Sparkman, Historical Development Study of USAF Turbojet and Turboprop Engines, 11.

74  Ibid, and Travers, The GE Aircraft Engine Story, 2-7.

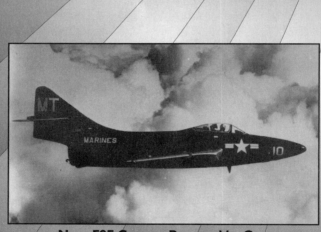

**Navy F9F Cougar, Powered by One
Pratt & Whitney J48 Turbojet**

# Chapter Eight

# Postwar Development Begins at Pratt & Whitney

## The J42, J48, and T34 Engines

Despite the research cited in earlier chapters, Pratt & Whitney (P&W) was not poised to enter the aircraft gas turbine engine business in 1945. The options open to the company were threefold. It could internally develop an engine based on previous research; it could license an already developed turbine from either General Electric or Westinghouse, having built, at the Navy's request, a limited number of Westinghouse J30 engines just after the end of the war; or it could license a British aircraft gas turbine engine from Rolls-Royce or another firm. The problem was that Pratt & Whitney was divided over whether or not to enter this new field at all. Richard Coar explained the differences in the Second Annual L.V. Smith Lecture:

> Most of Pratt's engineers at the time wanted nothing to do with anything requiring as much technical literacy as a turbine did; even five years later there would be shouting matches in the executive dining room between the turbine and anti-turbine forces...

> [Frederick B.] Rentschler believed the company had about five years (to 1950) before the piston engine business disappeared, to be replaced by turbine engines. He and Hobbs believed the company should stand on its own, not take someone else's design. Despite some internal dissension, the loudest coming from his Vice Chairman, Eugene Wilson, Fred convinced United's board to approve building turbine development facilities at a cost that exceeded the company's then net worth.[1]

These facilities were to become the famous Willgoos Laboratory, the establishment of which were to save the company much time and effort in its development of P&W engines.

P&W's management turned down two offers right away. GE came to P&W in 1945 with an offer to produce all of GE's turbine engine designs. Then P&W declined a no-money-down offer by Britain's Rolls-Royce to produce the 5,000-pound-thrust Nene turbojet engine. How then did they finally end up in the turbine engine business? Richard Coar relates the chain of events:

> About this time, 1946, Pan Am Airways hired Phil Taylor to take another look and advise Pan Am on what to do about turbine powered aircraft. After visiting all the contractors and experts around the world, Pan Am concludes that the time is not yet, but Rolls-Royce is clearly the leader. Within the year Taylor negotiates and buys the Nene license that P&W had rejected when it was free. Then in 1947, the United States Navy decides that it needs the 5,000 pound thrust Nene to supersede the 4,000 pound thrust J33 in its F9F jet fighter. Admiral Harrison asks P&W to build the Nene because Taylor has no facilities. Hobbs is reluctant, not wanting the distraction, and tries to stall the Navy by telling them they'll have to pay for everything including the license. The Navy quickly said yes.[2]

The Nene started life as a Rolls-Royce-produced variant of the Whittle W.2B turbojet engine, which Rolls had started to design in February 1944. The first design drawings of the new engine were sent to Rolls-Royce Barnoldswick in June 1944 and the first test runs took place in August 1944.[3] Rolls-Royce designed the Nene for an initial thrust of 3,300 pounds, but the engine soon proved capable of much more. It developed 4,000 pounds of thrust in its 50-hour test in December 1944 and its 100-hour test in January 1945, then 4,500 and finally 5,000 pounds of thrust in a test in February 1945.

In July of 1945 the U.S. Army Air Force test-flew the Nene in a Lockheed P-80 Shooting Star jet fighter. The Royal Air Force continued flight testing in an Avro Lancaster bomber. Also in July, the U.S. Navy authorized studies for a new jet night fighter called the XF9F-1. Grumman

Aircraft began work in September 1945 in answer to a Navy Request For Proposal (RFP) for a jet-powered carrier aircraft. On April 22, 1946, the Navy issued a contract letter of intent to Grumman for the two-seat, four-jet XF9F-1. This was later revised on October 9 to provide an XF9F-2 single-seat, single-jet day fighter.

Rene Francillon, in *Grumman Aircraft Since 1929*, relates how Grumman chose the Nene centrifugal turbojet for the XF9F:

> As first informally proposed to the Navy in June 1946, Design 79 (the XF9F) was planned to be powered by either a 3,750 to 4,000 pound thrust centrifugal-flow turbojet, such as the Allison J33 or the GE J35, with wing root intakes and a single exhaust beneath the rear fuselage, or by two wing-mounted 3,000 pound thrust Westinghouse J34 axial-flow turbojets or Rolls-Royce Derwent centrifugal-flow turbojets. Alternatively, during the early summer of 1946, Grumman proposed the use of a 5,000 pound thrust Rolls-Royce Nene centrifugal-flow turbojet which Taylor Turbine Corporation was proposing to build under license in the United States. BuAer [the Navy's Bureau of Aeronautics] considered the Nene to be the most promising powerplant but was concerned that the newly-organized Taylor Turbine Corporation would not be able to produce enough engines in a timely fashion.

> On June 30, 1946, the Naval Air Materiel Command ordered from Rolls-Royce two Nene turbojets for testing at the Aeronautical Engine Laboratory in Philadelphia. One of these engines completed its Navy 150-hour test at 4,500 pounds of thrust in December of that year. Although Taylor Turbine Corporation and Rolls-Royce had signed a licensing agreement on August 8, 1946, Pratt and Whitney started negotiations in April 1947 to take over manufacturing and sales rights and received a letter of intent from the United States Navy on May 29 for production of J42 engines.[4]

On July 2, 1946, a conference at the Bureau of Aeronautics recommended that the XF9F-2 be developed with a single Nene engine. On November 18 a Nene I sent to the United States for Taylor Turbine Corporation passed an official 150-hour type test at the Naval Air Materiel Center, Philadelphia.[5] On January 27, 1947, the Navy's Aeronautical Board approved BuAer's proposal that the Nene engine be manufactured by one of the three leading American engine producers. P&W was given the contract to "Americanize" the Nene. The Navy stipulated that the first Nene had to come off the assembly line by November 1948.

## P&W Development of the J42 Turbojet Engine

P&W began work on the J42 (the "Americanized" Nene) under Bill Gorton's direction in May 1947. The company received the first drawings from Rolls-Royce on July 15, 1947,[6] then had to engineer the British engine for mass production, as it was not being produced in mass quantities in Britain at the time. British blueprints—more than 1,100 of them—had to be redrawn to American standards. A total of 5,300 special production tools had to be designed and procured. Nine thousand operation sheets had to be written for shop guidance, and 225,000 square feet of factory area had to be converted to jet production facilities. In addition, more than a thousand design changes were required from the time the engine drawings arrived in Connecticut until the first production J42 rolled off the line. The entire front end of the engine had to be redesigned to conform with standard American accessories.[7]

Richard Coar describes the "Americanizing" of the Nene:

> First we had to learn what Rolls-Royce blueprints meant: among other things, everything was drawn backwards, then there were notes like "fettle to fit," "this dimension important," "BOC," or "this dimension must stand proud."

> I would describe our working relation with Rolls-Royce as a bit tentative. Very difficult to get straight answers because they didn't want to teach us too much. Many times we concluded we'd been "redcoated" again. Aspirin became known as Nene pills. But we did learn a lot that helped later in our own designs: a whole new field of metallurgy; how to make sheet metal structures; quality control procedures more stringent than before; and how not to design a fuel system.[8]

P&W's design team released the first drawings to Production on August 6, 1947 and the company negotiated a production contract for the F9F-2 production set.[9] Fuel pump problems continued to plague J42 production during its early months, and full assembly of the engines was stopped entirely for several months while the problem was dealt with. The J42 originally used the Nene engine combustion system without change. The problem with using gasoline, the Navy's alternative fuel, was with fuel pump gross failures. The Nene's high-pressure fuel-injection system required about 100 psi from the fuel pump, too high for a gear-type pump. This pressure was supplied by a Lucas-designed, Bendix U.S. produced variable-stroke piston pump. The design worked only marginally well with Navy jet fuel, and quickly failed using lower-viscosity gasoline. Adding 3 percent oil to the gasoline provided a temporary fix. Jack McDermott, later a J58 project engineer, spearheaded the crash program that redesigned the pump so that it would endure gasoline as well as salt-water slugging (carrier tanks used salt water ballast). The scaled up J42, or J48, used the same high-pressure fuel-injection system. Again, combustion was not a problem, except for a hiatus when Coar made an "insignificant" change to the fuel nozzle—an error soon corrected. On the J48 the pump problem was avoided using his new gear pump design capable of 1000 psi, about twice previous experience. In November 1947 P&W successfully ran a J42 for 150 hours on a fuel mixture of 97 percent gasoline and 3 percent oil. Meanwhile, the XF9F-2 first flew on November 21, 1947, with a Taylor Turbine-supplied Nene engine imported from Britain.

The first successful run of the P&W redesigned J42 (Figure 8-1) was on March 6, 1948, and the first production J42 was built on September 23, 1948.[10] The official "wet rating" of the J42 in October of that year was 5,750 pounds of thrust.[11] On November 24 came the first flight of a P&W-built J42 engine in an F9F-2 (Figure 8-2). The first production J42 was delivered to the Navy on November 30, 1948.[12]

**Figure 8-1. Cutaway of J42 Engine**
*(Illustration courtesy of Pratt & Whitney)*

On January 10, 1949, a J42 completed a 150-hour qualification test using straight gasoline and in March a P&W-designed J42 with afterburner passed a 50-hour test. Total test time on the J42 was already 8,411 hours.[13] P&W shipped their twenty-fifth production J42 on March 31. The first production J42 capable of operation on straight gasoline was delivered to the Navy on June 30. In August, VF-115 was the first Navy squadron to receive F9F-2 aircraft. The one-hundredth production J42 was shipped on September 30, 1949.

On August 5, 1950, operating from the carrier "Philippine Sea," the first strikes over Korea by F9F-2 aircraft from VF-111 and VF-112 were made. On November 9, Lt. Commander W.T. Amen became the first Navy pilot to shoot down a MiG-15 jet fighter while flying an F9F-2. On April 2, 1951, F9F-2s flown by VF-191 made a bombing attack on railroad bridges near Songlin, North Korea. This was the first time the Navy had used jets as fighter-bombers.

**Figure 8-2. Grumman F9F-2 Panther**
*(Photo courtesy of National Air & Space Museum)*

The company shipped their five-hundredth production J42 on June 14, 1950. By July 3, 1950, the J42 had accumulated over 10,000 hours of service flying. Between 1949 and 1950 the J42 overhaul interval improved dramatically from 150 to 300 hours. On March 15, 1951, Pratt shipped its one-thousandth production J42 and by June 30 of that year production of J42s was completed. Over 1,139 J42-P-4s, J42-P-6s, and J42-P-8s were shipped between March 1948 and June 1951 for installation in F9F-2s and re-engined F9F-3s.[14] In all, the J42 accumulated over 100,000 hours of service flying.

In August 1951 Grumman completed production of the F9F-2-series fighter, having completed a total of 1,385 Panthers (one source says 761)[15]. All F9F-2 aircraft in the last squadron, VF-123, were retired as fighter aircraft in June 1956. The Panther was relegated to training service until June 1958, when this remarkable aircraft ended its active service.

## Design and Development of the P&W JT7 (J48) Turbojet Engine

Rolls began development of the Tay in 1944 in their Barnoldswick development facility under the leadership of Stanley (later Sir Stanley) Hooker. The centrifugal Tay was a Nene redesigned to 115 pounds per second of airflow and incorporated many detailed improvements. It was initially rated at 6,250 pounds of thrust, and proved to be the last centrifugal turbojet development program at Rolls-Royce. The engine program was terminated in 1945, mainly due to a desire by Rolls-Royce's Chairman, Lord Hives, to both bring the jet engine programs "under heel" and push axial turbojet development. Part of the problem lay in the bias that many in the aircraft engine community had built up against both Whittle and centrifugal turbojets. Gunston explains in *World Encyclopedia of Aero Engines*:

> Part of the trouble lay in the belief, fostered during Whittle's early struggle by such experts as Griffith and Constant, that not only were axials better than centrifugals, but that the latter were a crude idea put forward by Whittle that would soon be rendered obsolete. Nothing could have been further from the truth, but in 1944 the centrifugal was limited by the strength of the available aluminum alloys to straight radial vanes and tip speeds around 1,500 feet per second. This means about 80% efficiency at a pressure ratio of 4. Today, titanium impellers with curved vanes and tip speeds exceeding 1,800 feet per second achieve 84% at a pr [pressure ratio] of 8.4 or more, which is far beyond what any axial could do in 1944! But Rolls-Royce decided to abandon the classic Whittle formula...[16]

Rolls-Royce's decision turned into P&W's opportunity. The company had already "Americanized" a foreign jet design and learned a great deal about developing and manufacturing jet engines. Acquiring another license to develop an existing design seemed to be the next logical step. Developing the Tay under license from Rolls-Royce would give P&W invaluable design and manufacturing experience, while getting ready to produce its own first-iteration jet engine development.

About 1946, Leonard Hobbs established a separate Technical and Research Group headed by Perry Pratt and Guy Beardsley Jr. to study, design, and begin testing P&W's own turbine engines. Americanization of the J42 and, later, development of the J48 were placed in the Production Engine Group under Arthur Smith, to avoid diluting the work on advanced concepts. The J42 and J48 work was led by Bill Gorton, assisted by Bill Brown, Roger Young, and Dick Coar. The J48 began as an Anglo-American venture with a Rolls-designed power section and a P&W-designed fuel system and accessory drives. Beyond the initial power section design and the supply of early experimental power sections by Rolls-Royce, the project was wholly a P&W development.

The J48 (Figure 8-3) was outstanding for its day in that it packed 30 percent more power into an engine with nearly the same overall dimensions as the J42, being only one-half inch larger in diameter and three inches longer than the J42 and weighing only 200 pounds more.

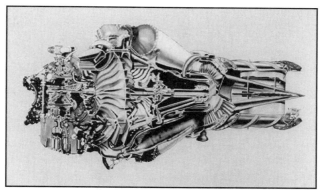

**Figure 8-3. Cutaway of J48 Engine**
*(Photo courtesy of Pratt & Whitney)*

The J48 engine series incorporated the first gear-pump fuel system, composed of a high-pressure gear pump with its own backup fuel system. A new alloy, Waspalloy, was developed for the turbine.[17] The J48 was P&W's first afterburning jet engine. This matching of the afterburner to the engine was accompanied by the same difficulties with "screech" that other contemporary jet engine manufacturers encountered.[18]

P&W produced 3,222 J48s for the Navy, 879 for the Air Force, and 5 commercial units for a total of 4,106.[19] Air Force variants of the J48 (JT7) included the J48-P-1 (JT7B), J48-P-3 (JT7), J48-P-5 (JT7E), and J48-P-5A. The J48-P-1 model was the prototype for the J48-P-3. The J48-P-5 was an improved version of the J48-P-3. The models after the J48-P-1 were all afterburning. The Navy models of the J48 included the J48-P-6, J48-P-6A (JT7A), J48-P-8 (JT7H) and J48-P-8A (JT7J). The J48-P-2 served as the prototype for the J48-P-6 and J48-P-6A. The J48-P-8 and J48-P-8A were both improved variants of the J48-P-6. The J48-P-6A and the J48-P-8A included afterburning.

## The New Technological Challenge

The outbreak of the Korean War in 1950 caught the United States by surprise. The jets of the Air Force, Navy, and Marines were thrust into the fight to keep the Russian and Communist Chinese-backed North Korean forces from overrunning South Korea. Although American fighter and fighter-bomber aircraft had little trouble gaining immediate control of the skies over Korea, that state of affairs was soon to change. American aircraft gas turbine engine technology, along with American military fighter technology, was soon challenged by Soviet technology. The catalyst to this challenge was the appearance of the Russian MiG-15 jet fighter in the air over Korea in November 1950. This fast Russian-built-Nene-powered swept-wing fighter suddenly made the current American jets obsolete. The straight-wing Air Force Lockheed F-80 Shooting Star and the best Navy jets, the straight-wing F9F-2 Panther and McDonnell F2H-2 Banshee, were suddenly second-best.

New-generation American jet fighters were ordered developed, and existing design programs for new and faster fighters were suddenly given much greater priority. Two of these new fighters, the North American F-86 Sabre for the Air Force and the Grumman F9F Cougar for the Navy, directly affected P&W's work with the JT7 (J48) engine.

North American Aviation began design and development of the swept-wing P-86 Sabre in the closing days of World War II. Re-designated the F-86 by the Air Force, there were only two operational squadrons of the F-86 when the Korean War broke out on June 25, 1950.

In March 1948 North American Aviation and P&W submitted a proposal to the Air Force to develop a variant of the F-86 called the F-86C. This was to be a modification to the F-86A, and was to incorporate the J48-P-1 engine. In May P&W delivered a mockup JT7B (J48-P-1) to North American for the F-86C.[20] The modifications to the F-86A soon became so extensive that the Air Force changed this model variant to the F-93 in September 1948.[21]

The first P&W model J48-P-6 (JT7A), incorporating an afterburner, ran on the company's East Hartford test stand. A mockup of this engine was sent to North American in December 1948.[22] In January 1949 P&W operated an afterburning J48-P-3 (JT7) on a North American F-93A.[23] Although two F-93A prototypes underwent flight testing by the Air Force in June and July 1950, the F-93 program was canceled by the Air Force in March 1951 in favor of the F-86D all-weather "Sabre Dog" interceptor version of the F-86 Sabre (Figure 8-4).[24]

**Figure 8-4. North American F-86D Sabre Dog**
*(Photo courtesy of U.S. Air Force)*

In September 1949 P&W began JT7 production with the J48-P-6 (JT7A) model. The installation of a J48-P-1 (JT7B) mockup engine in the Lockheed F-94B fighter took place in November. North American also installed a J48-P-1 model in the F-93A that same month. The first flight test of the F-93A powered by the J48-P-1 on January 24, 1950, required six 1,000-pound-thrust jet-assisted takeoff (JATO) units, because the afterburner for the engine was not yet available. Bill Brown, who played a key role in both J42 and J48 development, recalls the afterburner problem and how it was solved:

> The only afterburner that was operable at that time was the Solar afterburner, and it wasn't very operable. It worked fairly well at sea level, if it didn't screech and bust up everything. I got the job of de-

signing and developing an afterburner, so I decided to go out and see whether NACA had any information. I finally convinced Bill Gorton that we had to get information or something. "We can't get it from Solar. They ain't going to tell us." Bill said, "Well you can go out to NACA, but don't tell them anything." I went out, as I knew some people there. They had been doing a little research work, which was good research, and they gave me all the data that they had. That gave us the basis of design for an afterburner nothing like the Solar.

Solar had something I'll have to call a flame holder, because I've forgotten what they called it. You almost couldn't see through it because it was so dense. It was made of little half circles all the way around, joined in the middle. The fuel nozzles were built as part of the flame holder system. It had all these little fingernail cuts in it, and they'd fire it, look up the back end of the flame and then go in and bend them this way and bend them that way until it had the desired flame pattern. Its cold loss, a pressure loss when not afterburning, must have been like ten percent fuel consumption. It just cut the cruise range by ten percent. I thought at the time, based on what I had learned at NACA, that we could build one that was less than six percent cold loss. We found that one of the biggest losses in the Solar afterburner was in the clamshell nozzle. The nozzle was elliptical and it wasn't all in one plane. Of course, it wasn't a true clamshell; it was a sphere with a piece cut out. We ran some model tests. This resulted in a circular exit, all in one plane. It was a lot more efficient than the Solar clamshell. We accomplished that by making two centers instead of both sides operating on the same center. In the closed position, it was all in one plane circular. We got the cold loss down to three percent, and also we were able to burn all the way up as high as the airplane would go. The older afterburners did not burn above ten or fifteen thousand feet...Lockheed was beginning to build an F-94, which was an all-weather fighter, with the Allison J33 and Solar afterburner. The J33 engine with the afterburner gave about 6,000 pounds of thrust while afterburning at sea level. The J48 engine and afterburner produced 8,500 pounds of thrust. Percentage-wise, it was quite a bit more than the J33. Lockheed and the Air Force decided that the F-94C would have the J48 and afterburner.[25]

In April 1950 Lockheed received a letter of intent from the Air Force for the purchase of the prototype YF-97 (YF-94) including a J48-P-3 turbojet.[26] This second application of the J48 was the "C" version of the Lockheed F-94 Starfire all-weather radar-equipped fighter (Figure 8-5). This was a fundamental redesign of the F-94A, which in turn had been redesigned from the F-80 Shooting Star fighter, and which had been developed solely by Lockheed with corporate money. The YF-94C prototype first flew on January 19, 1950, powered by a J48-P-5 (JT7E).[27] The Air Force was impressed enough by the Starfire's capabilities that they immediately placed an order for 110 of the aircraft.[28]

At this time, matching afterburners to engines and airframes was still an inexact science. The period between first flight and first production delivery was plagued by what P&W called "rough afterburner operation." The problem was that the roughness persisted at altitude even after the modification of the afterburner spray bars, and that the afterburner fuel flow could not be reduced sufficiently to stay within the 720°C tail pipe temperature limit. Further testing revealed

**Figure 8-5. Lockheed F-94 Starfire**
*(Photo courtesy of U.S. Air Force)*

that afterburner roughness was started by pressure disturbances in the combustion chambers and compressor. P&W made a new engine iteration, incorporating a new larger turbine and a second flame ring mounted aft of the original flame ring in the afterburner. The changes alleviated compressor surge and the afterburner overpressure at altitude. The new and bigger turbine engine permitted slower acceleration of the engine to full rpm and produced more thrust at all altitudes than earlier engines. The new afterburner also maintained maximum revolutions per minute to approximately 40,000 feet without exceeding the new temperature limit of 755°C.[29]

Other engine problems surfaced during flight testing. Five prototype J48-P-1s and two production J48-P-3s suffered bearing failures. On September 18, 1951, a meeting was held at the Air Materiel Command at Wright-Patterson Air Force Base, at which representatives of both P&W and Lockheed were present. The entire F-94C and J48 program including flight testing was reviewed. The Air Force and company representatives decided that eight of the twenty J48-P-3 engines already produced would be equipped with a new accessory case. These eight engines would be used to support the first two production F-94Cs until J48-P-5 engines were available. All subsequent J48-P-5 engines would be equipped with the modified accessory case.

The first delivery of production J48-P-5s to Lockheed and the first flight of a production F-94C Starfire occurred in August 1951. By January 1952 a total of 546 F-94C aircraft were on order, all powered by the J48-P-5. By February this number had increased to 581. In March the F-94C successfully passed a full-scale wind tunnel test at Moffet Field. There were, however, more engine tribulations to come for P&W.

In April 1952 all F-94C aircraft were grounded by the Air Force as a result of fuel nozzle failures experienced in East Hartford. During flight tests, pilots experienced high frequency rumble from idle to about 45 percent rpm, a mild power surge in the region of 80 to 85 percent rpm and the necessity to throttle the engine revolutions per minute during an afterburning climb. P&W felt the high-frequency rumble would be eliminated by changing the fuel-pressurizing valve. They also installed "shotgun" pyrotechnic emergency ignitors on all engines before delivery, for air starts.[30]

In May 1952 F-94C flight testing resumed. Four F-94C aircraft were accepted and delivered to the Air Force in June. Also in June, the first three F-94C aircraft equipped with JT7E (J48-P-5) engines were delivered to the Air Materiel Command, the development and procurement agency for aircraft and aircraft engines for the Air Force. The Air Force officially "unveiled" the Starfire in July.[31]

The Air Force, however, was dissatisfied with the J48 engine. It requested that Lockheed investigate and determine the cost of installing an Allison J33-A-29 (afterburning version) centrifugal turbojet in the F-94C. P&W countered by offering the afterburning versions of the J48-P-8 engine on a trial basis and shipped the J48-P-8 (JT7J) to Lockheed in October.[32] Although the Air Force ultimately proved uninterested in the J48-8 version, P&W had bought enough time with their proposal to get the major problems with the J48-P-5 straightened out. On October 30, 1952, the first flight of the production F-94C with the J48-P-5 engine took place.[33]

In April 1953 the first Air Defense Command Base was activated with the F-94C at Otis Air Force Base in Massachusetts. In August of that year the second operational wing flying the F-94C was established at Langley Air Force Base in Virginia. The F-94C Starfire had an excellent record as a night-fighter in Korea. The final two F-94C aircraft powered by J48-P-5s were delivered to the Air Force in May 1954, completing the contract at 387.[34]

The third major application for the J48 was in the Grumman F9F series fighters; the F9F-5 Panther and the F9F-6 Cougar (Figure 8-6) swept-wing, single-seat, carrier-based fighters. In September 1949 the first JT7B (J48-P-1), a 7,000-pound-thrust, nonafterburning engine, was delivered to Grumman for installation in their F9F-5 Panther fighter.

**Figure 8-6. Grumman F9F-6 Cougar**
*(Photo courtesy of National Air & Space Museum)*

The first flight of the F9F-5 Panther powered by the J48-P-6 took place on December 21, 1949.[35] In December 1949 P&W also received an order for 264 J48-P-6s from the Navy for the Grumman F9F-5 Panther. They delivered the first three production J48-P-6s that same month. Two went to the Air Force for the F-93 and one went to the Navy for the F9F.[36] For the Navy aircraft, the J48-P-6 served as the prototype engine for the J48-P-8 and J48-P-8A series engines. The first production F9F-5 Panther with a J48-P-6 engine was delivered by Grumman on November 5, 1950.

The appearance of the MiG-15 in Korea in November 1950 made dramatic improvements in American fighters imperative. In December 1950 Grumman and the Navy agreed to expedite the development of a swept-wing fighter. The contract for the design of the Cougar was given to Grumman Aircraft on March 2, 1951. The new fighter was designed from the beginning to use the P&W J48-P-6 (JT7A). Grumman had had good experience with the P&W J42 turbojet and wanted to incorporate the more powerful J48 in the new design.

In July 1951 P&W delivered the first JT7H (J48-P-8) prototype to Grumman Aircraft. Grumman concurrently tested both the J48-P-6 and J48-P-8 models of the J48, but flew the -8 model first in the Panther before authorizing its use in the Cougar. The prototype of the F9F-6 Cougar first flew on September 20, 1951, powered by a P&W J48-P-6.[37] On October 25, 1951, Grumman delivered to the Navy the first production F9F-5 Panther powered by the new J48-P-8 engine.[38] The initial engine for the F9F-6 Cougar was the J48-P-6A, an afterburning version of the -6, which was delivered to the Navy on December 28, 1951. The last J48-P-6-powered F9F-5 (a -5P photo-reconnaissance aircraft) was delivered to the Navy on August 11, 1952.[39] The J48-P-6 and -6A also saw service with the F9F-6, -6D, -6K, -6K2, and -6P models, as well as a retrofitted F9F-7 variant of the Cougar.[40]

P&W began production of the J48-P-8 in March 1952 and delivered their first production unit to Grumman in September.[41] The first flight of an F9F-6 Cougar with a -8 model engine was in September 1952.[42] The J48-P-8 also saw service with the F9F-7 and the F9F-8 variants of the Cougar.[43]

The last twenty-four J48s were produced in 1959, for a total of 4,108 engines. The last F9F-8T Cougar (powered by a J48-P-8A) was delivered to the Navy on February 2, 1960.[44]

The J42 and J48 centrifugal-turbojet engines enabled P&W to enter the turbojet field and quickly achieve production expertise and capacity, while leaving the company free to work on designing and developing its own next-generation turbojets. The J42 and the J48 were also the last pure-centrifugal turbojets. They represent the end of a key developmental period in aircraft gas turbine engine technology. The centrifugal turbojet was a necessary first step in that technology.

# The P&W PT-2 (T34) Turboprop Engine

While P&W was Americanizing, developing, and producing the J42 and J48 centrifugal turbojets, it was also pursuing an in-house research and development program under Perry Pratt. The first design explored was the Kalitinsky PT-1 engine described in Chapter Three. The second program was the PT-2 or T34 axial-flow turboprop engine, on which work began on July 1, 1945. This engine, described as the "guinea pig," was the company's first venture into axial-flow design and the first gas turbine completely designed by P&W ever to reach flight test stage.[45]

The initial design goal was to develop a stainless steel turboprop engine that would develop 3,550 horsepower. The first attempt to run the T34 took place in September 1947, but the engine would not sustain itself. After the compressor was redesigned, the engine was tested again in December 1949 and produced 5,375 shaft horsepower. It had a thirteen-stage compressor which handled 65 pounds of air per second at a pressure ratio of 6.7:1, a cannular combustor, and a three-stage turbine. It passed its required 50-hour pre-flight ground test at 5,700 shaft horsepower on February 22, 1950. Its first flight (in the nose of a Boeing B-17) was on August 5, 1950.[46]

With improvements, the T34 ultimately delivered 7,500 equivalent shaft horsepower (with water injection). The T34 went into production in 1953, and P&W built 485 engines. The T34 was incorporated into the design of the Douglas C-133 Cargomaster transport, the first U.S. Air Force transport specified for turboprop power. The first flight of the C-133A was on April 23, 1956, with four P&W T34-P-3 engines. Deliveries of the C-133A began in August 1957, and with the -B series, saw service for the Air Force until 1961. P&W developed a total of three models of the T34, the T34-P-3, the T34-P-7, and T34-P-9W.[47]

Richard Baseler, the T34 project engineer who was later P&W's vice president of engineering, succinctly summed up the company's view of the T34:

> We bit off more than we were able to cope with at that particular state-of-the-art. And yet a lot of very useful work was done during that period.[48]

The development experience provided by the PT-2/T34, the J42, and the J48 proved invaluable in P&W's first major success, the J57, as will be described in the next chapter.

## Endnotes

[1] Coar, Richard J, Second Annual L.V. Smith Lecture, November 16, 1989, 14.

[2] Ibid, 14-15.

[3] Whittle, Frank, Jet: The Story of a Pioneer, London: Frederick Mueller, 1953, 278.

[4] Francillon, Rene J, Grumman Aircraft Since 1929, Annapolis, MD: Naval Institute Press, 1989, 314-315.

[5] Neville, Leslie E. and Silsbee, Nathaniel F, "The AAF and American Industry Pull a Miracle," from Jet Propulsion Progress, New York: McGraw-Hill Book Company, 1948, 50.

[6] P&W Aircraft Engine files, Resume of Engine Development Histories, East Hartford, CT: P&W Aircraft, Division of United Aircraft Corporation, 1975, 7, and Hotz, Robert, "The Turbo-Wasp Proves Itself," Bee-Hive (Summer 1950), 6.

[7] Hotz, "The Turbo-Wasp Proves Itself," Bee-Hive, 6.

[8] Coar, Second Annual L.V. Smith Lecture, 15.

[9] P&W Aircraft Engine Files, Resume of Engine Development Histories, 7.

[10] Ibid.

[11] Gunston, Bill, World Encyclopedia of Aero Engines, Second Edition, England: Patrick Stephens Limited, 1989, 119.

[12] P&W Aircraft Engine Files, Resume of Engine Development Histories, 7.

[13] Ibid.

[14] Francillon, Grumman Aircraft Since 1929, 316.

[15] Angelucci, Enzo, The Rand McNally Encyclopedia of Military Aircraft, New York: The Military Press, 1983, 426

[16] Gunston, World Encyclopedia of Aero Engines, 148-149.

17  Lippencott, Harvey H., Interview on November 22, 1991.

18  Ibid.

19  Ibid.

20  P&W Aircraft Engine Files, Chronological History of JT7, West Palm Beach, FL: Government Products Division, P&W Aircraft Engines, United Technologies Corporation, 5-1.

21  Ibid, 5-2, and Bowers, Peter M. and Swanborough, Gordon, United States Military Aircraft Since 1909, Washington, DC: Smithsonian Institution Press, 1989, 482.

22  P&W Aircraft Engine Files, Chronological History of JT7, 5-1.

23  Ibid, 5-2.

24  Ibid, 5-6.

25  Brown, William H, Interview on August 11, 1987, From The Memoirs of Ernest C. Simpson, Aero Propulsion Pioneer: Collected Oral History Interviews, Martin, Thomas; Queener, Catherine; and St. Peter, James J.; editors, Wright-Patterson Air Force Base, OH: Aero Propulsion Laboratory, Air Force Wright Aeronautical Laboratories, Aeronautical Systems Division, 1988, 665 and 666.

26  P&W Aircraft Engine Files, Chronological History of JT7, 5-5.

27  Bowers and Swanborough, United States Military Aircraft Since 1909, 376-377.

28  Ingells, Douglas J, L-1011 Tristar and The Lockheed Story, Fallbrook, CA: Aero Publishers, Inc., 1973, 136.

29  P&W Aircraft Engine Files, P&W Aircraft Engine Listings: Index of Aircraft Engines, West Palm Beach, FL: Government Products Division, P&W Aircraft Engines, United Technologies Corporation, 1972, section 5, 10.

30  Ibid, 12.

31  P&W Aircraft Engine Files, Chronological History of JT7, 5-12.

32  Ibid.

33  Ibid, 5-14.

34  Ibid, 5-17.

35  Ibid, 5-13.

36  Ibid, 5-14.

37  Francillon, Grumman Aircraft Since 1929, 334.

38  P&W Aircraft Engine Files, Chronological History of JT7, 5-9.

39  Ibid, 5-13.

40  Francillon, Grumman Aircraft Since 1929, 334-343.

41  P&W Aircraft Engine Files, Chronological History of JT7, 5-11 and 5-12.

42  Ibid, 5-12.

43  Francillon, Grumman Aircraft Since 1929, 334-343.

44  P&W Aircraft Engine Files, Chronological History of JT7, 5-22.

45  Lippencott, Harvey H, "P&W Enters the Jet Age," from "Classic Turbine Engines," edited by Robert B. Meyer, Jr. Casting About Volume 85, Number 4, 7.

46  Ibid, 7-8.

47  Francillon, Rene J., McDonnell Douglas Aircraft Since 1920: Volume I, Annapolis, MD: Naval Institute Press, 1988, 509-510.

48  Lippencott, "P&W Enters the Jet Age," Casting About, 8.

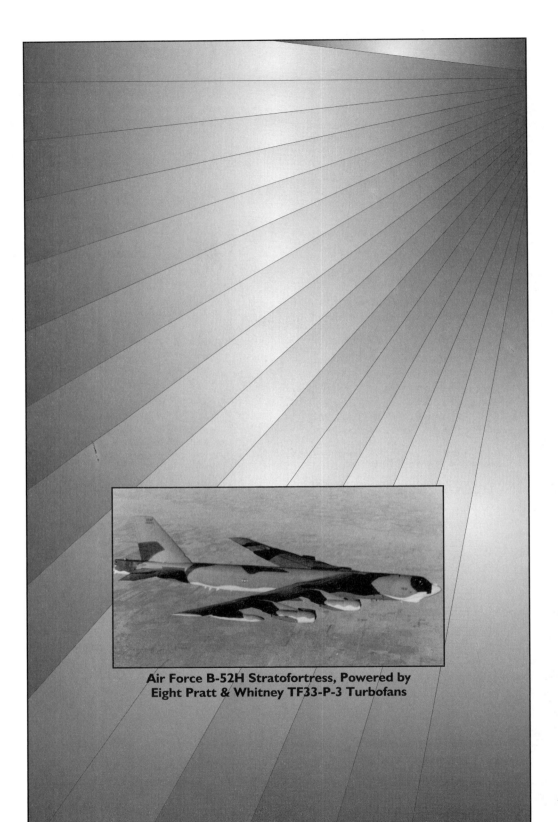

**Air Force B-52H Stratofortress, Powered by
Eight Pratt & Whitney TF33-P-3 Turbofans**

# Chapter Nine

# The Multiple-Spool Concept at Pratt & Whitney

Unlike the early work by Sir Frank Whittle and Dr. Hans von Ohain, the next step in American aircraft gas turbine technological evolution took place in an established aircraft engine company. Ernest C. "Cliff" Simpson, who was then chief of the Turbine Engine Division of the Air Force's Aero Propulsion Laboratory (becoming the Propulsion Directorate of the Air Force Research Laboratory in 1998), relates how the Air Force saw the then-current state of affairs in aircraft gas turbine technology:

> In the late forties, the propulsion community in the Air Force sat down to determine how well they were doing on the priority list previously established. The life picture was improving well and, although many of the improvements had not been installed or seen service, the rate of improvement was high and it was essential to at least the start of planning the attack on the second most 'stinko' element of the turbine engine — its fuel utilization. Since someone had to build quality into the next mechanical marvel, we made free use of the ability of industry to study and design engines...

> It is relatively easy to theoretically determine how to get a 25% improvement over the then existing engines; the rub comes in making the assumptions come true. The perception of the Air Force guy on the behavioral pattern of the contractor is, I believe, interesting. At the time, there were five manufacturers of propulsion devices for large aircraft. They were General Electric, P&W, Curtiss-Wright, Westinghouse, and Allison. All had properly done their thermodynamics, their preliminary designs; yet two distinct and separate conclusions were drawn from essentially the same set of engineering study data. The size or thrust of the engine needed was approximately 10,000 pounds thrust, a thrust/weight ratio on the order of three, and the best fuel consumption would win. Thermodynamics said that a 25% improvement could be achieved by having efficient components, keeping about the same turbine inlet temperature, but mainly by doubling the pressure ratio. P&W had one opinion, everyone else had another. The opposing opinion to P&W was most clearly presented by GE, so their version is used.

> The opinions can be summarized in that P&W considered 12.6:1 pressure ratio to be optimum and everyone else said 6:1 which (6:1) would get about a 10% improvement in fuel consumption. The opinion for 6:1 was based on a study of the effect of leakage on Cycle Selection. GE assumed that leakage could be studied by using a hypothetical orifice and noting that, as pressure went up, so did leakage, and not only that, but as pressure went up, the loss per unit leakage went up. If leakage characteristics were selected compatible with then current state-of-the-art leakage, the optimum pressure ratio was about 6:1. This was the loudly expressed opinion of four-fifths of the industry. P&W's conclusion was that better air sealing was essential and 12.6:1 was the best pressure ratio. P&W, after stating for eight years "Turbines and the Brayton Cycle are no damn good," retracted this position and became more aggressive than any other manufacturer.[1]

In an article for Howmet Manufacturing's magazine *Casting About*, Leonard S. "Luke" Hobbs described for author Harvey H. Lippencott how P&W viewed their position in 1949-1950:

> We faced a mighty tough situation. Not only were we five years behind the other companies, but some of them could draw upon years of experience in the steam turbine field. We were running a poor race. We decided that it would not be enough to match their designs; that to get back into the race we must 'leap-frog' them — come up with something far in advance of what they were thinking about.[2]

## Design and Development of the P&W JT3/J57 Turbojet Engine

Once Hobbs' new Technical and Research Team completed designs of the PT2 (described in Chapter Eight) in March 1946, P&W began design of their "next step" engine, which they designated the JT3-6. P&W chose a design goal of 7,500 pounds of thrust. Detail design of the JT3-6 began in May 1947. This engine design incorporated a constant diameter of 36 inches, with a pressure ratio of 6.

The idea for dual-spool compression (two compressors each with its own turbine drive as opposed to the variable-speed coupling to a single turbine used by Price in the L1000) was investigated by P&W's R.G. Smith and W.H. Sens in the spring of 1946. Why dual spools? The dual-spool concept was one of two ways to deal with the problem of off-design turbine engine performance. Turbine engines are designed to operate efficiently at cruise. Jet aircraft, however, do not operate at a constant speed. When a single compressor operates at a slower or faster rate than designed optimums, power decreases and fuel consumption increases. The challenge was to get an engine design that would have some performance flexibility. The two-spool design let the engine operate nearer optimum while changing speeds and power settings.

The construction of the Andrew Willgoos Laboratory complex was key to the successful development of the JT3. In late 1946 Leonard Hobbs realized that the existing laboratory and test facilities at P&W were inadequate for aircraft gas turbine design, development, and testing. He went to the United Aircraft Corporation board of directors and proposed that laboratory and testing facilities costing $15 million be built. This was an unusual request in that the proposed expenditure was more than the total net worth of the company! The board, however, approved the request, although not without some acrimonious discussion. Construction of the facility, which would be named for P&W's Chief Engineer, Andrew Van Dean Willgoos, began in March 1947. This complex provided key test facilities for both complete engines and components. In it, an engine could be operated at conditions simulating flight speeds of Mach 3 at a simulated altitude of 90,000 feet for 24 hours a day. High-altitude conditions could be reproduced in several scales. By July 1950 the facility was complete and ready to support the JT3 engineers, who had in some cases already developed components.

Richard Coar, retired executive vice president at United Technologies Corporation, relates how P&W's then engineering manager, Leonard S. "Luke" Hobbs, mustered funding support for the engine that became the renowned J57:

> Admiral Harrison, then Chief of the Navy's Bureau of Aeronautics, sent out a letter to its contractors asking for an expression of ideas on the next step in jet engines. Harrison's request was not taken seriously by Pratt's senior management but I did see the letter before it went into the wastebasket. Soon thereafter, the Navy announces the award of a development contract to Westinghouse for the J40, sort of a scale-up of the Air Force's GE J47. There's consternation in Connecticut. Hobbs rushes to Washington to see Harrison and ask how could the Navy award such a contract without giving everyone a chance to bid? Harrison replies: I did, but you never answered my letter. Luke sees there's no hope now that the Navy will support Pratt's home-grown efforts, so he must get the Air Force on board quickly to preempt this Navy action. After some three years of study, with help from its consultants at Harvard and MIT, Pratt's turbine team had by now concluded that a pressure ratio 12 axial flow jet in the 10,000 horsepower class would be a winner in the game, having 40% more thrust and 20% better fuel consumption than the J47. So Hobbs goes to Wright Field and suggests privately to the Air Force general in charge that the Air Force fund Pratt's new engine. The objective, of course, was to keep the Navy from getting the upper hand with a better airplane.

> The general says no, Congress would never let us get away with what looks like an obvious duplication of the Navy program. After more discussion, Hobbs and the general agree to start the new engine as a turboprop program, which wouldn't look like duplication of effort. Concurrently the Air Force would start Boeing on the design of a turboprop-powered B-52 bomber using this new engine, to supersede the B-47. Then, as soon as the smoke cleared, the Air Force would redirect Boeing to design the B-52 around jets, and redirect Pratt's turboprop program using its high pressure compressor to develop a 10,000 pound thrust jet for the B-52. This is about the way it came to pass, except that to accelerate the program the Air Force had Boeing change to a jet design based on J40s before the turboprop-to-turbojet switch was made at Pratt.

This was the second time Hobbs saved P&W from oblivion, and he was very proud of what he called "this chicanery." But Hobbs was a very quiet man, and this chapter passed into history with very few people knowing what really happened.[3]

Coar goes on to say that although "this all sounds as though the Air Force was politically inspired to go the B-52/J57 route, in fact there was sound engineering basis for the decision, and the program got wholehearted support from the Air Force technical community." This is corroborated by Cliff Simpson, at that time the chief of the Turbine Engine Division in the Air Force's Power Plant Laboratory at Wright-Patterson Air Force Base.

P&W launched the dual-spool idea in a turboprop design called the PT-4 in an engineering order dated September 2, 1947. The Army Air Force called it the XT45. The contract called for development of a 10,000-horsepower turboprop engine, employing a thirteen-stage axial-flow compressor with a compression ratio of 8:1. The design of the PT-4, however, was developed so that it could easily be converted to a turbojet, so when the Air Force changed the specifications in 1948 to specify a large, twin-spool turbojet engine in the 10,000 pound thrust class, the PT-4 became the JT3 again.

Design work began on the new JT3-8 turbojet engine on March 8, 1948, under the direction of Assistant Chief Engineer Perry Pratt and his Technical and Research Group, reporting directly to Hobbs. Mechanical design was directed by Andrew Willgoos, P&W's chief engineer. Although Boeing helped lobby for turbojet power for the XB-52, it was not committed to P&W for the engines. Boeing told the Air Force that either the new JT3 design or the Westinghouse J40 design would do, so P&W now had a competitor for the new bomber's engines. The company "pitched" the JT3 to the Air Force on the basis of improved power and lower specific fuel consumption, promising that the prototype would develop 8,700 pounds of thrust with a specific fuel consumption of 0.795 (pounds of fuel per hour per pound of thrust) at takeoff, with an eventual specific fuel consumption of 0.76. P&W emphasized that reduced specific fuel consumption translated into increased range potential for the B-52.

The JT3-8 was the first JT3 model tested. It was run for the first time on June 27, 1949, but yielded only 6,500 pounds of thrust because of seal leakage, compressor deficiency, and "obesity due to a faulty design approach."[4] The next model, the JT3-10A, lost 5 percent of its airflow to leakage, which cut its overall thrust and increased its fuel consumption. As Bill Gunston describes this initial testing, "even as they were built, rig testing indicated poor performance, mainly because of the very small high-pressure compressor blades, poor turbine disc design and excessive weight."[5]

On May 5, 1949, Perry Pratt, the assistant engineer for advanced engines, and Hobbs proposed to scrap the JT3-10A design and go with something different.[6] The Air Force agreed to the redesign later that month.

Pratt and his team totally redesigned the JT3. They changed to a constant-inner-diameter rotor disk on the JT3-10B instead of the constant outer diameter of previous models. This change was an attack on the leakage and pressure-ratio losses in the old design. The constant-inner-diameter rotor improved both efficiency and sealing characteristics. The compressor exterior was pinched at the high-pressure end, which reduced the engine weight by 600 pounds. An added bonus was that the wasp-waist design permitted an engine accessory arrangement that reduced nacelle diameter with an accompanying reduction in nacelle drag.[7] This new design was released to the experimental department for construction of the new engine on October 1, 1949.[8] On December 1 the Air Force ordered eighteen YJ57-P-3 prototype engines with specifications calling for 8,700 pounds of thrust and on December 6 the first drawings were released to the production department to begin building prototype engines. With the redesign, P&W's $4.6 million worth of prior design and development money spent on experimental hardware had been justified.[9]

The new engine was tested on January 21, 1950, eight months after redesign.[10] It was a redesigned JT3-10B, now called the JT3A by P&W and the J57 by the Air Force (Figure 9-1). The new engine still had problems, mainly with bearings and compressor blade vibration, which took an additional three years to work out. The Air Force stuck with the engine, however. Cliff Simpson described how the Air Force dealt with the interval:

> The old Power Plant Laboratory decided to pursue the T45, which was altered to the J57 about one year later. So, for the next three years, we took the gaff [guff] from the remaining big four in industry, with them attempting to prove we were pounding sand down the proverbial rat hole. In addition, topside [Air Force higher command] listened to the four outs [the four other engine companies] with greater acceptance than we could gain. We had no recourse but to dig in and hold as best we could. I have always greatly admired Colonel Russ Minty and Opie Chenoweth for their determination and guts in the face of such majority opinion. It was truly a case of 'everyone's out of step but me.'

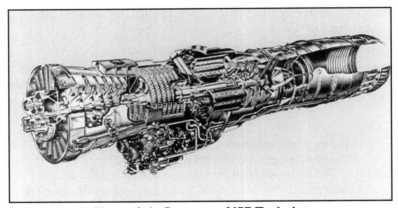

**Figure 9-1. Cutaway of J57 Turbojet**
*(Illustration courtesy of Pratt & Whitney)*

> In mid-1951, we learned how the survivors at Lucknow [the siege of Lucknow during the Indian Mutiny in 1857-1858] felt when they heard the skirling of the pipes in the distance. At the time, one of my chores was analysis and one of our chief tormentors was back to prove one more time that we were stupid, inept, incompetent and other less desirable epithets. Although he went to the front office one more time, they apparently decided that they could not stand this explanation one more time; so it became my job to listen once more. The two of us were sitting in a small conference room with the presenter's back to the door and (were) about one-third through the 'ultimate proof of stupidity.' John Coyle came down the hall and into the Commander's office with a standard telephone slip in his hand. When he came out shortly, he saw me and handed me the slip. In Johnny's handwriting it said, "J57 Ran last night - thrust 9,000 pounds, specific fuel consumption .80." I read it and said "Johnny, this is test data - right?" The reply was "You bet!" I handed the slip to our tormentor with, "I don't want to listen anymore." It was like a boulder lifted off my chest. But the other guy didn't speak to me for twenty-two years...[11]

It took only a few months before high-pressure-ratio turbojets were being proposed by GE (the J79 on February 29, 1953); Allison (the J35-A-23 and later the J71); and Curtiss-Wright (the J67, the original Bristol Olympus); Westinghouse never learned and continued with turbojets which had pressure ratios of 6:1 or 7:1.[12]

The test run at 9,000 pounds of thrust took place on March 9, 1951, as the J57 completed its 50-hour test.[13] Richard Coar described some of the developmental problems of the J57:

> The two spools weren't really the development problem that the bearings and seals were. Although the J57 never was stall free, it was rugged enough to withstand hundreds of stalls. In contrast, some of

the other axial engines had to go back to the shop after one hard stall. When the J57 went into prototype production I inherited its control and fuel system. The engine had one bad feature found also in the J47 — a vacuum tube electronic control. With its hundreds (perhaps thousands) of discrete parts, high control system reliability was theoretically impossible, a truth rapidly confirmed in the first B-52 flights. To quote Guy Townsend, the Air Force test pilot: 'I never had an eight-engine takeoff, always seven. You didn't know which seven, but they kindly failed one at a time.' We did manage to keep the prototypes flying, but quickly qualified the production engine using the kind of hydromechanical control that had worked well on the J42 and J48.[14]

## Compression System

The original J57/JT3 was made of steel, with later versions incorporating a titanium low-pressure compressor. The airflow through the J57 exceeded 200 pounds per second, and the compressor was correspondingly large. Blading in the initial rows was almost of ducted-fan caliber. The compressor had nine low-pressure stages, with compressor casing diameter decreasing to about 27 inches in the high-pressure compressor stages. There were seven high-pressure stages delivering air at about 190 pounds per square inch and at about 460°C. The two-spool compressor required two concentric drive shafts joining the turbine stages to their respective low- and high-pressure turbines. The tube between the high-pressure turbine and the rear compressor was fairly straightforward, but the driveshaft between the low-pressure (rear) turbine and the low-pressure (front) compressor posed some problems. Since this shaft lay inside its hollow companion, its diameter was constricted; accordingly, the rear turbine had to be brought up as close to its compressor as possible if a reasonable drive was to be achieved. The compressor and turbines were complete entities in themselves.[15]

## Combustion

In developing the combustion system for the JT3, P&W combustion engineers rejected both the can and annular types of combustion chambers. The simple can-type combustion chamber was rejected because, if excessive pressure drop was to be avoided, the cans would have to be reduced in length. A can-type system is not amenable to such reduction. Conventional annular systems were also rejected. Given the high internal pressures of the JT3, conventional annular chambers of reasonable weight would have buckled and burst within a short time. The JT3's unique combustion system was called the step-wall system.

From the compressor the air passed into a heavy, machined diffuser section. The internal static pressure rose still further here at the expense of velocity. The hot, dense air then entered the annular combustion zone, which housed eight flame tubes of P&W design. These cans were built-up assemblies of rings pressed from Inconel alloy. Part of the airflow entered the can through large holes to cool the flame, while the boundary layers flowed in through peripheral slots between the rings, thereby cooling the metal of the can itself. In the center of each can was a unique intake for cooling air, so the formation of a hot core was avoided. Around the front of each assembly were arranged six fuel injectors, making a total of forty-eight. These injected a fine spray downstream, achieving good mixing through baffles at the upstream end. This system permitted combustion within a very short distance. Each can was virtually a miniature annular combustion chamber. With this system, P&W achieved a combustion efficiency of 100 percent at sea level, 99 percent at 30,000 feet, and 95 percent at 50,000 feet.[16]

## Turbine

From the combustion chamber the hot gas flowed into a single-stage high-pressure turbine, which extracted most of the work from the air. Then the air flowed through a two-stage, low-pressure turbine which drove the low-pressure compressor section.[17] The last iteration of the J57, the J57-P-420, incorporated air-cooled first-stage turbine vanes.

## J57 Engine Family

The J57 delivered an average pressure ratio of 12.6:1. The highest thrust rating was 13,700 pounds wet (J57-P-43s and P-59s in the B-52F/G and the KC-135As) or 19,600 pounds with afterburner (the J57-P-420 in the F-8J fighter).[18] The JT3 flew for the first time under the wing of a B-50 on March 8, 1951.[19] The first prototype engine was delivered to Boeing on June 3, 1951. The JT3 completed a 150-hour test in the J57-3 production configuration in November 1951 and eight J57-P-3s powered the YB-52 (the second Boeing prototype) on April 15, 1952. The first production delivery of J57-P-1As to Boeing was on February 28, 1953, and the first production delivery of the J57-P-29W (or first improved "B" version) took place on January 19, 1955. The first production delivery of the J57-P-43W (or second improved version) occurred on October 31, 1956.

Aside from its service in the "Century-Series" fighters, the most famous application of the J57 was in the Boeing B-52 Stratofortress strategic bomber. The Boeing B-52 was originally intended to be a straight-wing turboprop heavy bomber. This design, called the Boeing Model 462, was offered to the Air Force with four T45 turboprop engines, each of 8,900 horsepower. This plan for a turboprop model was curtailed after a conference between the Boeing design team and the Air Force. Peter M. Bowers, in Boeing Aircraft, relates the fateful meeting:

> In October 1948, a team of Boeing's top designers went to Wright Field to discuss final details of the turboprop model with the Air Force. They were told that Air Force studies had indicated that the existing design was incapable of doing its assigned job. The turboprop project would be canceled, but the Air Force was interested in a comparable model using the new P&W J57 jet engine and asked what Boeing could do in that direction. The events of the next few days read almost like fiction. The Boeing team took the new Air Force requirements back to their Dayton hotel and studied them. The next morning, a Friday, they telephoned the project officer at Wright Field to tell him that a new Boeing proposal would be submitted on Monday. Working feverishly over the weekend and using memory of recent research supplemented by some information on the private jet bomber studies that had been brought to Dayton in the briefcases, six engineers worked out the basic design of a new eight-jet swept-wing heavy bomber. Typed by a public stenographer and accompanied by a balsa wood model that one engineer built with materials obtained from a local hobby shop, the proposal was submitted to the Air Force as promised on Monday.[20]

Compare this anecdote with Richard Coar's recollection earlier in this chapter.

The design studies and wind tunnel tests of the new design so impressed the Air Force that it issued Boeing a letter of intent for the manufacture of production B-52 tooling in March 1951. Boeing completed the first prototype XB-52 on November 29, 1951. This was more than a year before the first test flight. The XB and YB models of the Stratofortress used eight J57-P-3 8,700-pound-thrust turbojets.

Initial production B-52s used J57-P-9W turbojets with water injection, while the B-52B models used the improved J57-P-19W, J57-P-29W, and J57-P-29WA engines. On January 18, 1957, three such B-52Bs completed a nonstop flight around the world in 45 hours and 19 minutes at an average speed of 520 mph for the 24,325 miles.[21]

The last B-52 to use the J57 engine was the B-52F, which was equipped with eight 13,750-pound-thrust J57-P-43W turbojet engines. The B-52 variants built after this aircraft were equipped with P&W TF33 (a derivative of the J57) turbofan engines. On January 11, 1962, a B-52H (Figure 9-2) equipped with eight 17,000-pound-thrust TF33-P-3 turbofans flew nonstop from Okinawa to Spain to set a new nonrefueled distance record of 12,519 miles (a record which stood until December 1986).[22] Boeing B-52Fs, B-52Gs, and B-52Hs saw service in Vietnam from June 18, 1965, to August 15, 1973, flying 126,615 combat sorties.[23]

**Figure 9-2. Boeing B-52H Stratofortress**
*(Photo courtesy of U.S. Air Force)*

The J57 powered the first supersonic aircraft in production anywhere, the North American F-100 Super Sabre (Figure 9-3). North American Aircraft (NAA) began the design of the F-100 (NAA designation was NA-180) on January 19, 1951, incorporating a low wing with 40-degree sweep and making extensive use of weight-saving titanium. Designated the first in the "Century Series" of new generation fighter aircraft, the "Hun," as it was affectionately called by Air Force pilots, had a top speed of 660 mph at a combat ceiling of 26,000 feet.[24] A J57-P-7 with afterburner took the YF-100 jet fighter prototype beyond Mach 1 on its first flight on May 25, 1953.[25] This was the first afterburning J57 and incorporated a steel compressor, delivering 9,700 pounds of thrust dry and 14,800 pounds of thrust in full afterburner mode.[26]

**Figure 9-3. North American F-100 Super Sabre**
*(Photo courtesy of U.S. Air Force)*

Beginning with the F-100B, later versions of the Super Sabre were powered by the J57-P-21. This model also had a steel compressor section and delivered 16,000 pounds of thrust with full afterburner.[27] P&W produced 1,073 J57-P-21s, with Ford Motor Company producing an additional 913 of this model. Some of the F-100D variants used the J57-P-21A (759 engines produced), and the F-100C variant used the J57-P-39. The J57-P-39 delivered 14,800 pounds of thrust.[28]

The F-100 Super Sabre entered service with the Air Force in September 1954 and saw service in Vietnam until 1971 in both fighter-bomber and "Wild Weasel" anti-radar roles. The last "Hun" was retired from active service on November 10, 1979, after twenty-five years of durable service.[29] This fighter was also exported to France, Denmark, Turkey, and Taiwan.

Another major application of the J57 was the General Dynamics F-102 Delta Dagger supersonic interceptor (Figure 9-4). This delta-winged aircraft, a supersonic single-seat fighter, was conceived as a total "weapons systems" package, incorporating air-to-air missiles and all-weather radar search and fire control. Convair received a contract, along with Lockheed and Republic, to build two prototype YF-102s on December 19, 1951. Although the original design proposal called for the Wright Aero J67 turbojet as the propulsion system, the engine was not ready when the airplane prototypes were completed. Convair decided to use the J57 for the Delta Dagger, and the J57-P-11 model of the engine was used in the prototypes and the first twenty production aircraft. The aircraft, however, did not perform up to expectations. When loaded with 1,194 pounds of armaments, 1,050 gallons of fuel, and nearly 2,000 pounds of electronics, the F-102 was 50 percent heavier than the F-86D at combat weight. Flight testing found severe buffeting at Mach 0.9, and therefore the aircraft could not deliver its anticipated 870 mph at 35,000 feet altitude. Although many prototype aircraft do not live up to initial expectations, what made the F-102 significant was the innovation used to increase its performance. What saved the delta-wing concept for Convair and the Delta Dagger was the application of "coke-bottling" or area rule to the F-102's fuselage. The area rule was developed by NACA scientist Richard Whitcomb and dramatically reduced drag at transonic speeds. Supersonic speeds were achieved with an F-102 redesign incorporating an area-ruled fuselage with a lengthened nose and tail fairings on December 21, 1954.[30] The first F-102A Delta Darts were delivered to the Air Force on May 1, 1956. Later F-102s were equipped with the J57-P-23 afterburning engine. The F-102 served with an excellent safety record from 1956 through 1973, including service in Vietnam.[31]

**Figure 9-4. General Dynamics Convair F-102
Delta Dagger**
*(Photo courtesy of U.S. Air Force)*

The third Air Force fighter application of the J57 was in the McDonnell F-101A Voodoo long-range fighter (Figure 9-5). Initiated in January 1952, the F-101 was originally designed as a high-speed fighter-escort for U.S. Air Force Strategic Air Command (SAC) bombers, but was also used as a penetration-escort, tactical/nuclear strike interceptor, reconnaissance and conversion training aircraft. Like the Navy's F-9F and the Air Force's F-100, the F-101 was designed as a response to the highly maneuverable MiG-15 encountered over North Korea. The F-101's initial design mission was to escort B-29 and B-36 bombers on their strategic bombing missions in the North. For this mission, long range, endurance, high power and maneuverability were essential. Although the McDonnell design team, led by Edward M. Flesh, had decided upon the Allison J71 turbojet as the power plant for the new fighter, the Air Force engineers at the Wright Air Development Center pushed for the even-more-powerful P&W J57. This choice proved to be very wise, as the J57 and the F-101 were a natural match (although there were a few intake problems with the aircraft and a few compressor stall problems with the engine). An F-101B made the U.S. Air Force's first supersonic intercept on June 9, 1958.[32]

**Figure 9-5. McDonnell RF-101A Voodoo**
*(Photo courtesy of U.S. Air Force)*

On December 17, 1953, P&W Engineering Manager Leonard "Luke" Hobbs received the prestigious Collier Trophy for 1953 from President Eisenhower. It was the first time in twenty-one years that the Collier Trophy had been awarded for the development of an engine.[33]

Gunston considers this engine:

> ...probably the most important engine in the world since 1945. It initially gave 10,000 pounds dry or 15,000 pounds with afterburner yet, because of its pressure ratio of 12.5, it set totally new standards in jet fuel economy. Almost certainly its use in short-range fighters was mistaken: they would have done better with a less-economical engine of half the J57's weight of about 5,000 pounds with afterburner. For the B-52 and many other long range aircraft the J57 opened possibilities previously only dreamed of, not least being the design of the 707 and DC-8 commercial jets using civil JT3C engines."[34]

The total full-scale test time accumulated by June 30, 1974, was 101,270 hours.

## Development of the J57 for the Navy

Although P&W did not originally envision producing the J57 for the Navy, they quickly agreed to produce models of the engine tailored to that service's requirements. The J57-P-4, J57-P-11, and J57-P-12 models powered the Chance Vought F8U Crusader (Figure 9-6), the first operational Navy carrier-based fighter to exceed 1,000 mph. After eight aircraft manufacturers competed for a Navy contract starting in September 1952, the Navy issued a contract for the F8U to Vought on June 29, 1953. The aircraft, powered by a J57-P-11 of 14,800 pounds of thrust with a titanium-shrouded afterburner, went supersonic on its maiden flight at Edwards Air Force Base on March 25, 1955. Production F8Us were first flown on September 20, 1955, and entered squadron service with VF-32 in March 1957. The Crusader went into service with the J57-P-12 providing 16,000 pounds of thrust. Major John Glenn made the first transcontinental supersonic flight in an F8U1P (photographic reconnaissance) Crusader on July 16, 1957. The west-to-east flight took 3 hours and 22 minutes.[35]

**Figure 9-6. Vought F8U Crusader**
*(Photo courtesy of U.S. Navy)*

The second major application for the Navy versions of the J57 was the Douglas Aircraft A3D (A3) Skywarrior strategic bomber (Figure 9-7). Led by Ed Heineman, Douglas engineers designed a heavy attack bomber with the capability to deliver a Mark 15 nuclear bomb, six 1,600 pound bombs, or six Mark 36 antishipping mines on a target up to 1,150 miles away at 621 mph—faster than the big Boeing aircraft the Air Force was building. The A3D-1's high wing was swept back 36 degrees. P&W provided J57-P-6 and J57-P-10 engines for the service squadrons, with deliveries to the Navy beginning in March 31, 1956. A total of 284 Skywarriors were delivered to the Navy. The Air Force version of this aircraft was designated the B-66. After service as a bomber, many of the Skywarriors were converted to tanker aircraft, where they served well.[36]

**Figure 9-7. Douglas A3D Skywarrior**
*(Photo courtesy of U.S. Navy)*

Douglas and the Navy decided in June 1953 to install the J57 in the Douglas F4D-1 Skyray (Figure 9-8). Although they originally assigned the Westinghouse J40 turbojet to the Skyray, production difficulties with the J40 were so great that both Douglas and the Navy decided to re-engine the fighter with the J57. The first re-engined Skyrays used the J57-P-2, but production versions used the J57-P-8. The J57-P-8 was also to be used in the F5D Skylancer, but the aircraft was canceled by the Navy.[37]

The civil version of the J57, the JT3C, entered scheduled service on October 26, 1958, with a time-between-overhaul (TBO) of 8,000 hours. The JT3C was later developed to a thrust (dry) of 13,000 pounds and a weight of 3,495 pounds, almost 1,000 pounds lighter than the original

**Figure 9-8. Douglas F4D Skyray**
*(Photo courtesy of National Air & Space Museum)*

B-52 engine, and with a TBO of 14,120 hours.[38] Between 1951 and 1960, P&W made 15,024 J57/JT3s. Ford Motor Company made a further 6,202 engines in Chicago. Gunston states:

> The JT3 fulfilled every hope in overcoming P&W's late start in gas turbines, and fortuitously the failure of the rival J40 gave it the United States Navy market which had not been expected. Obviously it was not an end but a beginning, and from a host of possibilities the first derived engines were the J75 and the JT4.

The J57 axial turbojet engine has probably been the most successful military engine program that P&W has ever put together. While the J42 and J48 got P&W started, the J57 established the company as a leading player in the technology. The J57 was a "home-grown" development program, based on solid research by the company and several academic institutions. By December 1984, when P&W ceased building J57s, the engine in its various models had accumulated over 100,000 hours on the test stand.[39] P&W has gained invaluable engineering experience in "growing" this engine into its many models. One of the most important engineering changes resulted in the JT3D turbofan, which for the first time made commercial airliners or transports practical as well as possible, offering an aircraft range unachievable with turbojets.

## The Design and Development of the P&W JT3D/TF33 Turbofan Engine

Although the JT3D engine has a company numeric designation lower than the P&W JT4 engine, it actually came later than the JT4. Designated the J75 by the Air Force, the JT4 was a powerful engine in its own right, but it wasn't meant to be a commercial development at all. Using the J75 program as a vehicle, the Air Force steadfastly provided support and funding despite many obstacles and disappointments, to develop titanium alloys and processing for use in aircraft engines. The triple-vacuum-melted titanium now used by most manufacturers to eliminate "low-cycle" fatigue in fan discs is a typical result. This work made weight reductions of about 40 percent possible in engine fan and compressor components. After its first 50-hour test, the JT4/J75 was completely redesigned to correct major compressor and bearing problems, yet in commercial service the JT4 achieved mature reliability faster than did the JT3 with its background of military flight experience.

The story of how the JT3D became a commercial engine for the first Boeing 707s deserves retelling, for it also illustrates how a company can overcome its own misperceptions and biases against technological change and the "not-invented-here" syndrome. The overcoming of P&W's bias against the turbofan made the JT3D (TF33) possible. Richard Coar related this story in the Second Annual L.V. Smith Lecture:

> It was early 1955 before Boeing and Douglas were offering four engine aircraft powered by JT3's (civil version of the J57). Like the Comet III, neither of these planes had transatlantic range. A 15,000

pound thrust engine was needed. Rentschler and the Pratt management were not ready to offer the 15,000 pound thrust JT4 for commercial use because at this time the J75 military version had not even flown. Debug the engine in military operation, then go commercial was Pratt's approach. Nevertheless Fred Rentschler finally succumbed to Juan Trippe's blandishments and offered the JT4.

In a surprise move, Pan Am then ordered 116 JT4 engines. This was before we had redesigned the production engine, and before Pan Am ordered any airplanes! This decision forced rapid convergence of the Douglas and Boeing designs to use the JT4 so both now had transatlantic range. As you know, the British Comets suffered structural failures in flight, and were withdrawn from service. So ended the British attempt at air domination...

A few 707's and DC-8's were fitted with Rolls Conway engines. These were bypass or fan engines and the cycle should have made them more fuel efficient than the JT4. In practice there was no significant difference in airplane performance, Conway versus JT4. This was probably the result of poor fan efficiency in the Conway. At this time studies by United Aircraft's Research Department showed clearly that a modest fan bypass ratio should give 15-20% better aircraft range. Walt Doll of P&W's technical and research operation put this data together in a speech for Wright Parkins to give in Rome at an airline conference. To Parkins, "fans were no damn good," (they weren't invented here). Just to make Parkins madder he didn't see his speech till he's over the North Atlantic. He spends the rest of the trip re-writing the speech, to say that fans are no damn good, then he comes home and sends letters out to the world's airlines saying that Pratt will never build a fan. Next he cancels the few Pratt projects funded at the Research Department, and revokes all the badges that let Research employees into the P&W engineering building. John Lee, head of United's research lab retaliated by calling in all badges that gave Pratt's employees access to the research lab...

After the DC-8 and B707 were introduced, GE decides to offer its J79 for commercial service and sold this CJ805 to American Airlines for the Convair 880 and an aft-fan version for the Convair 990. GE had decided that the way to make money in the airline business would be to make a cheaper version of the military engine. As it stood, the military J79 already wasn't doing well, and you can imagine GE's troubles with the 880 and 990. Eventually GE withdrew from that market. What's important in our story is that GE almost convinced American Airlines to buy 707's with GE aft-fans. Here the monkey wrench came from Maynard Pennell, the 707 designer, who gets Art Smith, Bill Gorton, and Perry Pratt to come to New York so he can convince them that if P&W doesn't do something in the way of a fan, American Airlines will go to the GE engines. This hits Pratt where it hurts, and Perry remembers the military fan I cobbled up for him back in 1954. So right there in the hotel the front fan was reborn - replace three JT3 front stages with two larger stages using JT4 transonic aerodynamics. Put two discharge nozzles right up front with the fan and you have a package that can be retrofitted in existing engines. A quick and dirty test is run almost overnight and proves the concept works. American Airlines buys. The operational people in the Air Force, meanwhile, see no need for this kind of engine, but Bill Irvine, Chief of Procurement, sees what it could do for a B-52. He overpowers the Air Force's bureaucratic inertia to issue demonstration contracts to both Pratt and GE for fan demonstrations. Pratt's continued testing convinces the Air Force Power Plant Laboratory to fly some front fan prototypes on a B-52. The range improvement turns out to be even more spectacular in the 707. The JT3D/TF33 now becomes the standard engine for 707's, DC-8's and B-52's.[40]

The roots of the JT3D/TF33 turbofan engine lay in the P&W X-287 or J91 turbojet engine for the Air Force Chemical-Fuel Bomber (CFB) WS-110A program. Only two experimental engines resulted from this program, which P&W ultimately lost in a competition with GE, but the transonic compressor design laid the groundwork for the much more successful JT3D (Figure 9-9).[41]

The P&W engine design team began work on the new engine on February 7, 1958, selecting the JT3 as the base engine to which the new transonic technology would be applied. The first two compressor stages of the J91 were scaled down to a 53-inch diameter, yielding an airflow of 450 pounds per second through the fan. The team then added a third low-pressure turbine stage and a new fan duct. The first test run of the new engine with its three fan stages was on June 13, 1958. The Air Force saw the value of the new engine and funded further development and production of a military version, designated the TF33. The JT3D/TF33 passed the 50-hour test on November 17, 1959, and had its first flight test on July 21, 1959. It passed its 150-hour Military Qualification Test on April 23, 1960, and the first TF33 was subsequently delivered to the Air

**Figure 9-9. Cutaway of JT3D/TF33 Turbofan**
*(Illustration courtesy of Pratt & Whitney)*

Force on May 31, 1960. The P&W team had accomplished a major technological feat: they had married the fuel efficiency of the JT3 engine to a front fan configuration.

By first applying the J91 transonic fan aerodynamic innovations to the JT3, P&W was able to come up with a turbofan engine that was both technologically superior to any comparable British engine and easily adaptable from a JT3 engine. All a mechanic had to do to convert a JT3 to a JT3D was to change over the compressor using a kit sent by the company. Although the conversion increased the weight marginally, the accompanying thrust was increased by 35 percent, fuel burn was reduced by 15 to 20 percent , and the takeoff noise was reduced by some 10 decibels.[42]

The impact of the JT3D on the airline industry was remarkable. Together with such new aircraft as the Boeing 707 (Figure 9-10), the JT3D provided the means for an unprecedented change in the world of commercial transport aircraft. Although P&W had already been supplying both Boeing and Douglas with the JT4 turbojet engine for the 707 jetliner and DC-8, the JT3D was something else entirely. With a practical turbofan engine offering both jet engine speed and competitive specific fuel consumption, an era of jet airliners and transports able to surpass piston-engined aircraft was now possible.

**Figure 9-10. Boeing 707**
*(Photo courtesy of Boeing Co.)*

The British were the first to build and fly a jet airliner; however, the de Havilland 106 Comet proved to be no match for the new Boeing 707. With its thirty-five-degree swept wings and its JT3D engines, the 707 cruised at 550 mph, 100 mph faster than the Comet 2.[43]

The first effect of jet aircraft on air transportation was to increase the speed with which the passenger was able to get to his or her destination. Additional factors, however, emerged to make jet air transport superior to piston-engine aircraft. Over a given period, a jet aircraft, whether flying passengers or cargo, could generate more revenue simply by being able to make more round trips over its route. Another unexpected benefit to companies was further revenue from greatly decreased down time; the smoothness of jet travel greatly reduced airframe fatigue and the subsequent frequent overhaul and component replacement. The problems associated with airframe fatigue caused by frequent altitude "cycles" on jet aircraft was still in the future.

Peter M. Bowers, in Boeing Aircraft Since 1916, points out a frequently overlooked early advantage that jet aircraft brought to commercial airlines: the ability of jet aircraft to carry more passengers.

> The early Boeing 707-100, with non-stop transcontinental range, seated 121 first-class passengers compared to 55 for the Boeing 377 and 69 for the Douglas DC-7B models that it replaced. Even the short-range Boeing 737-100 and the Douglas DC-9 that preceded it by two years, seat 107 and 80, respectively. All jetliners have gone through subsequent stretches of the cabin area to increase their capacity.[44]

The turbofan had an important impact on the air freight industry as well. Airlines began using passenger jets to also carry cargo, and the freight lines were forced to buy jet aircraft to stay competitive. With the use of both pallets and standard-sized containers, airlines and air-freight companies employed the point-to-point speed of jets more than they had ever before.[45]

Production of the JT3D ended in 1985 at about 8,600, most of them conversions. Late models of the Military TF33, the TF33-P-7 and TF33-PW-100, have seven low-pressure stages and ratings of 21,000 pounds of thrust. The commercial version of the TF33, the JT3D, is still being produced, although commercial operators still must make more costly modifications to their JT3Ds to comply with tougher FAA Stage 2 noise standards.[46]

## Design and Development of the P&W JT8 (J-52) Turbojet Engine

The JT8 was a scaled-down version of the very successful JT3 turbojet engine program. Although the engineering order initiating the JT8 program came on February 16, 1953, actual engine design work started on August 14, 1954. The JT8 (Figure 9-11) incorporated five low-pressure and seven high-pressure compressor stages in a dual-spool configuration, and one low-pressure and one high-pressure turbine. The engine was released for experimental use in April 1955, with the first experimental engine test run on December 30, 1955.[47]

**Figure 9-11. Cutaway of JT8/J52 Turbojet**
*(Illustration courtesy of Pratt &Whitney)*

The JT8 passed its flight test on October 9, 1957, in a B-45 test bed aircraft. The engine was released to production on May 29, 1958, and passed its 50-hour test on July 29, 1958. The first delivery of a prototype engine, an XJ52-P-1, was on August 23, 1958, and the first YJ52-P-1 was shipped on October 26, 1958.

The first scheduled production delivery was on October 23, 1959. This was the "A" series of the engine, designed for a missile application and designated the J52-P-2 and J52-P-4. None were shipped, however, due to cancellation of the production contract.

The first production "A" series engine actually delivered was the J52-P-3. It had its first missile free flight on April 23, 1959, in the AGM-28 Hound Dog missile and passed its 150-hour Military Qualification Test on July 2, 1959.[48] The man-rated version of the J52, the YJ52-P-6 model, had its first test run on March 11, 1959. This was the first of the increased-thrust "B" Series.

The J52-P-3 had an axial-flow compressor, nine through-flow combustion chambers arranged in an annular chamber, and a two-stage reaction turbine. The multistage axial compressor consisted of a five-stage low-pressure unit and a seven-stage high-pressure unit. The low-pressure unit was connected by a through-shaft to the second-stage turbine wheel, and the high-pressure unit was independently connected by a hollow shaft to the first-stage turbine wheel. The engine was equipped with a convergent-divergent exhaust nozzle suited for high-Mach-number operation. The P-3 was the same as the P-1 except that it was 80 pounds lighter, did not incorporate titanium, and consumed less fuel.[49]

The first YJ52-P-6 man-rated engine was delivered on December 9, 1959, with delivery of the "B" series of the production YJ52-P-6 engine beginning on October 31, 1960, when the model passed its Preliminary Flight Ratings Test. On April 19, 1960, the YJ52-P-6 model made its first flight in the Grumman A-2F, which later was redesignated the A-6A Intruder, and on July 26 the YJ52-P-6 passed its 150-hour Military Qualification Test, providing the go-ahead for the first production engine deliveries to Douglas. The Navy awarded P&W a development contract for a growth version of the J52, the J52-P-8 (or JT8B-3) on June 29, 1962.

The first flight of the Grumman A-6A was on July 12, 1960. Ray Wagner describes the Intruder in *American Combat Planes*:

> Grumman's Intruder was the first jet-attack type designed for both limited and nuclear warfare, and its accuracy and weapons capacity enabled it to replace the last prop-driven A-1 in Navy service. Originally designated A2F-1, the A-6A was designed for short take-off and landings, long-range, all-weather location of targets, and low-level attack with conventional or nuclear bombs, rockets, or missiles.
>
> Two P&W J52-P-6 jets were mounted below the wing roots of wings swept back 25° with full-span leading-edge slots, slotted flaps, and flapperons (spoilers serving as ailerons). The two crewmen sat side-by-side, with the bombardier-navigator operating a digital integrated attack navigation system (DIANE) that included search and track radar, a computer, and two screens for presenting both the ground and the airspace ahead of the aircraft. They could attack without any outside visibility at all, but no guns were provided. The wings folded upwards and a flight-refueling boom was placed above the radar nose.[50]

The first production deliveries of the Grumman A-6A with the J52-P-6 started on July 24, 1963.[51] A variant to the A-6A, the EA-6A, which contained countermeasures equipment, shows how flexible this aircraft became as it evolved.

P&W delivered a J52-P-8 mockup to the Navy on October 25, 1960, for the Douglas A-4 Skyhawk (Figure 9-12). Wagner describes the Skyhawk:

> One of the most successful attack aircraft in Navy service was the simple design called Heineman's Hot Rod, after the Douglas chief engineer who insisted on reversing the trend towards constantly increasing weight and cost. Designed to deliver a tactical nuclear weapon, the single-place A-4 had a low delta wing small enough not to require folding on carrier decks. Armed with two 20-mm guns in the

wing roots with 100 rounds per gun, the Skyhawk had provisions for a Mark 7 or Mark 8 nuclear store under the fuselage and wing racks for 300-gallon drop tanks or conventional bombs; a total of 5,975 pounds of bombs could be carried on the first model.[52]

**Figure 9-12. Douglas A-4 Skyhawk**
*(Photo courtesy of National Air & Space Museum)*

The Navy had ordered twenty developmental models of this aircraft on June 13, 1952, and the first flew as the XA-4D-1 on June 22, 1954. Initial models were powered by two Wright 7,200-pound-thrust J65-W-2 (an American version of the British Sapphire) engines, but the Navy eagerly seized on the J52 when it authorized purchase of two A-4D-5 aircraft with P&W J52 engines on July 30, 1959. The first of these aircraft flew July 12, 1961, and 498 production models, now designated A-4E, were delivered from May 1962 to April 1966. The J52-powered Skyhawks joined the fleet in December 1962. The J52 in the A-4E entered combat with the first direct intervention in the Vietnam War on August 5, 1964, when 15 A-4Es joined 49 other Navy attack aircraft for an air strike on North Vietnam.[53]

A P&W pre-production J52-P-8 engine completed flight tests in the A-4E on May 10, 1963. The engine and aircraft completed anti-icing and cold-start testing at Eglin Field on December 20.[54] The J52-P-6 engine completed its 150-hour Military Qualification Test at J52-P-8 ratings on October 10, 1964 and the J52-P-8 completed its MQT on June 7, 1965. The first flight of the J52-P-8-powered TA-4F was made on October 15, 1965.[55] First production deliveries of the J52-P-8A began on August 31, 1965.[56] October 18, 1965, marked the first flight of the A-6A with the J52-P-8A engine. The J52-P-8A completed a 150-hour endurance test at maximum temperature ratings on February 10, 1966, and on October 20, 1967, its time-between-overhaul (TBO) was raised to 750 hours. On February 15, 1968, the J52-P-8A completed a 215-hour endurance test at J52-P-8B ratings and it completed a 150-hour endurance test on a finalized reduced-smoke burner on June 24, 1968.[57]

P&W received a Phase I development contract for a third improved version of the "B" series of the engine, the J52-P-408 (or JT8B-5), on February 20, 1969, and completed Model Qualification of the J52-P-408 in a B-45 Flying Test Bed on January 23, 1970. Five days later, the YJ52-P-408 completed its Preliminary Flight Rating Test and was accepted by the U.S. Navy. On March 16, the engine completed a test for Demonstration of Altitude Performance Guarantees. Finally, on May 8, 1970, the J52-P-408 engine completed its Model Qualification Test.[58] On July 1, 1969, Douglas shipped the first J52-P-408 conversion kit. The first experimental test run of it was on July 15, 1969. On November 10 of that year, P&W shipped the first XJ52-P-408 ground test engine to Douglas, followed by the first YJ52-P-408 flight test engine on March 31, 1970. The YJ52-P-408 first flew in the Douglas A-4M on April 10, 1970. By May 8 of that year the engine passed its 150-hour Military Qualification Test and was approved by the Navy. P&W

delivered the first production J52-P-408 to the Navy on June 30, 1970.[59] The J52-P-408 turbojet ultimately produced 7,500 to 11,200 pounds of thrust.

A J52-P-408 powered the first flight of the Grumman EA-6B Electronics Counter-Measures aircraft (Figure 9-13) on January 14, 1972. In September the A-4F, powered by the J52-P-408, was selected as the aircraft for the "Blue Angels" flight demonstration team.[60] In October 1974 the J52-P-408 was cleared for 1,250 hours time-between-overhaul, and in November of that year, Kuwait ordered 36 J52-powered A-4s for delivery starting in 1977. By January 1, 1975, more than 1,550 J52-powered A-4s and 600 A-6s had been delivered. By October 1, 1975, over 4,250 J52 engines had been delivered including over 550 J52-P-408s, and over 48,700 engine development hours had been completed on the engine, including 6,637 hours on the J52-P-408. Most impressively, by that date over 4.8 million engine flight hours had been accumulated, including over 153,000 J52-P-408 flight hours.[61]

**Figure 9-13. Grumman EA-6B Prowler**
*(Photo courtesy of U.S. Navy)*

The JT8 never found a commercial market, but the J52 military version was produced until 1986.[62] Just as the JT3 was the forerunner of the JT8, the JT8 was the forerunner of a derivative engine that was to change the commercial engine world.

## Design and Development of the JT8D Turbofan Engine

While the JT8/J52 design had little commercial success but found a military application, the JT8D (Figure 9-14) turbofan engine saw only limited use by the military but was very successful in the commercial arena. It achieved an outstanding measure of success first with Boeing in the 727, then with McDonnell-Douglas and other commercial airframe developers. Bill Gunston, in his *World Encyclopedia of Aircraft Engines*, states:

> In sharpest contrast [with the JT8] the derived JT8D turbofan, produced in 1960-61 to power the 727, has had hardly any military sales (apart from the Volvo Flygmotor RM8), yet it has probably been the most profitable gas turbine in history, with 12,000 having logged 245 million hours at the time of writing...[63]

The JT8D turbofan design was started by P&W with an engineering order dated March 1, 1960. Actual design of the engine began on April 1, 1960. The JT8D design differed from the JT8 in that the low-pressure spool was changed to have two fan and six low-pressure stages. This arrangement was driven by a three-stage turbine. The airflow in the engine was roughly doubled, from 136-143 pounds per second to 315-331 pounds per second with an overall pressure ratio of about 16.[64] The P&W design team was able to save considerable time on the engine; it was released to experimental on November 30, 1960.[65] P&W expertise had already been recognized in that the 14,000 pound JT8D-1 had been ordered by Boeing the preceding month to power the three-engine 727. All experimental drawings of the engine were released in December of that year.

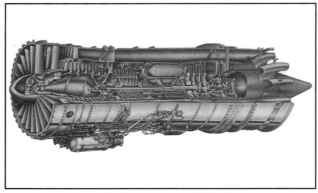

**Figure 9-14. Cutaway of JT8D Turbofan**
*(Illustration courtesy of Pratt & Whitney)*

The JT8D first ran on April 7, 1961. On October 21, the JT8D-P-1 passed its first 150-hour endurance test and first deliveries of the prototype JT8D began in April 1962. The first flight test of the pod-mounted prototype JT8D-P-1 engine was on May 1, 1962, in a Boeing 367-80 flight test aircraft.[66] This was followed on June 22 by the first flight test in a B-45 test bed. The turbofan passed its 150-hour Military Qualification Test and was cleared for prototype delivery on December 28, 1962; the first prototype JT8D-P-1 was delivered on May 1, 1962. The first production JT8D-P-1 was FAA certified on February 9 and delivered on February 27, 1963.[67] At the same time, the JT8D-P-5, a derated version with 12,000 pounds of thrust, was FAA certified. The first flight of a JT8D-P-1-powered 727 tri-jet aircraft was later that same month, and the first production P-1 engine was delivered on February 28. In April, Douglas announced that it would produce the twin-engine JT8D-powered DC-9. In December 1963 the Boeing 727 completed a 94,000-mile trouble-free world tour. The JT8D started commercial service in the Boeing 727 in February 1964 with Eastern Airlines and in the Caravelle Super B with Finnair in August 1964.[68]

The JT8D engine also powered the McDonnell Douglas DC-9 (Figure 9-15) and its "stretch" variants, the DC-9-10, DC-9-20, and DC-9-30. While the P&W JT3C and JT3D engine had helped the Boeing 707 jet transport to seize the bulk of the jet transport business starting in 1954, the JT8D engine really helped McDonnell Douglas get back into the thick of the commercial aircraft business in 1965. Bill Yenne, in *McDonnell Douglas: A Tale of Two Giants*, described the launch of the DC-9:

> With the exception of the enigmatic DC-5, the trend with each model of Douglas Commercial transports since the beginning was to be larger than its predecessor. The plane that the company announced in 1962 broke that trend. The proposed DC-9 was smaller than either the DC-8 or the DC-7, and the basic version carried fewer passengers than some versions of the DC-6 and DC-4. The idea was to develop a jet transport for the short-range markets of the world. Boeing had seized the long- and medium-range markets with its 707 and 720, and the new 727 would be another medium-range jetliner. Boeing had come to dominate the commercial market more completely than any company since Douglas stunned the market with the DC-3. The Seattle plane maker, however, still had shown no intentions of getting into the short-range jetliner market (it would, eventually, with its 737) and Douglas felt it could easily compete with the smaller companies who were already there.
>
> The DC-9 Series 10 first flew on February 25, 1965 and made its first in-service flight for Delta Airlines on December 8, 1965. It was 104 feet and 4 inches long, 83 feet shorter than a DC-8 Super Sixty, 46 feet shorter than a standard DC-8 and very different in appearance. The forward fuselage was similar but the rest of the design was decidedly dissimilar. The DC-9 had two engines instead of four, and they were located at the aft fuselage rather than on the wing. The horizontal tail surfaces were located at the top of the vertical tail plane like the Boeing 727 and the BAC 111, which also had their engines located aft.[69]

**Figure 9-15. McDonnell Douglas DC-9**
*(Photo courtesy of McDonnell Douglas)*

Delta Airlines inaugurated DC-9 scheduled service with the P&W JT8D-P-5 turbofan engine on November 29, 1965.[70] The DC-9-20, developed for Scandinavian Air Services, had a DC-9-10 fuselage but the DC-9-30's wing. The first flight of the DC-9-30, 15 feet longer than the DC-9-20 and DC-9-10, was on August 1, 1966. The DC-9-40, 6 feet longer than the DC-9-30, first flew on November 28, 1967. The first DC-9-50 flew on December 17, 1974. It was 29 feet and 2 inches longer than the DC-9-10 series and 8 feet longer than the DC-9-40 series.

McDonnell Douglas made 976 commercial DC-9s. The company also made 20 military versions of the DC-9 as the Air Force C-9A Nightingale, and 14 C-9B Skytrain IIs for the U.S. Navy.[71] Meanwhile, Boeing had announced the start of its 737 program, a short and mid-range transport to compete with the DC-9.[72]

The first "improved" version of the JT8D was the JT8D-P-7. It was certified on March 24, 1966, and first delivered from production on September 9, 1966. The JT8D-P-7 extended the JT8D-P-1's sea level takeoff thrust rating of 14,000 pounds from 59°F to 84°F. A second improved version of the engine, the JT8D-P-9, was delivered from production on July 27, 1967, and FAA certified in September 1968. [73]

The JT8D-P-9 and JT8D-P-9A turbofan were forward-fan-type engines with a twin-spool axial compressor. They had nine can-annular burners in the combustion chamber, and were provided with a multistage turbine. The multistage axial compressor consisted of a low-pressure unit (which included the fan stages) and a high-pressure unit. The low-pressure unit was connected by a through-shaft to the turbine wheels and the high-pressure unit was connected independently by a hollow shaft. The engine was equipped with a full-length, annular fan-discharge duct which surrounded the basic conventional convergent exhaust nozzle. A hydromechanical fuel control governed the rotor speed of the high-pressure compressor and scheduled fuel flow to provide the thrust called for by the throttle setting in the cockpit of the aircraft. A thrust reverser was also provided.[74]

The JT8D-9 powered the Boeing 727 and 727-200, the 737, the McDonnell Douglas DC-9-30 and DC-9-40 airliners, the C-9A and C-9B transports, and the Aerospatiale Caravelle series of commercial aircraft.[75] By September 1969, over 5,000 JT8Ds had been delivered, an incredible number for just over nine years.

A third improved version of the engine, the JT8D-P-11, was first produced on November 12, 1968. Delivering 12,600 pounds of thrust, it powered the Boeing 727-200, and the McDonnell Douglas DC-9-20, DC-9-30, and DC-9-40 model commercial aircraft.[76]

After 1970 the JT8D combustion system was modified to reduce smoke. April 8, 1971 marked the production delivery of the fourth improved version, the JT8D-P-15. The engine was also FAA-certified in that month.[77] The JT8D-P-15 was the first JT8D engine equipped with full noise treatment. This meant turbine case acoustical treatment, as well as the fan duct treatment now in use. The fan duct noise treatment has been installed in over 200 engines with over one million trouble-free hours in these parts. The P&W JT8D-P-15 delivered 13,750 pounds of thrust and powered the Boeing Advanced 727-200,[78] and Advanced 737-300, the Dassault Mercure (in June 1974),[79] and the McDonnell Douglas DC-9-30, DC-9-40 and DC-9-50 commercial aircraft.[80]

On February 15, 1973, P&W announced the availability of the next growth model of the JT8D series, the JT8D-P-17, at 16,000 pounds of takeoff thrust. The JT8D-P-17 was certified in February 1974. By April 1974, JT8D time-between-overhauls had reached 16,800 hours at Delta Airlines. In June 1974 the JT8D-17/Advanced 727-200 had received its FAA certification and the first delivery was made to Mexicana Airlines. By April 1976 the JT8D had accumulated over 100 million flight hours. On July 5, 1976, Douglas announced start of the JT8D-P-17-powered advanced DC-9-50 program with sale of 10 to SwissAir. On November 14 of that year, Boeing certified the advanced 727-200 at 208,000 pounds gross weight.[81] On October 15, 1974, P&W announced a growth version of the JT8D-P-17 model, the JT8D-P-17R rated at 16,400 pounds of takeoff thrust (with an additional 1000 pounds of thrust in reserve). By July 1975 over 90 million JT8D flight hours had been accumulated. On April 29, 1976, the FAA certified the JT8D-P-17R. By April the 100 million JT8D flight hour milestone had been reached. Production deliveries of the JT8D-P-17R model engine began to Boeing in May 1976. On June 9 of that year engine number 8,000 (a JT8D-P-15 to Boeing) was shipped.[82]

A refanned JT8D-P-200 series was marketed by P&W for the very successful McDonnell-Douglas MD-80 series of airliners. This new model increased the JT8D's thrust from the 14,000-17,400 pound thrust class to the 20,000-21,700 pound level, with greatly reduced specific fuel consumption and noise.[83]

The JT8D-P-209 was first run on a test stand in May 1976. The program, initially run under very tight security, was not even announced until March 1977. In October of that year the JT8D-209/MD-80 program was announced. In July 1978 the JT8D-P-209 completed a 1,000-hour cycle test and the production contract between P&W and McDonnell Douglas was signed the following November. The JT8D-P-209 passed a 150-hour endurance test in May 1979 and was certified the next month. The first flight of the MD-80 was in October 1979. The JT8D-P-209 started commercial service in October 1980. An improved version, the JT8D-P-217, was certified in October 1980 as well.[84]

The advanced JT8D-P-217 model engine was used to power the McDonnell Douglas MD-82 in its first flight, in July 1981. The first JT8D-P-217-powered MD-82 was delivered in August that same year. Two months later the JT8D-P-217A was certified, and the first JT8D-P-217A-powered MD-82 was certified in August 1982. The first delivery of a JT8D-P-217A-powered MD-82 was in December 1982.

By May 1980 over 10,000 JT8Ds had been produced and delivered. In January 1982 the JT8D-P-15A, JT8D-P-17A and JT8D-P-17AR had been certified. By January 1983 the engine had accumulated over 200 million flight hours and by March of 1983 the JT8D-P-217 and JT8D-P-217A had accumulated over 688,000 flight hours.[85] P&W started development of the JT8D-P-219 version of the engine in February 1983.

The JT8D set a high standard for P&W in service. The company had successfully followed up on its first commercial transport success, the JT3D, and had laid the groundwork for the even more successful JT9D in the commercial arena. The company had gained a great deal of experience with turbofans, and was eager to launch its next effort.

The next two engines that we will look at were developed in direct competition to each other. The prize was the propulsion contract for the next generation of Air Force heavy transport aircraft, the aircraft that eventually became the C-5A Galaxy. One engine company won, only to see its competitor's engine run away with the much more lucrative commercial turbofan market. Both engines, however, proved over the long term to be the best high-bypass turbofans produced to that date in the United States.

In the early 1960s GE and P&W were ready to enter into the next stage of competition in the commercial turbofan market. P&W was fresh off the success with the JT8D program and was anxious to maintain its position in the commercial market. GE had just finished developing its first-generation building block engines and was anxious for an application for them. The competitive arena was to be the Air Force's Cargo Experimental-Heavy Logistics System (or CX-HLS) competition.

The competition was driven by the Air Force's need for a heavy transport with greater capacity and slightly longer range than the current Lockheed C-141 Starlifter. Rene Francillon, in *Lockheed Aircraft Since 1913*, describes the Air Force's situation:

> The Air Force Specific Operational Requirement to which the C-141A Star Lifter was designed had failed to provide for a fuselage cross-section of sufficient size to enable the carriage of large pieces of Army equipment, such as heavy tanks and troop-carrying helicopters. Thus, while the C-141A proved a reliable aircraft and markedly augmented Military Air Transport Service's airlift capability, it did not provide the level of flexibility required to implement fully President Kennedy's policy of offsetting reductions in overseas-based troops with greater flexibility of home-based forces. To a certain extent this deficiency could be overcome by pre-positioning heavy and bulky items of equipment at selected overseas depots - with personnel and lighter equipment to be flown in by C-130s and C-141s in time of emergency - but the Army still wished for the Air Force to be capable of airlifting a larger percentage of its combat weapons. Consequently, to obtain the necessary aircraft the United States Air Force and the industry began working during 1963 on parametric design studies for the CXHLS.[86]

After the Air Force used these studies to more accurately configure their requirements, three-month design contracts were given to three airframe builders (Boeing, Lockheed, and Douglas) and two engine companies (P&W and GE).

The design contracts were meant to respond to a new procurement policy in the Pentagon, called "total package procurement" (TPP). The TPP concept was also called the "Charles Plan" for its developer, then Assistant Secretary of the Air Force for Installation and Logistics Robert H. Charles. Under this concept the manufacturers were to compete for a whole program of research, development, testing, evaluation, and production under a single contract. This contract would also clearly set price, schedule, and performance commitments.[87]

The new aircraft had clear operational requirements. It had to be able to take off at maximum weight from an 8,000-foot runway and land on a 4,000-foot semi-prepared strip. Payload was set at 125,000 pounds over a stage length of 8,000 miles. The maximum payload was set at 250,000 pounds. The overall design life of the aircraft was set at 30,000 flying hours.[88]

All five companies submitted proposals and designs in April 1965, with GE submitting its TF39 turbofan and P&W submitting its JTF-14E turbofan. In August of that year the Air Force announced GE the winner of the engine competition with the GE1/6 to go into production as the TF39-GE-1. Lockheed won the airframe competition two months later.[89] Detailed discussion of the high-bypass ratio turbo for engines will be presented in Chapter 16.

## Endnotes

1   Simpson, Ernest C., The Memoirs of Ernest C. Simpson, Aero Propulsion Pioneer, James St. Peter, editor, Wright-Patterson Air Force Base, OH: Aero Propulsion Laboratory, Air Force Wright Aeronautical Laboratories and Special Staff Office, Aeronautical Systems Division, 1987, 39-40.

2   Lippencott, Harvey H., "P&W Enters the Jet Age," from "Classic Turbine Engines," edited by Robert B. Meyer, Jr., Casting About Volume 85, Number 4, 8.

3   Coar, Richard J, Second Annual L.V. Smith Lecture, November 16, 1989, 18-19.

4   Lippencott, Harvey H., "P&W Enters the Jet Age, Part II," from "Classic Turbine Engines," edited by Robert B. Meyer, Jr., Casting About Volume 86, Number 1, 10.

5   Gunston, Bill, World Encyclopedia of Aero Engines, Second Edition, England: Patrick Stephens Limited, 1989, 120.

6   P&W Aircraft Engine Files, Resume of Engine Development Histories, East Hartford, CT: P&W Aircraft, Division of United Aircraft Corporation, 1975, 10.9.

7   Lippencott, Casting About, Number 1, 10.

8   P&W Aircraft Engine Files, Resume of Engine Development, 10.

9   Lippencott, Casting About, Number 1, 11.

10  P&W Aircraft Engine Files, Resume of Engine Development, 10.

11  Simpson, Memoirs, 40-41.

12  Ibid.

13  P&W Aircraft Engine Files, Resume of Engine Development, 10.

14  Coar, L.V. Smith Lecture, 21-22.

15  W.T.G., "Two-Spool Turbo-Wasp: Characteristics of the P&W J57," Flight (November 25, 1953), 698.

16  Ibid, 698-699.

17  Gunston, Aero Engines, 121.

18  Ibid.

19  P&W Aircraft Engine Files, Resume of Engine Development, 10.

20  Bowers, Peter M., Boeing Aircraft Since 1916, Annapolis, MD: Naval Institute Press, 1989, 394-395.

21  Ibid, 394-399.

22  Ibid, 403-405.

23  Ibid, 408-409.

24  Wagner, Ray, American Combat Planes, Garden City, NY: Doubleday & Company, 1982, 462-463.

25  Bowers, Peter M. and Swanborough, Gordon, United States Military Aircraft Since 1909, Washington, DC: Smithsonian Institution Press, 1989, 491., and Koyen,

Kenneth, "Supersonic Fighter No. 1," Bee-Hive (Fall 1953), 3-6.

26  P&W Aircraft Engine Files, Engine Listings, D-21.

27  Ibid, D-28.

28  Ibid, D-32.

29  P&W Aircraft Engine Files, Engine Listings, 464.

30  Wagner, American Combat Planes, 467.

31  Ibid, 468.

32  Francillon, Rene J, McDonnell Douglas Aircraft Since 1920: Volume II, Annapolis, MD: Naval Institute Press, 1990, 155.

33  No Author Listed, "The New Margin in Power., Bee-Hive (January 1954), 3-6.

34  Gunston, Aero Engines, 120-121.

35  Wagner, American Combat Planes, 318.

36  Wagner, American Combat Planes, 490, and Yenne, Bill, McDonnell-Douglas: Tale of Two Giants, Greenwich, CT: Bison Books, 1985, 53-57. [

37  Wagner, American Combat Planes, 510.

38  Gunston, Aero Engines, 121.

39  P&W Aircraft Engine Files, Resume of Engine Development, 10.

40  Coar, L.V. Smith Lecture, 26-28.

41  Gunston, Aero Engines, 122.

42  Gunston, Bill, Aero Engines, 122.

43  Bowers, Boeing Aircraft, 413.

44  Ibid, 414.

45  Ibid, 415.

46  Gunston, Aero Engines, 122.

47  P&W Aircraft Engine Division of United Technologies Corporation, Aircraft Engine Listings, East Hartford, CT and West Palm Beach FL: P&W Aircraft Engine Division, United Technologies Corporation, 7.1.

48  Ibid, 7-1, and P&W Aircraft Engine Files, P&W Aircraft Engine Listings: Index of Aircraft Engines, West Palm Beach, FL: Government Products Division, P&W Aircraft Engines, United Technology Corporation, 1972, 8.

49  P&W Aircraft Engine Files, Chronological History of JT8, West Palm Beach, FL: Government Products Division, P&W Aircraft Engines, United Technology Corporation.

50  Wagner, Ray, American Combat Planes, Garden City, NY: Doubleday & Company, 1982, 496.

51  P&W Division of UTC, Aircraft Engine Listings, 7-1.

52  Ibid, 491.

[53] One of the A-4Es was shot down by antiaircraft fire and the unfortunate pilot was subjected to the longest POW experience ever endured by an American. Ibid, 493.

[54] P&W Division of UTC, Aircraft Engine Listings, 7-1.

[55] Ibid, 7-2.

[56] P&W Engine Files, Chronological History of JT8.

[57] P&W Division of UTC, Aircraft Engine Listings, 7-2.

[58] P&W Engine Files, Engine Listings: Index of Aircraft Engines, 8.

[59] P&W Division of UTC, Aircraft Engine Listings, 7-2.

[60] Ibid, 7-3.

[61] Ibid.

[62] Gunston, Bill, World Encyclopedia of Aero Engines, Second Edition, England: Patrick Stephens Limited, 1989, 122.

[63] Ibid, 123.

[64] Ibid.

[65] P&W Aircraft Engine Files, Resume of Engine Development Histories, East Hartford, CT: P&W Aircraft, Division of United Aircraft Corporation, 1975, 8-9.

[66] P&W Division of UTC, Aircraft Engine Listings, 9-1.

[67] Ibid, 8-1 and 9-1, and P&W Engine Files, Resume, 8-9.

[68] P&W Division of UTC, Aircraft Engine Listings, 9-1.

[69] Yenne, Bill, McDonnell-Douglas: Tale of Two Giants, Greenwich, CT: Bison Books, 1985, 144.

[70] P&W Division of UTC, Aircraft Engine Listings, 9-1.

[71] Ibid, 155.

[72] P&W Division of UTC, Aircraft Engine Listings, 9-1.

[73] Ibid, 8-1, and P&W Engine Files, Chronological History of JT8, and P&W Engine Files, Resume,16.

[74] P&W Engine Files, Chronological History of JT8, 16.

[75] P&W Aircraft Engine Files, List of Planes, Missiles, Space and Marine Vehicles and Industrial Installations Powered by P&W Aircraft Engines, East Hartford, CT: Public Relations Division, P&W Aircraft Division of United Aircraft Corporation, 1970.

[76] Ibid.

[77] P&W Division of UTC, Aircraft Engine Listings, 8-1.

[78] On 23 June 1972 first JT8D-15 powered advanced 727-200 at 191,000 lb. gross weight delivered to All Nippon Airlines. Ibid, 9-2.

[79] First flight was on September 7, 1971 and the engine was in service by June 1974. Ibid.

[80] P&W Engine Files, List of Planes, Missiles, Space and Marine Vehicles and Industrial Installation.

[81] P&W Division of UTC, Aircraft Engine Listings, 8-1 and 9-2.

[82] Ibid, 9-3.

[83] Gunston, Aero Engines, 123.

[84] P&W Division of UTC, Aircraft Engine Listings, 8-1.

[85] Ibid.

[86] Francillon, Rene J, Lockheed Aircraft Since 1913, Annapolis, MD: Naval Institute Press, 1987, 450.

[87] GE Company, Eight Decades of Progress: A Heritage of Aircraft Turbine Technology, Cincinnati, OH: GE Aircraft Engines, 1990, 150.

[88] Francillon, Lockheed Aircraft, 451.

[89] Ibid.

**UH-1 Huey, Powered by One Lycoming T53 Turboshaft**

# Turboshaft Development

## The T53, T55, T58, T64, and T700 Turboshaft Engines

In principle the turboshaft gas turbine is very similar to a turbojet engine. The difference is that it transmits most of its output through a shaft, rather than through a large velocity jet. Turboshafts are used mostly in helicopters, but are also used for power generation, ship propulsion and vehicle (main battle tank) propulsion. We will use helicopters as the principal example in this chapter.

Like a turbojet, the turboshaft engine consists of a diffuser, compressor, combustion system, turbine, and exhaust nozzle. Unlike a turbojet, it may also have a system of reduction gears and a drive shaft for the helicopter rotor. The diffuser, compressor, and combustion chamber function in the same manner as in the turbojet engine. However, the turboshaft engine may use one turbine to drive the compressor and another to drive the output shaft. When the energy to drive the compressor and the load is extracted from the high-temperature gases, little is left for producing jet thrust. Since the shaft rotational speed of gas turbine engines is very high, a reduction gear must be placed between the turbine output shaft and the helicopter rotor shaft to enable the helicopter rotors to operate efficiently.

The keys to aircraft turboshaft design are light weight, a high power-to-weight ratio, low specific fuel consumption, durability, reliability, and stable selective constant-speed control.[1] There have been many successful turboshaft designs in the history of the aircraft gas turbine in the United States, but the five engines covered in this chapter provided the important technological innovations.

The story of the aircraft turboshaft is largely the story of the helicopter, since without the helicopter, the turboshaft would not have been developed to the extent that it has been today. Thus like the turbojet itself, the development of the helicopter has been of necessity a military development. The value of vertical flight has been seen by the military since the invention of the first helicopters. In 1918 the Army's Air Service investigated the helicopter's potential for vertical takeoff flight in restricted landing areas. The Air Corps established the Autogyro School at Patterson Field in Fairfield, Ohio, on April 15, 1938. The Air Corps (soon to become the Army Air Forces) also supported the infant helicopter programs of Igor Sikorsky, Frank Piasecki, Stanley Hiller, and Charles Kaman, funding their research and prototype developments and purchasing quantities of their aircraft, largely from Sikorsky. The U.S. Navy also appreciated the helicopter's capabilities as an antisubmarine weapon and as "plane guard" (replacing destroyers in that duty) while launching and recovering aircraft and became an early and enthusiastic supporter of helicopter research and development. The U.S. Coast Guard became one of the earliest supporters of helicopter development, seeing the value right away of the helicopter in search and rescue operations. The Coast Guard established one of the very first helicopter training schools at Floyd Bennett Field in Brooklyn, New York, in November 1943.[2]

The U.S. Marine Corps were pioneers in the combat use of helicopters. As the amphibious fighting force of the Navy, the Marines were to stress the use of helicopters to overfly potentially hostile beaches and to supply troops in the field. In 1948, in the Key West and Newport Agreements, the Air Force, Navy, and Army defined their aviation service roles and missions. The Air Force agreed to furnish close combat and logistical support to the Army. The Army retained its light aircraft, to be used only for liaison and spotting for artillery.

The aviation roles and missions agreement between the Air Force and Army was amended in May 1949, limiting the Army to fixed-wing aircraft under 2,500 pounds and helicopters under 4,000 pounds. Furthermore, these aircraft types to be used by the Army were to be unarmed.

Although the services first became interested in the helicopter during World War II, Korea marked the turning point for the use of helicopters by the military. The Korean War had little impact on the Air Force's ideas about the helicopter's role (apart from the increased use of helicopters in air/sea rescue), but the Army found the aircraft missions limitations imposed by the 1949 Air Force/Army agreement to be a problem as they began using helicopters to evacuate battlefield casualties and provide limited logistical movement of troops. It was the U.S. Marines, however, who made the first initial use of the helicopter in the forward battle area in Korea. In early 1950 the first transport helicopter squadron in history, HMR-161, was formed by the Marine Corps at El Toro Naval Air Station in California, with Sikorsky H-19 piston-engine-powered helicopters. On August 31, 1951, Squadron HMR-161 arrived in Korea. Two weeks after its arrival, it executed its first resupply and casualty evacuation lift, moving 19,000 pounds of cargo seven miles to the engaged 2nd Marine Battalion, 1st Marines, and evacuating 74 casualties in 2.5 hours. This was the first of many operational combat missions for Marine helicopter aviation.[3]

The most spectacular use of helicopters in Korea culminated four years of Marine experimentation with the tactical transport of combat troops. On September 20, 1951, in "Operation Summit," twelve Navy Sikorsky HR2S-1 (H-37) helicopters (Figure 10-1) lifted a company of 228 fully equipped Marines to the top of a 3,000 foot hilltop in central Korea. They followed up this deployment with the delivery of nine tons of food, ammunition, and other supplies. This is the first known use of what the Marines termed "vertical envelopment." The trek to the top of this strategic hill would have taken two days by foot. It took four hours by helicopter. The Marines followed this mission up within a month in "Operation Bumblebee," by moving an entire battalion to the front in full view of enemy forces, requiring just 6 hours and 15 minutes to accomplish the airlift.[4] Soon after that, everyone in any command capacity over the level of battalion commander wanted his own helicopter. Although this tactical airlift capacity demonstrated the future power of the helicopter to radically change the nature of small and medium level combat, it was in a more humanitarian way that the helicopter became famous in Korea.

**Figure 10-1. Sikorsky HR2S-1 (H-37)**
*(Photo courtesy of U.S. Army)*

The helicopter became most well-known in Korea through its missions in CASEVAC, or casualty evacuation. Everyone in America has seen at least once the famous opening scene from the hit television series M*A*S*H of the bubble-canopy helicopter sweeping in from above with its load of wounded American soldiers to the field hospital. This "mission of mercy" of the helicopter was very real. In *Helicopters at War* David Wragg observes:

> Compared with World War II, deaths among casualties reaching first-aid posts in Korea were down from 4.5% to just 2%, simply as a result of being able to use helicopter casualty evacuation, or CASEVAC. The extensive use of the helicopter in this role during the Korean War shortened the time necessary to get a wounded man to a first-aid station, and reduced the very real risk of further injury or complications arising during transport over rough ground and indifferent battle-front roads.
>
> Obviously the wounds and injuries requiring the most careful handling and least suited to rides in a bumpy jeep or field ambulance were the head and stomach wounds. Before the Korean War, or perhaps one should really say, before the arrival of the helicopter, between 80-90% of soldiers with such wounds died, but fast and relatively smooth helicopter transit to the hospital reduced this appalling figure to 10%.[5]

By April 1951 CASEVAC missions were being performed by both S-55 and Bell 47 (Figure 10-2) helicopters. In the first two months of operation the first Mobile Army Surgical Hospital (or M\*A\*S\*H) was able to transport over 2,000 wounded soldiers using only eleven helicopters. And this was done under fire and often only one wounded soldier at a time.[6] Helicopters also served a vital role as a rescuer of downed pilots, the Sikorsky H-19 being the helicopter most used for this role.

**Figure 10-2. Bell Model 47 Helicopter**
*(Photo courtesy of Bell Helicopter)*

In the late 1940s and early 1950s, while the Marine Corps and the Navy were working together to develop the vertical envelopment theories of helicopter use in combat, the Air Force and Army were fighting with each other. The prize was aviation missions and concepts. The stakes, as the Air Force saw them, were immense. The battlegrounds were medium- and short-range logistical aircraft and close air support aircraft. The Air Force had only recently become a separate service, and saw itself as the wielder of the nation's air weapons as well as the natural home for all logistical movement of men and material by air. It had already created the Materiel Air Transport Service (MATS) to coordinate the development, purchase and coordination of such aircraft. The Army, on the other hand, was still concerned about the ability to provide close air support to its combat troops. It had seen the apparent thrust of the Air Force towards strategic and nuclear aircraft, and felt that the Air Force had lost sight of the need for tactical support of ground forces.

The Secretaries of the Army and Air Force signed a memorandum of understanding at the urging of Secretary of Defense Robert A. Lovett on November 4, 1952. The agreement raised the weight limit of Army fixed-wing aircraft to 5,000 pounds and eliminated the weight limit for helicopters. The agreement also gave the Army two new air missions for topographic survey and medical evacuation of front-line battlefield casualties.[7]

Camp Rucker (now Fort Rucker) in Alabama was established as the Army Aviation Center in the mid-1950s. The Army Aviation School was founded there to train helicopter pilots (with the rank of warrant officer) and to explore "airmobility" concepts. They applied the lessons they learned during their limited helicopter operations in the Korean War. Both the Army and Marine Corps sent military attaches to Algeria from 1955 to 1962 to study the French Army's massive use of helicopters in their colonial guerrilla war. The information they gained was evaluated by the Army planning staffs in the Pentagon and integrated with ongoing U.S. Army experiments in helicopter tactics. The Army also began building its own helicopter support "establishment" so that it would not be dependent upon the Air Force for its aviation research, development and procurement. With the transfer of some Air Force civilian personnel from the Air Force's Power Plant Laboratory to the Army in the mid-1950s, the Army built its own expertise in the definition of military aircraft mission requirements necessary for the procurement of aircraft to serve field operations.

The Army used a two-tiered approach to its helicopter research and development. The first involved using the most modern helicopters to fully investigate the potential of small-, medium-, and large-scale logistical movements of troops via helicopters, using such late models as the Vertol CH-21 Shawnee, Sikorsky CH-34 Choctaw, and CH-37 Mojave. The second approach involved the arming of a small number of the Army's helicopters. In June 1954 the Army authorized Colonel Jay Vanderpool to organize a provisional platoon of armed helicopters. His operations over the next several years yielded valuable theoretical and practical experience for the Army's pilots.

All of the missions described above were performed very well by the first and second generation of helicopters, all powered by piston engines. The very success of the helicopter, however, worked against the piston engine. All of the services wanted helicopters that could carry more cargo, fly farther, evacuate more wounded, and stay on station longer. New helicopter designs were able to meet these new mission requirements, but piston engine designs could not. Enter the turbine engine. Aircraft turbine engine design had advanced to the point that spin-off technology in large turboprop engines had become possible. Avco Lycoming (later Textron Lycoming, now AlliedSignal), General Electric, and Allison Division of General Motors (now owned by Rolls-Royce) also began looking at small turbojets, turboprops, and, more importantly for helicopters, small turboshaft engines

Lycoming was awarded a contract by the Air Force (still acting for the Army) in June 1952 for a 600-shaft-horsepower turboshaft, the concept that became the T53. The move to develop a turboshaft for the next generation of Army helicopters made sense for several reasons. First, the aircraft gas turbine engine was technologically ready for a turboshaft. Second, turboshafts for helicopters were simpler and lighter than piston engines. The piston engine on the Sikorsky H-19 weighed about 1,056 pounds. That was 500 pounds more than the heaviest of the later turboshaft engines of the Huey. The turboshaft was also smaller and could be mounted on top of the helicopter, saving payload room. Finally, a turbine engine is easier to start and does not require time to warm up before flight. The sole disadvantage in the early days of the first turboshafts was that they did require more fuel.[8]

In February 1954 the Army announced a design competition for a new utility helicopter. The requirements were a payload capacity of 800 pounds and a round-trip range of 200 nautical miles with a cruising speed of 114 mph. The first designated mission for the new aircraft would be as instrument flight trainers for the Army Aviation School. The mission profile of the new helicopter also included troop transport, cargo lifts, and CASEVAC. The new helicopter had to be more reliable and maintainable in the field than previous helicopters and it had to be air-transportable in the cargo bay of the Air Force's C-124s and C-130s.[9] Bell Helicopter won the design competition (designed under weapon system designation SS443-L) on February 23, 1955.[10] Aware of the Lycoming work on the T53 turboshaft design, Bell incorporated the not-yet-finished turboshaft in its winning proposal. In June 1955, the Army awarded Bell Helicopter the contract to build three new T53-powered helicopter prototypes. The new helicopter was designated the XH-40. Bell called it the model 204.

Bell Aircraft was experienced in the helicopter business, having designed and flown their first helicopter in 1943. The Helicopter Division headed by Lawrence Bell was established in 1951. Their Model 47 helicopter was the first helicopter to be granted a commercial license by the Federal Aviation Administration and was probably the most popular helicopter ever produced before the Huey. The military version, the OH-13, was a veteran of Korea. The H-40 eventually became the UH-1 Huey, used for med-evac, training, and utility missions.

General Hamilton Howze was named first director of the Army Aviation Directorate, established in 1956. This directorate was to be the organization for research and development, purchasing and training for the Army's aviation mission requirements.

In January 1960 the Army convened the Rogers Board to examine the state of Army aviation. One of the board's recommendations was for the Army to investigate the "airmobile" concept. This recommendation led in the spring of 1962 to the establishment of the Army Tactical Mobility Requirements Board with General Howze as president. The Howze Board used field tests, war games, research, overseas visits, interviews, and think-tank studies in the formulation of their recommendations, which they submitted to Secretary of Defense Robert McNamara in August 1962. Specifically, the Howze Board recommended formation of the Air Assault Division and the Air Cavalry Brigade, both of which would replace their wheeled vehicles with unarmed helicopters and light aircraft. These new formations would also replace most of their artillery and armor with armed helicopters. The Pentagon authorized the organization, training, and evaluation of both units in January 1963. However, events in Vietnam were rapidly overtaking the U.S. military.[11]

The first major commitment of combat power to Vietnam was marked by the deployment of the U.S. Army's 8th and 57th Light Helicopter Transportation Companies with Boeing Vertol H-21s to Vietnam on December 11, 1961. Their purpose was to transport troops of the Army of the Republic of Vietnam (ARVN) into battle against the guerrillas. They carried out their first airlift of ARVN troops and their American advisors into combat on December 23, 1961. By mid-1962 five companies of Army helicopters were 'in-country' in Vietnam. They were followed in April 1962 by the Marine Corps's helicopter squadron HMM-362, equipped with Sikorsky H-34 helicopters.[12]

The need for increased horsepower for the helicopters in Vietnam was underscored for the first time when one of the Army's helicopter companies had to trade bases with the Marine HMM-362 from their mountain base to a lowland base because the H-21 could not deliver enough power to operate in higher altitudes.

In 1962 Secretary of Defense McNamara authorized the arming of certain helicopter types in Vietnam with light automatic antipersonnel weapons. Three years later Secretary McNamara authorized an Army review of its future aircraft requirements. On February 19, 1965, the Army awarded contracts for the program definition of an attack helicopter. The first flight of the AH-1 Huey Cobra was on September 7, 1965. Powered by a Lycoming T53, it became operational in Vietnam by November 1967.

On April 6, 1966, Air Force Chief of Staff General John P. McConnell and Army Chief of Staff General Harold K. Johnson signed an agreement further delineating aircraft mission responsibility between the Air Force and the Army. The Air Force merged the Army's short-range air transport mission, along with the Army's 160 de Havilland CV-2B Caribou aircraft, into their Military Air Transport Service (MATS). In turn the Air Force relinquished all claims to helicopters for airlift, fire support, and supply of Army forces.

From a base of about 2,600 utility helicopters in 1960, the Army Aviation Directorate's air fleet grew to over 12,000 aircraft in 1970, of which over 10,000 were helicopters. The Army had over 24,000 helicopter pilots on active duty, making it the world's third-largest air force (behind only the Soviet Air Force and the U.S. Air Force).

## Design and Development of the Lycoming T53 Turboshaft/Turboprop Engine

In April 1952 Avco-Lycoming responded to Air Force Request For Proposal (RFP) No. 345609, which called for a single-shaft turboprop engine of 500 to 700 horsepower. The RFP also stressed simplicity of design and a rugged compressor. Lycoming sent a proposal to the Air Force to develop two engines for Army use. The first design was the LTC1 single-shaft, axial-radial compressor design. The second was the LT single-shaft all-axial compressor design. Both designs could be modified for a free turbine. Lycoming won the design competition and received a contract in July 1952 to develop their LTC1 design as a turboshaft with a free turbine. The Air Force development contract called for 600 shaft horsepower.

The T53 was Lycoming's entry into the aircraft gas turbine field. Its design reflected the development philosophy of Dr. Anselm Franz. Brought to Wright Field from Germany by the U.S. Army Air Forces after WWII where he had led the Junkers Jumo 004 turbojet design team, Franz had come to Lycoming with the desire to build and develop small, rugged, and versatile gas turbine engines for land, sea, and air. The T53 was his first design for Lycoming.

The initial design of the engine was done in Williamsport, Pennsylvania, by Dr. Franz, Heinz Moellmann, and Eugene Clark. Donald Weidhuner was the Army liaison for the effort. In October 1952 Lycoming moved the T53 project to Stratford, Connecticut. In 1953 Dr. Heinrich Adenstedt, Dr Siegfried Decher, and Dr. Friedrich Bielitz joined the design and development team, reuniting much of what had been the original Jumo 004 team from Germany. Joining them were a number of young Westinghouse engineers.[13] In June 1953 Wolfgang Stein joined the T53 design team. Hans Berkner joined the team in 1954.[14]

The T53 was designed to be small, powerful, fuel-efficient, rugged, and easily maintainable in the field. It is a two-shaft axial-centrifugal flow free turbine turboshaft engine with five axial compressor stages followed by a single titanium centrifugal stage. Early rotors were composed of a steel first stage and four aluminum stages; current engines are fitted with a titanium drum rotor comprised of electron-beam-welded discs. Early models of the T53 used a single-stage turbine wheel to drive the compressor section via the outer concentric shaft. Franz had initially decided to use a centrifugal compressor as the high loading stage of his compressor to avoid both compressor stage matching problems and to make the engine more rugged overall. As this single-stage arrangement was not very efficient, Franz added a second centrifugal stage to the first. This increased the compressor pressure ratio to about 6 for better fuel economy. This original design, designated the LT-X, had the engine's accessories arranged on the front of the engine.

When the Lycoming and airframe design teams looked at this engine design, they realized that the engine would be too large in diameter, so Lycoming replaced the first centrifugal compressor stage with five axial stages, thereby reducing the frontal area of the engine considerably. When they wrapped the engine accessories around this smaller axial compressor, they found that the engine regained its original diameter.

The Lycoming engine design team decided on a reverse-flow annular combustor wrapped around the turbine assembly (similar to the Whittle combustor designs). The design was based on a concept by Franz, although a combustor team led by Sig Decher actually designed and built the first one. A combustor test of the Franz concept was the first component test run at the Lycoming facility. The combustor was designed with safety as a primary design consideration, providing four layers of steel surrounding the turbine.[15] The first combustor had twelve vaporizing tubes, but the combustor team reduced that number to eleven. In 1953 they established the T-cane design of the combustor vaporizer.[16] From late 1955 to June 1956 they encountered a significant coking problem with the T53 combustor walls and T-canes. The build-up would break off and in some instances clog the turbine openings. The team solved the problem by changing the shape of the vaporizers which changed the air distribution in the primary zone to increase mixing and eliminate rich fuel-air ratio pockets. That combustor design stayed in place up to the development of the L-11 model.[17]

A single-stage free power turbine drove the gearbox, which was front-mounted, via the inner coaxial shaft. The turbine blades were of solid, uncooled steel, as were the vanes. Discs were spline-mounted to the shaft. The shaft was kept short to eliminate vibration problems. Maximum power turbine speed was 21,300 rpm at all conditions including takeoff. The engine fuel controls were hydromechanical.

In May 1953 the Air Force and Army raised the horsepower design goal of the T53 from the original 600 shaft horsepower to 720 shaft horsepower, then to 860. The entire engine first ran in April 1955.[18]

One of the early problems encountered by the design team was vibration of the power turbine shaft. The slender shaft had a low natural frequency that caused a vibration at the bearing points. Since the bearing design requirements were set (and therefore the diameter dimensions at those points were set), the team resorted to a bit of engineering legerdemain. Using an idea by Dr. Friedrich Belitz, which he called "the pregnant worm," the team redesigned the power turbine shaft as a variable-diameter shaft. The power shaft would have twice the diameter, and thus a higher natural frequency, between the two bearing points as at the points themselves. The team also encountered the other problems associated with a first-engine development, such as failure of compressor disks and blades, weakening of turbine blades, engine control problems, and, peculiar to turboshafts (and turboprops), the matching of frequencies between turbine blades and gearing.

When the first prototype T53 (Figure 10-3) was delivered to test in September 1955, Lycoming had to improvise jet engine test facilities. The company first built a test rig for

**Figure 10-3. Cutaway of T53 Turboshaft**
*(Illustration courtesy of Lycoming)*

combustor experiments and then assembled turbine test facilities in an old building behind the Stratford plant. This building had been first used by Pratt & Whitney for testing combustors in the late 1940s. Old vacuum pumps were the only equipment remaining in the building. Lycoming augmented the vacuum pumps with a diesel supercharger from a locomotive. The output from the supercharger served as the air supply. Lycoming also installed an electrical heater and a high-speed water brake to control the test turbine speeds.

The first 50-hour test of the T53 took place in June 1956 and the 150-hour benchmark test of the T53 occurred in June 1958.[19] Although the T53-L-3 combustor underwent six 150-hour tests and worked well, the T53 engines and their combustors could not pass a "green run" once production began. A green run is an inspection test to determine that the engine works the way it ought to. The combustor team could not initially determine what was causing the combustor failures. George Opdyke related "that it was a very difficult problem to solve. We finally determined that some parts had been mis-assembled so that some cooling gaps were too small. When the parts were corrected, there were no problems." This is a good example of how a very simple problem in manufacture and assembly can hold up an otherwise excellent design for weeks.

The first flight of the T53 turboshaft was in a Kaman Model K600-1, later developed into the H-43 Huskie (Figure 10-4), on September 27, 1956. The first flight of the Bell XH-40 helicopter prototype took place on October 22, 1956. As a result of this successful first flight and the subsequent flight test program, Bell received a contract for six YH-40 aircraft for service tests. With the T53, the XH-40 had a gross weight of 5,800 pounds (of which 2,200 pounds was cargo), a top speed of 138 mph, and a cruising speed of 125 mph. Maximum range was over 254 nautical miles.[20]

**Figure 10-4. Kaman H-43 Huskie**
*(Photo courtesy of U.S. Army)*

The YH-40s were delivered by August 1958. The T53 by this time produced 860 horsepower, temporarily derated to 770. The Army ordered nine more pre-production aircraft, the first of which was delivered by June 30, 1959.[21] Further production contracts for the UH-1A were placed at this time. The H-40 (the Air Force designation until 1962) was redesignated by the Army as the UH-1 and production aircraft were later designated UH-1As. Although the company name for the aircraft was the Iroquois (due to the Army practice of naming helicopters after Indian tribes), the helicopter entered aviation as the "Huey" (Figure 10-5). The name became an official part of the helicopter design when Bell began putting the words "Bell" and "Huey" on the left and right rudder pedals respectively. Total cost to the Army for the three prototype XH-40s and the six YH-40s was just under $30 million.[22]

**Figure 10-5. Bell UH-1 Huey**
*(Photo courtesy of U.S. Army)*

Avco-Lycoming delivered the first T53-L-1A production engine in December 1956 at 860 shaft horsepower.[23] In late 1958 the company began production of the T53-L-5 at 960 shaft horsepower. The engine was flight-qualified in April 1958. By mid-1958 Avco-Lycoming had already accumulated over 12,000 hours of running time on the T53, of which 3,500 hours were in the field on aircraft.[24] The T53 was also used in many experimental applications: the Boeing Vertol VZ-2 experimental tilt-wing aircraft; the Ryan deflected slipstream research aircraft; and several experimental lift-fan designs.

The initial T53, the T53-L-1A, was certified at 860 shaft horsepower for turboshaft applications in April 1958. The first production UH-1A Huey left the Bell factory in September 1958 with this engine installed. The helicopter then had a maximum speed of 148 mph, a gross weight of 8,500 pounds, and a range of 335 nautical miles.[25] The T53 L-3 turboprop version was also initially produced for the Grumman OV-1 Mohawk fixed-wing observation aircraft.

One hundred seventy-three UH-1As were produced and first deployed to Panama, Korea, and Europe in 1960.[26] In January 1962 the first UH-1As were deployed to Vietnam with the 57th Medical Detachment (Helicopter Ambulance). These were to be the first of thousands of Hueys to be used in Vietnam. In June 1959 Bell began development of an improved model of the UH-1 as the YUH-1B. This model was powered by the 960-shaft-horsepower Lycoming T53-L-5 engine. Later models of the UH-1B were powered by the 1,100-shaft-horsepower T53-L-9 or T53-L-11. This new model helicopter had an enlarged cabin and increased-chord rotor blades of honeycomb construction. The first flight of the YUH-1B was in 1960 and delivery of the first of a total of 1,010 UH-1Bs began in March 1961. Deployed to Vietnam, the UH-1B served principally in utility and armed escort roles.[27] Jim Mesko, in Airmobile: The Helicopter War in Vietnam, describes the role of the armed helicopter as deployed to Vietnam in September 1962:

> This pioneer organization, designated the Utility Tactical Transport Helicopter Company (UTTCO), was composed of fifteen UH-1As armed with a weapons system fabricated on Okinawa. This first weapons system consisted of two .30 caliber machine guns and sixteen 2.75 inch rockets mounted on the Huey's landing skids. Upon arrival in Vietnam the unit was assigned to Tan Son Nhut where it supported the H-21s of the 33rd, 57th, and 93rd Helicopter Companies. This first element of UTTCO soon received reinforcements when eleven UH-1B model Hueys arrived in November. These differed from the A models in two important ways. The B model had a more powerful engine which allowed it to carry more armament, and it had a factory installed weapons pack of four M-60 machine guns and a different set of mounts for the sixteen 2.75 inch rockets.

Under the direct control of Military Assistance Command, Vietnam (MACV), this unit was to test the role of the helicopter as an 'escort' or 'gunship' for troop-carrying helicopters. The 'escort' role evolved into three distinct segments: the 'en-route phase', the 'approach phase', and the 'landing zone (LZ) phase'. During the en-route phase, the helicopters flew at a relatively safe altitude with little danger from ground fire. During the approach phase the helicopters dropped down on the deck when they were several miles away from the Landing Zone. These phases required little from the armed Hueys unless a ship went down due to mechanical failure or ground fire. Then one of the escorts would be detached to cover and provide support for the crew during rescue operations. However, it was during the Landing Zone phase that the escort carried out its most important role. Throughout this part of the operation the escorts were constantly over the Landing Zone providing support for the transport helicopters (slicks). Initially, the armed Hueys would go into the landing area ahead of the slicks to find out if it was occupied by the enemy. If ground fire was encountered it was considered a 'hot' Landing Zone and the escorts tried to suppress the enemy fire with their guns and rockets. Throughout the landing, the armed Hueys remained over the Landing Zone to cover the vulnerable slicks. Thus, they were exposed for a long period of time to enemy fire, particularly if the landing area was small and could only take a few troop carriers at a time.[28]

## The Sand Ingestion Problem

Although the T53, like all new aircraft engines, had its share of minor troubles in the field after its introduction, there was one major field problem that required a substantial effort by the company to fix immediately. That was the problem of sand ingestion and erosion of engine parts. First encountered by those squadrons operating close to the sandy beaches of South Vietnam (particularly around Da Nang), the problem was brought to full exposure during operations in South Vietnam's central highland provinces. The ingestion and subsequent erosion caused compressor stalls and even worse, engine surges, which can destroy an engine. Lycoming and Bell undertook a crash program to develop a particle separator to screen the engine from most of the sand particles. They came up with an inertial-type separator that collected most of the sand in a separate compartment which could be emptied overboard after each flight.

## T53-L-3 Turboprop

Lycoming also developed turboprop models in parallel to their turboshafts, the difference between turboshaft and turboprop being a gear box change for lower output revolutions per minute to the prop and control module. The first application for the T53 turboprop came in September 1959 when Lycoming delivered the first 960-shaft-horsepower T53-L-3 to Grumman for installation in their OV-1 Mohawk, the first turboprop aircraft developed for the U.S. Army. The OV-1D was designed and produced as an observation/photographic aircraft with short-take-off-and-landing (STOL) performance and rough-field capability to fulfill the battlefield surveillance requirements of the Army and Marine Corps (the Marine Corps later withdrew from the program). First flight of the OV-1 was on April 14, 1959. The Mohawk served in Vietnam in OV-1A, OV-1B, OV-1C, and OV-1D versions.[29]

## T53-L-5 Turboshaft

The first UH-1Bs were powered by the 960-horsepower T53-L-5. Lycoming qualified this model in December 1959 and delivered the first production engines to Bell Helicopter in February 1960. The T53-L-5 differed from the T53-L-3 model in that it incorporated a high speed main reduction gear assembly and power control. Production was completed in January 1962 and only 182 of these engines were produced.

## T53-L-9 Turboshaft

By June 1961 Lycoming had the first T53-L-9 model series available for the UH-1B/C. The T53-L-9 delivered 1,100 horsepower through an increase in turbine inlet temperature to

1725°F, an increase of 75° over the L-5 model. The T53-L-9 boosted the Huey's maximum gross weight by 1,300 pounds, its load-carrying capability by 1,500 pounds, and its speed by 29 mph. For CASEVAC the Huey UH-1B could now carry eight passengers or three litters. This engine also powered the first commercial Huey, the Model 204B. This helicopter could carry nine passengers or 140 cubic feet of cargo.[30]

## T53-L-11 Turboshaft

The Army discovered in their airmobile operations that five to seven armed Hueys could escort twenty to twenty-five unarmed "slicks". However, the armed Hueys were capable of only 80 knots and could not catch up to the slicks if they were delayed at liftoff or were forced to attack a target along the way. The Army realized that a more powerful engine for the armed Huey was needed. Lycoming was ready to respond. The T53-L-11 model became available in 1962 and in August 1963 Lycoming began delivery of the T53-L-11 series engines (T53-L-11, T53-L-11A, and T53-L-11B). This was the same engine as the T53-L-9 except for the multifuel combustor and modified fuel controls, which gave it better acceleration and the ability to operate on either JP-4 or JP-5 fuel.[31] Coupled with the completely new and improved rotor system, the UH-1C was a much better gunship. The rotor system had a much wider chord and a new, flexible rotor head assembly which greatly increased maneuverability. The UH-1C could now run at 126 mph for a longer distance of 260 nautical miles, made possible by an increased fuel tank of 242 gallons (from 165 in the UH-B model Hueys).[32] Many of the UH-1C Hueys were retrofitted with the later T53-L-13 turboshaft engines. By September 1965 the Bell UH-1C, with the Lycoming T53-L-11 standard, had replaced the UH-1B. A total of 767 UH-1Cs was produced.[33]

Now that the Army had an updated gunship, it set out to harness the new and improved T53-L-11 to a bigger "slick." Bell Helicopter responded with the YUH-1D design. With Army approval, they began ground and flight tests of the bigger helicopter. The first flight of the Bell Model 205 YUH-1D was on August 16, 1961.[34] The Bell Helicopter team based the new YUH-1D on the Bell model 205 design, with an 1,100-shaft-horsepower Lycoming T53-L-9 or T53-L-11 turboshaft engine, the larger rotor diameter introduced in the UH-1C and a redesigned cabin that increased overall fuselage length by 3.5 feet. This gave the YUH-1D an 80-cubic-foot increase over the smaller Hueys, allowing accommodation of up to twelve troops in addition to the pilot. If used strictly as a passenger transport, the UH-1D could be fitted with as many as fifteen seats, including the pilot and co-pilot. For casualty evacuation it could handle six litter patients.[35] On August 9, 1963, Bell began deliveries of the UH-1D to the Army. A total of 2,008 were built.[36] Bell also began deliveries of the UH-1H to the Air Force after Bell won a competition for a missile-site support helicopter in 1963. Designated the XH-48A in prototype form but later UH-1F, this variant differed from Army models in that it was powered by the 1,000-shaft-horsepower General Electric T58-GE-3 engine.

## T53-L-13 Turboshaft

In 1966 the T53-L-13 model became available (Figure 10-6). Rated at 1,400 shaft horsepower, it represented a major improvement in the basic design with only a marginal increase in the engine frame size. The changes to the T53 included transonic first- and second-stage compressor blades of wider chord and variable inlet guide vanes. Transonic stages increased airflow and pressure ratio, and the variable inlet guide vanes increased stall margin and provided better compressor stage matching over a wider speed range. Combustor changes included improved alloys to increase heat and corrosion resistance in the hot section and atomizing fuel injectors for the increased combustion intensity required and for operation on alternative fuels. Lycoming also added an additional turbine stage in the gas producer and power turbine sections. The gas producer turbine incorporated hollow air-cooled steel blades and vanes, which increased turbine

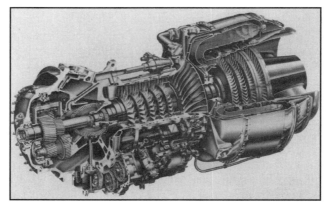

**Figure 10-6. Cutaway of T53-L-13 Engine**
*(Illustration courtesy of George Opdyke)*

inlet temperature (TIT).[37] The decision to incorporate variable inlet guide vanes and atomizing fuel nozzles was a late change in the T53-L-13's design. The atomizers were added to the T53-L-13 at the last minute when the Army and Air Force multifuel use requirements came out.[38]

On March 11, 1966, the Army announced plans to procure Bell AH-1 Huey Cobra gunships. These were the first dedicated all-attack helicopters to see service in the Vietnam War and were a product of the Army's need for an Advanced Aerial Fire Support System (AAFSS) to provide close-in fire support for airmobility operations. The Bell Model 209, the AH-1G Huey Cobra (Figure 10-7) proved to be a most effective helicopter in Vietnam.

**Figure 10-7. Bell AH-1 Huey Cobra**
*(Photo courtesy of U.S. Army)*

A team headed by Bell engineer J.P. Duppstadt began to design the Model 209 in March 1965. What made the AH-1 so timely was that Bell decided to take many of the features of the AH-1 from its UH-1 design and from several attack helicopter prototypes, such as their Sioux Scout and Model 207 prototypes. From the Model 207 came the stepped tandem seating, stub wings, and remote-control turret. From the UH-1C came the Bell high-performance rotor system and cambered vertical fin, as well as the majority of the principal internal dynamic components. The Huey Cobra also used the dependable T53-L-13 turboshaft engine, later upgraded to a T53-L-703 turboshaft of 1,800 horsepower.

The first flight of the Model 209 was on September 7, 1965. On October 25 Bell 209 No. N209J set an official world speed record in its class of 200 mph. By November of that year the Huey Cobra won a comparative "fly-off" against the Sikorsky S-61A, the Boeing Vertol CH-47, and the Kaman UH-2. On April 4, 1966, the Army awarded Bell a development contract for two prototype Huey Cobras and nine days later gave the company a contract for 100 helicopters.[39] In *The Huey and Huey Cobra*, author Bill Siuru relates why the Army chose the Huey Cobra:

> The Army favored the Bell 209 for two principal reasons. First, being based on the Huey, it could be placed in production rapidly. Even more importantly, it could be deployed into the field quickly — just eighteen months after the contract go-ahead date. Commonality with the Hueys meant it could share much of the existing parts inventory, and maintenance crews could service the Huey Cobra with little or no retraining.

> Secondly, there was the design itself. Powered by the Lycoming T53-L-13 1,400 horsepower engine, the AH-1G had a maximum cruise speed of over 150 knots (171 mph), and 190 knots (216 mph) in a shallow dive. Thus it had no trouble flying escort for any of the modern troop-carrying transport helicopters. Since the AH-1G used the Bell 540 door hinge rotor head assembly, it had outstanding maneuverability. Even though weighing essentially the same as the Hueys, it could go faster because of its 36-inch-wide, slimline design...[40]

The first AH-1 with its T53-L-13 engine arrived in Vietnam on August 19, 1967, and the first combat mission was flown on September 4. In January 1968 the AH-1G Huey Cobra performed beyond expectations, either providing suppressive fire against enemy strongholds or blunting enemy attacks during the Tet Offensive.

In September 1967 the UH-1H replaced the UH-1D in service and became the backbone of the U.S. Army in Vietnam. Not only could the new Huey haul up to 220 cubic feet of cargo internally, but it could also carry loads of up to 4,000 pounds from the floor-mounted hook. The range of the new Huey extended to 250 nautical miles and could reach 600 nautical miles with external fuel tanks. The Army spread out orders for this aircraft from 1966 to 1976, making it the most produced Huey variant at 5,435.[41] The T53-L-13 also provided power for the Navy's adaptations of the Huey, the UH-1L, TH-L, UH-1M, and the HH-1K models, as well as the commercial Model 205-A1.

## T53-L-703 Turboshaft

The T53-L-703 model became available in 1973, offering 1,800 shaft horsepower. Derived from the basic T53-L-13, the T53-L-703 offered improved hot-section components. Conversion kits for the T53-L-13 were made available and were used in the Army's AH-1s. In January 1974 Bell Helicopter offered to build the Army an interim tank-killer variant of the AH-1 equipped with the TOW (Tube-launched, Optically-tracked, and Wire-guided) antitank weapon system. With Army acceptance, the new helicopter was designated the AH-1Q. The more powerful T53-L-703 engine enabled Bell Helicopter to produce the AH-1S, offsetting the much-increased weight of the AH-1Q. Most of the Army's AH-1Gs were also upgraded with this new variant, starting in 1976 and ending in 1982.[42] In 1977 Bell delivered the last T53-powered UH-1 to the Army. Over 9,400 UH-1 helicopters were built before the line was closed down. Worldwide production of the Bell UH-1/204/205 series powered by the T53 as of the start of 1993 totaled 12,066 aircraft, including aircraft built in the United States, Italy, Germany, and Japan.[43] The last deliveries of the new-build AH-1S aircraft to the Army were made in 1985.

Lycoming completed the initial series of U.S. T53 production in the mid-1980s but is currently engaged in a series of upgrades for the existing UH-1 and AH-1 fleets. The T53-L-70X, currently in the final stages of development, offers 1,900 to 2,000 shaft horsepower. It features a stainless steel compressor casing, a cooled deflector, and a thermal barrier coated combustor. Textron Lycoming is also working with Bell Helicopter Textron on a low-cost Fleet Life Extension Program (FLEX) to extend UH-1 service life.[44]

The T53 engine is still being produced today by Lycoming and coproducers in Taiwan, Japan, Germany, and Italy. Through June 1993 Textron Lycoming and its licensees had built an estimated 17,694 T53 turboshaft engines of various models. Apart from the sheer volume of production over the last forty years, the T53 represents an outstanding achievement in aircraft gas turbine engine design, development and production. It was the first aircraft gas turbine of its power class to be completely designed and developed in the United States and was the first mass-produced U.S. helicopter engine.

The T53 served as a major catalyst in the Army's drive to expand its aviation role within the military. The ability of the Huey and the T53 to fill distinctly different combat aviation roles for the Army was the key to their mass production, which, in turn, was the key to the Army's phenomenal aviation growth during the Vietnam War.

## Design and Development of the Avco-Lycoming T55 Turboshaft Engine

With the success of the T53, Lycoming began to think about "growing" the engine as an entry into the high-power turboshaft engine market. The plan was to modify the T53 into a higher-power engine with higher airflow while maintaining much the same dimensions and leaving room for thrust growth. The Lycoming design team was expanded for the new engine. By April 4, 1953, Lycoming had produced an initial proposal for the LTC4 and LTE4 engine models,[45] followed in September with a second proposal. The LTC4 was an axial-radial compressor design and the LTE4 was an all-axial compressor design. Both were designed to a 1,500-horsepower requirement.[46]

In April 1954 Avco Lycoming won the Air Force contract for design and development of a turboprop in the 750-1,500 horsepower range. Their LTC4 axial-radial design became the T55 (Figure 10-8).[47] In June 1954 they were awarded the final contract,[48] and by March 1955 the design team had completed the preliminary design of a 500-pound, 1,500 horsepower LTC4. The gas generator for the design ran on the test stand from December 1955 to June 1956, at which time the entire engine first ran.[49] The T55 benefited from T53 experience in that it had a lower weight, smaller envelope, and improved fuel consumption.

**Figure 10-8. Cutaway of T55 Engine**
*(Illustration courtesy of George Opdyke)*

The T55 was a two-shaft, axial-centrifugal-flow free turbine aviation turboshaft. The compressor consisted of seven axial stages followed by a single centrifugal stage. The two-piece magnesium alloy stator casing had one row of variable inlet guide vanes and seven rows of steel stator blades bolted to a steel diffuser casing. The combustor was an annular reverse-flow type with a steel outer shell and inner lining. The turbine consisted of two mechanically independent axial turbines. The gas generator turbine for the first models of the T55 was a single-stage turbine; subsequent models beginning with the T55-L-9 had two stages with core-out cast steel blades having inner cooling airflow. The two-stage power turbine had solid steel blades. The engine was a simple, rugged design, which would not press the then-current Lycoming technology very far. The T55 also continued the Lycoming design philosophy of a "universal engine;" it was initially designed as a turboprop or turboshaft for aircraft main propulsion, tank engine use, or as a ground-power engine.[50]

The T55 was entered into the engine competition for the propulsion system for Weapons System SS471L, a medium-lift vertical takeoff and landing (VTOL) transport. The Army announced in late 1956 that it wanted to replace its piston-engine-powered H-37 transport helicopter with a turbine engine helicopter. The aircraft that won the competition and became slated for first use of the T55 was the Boeing-Vertol Corporation CH-47 (Model 114) Chinook helicopter (Figure 10-9), developed from an Air Force/Army design requirement for a "battlefield mobility" helicopter.[51] The Chinook was designed to carry a maximum of 40 troops with full equipment. The contract for the production of the first five Chinooks was given to Boeing-Vertol in June 1959.

**Figure 10-9. Boeing-Vertol/CH-47 Chinook**
*(Photo courtesy of U.S. Army)*

The Air Force/Army changed the Avco Lycoming contract from a turboprop to a turboshaft engine in April 1957. The T55-L-1 (LTC4A-1) turboprop was laid out in Lycoming Specification 124.2.2 on August 7, 1957. This model was available only in a "YT," or preliminary design, version and was to be superseded by a proposed advanced version. Designed to produce 1,600 maximum shaft horsepower at a specific fuel consumption of 0.682, it completed a 50-hour test in December 1957. The dry weight of the engine was 695 pounds. The T55-L-1 turboprop was followed on June 1, 1959, by the T55-L-3 (LTC4B-2) turboshaft. Only prototype and test versions of this 600-pound engine were built. It completed its 50-hour test in March 1959.[52] This variant is the ancestor of the outstanding T55 series of turboshafts that followed.[53]

## T55-L-5

The first production version of the T55 was the T55-L-5 (or LTC4B-7) at 2,200 shaft horsepower. Its maximum design pressure ratio was 6.6:1. This was the first engine produced for the first YHC-1B service test Chinooks (which were rolled out in the spring of 1961), as well as the first production HC-1B Chinooks. The T55-L-5 was 44 inches long and had a diameter of

24.25 inches and weighed 570 pounds dry. The first one ran in April 1959. The engine passed its 50-hour Preliminary Flight Rating Test in February 1960 and its 150-hour Qualification Test in January 1961. The first flight of the T55-L-5-powered Chinook was on September 21, 1961, at the Philadelphia Airport.

The Army began procurement of the Chinook and the T55 engine in 1960, with an initial contract for five helicopters. The HC-1B designation was changed to the CH-47A in 1962. Lycoming began delivery of production T55-L-5s to Boeing-Vertol in February 1961 and Boeing Vertol began deliveries of production aircraft to the Army on August 16, 1962. The Army designated the Chinook as its standard medium transport helicopter in October 1963.[54] The last 146 production T55-L-5s were delivered to Boeing Vertol in 1963.

## T55-L-7

While producing the T55-L-5, Lycoming was already working on a higher output version of the T55, the T55-L-7 (Lycoming Model LTC4B-8). This uprated version incorporated compressor and combustor improvements to permit higher power output, the most important in the combustion section, where the vaporizing fuel tubes were replaced by atomizing fuel injector nozzles. These new nozzles served to eliminate an ongoing combustor "hot spot" problem by providing more even temperature distribution in the combustion chamber.[55] This engine did not have to undergo a 50-hour test and passed its 150-hour Military Qualification Test in May 1963. First production deliveries of this 2,650-shaft-horsepower engine began in July 1963. The T55-L-7 powered the CH-47B Chinook, which entered service on May 10, 1967. A total of 1,471 T55-L-7 turboshaft engines were produced and saw extensive service in the Vietnam War.[56]

## T55-L-11

As in any successful engine/aircraft application, the Army began pressing Lycoming to get more power out of the T55. The company's next variant, the T55-L-11 (or LTC4B-11B), was an attempt to grow the engine more quickly than the technology could advance. The T55-L-11 was an uprated and redesigned T55-L-7, rated at 3,750 shaft horsepower. The changes in this variant included the use of variable-incidence inlet guide vanes in place of fixed vanes, and a redesign of the first three compressor stages to accommodate transonic airflow as opposed to subsonic. The engineers added a second turbine wheel to the compressor turbine and the first-stage blades and stator vanes were air-cooled. The engine achieved its qualification in July 1968, and the first engines were delivered in August 1968. This engine was installed in the CH-47C, which first flew on October 14, 1967.[57] During its extensive service in Vietnam, the engine encountered significant service problems resulting in some in-flight failures, and in-field corrections. A total of 1,009 of the T55-L-11 engines were produced until 1984 in series designated A, B, C, and D.

## T55-L-712

The next T55 engine in the series, the T55-L-712, directly addressed the problems of reliability, maintainability, and durability while maintaining the high performance of the T55-L-11D. Lycoming went to wide-chord compressor blades without inlet guide vanes, and a one-piece rotor. This new engine achieved and held a time-between-overhaul rating of 2,400 hours, a considerable improvement over the T55-L-11D. Rated at 4,500 shaft horsepower, the T55-L-712 powered the updated HC-47D Chinook. The first flight of the new model Chinook took place on May 11, 1979. Between 1980 and 1985, 328 earlier Chinook models were modified to the CH-47D configuration with the T55-L-712.

## T55-L-714

In 1987 the Army contracted with Boeing Helicopter for the development of a CH-47E for Special Operations Forces. This variant of the Chinook was powered by T55-L-714 engines rated at 4,868 shaft horsepower with maximum continuous power of 4,168 shaft horsepower. The T55-L-714 turboshaft gave improved performance for hot-weather and high-altitude operations.[58]

## T55-ACE

In 1990 Lycoming began work on their next-generation T55 engine, the T55-ACE (Advanced Chinook Engine). This was to be an uprated variant, moving into the 6,000-shaft horsepower range and offering increased time-between-overhaul, and improved specific fuel consumption over the T55-L-712 (by 13 percent). Testing of a fully configured engine began in 1993.[59] The T55-ACE owes its improved performance to an improved compressor derived from technologies developed under the Defense Department's Integrated High Performance Turbine Engine Technology Program (IHPTET). The ACE delivers increased performance and specific fuel consumption while maintaining the same installation envelope as the T55-L-714.[60]

Although the T55 is remembered mostly as a helicopter engine, the core of the T55 led to the development of the first high-bypass turbofan, the ALF 502, used in the Canadair Challenger 600 and the BAe 146. The core also was the basis for several stationary and marine power plants including the TF40 which powers the Navy's LCAC (Landing Craft Air Cushion) used in the 1989 Gulf War.

## Design and Development of the General Electric T58 Turboshaft Engine

The creators of the General Electric T58 were not in the large company organization set up in Lockland (the name was changed to Evendale when the local village incorporated), but in fact were the engineers at the relatively smaller Aircraft Accessory Turbine Department at Lynn, Massachusetts. This group was composed mostly of engineers who had not wanted to make the move to Ohio, preferring to stay in Massachusetts. Although the department was engaged in developing and producing accessory air turbines for electrical and hydraulic drives in aircraft, and in producing aircraft turbosuperchargers as well, the engineers also wanted to produce small gas turbines for primary power plants. They tried in 1951 for an Air Force contract but lost to Lycoming's T53. General Electric then turned to the Navy to develop the market for a GE-built small gas turbine engine.[61]

## The Development of the T58-GE-2

GE submitted the initial proposal for a small engine to the Navy in January 1953.[62] The Navy contract was originally for a 600-shaft-horsepower turboshaft engine, but General Electric proposed an 800-shaft-horsepower engine that weighed 400 pounds without a gearbox.[63]

On October 1, 1953, General Electric reorganized and decentralized the Aircraft Engine Division. One of the new departments that were subsequently established was the Small Aircraft Engine Department, headquartered in Lynn. The new manager of this department was Jack Parker, an engineer who was to rise far in the General Electric management hierarchy.[64]

The design of the T58-GE-2 started in June 1953 when the company received the Navy contract, and was completed in March 1954.[65] In May of that year, however, General Electric became convinced that the XT58 was not large enough. Market and mission evaluations indicated that a shaft horsepower of about 1,000 was better. General Electric also recalled their weight problems with the J73 turbojet, and wanted a less conservative (and therefore lighter) engine.

The engineers made a new preliminary design of a 1,000-shaft-horsepower engine. They scaled down the J47's compressor to integrate it into the T58's design. When the redesign was ready, the company presented it to the Navy. The new design promised 1,050 shaft horsepower with a weight of 250 pounds. This meant a power-to-weight ratio of 4:1, unheard of at the time. Nevertheless, the Navy, after studying the proposal for two weeks, approved the new design for the T58-GE-2 (Figure 10-10) in September 1954.[66] They also provided $10 million more for development of the new design.

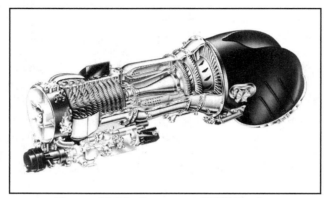

**Figure 10-10. Cutaway of T58 Engine**
*(Illustration courtesy of GE)*

The compressor for the T58 was the first variable-stator, high-pressure compressor ever designed for that small an application. The compressor in its final design configuration was a ten-stage, axial configuration of which the first three stages were transonic, using variable geometry. While the designers hoped to achieve a compressor efficiency of approximately 75 to 78 percent, the compressor when tested actually achieved an efficiency of 85 percent. This was achieved with compressor blades which in the last stages of the compressor were smaller than the average thumbnail.[67] The combustor and two-stage turbine were conventional.

William Travers, in *The General Electric Aircraft Engine Story*, explains one of the difficulties associated with scaling down turbine engine technology:

> The manufacture of tiny compressor blades for the new small aircraft engines, like the T58, posed a real challenge, because accuracy and reasonable cost were absolutely necessary. Two manufacturing plants at Ludlow and Rutland in Vermont were used for development and production of blades and vanes, where a "pinch and roll" process was developed for production of these small aircraft compressor blades.[68]

The T58 was also the first General Electric engine to incorporate an annular combustor. The free power-turbine assembly used a single stage to drive the output shaft.[69] Travers describes two of the early T58 development problems:

> When the T58 compressor was first designed, engineers did not sufficiently allow for the boundary layer, which restricts air flow, and is a significant consideration in very small compressors. They completely redesigned the T58 compressor and had it operating on an engine in less than eight months. The first engine had gone to test in March 1955, and would not run. But in December 1955, the T58, equipped with the new compressor 'operated like a charm.' In this crash program, there had been no time for either component testing or blade instrumentation, and, as a result, during the first engine tests, the first stage blade broke off from vibratory excitation. With this blade fixed, the T58 project was on its way toward engine qualification. The technical management vowed that the T58 was the last new engine that General Electric would ever run without blade instrumentation.[70]

The first run of the T58-GE-2 was in April 1955, and after its success a manufacturing proposal was submitted to the Navy in May 1955.[71] The T58-GE-2 passed its Preliminary Flight Rating Test (50 hours) in August 1956, and passed its Military Qualification Test (150 hours) in August 1957.[72]

The T58-GE-2 first flew on January 30, 1957, in a Sikorsky HSS-1F (H-3) helicopter. As this was an old design aircraft, the Sikorsky engineers argued for installing two T58-GE-2s in a new helicopter design, the S-61 (redesignated by the Department of Defense the SH-3A), or Sea King, which flew for the first time in March 1959. The engine was also installed in the Kaman UH-2 Sea Sprite (Figure 10-11).[73]

**Figure 10-11. Kaman UH-2A Sea Sprite**
*(Photo courtesy of U.S. Navy)*

## The T58-GE-6

The T58-GE-6's design was started in August 1957, was first test-run in March 1958, and passed its Military Qualification Test in August 1958. The first flight of the T58-GE-6 was in April 18, 1958, and production was begun in April 1962.[74]

## The T58-GE-8

The T58-GE-8's design started in August 1958, incorporating such features as improved turbine nozzles and compressor modifications to improve performance and durability. The first test run of the T58-GE-8 was in November 1958. It passed its Preliminary Flight Rating Test in August 1959 and its Military Qualification Test in July 1960.[75]

The T58-GE-8 first flew on March 11, 1959, in a Sikorsky SH-3A helicopter.[76] The T58-GE-8 was also installed in many other helicopters, among them the Boeing-Vertol CH-46A Sea Knight, which flew for the first time in August 1962.[77] In October of that year the Marine Corps chose the UH-46A as its standard medium assault helicopter and ordered fifty.

The T58-GE-8 was also installed in the Kaman UH-2A, which flew for the first time in July 1959.[78] Additional installations included the HH-52A Seaguard search/rescue helicopter; SH-2D/-2F and YSH-2E antisubmarine helicopter; and the UH-3A Sea King utility helicopter. The first production of the T58-GE-8 was in November 1960. Production terminated in 1984.[79]

## The T58-GE-1

The first production of the T58-GE-1 was in January 1963, for installation in the CH-3C helicopter. The first flight of the engine was in June 1963.[80]

## The T58-GE-3

The first production run of the T58-GE-3 was in September 1963.[81] The first flight of the engine was on February 20, 1964, in the Bell UH-1F.[82] The major application of the 1,270-horsepower T58-GE-3 was in the Air Force adaptation of the Bell UH-1F Huey. This helicopter was based on the Bell Model 204 series, but with the T58-GE-3 instead of the Lycoming T53. The Air Force bought the Bell helicopter primarily to support the ballistic missile forces in the continental United States, although they also used it for rescue and recovery and aerial psychological warfare. The Air Force eventually contracted for and received 120 UH-1Fs and an additional 26 TH-1Fs.[83]

## The T58-GE-10

The design of the T58-GE-10 was begun in March 1961. The first run of the 1,400-shaft-horsepower T58-GE-10 was in May 1962. The T58-GE-10 was shipped for installation in May 1965, and passed its 150-hour endurance test in November 1965.[84] The first flight was in December 1963 in the SH-3D.[85]

The T58-GE-10 saw service (two engines each) in the CH-46D/46F cargo/transport (Figure 10-12), the UH-46D Sea Knight utility, and the SH-3D/3H Sea Knight antisubmarine helicopter. In its CH-46D form the Sea Knight could carry twenty-six combat troops plus three crew, or an internal cargo payload of up to 10,000 pounds. The Sea Knight could also carry an under-slung load on a central hook. A total of 266 CH-46Ds were built for the Marine Corps. Both CH-46 and UH-46 (Army) versions saw combat in Vietnam from March 1966, with over 100,000 combat hours logged by August 1968.[86]

**Figure 10-12. Boeing-Vertol CH-46D Sea Knight**
*(Photo courtesy of U.S. Navy)*

## The T58-GE-16

This 1,870-shaft-horsepower variant of the T58 was first installed in an upgraded version of the CH-46, called the CH-46E. The Navy began conversion of CH-46Ds in 1973 and completed conversion of 272 of them to E models by 1984.

## The CT58

The CT58 turboshaft engine was certified in 1959 by the CAA.[87] The four major commercial derivatives of the T58 model were the CT58-100-2 of 1,050 horsepower; the CT58-100-1, a down-rated version at 730 horsepower; the CT58-110-1, of 1,350 horsepower at 59°F ambient day conditions; and the CT58-140-1, of 1,400 horsepower at 80°F ambient day conditions.

Commercial installations included the Sikorsky S-61 and S-62 helicopters and the Boeing Vertol V-107 helicopter. Commercial customers were mostly located in major metropolitan centers, with the three biggest being Los Angeles Airways, San Francisco Airways, and New York Airways.

The T58 was the first General Electric aircraft gas turbine engine to be licensed to a foreign manufacturer. De Havilland Engines in Great Britain produced and sold it as the Gnome turboshaft engine. Total production of the T58 turboshaft engine came to 8,536 engines as of December 31, 1988.

## Summary of T58 Engine Development

The T58 proved to be an important aircraft gas turbine engine development program for GE. It got the company involved in the field of small gas turbines and its engineers were able to apply their new variable-geometry compressor experience to the smaller turbine engine. The T58 program also gave them their first experience in direct contracting with the Navy (although the Air Force bought the T58 for several of its helicopter programs as well). This Navy experience was to serve them well in future turboshaft developments, like the T64, as well as future turbojet and turbofan developments. Perhaps most important, the General Electric development of the T58 series of engines helped the company prove that a small engine could be produced with overall quality comparable to a large turbine engine.

## Design and Development of the T64 Turboshaft/Turboprop Engine

While the T58 turboshaft was being designed and developed, General Electric engineering teams were traveling across the country, talking to airframe developers to discover what the market requirements were for the next generation of turboshaft engines, but they were also out to emphasize the next basic technological direction for aircraft gas turbines: the idea that the aircraft engine should be assessed as part of an overall integrated transport system. Engines should not be fitted to aircraft or vice versa, but both should be considered concurrently in the design and development process. This was especially important in the field of helicopter development as every ounce of weight saved has a measurable impact on performance.

The General Electric marketing efforts showed that there would be a near-future need for a small turboshaft engine in the 2,500 horsepower range with the highest possible thermodynamic efficiency. The Navy came to the same conclusion and held a design competition, which General Electric won. The company launched a preliminary design during 1954.

One of the basic parameters in gas turbine design is the compressor's pressure ratio. Compressor losses are relatively simple to constrain when the pressure ratio is kept below 12:1. Above that limit the losses increase disproportionally and more stages must be brought in to handle the flow, thereby increasing the engine weight. For a long time General Electric pursued a 2,500-horsepower engine with five turbine stages. Although the company felt that a five-stage turbine design offered the best potential for a growth engine, the design team also felt that the initial product of their efforts should be a lighter engine with a four-stage turbine (two compressor and two power stages). They knew that they were paying a penalty in both higher engine cost and higher pressure-ratio in the turbine. They decided that the relatively higher cost of the overall aircraft would offset the higher cost of the engines and that the weight penalty of a higher pressure ratio would be worth paying for.[88]

GE decided to go with a pressure ratio of 12.5:1, the highest ratio yet adopted in any single-spool turboshaft engine. It was a very ambitious goal. The engine mass flow was fixed at 25 pounds per second in order to achieve the desired level of 2,500 horsepower. General Electric also decided to strive for an overall lower specific fuel consumption than in the T58. Armed with this goal, General Electric immediately began component evaluations.[89]

It is important to note here that General Electric continued design and development of the T64 in 1954 and 1955 significantly beyond the initial development requirements laid down by the Navy. When the engineers at the Navy Bureau of Aeronautics questioned GE's ability to achieve their compressor pressure ratio goals, the company submitted to the Navy the compressor design map with a series of actual test points shown on it.[90]

Early in 1956 General Electric made an unsolicited proposal to the Navy for the development of the T64. The point of the proposal was that the T64 would suit a variety of current and future applications and could be easily installed in whole families of aircraft, including many already in production with piston engines. General Electric emphasized that the cost-effectiveness of the T64 would come from an increased capability in helicopters and even fixed-wing aircraft, which would in turn result in a reduction in the number of aircraft required. When this conclusion began to agree with the Navy's own studies, the Navy decided on an engine competition. General Electric naturally won and received an engine development contract in September 1957.[91] Travers describes the contract award in 1957:

> Very early, the General Electric sales people recognized that the desires and requirements of potential evaluators were important. The engineers at Lynn worked so closely with the Navy's engineers that there grew a feeling that the design of the T64 was 'Navy.' This relationship paid off later when trouble developed and Navy engineers came to Lynn and helped work out the problems. The philosophy of the T64 Project was to tell the Navy everything and quickly. The initial development contract was for $58.5 million for four years, in a relatively leisurely program working towards a definite application.[92]

The contract was a cost-plus-fixed-fee type, and covered the development up to the 150-hour qualification of turboprop, turboshaft, and direct-drive engines, in both single and twinned configurations, all using the same gas generator.[93] The General Electric engineers thought it made good sense...

> to develop an engine with a basic gas generator section which could readily be converted from a turboshaft to a turboprop with a minimum of effort and a maximum of parts interchangeability. Four engine configurations resulted, all utilizing the identical basic power unit and differing only in speed decreaser gearing and accessories.[94]

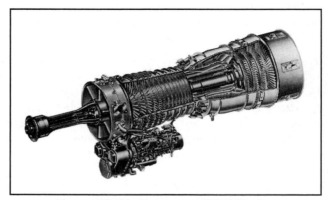

**Figure 10-13. Cutaway of T64 Engine**
*(Illustration courtesy of GE)*

The T64 (Figure 10-13) represented a 'new sheet of paper' engine design for GE. The engine was designed to function in turboshaft and turboprop configurations, and it was the first turboshaft designed to operate in the vertical orientation.

Based on J93 turbojet engine compressor technology, the fourteen-stage axial-flow compressor developed a pressure ratio of 12.6:1. The inlet guide vanes and first four stages of stators were variable to assure high-compression starting and fast acceleration without stalling, and the inlet guide vanes and first two stator stages were shrouded at their inner diameter for added ruggedness and reliability.[95] The compressor was made of titanium to meet the Navy's requirements for corrosion resistance.

Incorporating elements of the T58 and J93 combustors, the T64 combustor was a full annular system consisting of an inner shell, outer shell, and connecting annular dome at the upstream end. The combustor contained twelve adjustable ferrules to accommodate the duplex fuel nozzles. Early problems with localized liner buckling and burning were eliminated by improving the louver cooling pattern and increasing the liner wall thickness. The General Electric team achieved a significant improvement in performance by reducing the combustor casing contour to increase the velocity of cooling air.[96]

The turbine casing was split in a way similar to the compressor casing, so that individual blades could be taken out of the rotor or casing without the engine leaving the test stand.[97]

The development program, as initially established, consisted of the design, development, and qualification of two engine models; the T64-GE-2 turboshaft (single-stage reduction gear) and the T64-GE-4 turboprop engines. During the development program, the basic engine rating was increased from 2,650 to 2,850 shaft horsepower, and the qualification of the T64-GE-6 turboshaft (basic power producer) and T64-GE-8 turboprop engines were added.[98] The engine's specific fuel consumption is still rated as the best for any turboshaft engine in service for helicopters.

GE also demonstrated with the T64 a significant number of "lessons learned" in terms of maintenance. John M. Fernberger describes those lessons:

> For instance, the compressor with a split casing and vane rings, plus moment-weighted blades, permits field replacement of all compressor blades and vanes without major disassembly. The fuel control, fuel pumps, and centrifugal fuel filter are grouped and attached to each other and the engine accessory drive pad by means of quick detach clamps so that they can be serviced from one access position. The fuel manifolds, nozzles, and ignitors are individually replaceable, and mounted so they can be removed without engine disassembly.[99]

This meant that with the engine installed, the compressor casing could be unbuttoned and any required blade could slide from the casing or rotor.

## T64-GE-2 Turboshaft

The design and initial development of the T64-GE-2 was completed in April 1960 and both the T64-GE-2 and T64-GE-6 models completed the Preliminary Flight Rating Test in April 1960. Testing of the engines began shortly thereafter. Travers relates:

> In 1962, the United States Navy became concerned about the T64 program after several futile attempts by General Electric to pass the Model Qualification Test. General Electric had many early development problems with the engine during the previous four-and-one-half years. Finally the T64 was able to pass the Model Qualification Test for both the turboprop and turboshaft versions.[100]

A history of the T64 on file in the General Electric Archives in Evendale states the following:

> Schedule delays for 150-hour endurance testing were primarily the result of time required to complete the Preliminary Flight Rating Test on the turboprop gearbox and time to thoroughly evaluate and assurance-test improvements resulting from deficiencies found in the first-stage compressor blading and first-stage turbine nozzle diaphragm encountered during official testing. Comprehensive corrective action and stringent test and inspection requirements produced the necessary results. Environmental, altitude and anti-icing testing to complete all requirements for full model qualification were completed in 1964 following completion of 150-hour endurance qualification requirements.[101]

The Navy wanted the T64 to pass extensive endurance qualification testing because of the projected mission of the engine, so the engine cycle had to be durable and reliable for long flights over water. The T64-GE-2 and T64-GE-6 engine passed its 150-hour Military Qualification Test in June 1963 and flew in the Sikorsky CH-53 helicopter in October 1964.[102]

## T64-GE-6 Turboshaft

This engine was a growth version of the T64-GE-2 and was developed for the CH-53 Sea Stallion helicopter, which first flew on October 14, 1964.

## T64-GE-4 Turboprop

From the beginning of the T64 development program, a turboprop version of the engine had been decided upon. During the period from May 1960 to May 1962, a T64-GE-4 turboprop underwent a 100-hour flight test program (356 engine hours) in the de Havilland Caribou. General Electric service representatives went to South America and helped introduce the de Havilland Buffalo to Brazil. The General Electric team also worked successfully to replace the Rolls-Royce Dart turboprops with T64s on Fiat's G.222 Transport and General Electric application engineers worked with the Japanese to equip their PS-1 flying boat with T64 power and re-engine their P2J patrol aircraft with T64s.[103]

A significant technological advance was realized with the incorporation of a titanium compressor for the T64, a first in turboshafts. Titanium was considered much more corrosion-resistant than stainless steel or aluminum. Travers describes the problems associated with titanium and the General Electric approach to overcoming them:

> Manufacture of the small titanium compressor blades presented a unique problem. To solve the problem a new process was developed in the Thomson Laboratory in Lynn, so that GE's Rutland Plant in Vermont could produce tiny compressor blades of titanium at a fraction of the cost. The 'pinch and roll' process, so successful on steel blades, was not satisfactory for titanium. A team developed precision 'oversize' forgings and then a process to chemical-mill the blades to final size. As the dies would wear, as they do in production, adjustments could be made to the chem-milling process.[104]

> As the production program got underway and the applications increased, all of which required more growth horsepower, General Electric reached an agreement with the Navy to develop a more powerful version. For the new growth engine General Electric specified the titanium compressor, advanced technology turbine air-cooling, segmented nozzle partitions, and a new shingle-type combustor. The engine grew from the 2,600-2,800 horsepower level to the 4,500-5,000 horsepower class.

As it turned out, the decision was made to go back to a steel-bladed compressor configuration for the T64-GE-415 and T64-GE-416 engine. General Electric also installed an integral spray system to flush deposits from the engine and to apply corrosion inhibitor to the internal parts. Two T64-GE-415s were installed in the RH-53D Sea Stallion reconnaissance aircraft, and three T64-GE-416's were installed in the CH-53E Sea Stallion cargo/transport helicopter (Figure 10-14).[105]

## Summary

The T64 program has been a significant technological and business success for GE. In a technological sense the delay in developing the engine models has been more than compensated for by the tremendous impact the engine had on the market. The T64 showed the tremendous capability inherent in small aircraft gas turbines to increase lifting power, extend cruise range, and improve reliability in an over-water environment. Both the Navy and the Air Force have made considerable use of T64 turboshaft engines in their rescue helicopters, where power, reliability and maintainability are crucial to operational success.

**Figure 10-14. Sikorsky CH-53E
Sea Stallion (Jolly Green Giant)**
*(Photo courtesy of U.S. Navy)*

The T64 program has been a significant technological and business success for GE. In a technological sense the delay in developing the engine models has been more than compensated for by the tremendous impact the engine had on the market. The T64 showed the tremendous capability inherent in small aircraft gas turbines to increase lifting power, extend cruise range, and improve reliability in an over-water environment. Both the Navy and the Air Force have made considerable use of T64 turboshaft engines in their rescue helicopters, where power, reliability and maintainability are crucial to operational success.

The T64 has also been very good to General Electric in a commercial sense. The T64 is still being produced by the company in Lynn, over thirty-five years after its inception. It has provided a significant production base for the Lynn Division, with production of over 3,215 turboprop and turboshaft engines.

## Design and Development of the T700 Turboshaft

The next engine, the T700, is very important to any history of the aircraft gas turbine engine in the United States. The T700 marked the beginning of a truly independent Army gas turbine engine program, wholly apart from the Air Force. The T700 was the first product of the Army Advanced Technology Demonstrator Engine (ATDE) program in the late 1960s. The program was effective, achieving all of its technical, reliability, and maintainability goals, but at the cost of overrunning its budget by a considerable margin. It provides a good look at how a military service and a company can work together to provide timely engine development.

GE entered into the ATDE program in 1967. Under ATDE, participating engine manufacturers were to design, engineer, and produce a new series of power plants for a new generation of utility and transport helicopters. Also in 1967 the Army issued requests for proposals to all aircraft gas turbine manufacturers for a new 1,500 horsepower engine requirement for a new Utility/Transport helicopter. General Electric responded with the GE12 demonstrator engine, a derivative of its 'building block' series of demonstrator engines. Both General Electric and P&W were awarded contracts for a 1,500 horsepower demonstrator turboshaft engine.[106]

The Army then decided to select one of the two demonstrator programs for development. The selection process was called the T700 competition, and it was a rigorous one. The Army was looking for a tough helicopter/engine weapons system to measure up to Vietnam War standards. The system had to operate in severe combat conditions and deliver greater reliability, maintainability, and survivability, plus high excess power. Both the GE12 and the P&W ST9 designs had compressors with pressure ratios around 14:1, the P&W compressor consisting of two centrifugal stages, and the GE12's compressor consisting of five axial stages and one centrifugal stage. The Army, however, announced that they would count the number of engine parts in the competition, and the P&W design had a compressor of around 70 parts, while the GE12's compressor had over 300.

GE's response to this problem was to greatly simplify the compressor. Engineers came up with the integral blade and disk or "blisk," a combination of blade and disk where each wheel and all of the blades were machined from a single piece of material. This helped scale the GE12's compressor down from 300 pieces to 12. With the efficiency of the axial-centrifugal compressor, General Electric won the competition and was awarded a four-year development contract in August 1967.[107] The task of developing this radically new turboshaft engine still lay ahead.

The T700 turboshaft development program offered several distinct technology development challenges to GE. First there was the fact that General Electric had never developed a helicopter engine for the Army, and the Army had never before managed a helicopter engine development program. Both were therefore on new ground. Next the engine had to be developed to very special U.S. Army requirements. The Army wanted an engine suitable for both a Utility Tactical Transport Aircraft System (UTTAS) helicopter, and for an Advanced Attack Helicopter (AAH). Technologically speaking, the T700 presented some specific challenges. It combined axial and centrifugal stages in its compressor, and General Electric had not done any centrifugal compressor design in many years. The axial part of the compressor had to run at 1,550 feet per second tip speed, a difficult requirement in itself. The pressure ratio also had to be high, about 17:1 in all, and finally, the specific fuel consumption had to be about 25 percent better than GE's T58. Moreover, General Electric had agreed to develop the T700 to meet the needs of the developing UTTAS helicopter design, which wasn't yet set. This meant that the T700 design and development team had to 'build in' performance improvement from the very beginning. The development contract called for a 30 percent improvement in part power specific fuel consumption, a 25 to 30 percent improvement in weight, and a "significant improvement in maintenance over the then-current state-of-the-art."[108]

GE was awarded the development contract for the T700 in March 1972. The company realized the best way to stay ahead of changing airframe developments was to keep abreast of the two competing airframe manufacturers' developments, so the T700 team worked very closely with both Bell Helicopter and Boeing-Vertol (formerly Piasecki), listening to what these two companies engineers had to say about engine requirements. From February to April 1971 General Electric engineers built a mockup and worked on a major layout of the T700 (Figure 10-15).

As development proceeded, the engine met the strict performance predictions, although not without its share of development problems. William Travers described these:

> At first, it had inadequate compressor stall margin, then a stage matching problem, and then a problem with turbine efficiency. Fortunately the competition dragged on and on, and General Electric took advantage of good results in its engineering component development programs.[109]

The T700 was the first jet engine designed with a radial compressor since 1950. The compressor achieved a 7:1 pressure ratio in five axial stages, and its blisks, wheels, and blades were one-piece designs. The combustor was a unique design from a Curtiss-Wright design contract. It featured vaporizing fuel nozzles that produced a very low pattern factor. The high-pressure tur-

**Figure 10-15. T700 Engine**
*(Photo courtesy of GE)*

bine featured air-cooled blades with short radial height and an aspect ratio of 0.5 (chord length twice blade height). All engine accessories were top-mounted. The engine installation featured an aircraft-mounted fuel pump, the first suction fuel system, and an integral particle separator to minimize sand and dust ingestion. The T700 also featured the first infrared suppressor ever devised for an engine. In terms of maintenance the T700 required only a twelve-piece toolkit for its repair.

The Army insisted on a simple engine design. They wanted an engine that would reduce the cost of engine procurement, maintenance, and logistical support, and that would have an enhanced survivability factor. The T700 design addressed all of those concerns. Its new component modular design and assembly claimed several technological firsts. One of them was the unique integral inlet particle separator, located in the front of the engine, which eliminated up to 95 percent of ingested foreign matter and sand. In addition, a variable-stator system that resisted sand and oil was conceived. A second unique element of the engine was its lubrication system, including special high-speed bearings, designed for a combat environment. Totally self-contained, the system was not dependent on the rest of the aircraft for operation. If the lubrication supply to the engine was lost due to hostile fire, the engine provided a "get home" mist lubrication system for an additional six minutes of flying time. In Vietnam six minutes was often enough time to clear enemy-held areas and get back to friendly zones of control, a real advantage to the aircraft's personnel. This proved important in Vietnam, as over 5,000 helicopters were lost during counter-insurgency operations.[110]

The component modules of the T700 were mechanically interchangeable; this included the accessory, compressor, combustor, and high-pressure turbine modules. There were no critical dimension or calibration checks required for installation. Only two men were needed to replace modules, and only ten tools from the standard Army AO7 tool kit were required.[111] The first T700 was delivered to the test stand in early 1973. On October 11, 1974, the T700 passed the 50-hour Preliminary Flight Rating Test and in March 1976 it passed the 150-hour Military Qualification Test.[112]

On May 13, 1976, General Electric was cited by the U.S. Army Materiel Development and Readiness Command "for its technical excellence in the development of the T700 engine." The remainder of the citation read:

> The engine has completed every major official test on the first run. There have been no program delays due to engine failure. The T700 incorporates features, both Army and contractor imposed, which

promise increased performance, greater reliability, ease of manufacture and reduced maintenance. The Aircraft Engine Group at General Electric is recognized for its outstanding support to the Army.[113]

The first production T700-GE-700 was delivered to the U.S. Army in March 1977. Installed in the first Sikorsky UH-60A Black Hawk helicopters (Sikorsky having won the UTTAS helicopter competition), it began a very successful and profitable relationship between Sikorsky and GE.

Sikorsky flew its first prototype YUH-60A on October 17, 1974. The YUH-60 incorporated a fully articulated, four-bladed main rotor with swept-back tips. It had a fixed undercarriage and could carry an infantry squad of eleven fully equipped troops. The helicopter was modified after flight testing with the raising of the main rotor by 15 inches above the fuselage and by the adoption of an all-moving tailplane instead of a fixed tailplane. The first production UH-60A (Figure 10-16) flew on October 17, 1978, and the first deliveries to the Army's 101st Airborne Division started on October 31, 1978. By 1987 the Black Hawk was also serving with the 82nd Airborne, and the 9th and 24th Infantry Divisions, as well as units in Panama, Korea, Hawaii, and West Germany. Indeed the UH-60 has been adopted for service by the Navy, Marine Corps, and the Air Force, as well as other nations, making it and the T700 engine a much-relied upon system today.[114]

**Figure 10-16. Sikorsky UH-60A Black Hawk**
*(Photo courtesy of U.S. Army)*

In the Army's Advanced Attack Helicopter (or AAH) program formulated in 1972, both aircraft finalists in the competition, Bell Helicopter and Hughes, used T700-GE-700's in their helicopters. The winner of the competition was Hughes (now part of Boeing via its acquisition through McDonnell Douglas), in December 1976. The helicopter, designated the AH-64 Apache (Figure 10-17), was designed to use advanced composite materials in its structure. It was designed to be able to absorb a great deal of battlefield damage and still fly and accomplish its anti-tank mission.

## T700-GE-401

The next significant model of the T700 engine was the T700-GE-401 model. This is the nautical version of the T700, incorporating modifications and changes to adapt the engine to an ocean environment. Some of the gas-path components have been made from corrosion-resistant materials, and the engine seals and cooling systems are different from the other T700 models. This program was initiated in September 1977 and the Navy awarded a development contract to General Electric for the engine in March 1978. The T700-GE-401 engine delivers 1,690 shaft horsepower, the increase coming from a higher turbine inlet temperature, an improved centrifu-

**Figure 10-17. AH-64 Apache**
*(Photo courtesy of U.S. Army)*

gal compressor impeller, and tighter overall clearances. The first mockup for the aircraft was completed in January 1978 and the first installation engine was completed in September 1979. The T700-GE-401 completed its 50-hour Preliminary Flight Rating Test in May 1979, and its 150-hour Military Qualification Test in November 1982. General Electric delivered the first production T700-GE-401 in December 1982. The T700-GE-401 is used in a twin configuration in the Navy's SH-60B Seahawk LAMPS MARK III helicopter.

The next improved version of the T700 was the T700-GE-401C/701C model. This model is rated at 1,798 shaft horsepower for the T700-GE-701C derivative and 1,890 shaft horsepower for the T700-GE-401C derivative. These models are considered part of the General Electric Step 2 Growth Series of the T700. Initial T700-GE-401C engines were delivered to the Navy in April 1988 and the first T700-GE-701Cs were shipped to the U.S. Army for their Black Hawk helicopters in January 1989. The T700-GE-401C/701C engines include improvements in aerodynamic, materials, and cooling technologies that have been incorporated into the engine's centrifugal compressor and high-pressure turbine.

A commercial turboshaft growth derivative of the T700, the CT7-6/6A, was developed by Alfa Romeo Avio and Fiat Aviazione. In March 1988 General Electric agreed to provide fourteen General Electric CT7-6 turboshaft engines for the three-engine EH 101 civil and utility helicopters to E.H. Industries (EHI) in Britain. As of January 1995 more than 8,530 T700's had been delivered worldwide.[115]

## Endnotes

[1]   Avco-Lycoming, "T53 and T55," Flight (January 17, 1958), 79.

[2]   Wragg, David, Helicopters At War: A Pictorial History, London, UK: Robert Hale, 1983, 70.

[3]   Condon, John P., Major General, USMC (Ret.),U.S. Marine Corps Aviation: Volume Five of a Commemorative Collection, Diamond Anniversary of the 75th Year of Naval Aviation, Washington, D.C.: Deputy Chief of Naval Operations (Air Warfare), Naval Air Systems Command, 1987, 30.

[4]   Wragg, David, Helicopters at War, 66, and Siuru, Bill, The Huey and Huey Cobra, Blue Ridge Summit, PA: Tab Books, Incorporated, 1987, 8.

[5]   Wragg, David, Helicopters at War, 66.

[6]   Siuru, The Huey and Huey Cobra, 8.

[7]   Davis, Richard G., The 31 Initiatives: A Study in Air Force - Army Cooperation, Washington, D.C.: Office of Air Force History, United States Air Force, 1987, 5-12.

[8]   Siuru, The Huey and Huey Cobra, 13.

9   Ibid, 9, and Bowers, Peter M. and Swanborough, Gordon, United States Military Aircraft Since 1909, Washington, D.C.: Smithsonian Institution Press, 1989, 78.

10  Bowers and Swanborough, United States Military Aircraft Since 1909, 78.

11  Mesko, Jim, Airmobile: The Helicopter War in Vietnam, Carrollton, TX: Squadron/Signal Publications, 1984, 4-5.

12  Ibid, 6.

13  Moellmann, Heinz, Stratford, Connecticut, Interview, September 16, 1987.

14  Ibid.

15  Opdyke, George, Stratford, Connecticut, Interview, April 22, 1994.

16  Ibid.

17  Opdyke Interview, April 22, 1994.

18  Moellmann Interview, September 16, 1987.

19  Moellmann Interview, September 16, 1987.

20  Wragg, David, Helicopters at War, 16.

21  Bowers and Swanborough, United States Military Aircraft Since 1909, 78.

22  Wragg, David, Helicopters at War, 16, and Williams International, History and Evolution of the Williams International F107 Cruise Missile Turbofan Engine, covers years 1955 through 1988, Walled Lake, MI, no date, 9.

23  Moellmann Interview, September 16, 1987.

24  Ibid.

25  Wragg, David, Helicopters at War, 16.

26  Williams International, History and Evolution of the Williams International F107, 9.

27  Bowers and Swanborough, United States Military Aircraft Since 1909, 79-80, and AP Rees, Elfan, World Military Helicopters, New York, NY: Jane's Publishing, 1986.

28  Mesko, Airmobile: The Helicopter War in Vietnam, 9.

29  Bowers and Swanborough, United States Military Aircraft Since 1909, 336-338.

30  Wragg, David, Helicopters at War, 114.

31  Schrader, J. Walton, Stratford, Connecticut, Interview, April 23, 1994.

32  Wragg, David, Helicopters at War, 30.

33  Bowers and Swanborough, United States Military Aircraft Since 1909, 81.

34  Wragg, David, Helicopters at War, and Rees, World Military Helicopters, 38.

35  Bowers and Swanborough, United States Military Aircraft Since 1909, 80-81, and Wragg, David, Helicopters at War, 40.

36  Bowers and Swanborough, United States Military Aircraft Since 1909, 81.

37  Forecast International, Gas Turbine Forecast: Book One, Reports and Forecasts, Newtown, CT: Forecast International, 1993.

38  Kuntzle, Charles, Stratford, Connecticut, Interview, April 21, 1994.

39  Rees, World Military Helicopters, 43.

40  Wragg, David, Helicopters at War, 55-56.

41  Ibid, 41, and Bowers and Swanborough, United States Military Aircraft Since 1909, 81.

42  Forecast International, Gas Turbine Forecast.

43  Ibid.

44  Ibid.

45  Anderton, David and Miller, Jay, Boeing Helicopter CH-47 Chinook, Aerofax Mimeograph 27, Arlington, TX: Aerofax, Incorporated, 1989.

46  Ibid.

47  Ibid.

48  Ibid.

49  Ibid.

50  DeBiasi, Victor, "Design Progress: T55 Stresses "Universal Engine " Concept," Space/Aeronautics, November 1958, 30.

51  Wragg, David, Helicopters At War: A Pictorial History, London, UK: Robert Hale, 1983, 158.

52  Aircraft Engine Marketing, Avco Lycoming Division, Summary of Specifications, Lycoming Gas turbine Engines Currently on Contract, Stratford, CT: Avco Lycoming Division, March 1968.

53  Ibid.

54  Bowers, Peter M. and Swanborough, Gordon, United States Military Aircraft1909, Washington, DC: Smithsonian Institution Press, 1989, 155.

55  Air Force Propulsion Characteristics Summary, T55-L-7 Turboshaft Engine, August 1963.

56  Bowers and Swanborough, United States Military Aircraft, 155.

57  Bowers and Swanborough, United States Military Aircraft, 155.

58  Gas Turbine Forecast, Textron-Lycoming T55 (Turboshaft), Forecast International/DMS Market Intelligence Report, 4.

59  Ibid.

60  Kandebo, Stanley W., "T55 Derivative To Run By Mid-Year," Aviation Week & Space Technology, March 8th, 1993.

61  Travers, William R, The General Electric Aircraft Engine Story, Cincinnati, OH: The General Electric Company, 1978, 3-13.

62  GE Company Archives File on the T58 turboshaft engine, Military and Commercial T58 Engines: Historical Dates, 1.

63 Travers, The General Electric Aircraft Engine Story, 3-14.

64 Ibid, and Avco-Lycoming, "Quarter Century of Progress Builds Helicopter Heritage," General Electric Aircraft Engine Group Headlines, no date, 1.

65 GE Company Archives File on the T58 turboshaft engine, Major Milestones In the T58 Engine Design, 1. and General Electric Company Archives File, Military and Commercial T58 Engines 1.

66 Travers, The General Electric Aircraft Engine Story, 3-14, and General Electric Company Archives File, Military and Commercial T58 Engines, 1.

67 W.T.G., "T64: Design Philosophy Behind GE's New Shaft Turbine, Flight (January 13, 1961), 63.

68 Travers, The General Electric Aircraft Engine Story, 3-15.

69 Avco-Lycoming, "T53 and T58," Flight, 79.

70 Travers, The General Electric Aircraft Engine Story, 3-14.

71 GE Company Archives File, Major Milestones In the T58 Engine Design, 1.

72 Ibid.

73 Travers, The General Electric Aircraft Engine Story, 3-14.

74 GE Company Archives File, Major Milestones In the T58 Engine Design, 1.

75 Ibid.

76 GE Company Archives File on the T58 turboshaft engine, T58 Program Chart, Evendale, OH: General Electric Aircraft Engine Group, no date, 1., and Pearson, Lee M. and Adrian O. Van Wyen, United States Naval Aviation: 1910 - 1980, NAV AIR 00-80P-1, Washington, D.C.: Office of Naval Operations, Naval Air Systems Command, 1980, 426-427.

77 GE Company Archives File, T58 Program Chart, 13.

78 Ibid, 14.

79 GE Company Archives File, Major Milestones In the T58 Engine Design, 1, and United States Navy, Propulsion Characteristics/Summary, NAVAIR No. 00-110A-3. Washington, D.C.: Naval Air Systems Command, 1984, 103-104.

80 Ibid, and General Electric Company Archives File, Major Milestones In the T58 Engine Design, 1.

81 Ibid.

82 Ibid.

83 Wragg, David, Helicopters at War, 93-98, and Rees, World Military Helicopters, 37.

84 United States Navy, Propulsion Characteristics/Summary, 105.

85 GE Company Archives File, Major Milestones In the T58 Engine Design, 1, and Rees, World Military Helicopters, 62.

86 Ibid, and United States Navy, Propulsion Characteristics/Summary, 105.

87 Avco-Lycoming, "Quarter Century of Progress Builds Helicopter Heritage," General Electric Aircraft Engine Group Headlines, 1.

88 W. T. G., "T64: Design Philosophy Behind GE's New Shaft Turbine, Flight, 63.

89 Ibid, and Travers, The General Electric Aircraft Engine Story, 4-8.

90 Ibid.

91 GE Company Archives File on the T64 turboshaft engine, T64 Program, 1.

92 Travers, The General Electric Aircraft Engine Story, 4-8.

93 W. T. G., "T64: Design Philosophy Behind GE's New Shaft Turbine, Flight, 63.

94 Fernberger, John M, "A Versatile Free Turbine," Interavia 1 (1963), 57.

95 Ibid. 58.

96 Ibid, 59.

97 W.T.G., "T64: Design Philosophy Behind GE's New Shaft Turbine, Flight, 64.

98 GE Company Archives File on the T64 turboshaft engine, T64 Turboshaft/Turboprop Development Data, 1.

99 Ibid, 58.

100 Travers, The General Electric Aircraft Engine Story, 4-8.

101 GE Company Archives File, T64 Turboshaft/Turboprop Development Data, 1.

102 Gunston, Bill, The Encyclopedia of the World's Combat Aircraft: A Technical Directory of Major Warplanes from World War 1 to the Present Day, New York: Chartwell Books Inc., 1976, 68-69.

103 Travers, The General Electric Aircraft Engine Story, 4-9.

104 Ibid, 4-8.

105 United States Navy, Propulsion Characteristics/Summary, 119.

106 Travers, The General Electric Aircraft Engine Story, 7-13.

107 Ibid.

108 Ibid.

109 Ibid.

110 Redding, Robert, and Bill Yenne, Boeing: Planemaker to the World, Greenwich, CT: Bison Books Corporation, 1983, 209.

111 Travers, The General Electric Aircraft Engine Story, 7-14.

112 GE Company Archives File on the T700 turboshaft engine, T700 General Information File, 4.

113 Ibid.

114 Bowers and Swanborough, United States Military Aircraft Since 1909, 536.

115 Falk, Eric, "United States Army's T700 Engine Completes Model Test Endurance Runs," General Electric Aircraft Engine Group Press Release No. AEG-376-18, 3.

**Air Force C-130 Hercules, Powered by
Four Allison T56 Turboprops**

# Chapter Eleven

# Turboprop Development

## The T40, T56 and T76 Engines

Immediately after World War II, the power plant deemed most likely to affect commercial aviation was the gas turbine/propeller combination—the turboprop. The biggest shortcoming of the turbojet was fuel efficiency, especially at lower altitudes and speeds, which meant it had a very short range. Whereas this was not a barrier to military fighter development, commercial airlines required "longer legs" in their operations. Enter the turboprop engine, with its propeller.

With a great deal less machinery, the turboprop obtains almost the same specific fuel consumption and efficiency at higher altitude and at slower speeds as does the most advanced reciprocating engine. The propeller also greatly improves takeoff and climb performance in terms of fuel economy, compared to a pure jet. In the first two decades of the aircraft gas turbine engine, the 1940s and 1950s, the turboprop was seen as the natural successor to the piston engine for certain types of aircraft. While the turbojet was seen as the premier military fighter application, the turboprop was seen as the proper application for long-, medium-, and short-range passenger aircraft as well as long-range freighter aircraft.

The turboprop, with its much lower specific fuel consumption and greater range, also provided a more comfortable transition technology to those unfamiliar with the still-exotic turbojet. Combining the propeller with the turbine did not seem as great a technological leap as going without a propeller at all, although developing turboprop technology did mean having to develop gearing to match turbine engine speeds. Airline executives during the period after the war, with declining military contracts and an abundance of surplus reciprocating engines available, also did not feel any urgency to buy turbojet engines. The turboprop did offer an increase in speed and power, and that was attractive to the airlines. In the United States, however, the military aviation establishments did not consider turboprop development to be as important as turbojet development.

In the mid to late 1940s, the Army Air Force and the Navy decided to pursue separate aircraft gas turbine engine development programs. In 1948, the Air Force stopped development of the turboprop engine altogether in favor of the turbojet. The Navy alone continued to develop both. Turboprop development languished until Allison came out with its remarkable T38 large turboprop engine, at which time a "marked change in attitude toward the turboprop" occurred.[1]

The Air Force's rediscovery of the turboprop was driven by the need for an efficient long-range transport capability. The United States was now a world superpower, with bases and strategic commitments all over the world. Both the Air Force and the Navy needed and wanted a long-range, strategic airlift capability. The Berlin Airlift of 1948-1949, although conducted with piston-engine aircraft, proved the value of strategic airlift. Now, fuel economy and range became as important as speed in the military aviation equation. In 1951 the Air Force's decision to reenter the turboprop development field with the T56 and the YC-130 transport brought renewed interest in the economics of the turboprop for transport use.

The Navy, however, perceived the turboprop also as a power plant for carrier tactical aircraft. The turboprop promised top speeds comparable to those of early jet aircraft. Turboprop development also promised to overcome the low-speed thrust and fuel-efficiency problems of the early turbojets. Both the Air Force and the Navy turboprop development programs led to engines that in turn caught the interest of the commercial aviation community. With most of the initial turboprop work paid for by military programs, the engine manufacturers could now present to the commercial aircraft designers a new capability.

In the commercial arena, the first flight of the Convair-built Turboliner in 1950 opened up the eyes of commercial airlines to the potential of the turboprop. Until the development of the turbofan engine, the turboprop remained supreme among commercial carriers and in military transport. In this chapter we will look at the development of two major turboprop applications, one a large turboprop for large aircraft, and the second a small turboprop for light military and business jet aircraft.

Two World War II naval warfare missions, antisubmarine warfare and long-range reconnaissance, had required the development of specific types of aircraft. The naval establishments of the Allies after the war sought to develop suitable aircraft for immediate and future requirements in both of these areas. The Navy believed that the turboprop offered substantial benefits for both types of aircraft, and it did not want the Army to be the sole sponsor of aircraft gas turbine engine research and development in the United States. The Army had brought the Whittle engine to the United States and had sponsored the aircraft gas turbine engine efforts of Nathan Price (first at Lockheed, then at Menasco). The Navy's aviation establishment wanted to make sure that the special needs of naval aviation were included in aircraft gas turbine engine research and development and therefore proceeded to sponsor work at Westinghouse on the 19A (military designation the J30) "Yankee" turbojet (Figure 11-1) and worked to move Pratt and Whitney into turbojet development. The Navy was also very receptive to the Allison proposals for turboprop development.

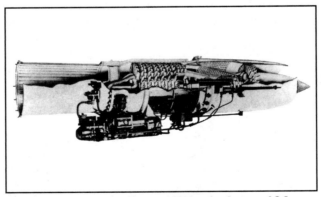

**Figure 11-1. Cutaway of Westinghouse 19A
Yankee (J30) Turbojet**
*(Illustration courtesy of Westinghouse)*

## Turboprop Development at the Allison Division of General Motors: The T38, T40, and T56

During World War II, the Allison Division of General Motors developed an outstanding reputation as both a designer and manufacturer of aircraft engines. After the war the Army Air Forces were committed to Allison's maintaining their aircraft engine manufacturing capability and even gave Allison the production contracts for two General Electric turbojets, the J33 and J35. Refining and producing the J33 and the J35 helped Allison through the transition from being simply a producer of jet engines to a designer and builder of turboprop engines. Producing these engines not only gave Allison experience in aircraft gas turbine tooling and production, but also earned the company a reputation within the military for reliability and service. The Navy, interested in long-range patrol aircraft, also began funding Allison research into turboprop engine design and development, beginning with the T38 turboprop in 1944.

## The Allison T38 Turboprop Engine

Allison decided to begin their turboprop research and development with an engine in the 3,000-shaft-horsepower class. The design team produced a concept for a turboprop engine with a nineteen-stage compressor producing a 6.2 pressure ratio, an eight-can combustion system, and a four-stage turbine. The size and shaft horsepower goals of the T38 set the standard for future Allison developments. The inlet diameters for the subsequent T40 and T56 stayed at relatively the same size as those of the T38. The T38 also began the Allison practice of mounting the turboprop gearbox via an offset prop shaft remote from the power section, making it possible to offer an engine that could be mounted without splitting an aircraft's wing structure.

Although the T38 never saw an application, the development program enabled Allison to gain valuable experience in original aircraft gas turbine engine design and development. The T38 was slated for installation in the E Model of the Convair T-29 transport, a military derivation of the Convair 240, but the T-29E (and its engines) was later canceled by the Air Force.[2] On April 19, 1949, Allison flew its first turboprop engine — a T38 — as the fifth engine on a B-17G test bed at Weir Cook Municipal Airport in Indianapolis.

Like all other engine manufacturers who decided to produce jet engines, Allison had to get through the "learning curve." Aircraft gas turbine aerodynamics and thermodynamics were not the same as those of the reciprocating engine. The mysteries of combustion proved to be a major hurdle for Allison to overcome, just as they did for all the other jet engine developers. Another problem peculiar to turboprop development that Allison had to overcome was gearbox frequency-matching vibrations.

Allison Division management was well aware of the military perception of Allison as a fighter engine company. Although the Navy supported the turboprop research at Allison, the military seemed more content to deal with GE and Pratt & Whitney for their bomber and transport engine business. Adding to the company's problems in breaking into the heavy aircraft engine market were the difficulties that General Motors automotive-trained engineers had in understanding the complexities of the aviation market.

Engineers at General Motors were used to the automotive marketplace, with its tough cost containment and efficient annual production of hundreds of thousands of units with only minor model changes. By contrast the aviation engine industry was notorious for bet-the-company, winner-take-all competitions. The money needed for research, development, and facilities to enter the aviation gas turbine engine field had to be spent up front. Allison, however, would be spared the need to confront this aspect of the business in the early days of their gas turbine engine work, as the Navy was committed to funding turboprop development.

## Design and Development of the Allison T40 Turboprop Engine

Allison signed a contract with the Navy for development of the Allison T40 turboprop engine on June 28, 1946, but Allison engineer Art Gaubatz and aerodynamicist O.P. Pracher are said to have designed much of the T40 during the 1945-46 union strike. As related in *Allison: Power of Excellence*, Allison engineer Bob Hicks described the T40:

The T40 was a complex Machine, including 14-foot dual-rotation propellers, two power sections, remote mounting of the power sections from the reduction gear, clutches, and all sorts of hardware. It was among the most difficult aircraft engine[s] to design and develop ever undertaken. Partly because of its complexity and partly because of inexperience in the industry at the time, the T40 never was very successful, but it did make some noteworthy achievements.[3]

The T40 (Figure 11-2) was based on the design of the Allison T38 power section, incorporating two T38s side by side, with a double gearbox, shafting, and decoupler mechanisms, yielding a total weight of 2,980 pounds.

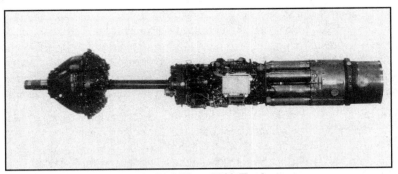

**Figure 11-2. Allison T40 Turboprop**
*(Photo courtesy of Allison)*

One of the crucial problems to overcome in the T40 development was vibration. The Allison engineers had learned a great deal from their experiences with the T38 gearbox and had designed an entirely new gearbox for the T40.[4] The new gearbox did not, however, solve their vibration problems. The engineers had to uncover all the vibration frequencies in the gearbox and then design each gear so that it would not experience these frequencies. Finding the meshing frequencies and measuring vibrations required the creation of new tools and mechanical innovations, such as damper rings and preloaded bearings. On May 24, 1948, Allison delivered the T40 to the test stand for its first 50-hour qualification test.[5] It ran for the first time on June 4. Most of the flight-testing was done in a B-17G flying test bed.

## The Allison T40 and the XP5Y

The first public disclosure of the T40 came in June 1948 when the Navy announced that the T40 would power the Convair XP5Y flying boat. Led by Convair's Herbert Sharp, the Convair XP5Y (Convair Model 117) program planned to produce a long-range patrol/air-sea rescue/antisubmarine warfare flying boat capable of operating from forward bases. The aircraft was huge (at 60 tons) and incorporated the latest aero and hydrodynamic designs. Heavily influenced by captured German flying-boat designs, it had a length-to-beam ratio of 10:1, a cantilever high wing, fixed floats on the wings, and a single tail unit adapted from the XB-46. The Navy ordered two XP5Y prototypes on June 19, 1946, with flight tests scheduled to begin in mid-1948.

Although the XP5Y was originally designed to incorporate Westinghouse 25D (T30) turboprops, industrial disputes at Westinghouse caused the T30 to fall behind schedule. This led to the Navy's decision to use Allison T40-A-4 turboprops instead. The T40 engines were ready for installation in the first XP5Y prototype by the end of 1949.

The first flight of the XP5Y, with the T40 turboprops driving 15-foot counter-rotating propellers, was on April 18, 1950, with pilot Sam Shannon at the controls. The flight lasted just 29 minutes.[6] Allison engineer Jim Holman related in *Allison: Power of Excellence*:

The ramp team — Convair engineering, Allison, and Aeroproducts people - came across with the changes that took us from an engine unable to get off the ground to the point where the XP5Y made a 40-hour endurance flight at tremendous speeds: the 2,890-pound engine produced 5,850 horsepower, more power at takeoff than any engine then developed, and drove the 86-ton boat over 400 mph, pretty fast in those days, and met Navy requirements on many technical issues.[7]

In fact the endurance record set by the XP5Y and its T40 engines was for an 8-hour, 6-minute flight in August of 1950.[8] Holman refers to the record-setting flight of the R3Y-1 Tradewind (Navy Bureau of Aeronautics Number 128488) with T40 engines in 1955. This aircraft flew from San Diego to Patuxent River, Maryland, in a record time of 6 hours at an average speed of 403 mph, a world record for seaplanes that has never been broken.[9]

The XP5Y mission was changed in 1949 to an ASW-only role, then later on to a mine-laying-only role. In August 1950 the Navy again changed the mission of the XP5Y to a transport role. On July 15, 1953, the XP5Y prototype suffered a loss of elevator control during a high-speed test dive and subsequently entered an uncontrollable divergent phugoid (porpoising) sequence, forcing the test crew of eleven to abandon the aircraft before it plunged into the ocean off Point Loma near San Diego.[10]

Allison purchased a Turboliner from Convair for use as a test bed and demonstration aircraft for Allison T40 and subsequent turboprops, replacing the B-17G. The first flight of the Allison Turboliner was on December 29, 1950, at Lindbergh Field in San Diego. The T38 was also flown for a short time in the Turboliner. By early 1950 Allison also had the Model 501 engine in the initial stages of development. On December 19, 1953, the T40 completed and passed the 150-hour Military Qualification Test at 5,850 shaft horsepower.

The installation and fight testing of the T40 in the XP5Y brought out another problem inherent in the operation of a dual-power-source engine, that of decoupling. Decoupling is the quick disconnection of the second power source on the T40 if the first power source is crippled. Holman recalls the Allison experiences with decoupling;

> Unless instantaneously removed from the power train by decoupling, the drag of a failed power section would immediately fail the second power section. Of course, reliable decoupling had to be verified on the test stand before any flights, and a realistic failure had to be simulated. One power section, No. 38, had an internal oil leak and its tailpipe flame grew longer and longer. We just knew that 38 would be a good one to have fail in a natural state so that we could test the decoupler, but it would never give up. It would throw a bright ten-foot flame out over the water of San Diego Bay where the test stand was. When the grunion ran, they liked that light, and everybody filled their lunch buckets and pails with grunion beneath our beacon.
>
> Since No. 38 wouldn't fail, somebody came up with the idea of drowning it with water. Well, the housings were magnesium and we really didn't want to put salt water through them. The base fire department came along and said, 'We'll just rig a hose and nozzle up there at the inlet, and that'll get the job done. That sounded fair enough. Not realizing that the pumper's high pressure nozzle was a straight on/off fitting, we got the engine running to simulate takeoff, and gave the signal. When they opened the valve, the blast of water through the fire section shrank the case and peeled off every blade and vane from stem to stern. Looking down through that thing all you could see was case and barrel. That wasn't too realistic, so we had to think of something else. Eventually, we threw a bunch of junk into one section until the compressor finally went down; the decoupler did its job, and we went on into flight status.[11]

## The T40 and the R3Y-1 Tradewind

The T40 turboprop did find a home in the Convair Model 3, designated the R3Y-1 Tradewind by the Navy. Allison delivered the first production T40 to Convair in April 1952.[12] Four short-shaft 5,332-shaft-horsepower T40-A-10s powered the first flight of the R3Y-1 on February 25, 1954. An assault transport version of the Tradewind, called the R3Y-2, first flew on October 22, 1954. John Wegg relates the fate of the Tradewind.

Three R3Y-2s and one R3Y-1 were converted for the tanker role with a four-point hose system with fuel taken from the wing tanks. Tests with Grumman F9F Cougars from VF-111 in September 1956 were the first simultaneous refueling of four receiver aircraft by any air tanker. A severe problem with turbulence was resolved by extending the inboard hoses further than the outer two, but use of the aircraft was in any case limited.

Seven R3Ys were delivered to VR-2 at NAS Alameda, California, between March and November 1956, to replace the Martin Mars on trans-Pacific services. On October 18, a new seaplane record of 6 hours and 45 minutes was established between Honolulu and NAS Alameda (at 360 mph) but the new type continued to suffer from engine problems and only a dozen or so flights were made to NAS Honolulu. On May 10, the Coral Sea Tradewind, the aircraft that had made the record-breaking run two years earlier, was written off in San Francisco following loss of control after a propeller ran away. Then, on January 24, 1958, the Indian Ocean Tradewind (all VR-2's aircraft were named) lost a complete gearbox while on a return flight to Alameda from Hawaii. Asymmetric power problems caused the R3Y-2 to hit a seawall.

There were no fatalities in either incident, but the Navy prudently grounded all Tradewinds immediately.[13]

The T40 was also used as the main power source for the Navy's Vertical Take-Off (VTO) aircraft program, powering both the Lockheed XFV-1 and the Convair XFY-1 VTO aircraft. The first takeoff and landing (in tethered position) of the Convair XFY-1 was on June 1, 1954, at Moffett Field. An Allison T40 also powered the Lockheed XFV-1 for its first flight in horizontal attitude on June 16, 1954.[14]

The Navy contract for the T40 basically established Allison in the turboprop business. In the words of one Allison engineer:

> They (the Navy) sealed our fate, detracted from our interest in the pure jet business. We carved a niche for ourselves, but it relegated us to third place in terms of gross sales.[15]

## General Motors and Aircraft Engine Development

Although the parent management at General Motors in Detroit often did not quite understand the marketing of aircraft engines, they did prove willing and able to take on the challenge of becoming a major player in the business. In 1955 General Motors management quickly agreed to undertake a major step in moving Allison into the aircraft engine development field. Allison engineer Jim Knott describes the perspective of management.

> Detroit sometimes just didn't seem to understand what we were doing, and yet they could be very receptive and responsive. Take for example the 1955 Plant 8 engine test facility, a $75 million project. Locally we'd convinced management that we had to do it. General Motors president Harlow Curtice and the executive committee came down to Indianapolis. In making the slide presentation, I described what the Air Force was planning, the coming of supersonics, the need for our proposed facility. Suddenly Curtice turned around in his front row chair and said, "Fellows, this sounds like a helluva deal to me, let's do it." The lights came on. Curtice was intrigued and convinced. Without that plant there would be no Allison today. From then on, we started to become a high tech outfit, conscious of high technology.[16]

Although the British were the first to recognize the potential of the turbojet and turboprop for commercial passenger and cargo use, it's fairly clear that the Allison T40 turboprop engine initiated the era of large-scale use of the turboprop as a commercial power plant for large aircraft in this country. From 1949 to around 1955, Britain enjoyed a substantial lead over the United States in turboprop development and production. This lead enabled the British to move ahead into actual jet aircraft operation, while America still produced the best large commercial aircraft designs (although still with reciprocating engines). And while the British were the first to inaugurate both turboprop and turbojet passenger service to the United States, American aircraft manufacturers such as Boeing, Lockheed, Convair, and Douglas soon began producing their own commercial jet designs. All four companies also directly benefited from U.S. military turboprop engine development, with Allison, GE, and P&W turboprop engines leading the way. The following is the story of how one such turboprop aircraft development program married two major technology innovators, Lockheed and the Allison Division of General Motors, to produce the world's greatest turboprop transport, the C-130 with the T56 turboprop engine.

## Development of the Allison T56 (Model 501) Turboprop Engine

Allison started design of the T56 engine series (Figure 11-3) in 1951. The Allison design team leaders were Jack Fetters, chief engineer for power turbine engines, and John Wheatley, chief project engineer. The principal component designers were Joe Barney for the compressor, Don Zimmerman for the turbine, and Victor Peterson for the reduction gear. One of the young engineers on the design team was Gordon Holbrook, who joined Allison from the Turbo Engineering Company and would eventually become Allison's director of gas turbine research and engineering.[17]

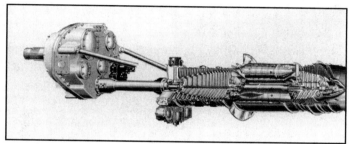

**Figure 11-3. Cutaway of Allison T56 Turboprop**
*(Illustration courtesy of Allison)*

Allison took the lessons learned from the T40 and T38 programs and applied them to the T56. By expanding the T56 from the T38 design and improving the combustion process (the T38 combustion system was a can-type, the T56's can-annular, or cannular), the T56 was ready for test in little under two years from start of design. The T56-A-1 passed its first 50-hour test in September 1953, by November of that year it was in production, and on December 12, 1954, it completed a 150-hour qualification test. This model and the subsequent T56-A-9 were to become known as the Series I. The T56's commercial derivative, the model 501-D13, was also ready in 1954 for certification testing by the government. For the next five years the engines would be tested and flown in the Allison Turboliner, the Convair 580, the Lockheed L-188 Electra, and both the prototype YC-131C and the YC-130A transports. The first flight of T56 in a B-17 test bed was on March 26, 1954. Allison engineer Bob Hicks recalls the company's test philosophy:

> One of the reasons that the T56 was so successful was the amount of testing done on the engine. It's been tested more thoroughly than any engine that I'm aware of over the last fifty years. Before the engine entered production, there had been, I believe, thirteen 150-hour tests run. Two engines had flown on a converted Convair for 1,000 hours each. Those same engines were then examined and some refurbishment done with very minimal parts replacements and then they were run another 1,000 hours on Allison test stands before the Electra program got underway. The engine was first flight tested in the B-17 test bed out of Allison Plant 10, and testing continued in the four-engine YC-130 and then, as the 501, in the Electra.[18]

## The T56 and the Convair C-131

Convair first flew a converted Model 340 with T56-A-3 turboprops on May 10, 1954, marking the beginning of an ambitious flight test program. The Air Force modified and instrumented two Convair 340s as C-131Cs (Figure 11-4) for test. Commencing on June 29, 1954, pilots of the 1700th Test Squadron of the Air Force flew all over the country under real operating conditions to test the ruggedness of the T56's design and to gain turboprop handling experience. The engine passed with flying colors with over 3,000 combined flight hours on the two aircraft.

**Figure 11-4. Convair C-131 Transport**
*(Photo courtesy of U.S. Air Force)*

Four C-131Ds were also modified in a similar fashion to use T56 engines. These were redesignated as VC-131Hs in 1965 for use by the 89th MAW, Special Missions, at Andrews Air Force Base.

## The T56 and the Lockheed C-130 Hercules

The most significant application of the T56 turboprop engine was in the Lockheed C-130 Hercules series of transport aircraft (Figure 11-5). In 1948 the Air Force had decided to curtail turboprop engine development, leaving that arena to the Navy and focusing on turbojets. The invasion of Korea, however, saw the Air Force scrambling to airlift military personnel and materiel to Korea, and the Air Force's Fairchild C-119 transport was hard pressed to do so. Korea pointed out the need for strategic and tactical airlift, and that meant developing turboprop technology.

**Figure 11-5. Lockheed C-130
Hercules Transport**
*(Photo courtesy of U.S. Air Force)*

The Air Force drew up a General Operational Requirement (GOR) for new and improved transport capability, specifying that the aircraft had to carry ninety paratroopers over 2,000 miles or a 30,000-pound load over a shorter distance, it had to operate from short and unprepared air-strips, and it had to be able to slow down to 125 knots for paradrops and fly even more slowly for assault landings.

With the approval of the Secretary of Defense, on February 2, 1951, the Air Force issued a series of requests for proposal (RFP) for the design of a medium transport aircraft to Boeing, Douglas, Fairchild, and Lockheed. The four aircraft manufacturers responded with proposals by April. Lockheed was declared the winner by the Air Force on July 2, 1951, and was awarded a contract for two YC-130 prototypes of the Hercules. Rene Francillon, in *Lockheed Aircraft Since 1913*, describes the design philosophy at Lockheed:

> To meet and, as far as possible, exceed the demanding specifications of the February 1951 RFP of the United States Air Force, the team of project engineers led by Art Flock designed under supervision of Willis Hawkins — then heading the Advanced Design Department — an aircraft which more than made up in functional efficiency what it lacked aesthetically. Key features of the project (Temporary Design Designation L-206) included a 41-foot, 5-inch/12.74-meter long cargo compartment of nearly square cross-section (10 feet/3.05 meters wide and 9 feet/2.74 meters high) for a total volume of 4,500 cubic feet; 127.4 cubic meters, and incorporating a rear loading ramp, a roomy flight deck (normal crew of two pilots, navigator, systems manager and loadmaster) in the extreme nose, high-mounted wing to achieve ease of loading and unloading with a truckbed-height cargo floor, and sturdy undercarriage with main wheels retracting into fairings on the sides of the fuselage. More unusual, in view of the fact that the L-206 was intended as a medium-sized tactical transport, was the decision to use four instead of two engines, with Allison T56 propeller turbines being selected.[19]

The maiden flight of the YC-130 Hercules took place at the Lockheed Air Terminal on August 23, 1954, with pilots Stanley Betz and Roy Wimmer at the controls.[20] Most of the flight testing was done at Edwards Air Force Base in California.

Allison shipped the first production engine, a T56-A-7, to Lockheed for the C-130 on January 10, 1955.[21] The T56-A-2, T56-A-3, T56-A-4, T56-A-5, and T56-A-6 models were assigned to configurations that never got applications.[22] Lockheed produced the first C-130 on March 10, 1955, and the maiden flight of the production C-130 with T56 engines took place on April 7, 1955.[23] The Air Force began flight testing the C-130 on October 10, 1956. Lockheed delivered the first operational C-130A-LM on December 9, 1956, to the Air Force's 815th Troop Carrier Squadron, 463rd Troop Carrier Wing in Ardmore, Oklahoma. The initial C-130 version was also delivered to Air Force units in Tennessee, France, and Japan. The Hercules performed well in several emergency deployments, first in July 1958 to Lebanon, in August 1958 to Formosa, and in July 1960 to the Congo, where the Hercules was the backbone of the United Nations airlift effort. The C-130A-LM was powered by either T56-A-1As or T56-A-9s at 3,750 estimated horsepower. On August 12, 1957, Lockheed selected Allison T56s for the C-130B-LM, the second production series of the Hercules, which flew for the first time at Marietta, Georgia, on November 20, 1958.[24]

On May 20, 1958, the Air Force awarded Allison $24.6 million to produce advanced T56s for the C-130B.[25] This was the beginning of the Allison Series II T56 models for both the Air Force and the Navy. The T56-A-7 and T56-A-8 models were used in the C-130B Hercules transport, with initial deliveries of 123 C-130Bs to the Air Force beginning in 1958. Lockheed, with the concurrence of the Air Force, also sold the C-130B to the air forces of Canada, Indonesia, Iran, Jordan, Pakistan, and South Africa. The Navy's E-2A also used the T56-A-8. The major difference between Series I and Series II T56s was a new turbine and new aerodynamics in the compressor.[26] The first run of the T56-A-8 model was in September 1958.[27] Although the T56-A-8 model was not required to pass a 50-hour Preliminary Flight Rating Test, it passed a required 150-hour endurance test in August 1959. Another Series II change came in the engine's reduction gear with the addition of a self-aligning planetary gear system. This change was also included in Series III engines.

On September 18, 1958, the Marine Corps bought the first two of over eighty C-130s with T56 engines they were to purchase in the next forty years.[28] Most of these C-130s were KC-130F-LMs, a tanker variant that the Marine Corps bought as GV-1s beginning in 1962.[29] On March 30, 1962, Allison was awarded a $2.6 million contract to deliver T56-A-7s for the Marine Corp's GV-1s.[30]

Lockheed delivered the first SC-130B to the Coast Guard on December 1, 1959.[31] The C-130 for the Navy was first ordered in 1959, and the first Navy aircraft was flown on January 22, 1960.

On September 23, 1960, the Air Force awarded Allison a $19.5 million contract for T56s, followed on December 1, 1960, with a further contract for $25.1 million for T56 development.[32] These contracts resulted in the development and production of an improved version of the T56, the T56-A-7 model, which first flew on an improved, longer-ranged version of the C-130 (the C-130E) on August 15, 1961. This was in keeping with one of the "iron laws" of military aircraft development: no matter what the initial weight of the aircraft or the initial power of the engine, the longer the aircraft stays in service and the more it is developed, the heavier it will get. This inevitable weight gain forces the engine developer to deliver more power. Allison's ability to "grow the engine" has been one of the key factors in the T56's long service life. The maximum takeoff weight of the C-130E increased from 124,200 pounds for the C-130A to 175,000 pounds for the E version. Allison kept up with this growth by improving the T56-A-7's power to 4,050 estimated horsepower.

The first flight of a C-130E was on August 15, 1961, with deliveries beginning in April 1962. The Air Force received 377 C-130Es, with 109 additional aircraft going to foreign air forces.[33] The longer-ranged E version of the Hercules entered service with the Air Force Military Air Transport Service, and on March 23, 1963, Allison-powered C-130Es also entered service with the Air Force Tactical Air Command.[34] It was also used in the Systems Command and other commands of the Air Force.

By the time the United States became involved in the Vietnam War, the C-130 Hercules had already been proven. In Vietnam the Hercules and its T56 turboprops really shined. Although the main mission of the Hercules was continual supply of isolated outposts and intra-theatre logistics work, the "Herc" was also used as a low-level covert transport, as a battlefield command and control center, for rescue operations, airborne refueling of tankers, and in its AC-130 variant as a gunship.

The T56 was a major moneymaker for Allison. To give a series of examples of the T56's worth to the company, we can observe a few of the transactions involved in the T56's history.

On June 6, 1964, Allison was awarded a $17 million contract for T56s for C-130 and E-2A Hawkeye aircraft.[35] On July 2, 1964, Allison was awarded $5.6 million by the Air Force for T56s for the C-130.[36] On March 4, 1965, Allison received a $5.8 million order for T56 engines from Lockheed-Georgia.[37] On July 22, 1965, Allison received another $4.7 million purchase order from Lockheed for T56s.[38]

On May 18, 1964, Allison announced their new T56 Series III turboprop, featuring a 20 percent increase in the power over T56-A-7s and T56-A-8s.[39] By 1965 Allison had begun production of the T56-A-14 (for the P-3 Orion), T56-A-15 (for the C-130 Hercules), and the T56-A-16/425 (for the E-2 Hawkeye). Series III T56s had a bigger turbine and a larger diameter inlet than previous models.[40] The Air Force C-130H Hercules used the T56-A-15 model, the

Navy's P-3B/C Orion antisubmarine warfare (ASW) aircraft used the T56-A-14 model, and the Navy's E-2B/C and E-2C-2 Hawkeye early warning aircraft used the T56-A-16/425. On April 7, 1967, an Allison T-56-A-15 completed a 5000-hour simulated test for flight endurance.[41] The T56-A-15 delivers 4,920 estimated horsepower derated to 4,508 estimated horsepower. The C-130H has been built by Lockheed for the United States and forty-two foreign military customers. The C-130H(CT) model is the designation given to eleven C-130E-Is fitted with T56-A-15s and improved electronic equipment as part of the "Combat Talon" special operations program.[42]

In May 1979 the Air Force awarded Allison, renamed Detroit Diesel Allison, an $8.7 million contract to start development of an advanced version of the T56 and a flight test program.[43] By 1981 the C-130 and all of its Air Force variants used about 293 million gallons of aviation fuel annually, only one indication of the importance of the aircraft and its engine to the Air Force.

The commercial variant of the C-130 Hercules is the L-100, which is powered by the commercial variant of the T56, the Allison 501. The first L-100 was powered by the Allison 501-D22 turboprop engine at 4,050 estimated horsepower. This same aircraft-engine configuration was used to obtain a Type Certificate on February 16, 1965. Twenty-one production aircraft were built, with the first delivery going to Continental Air Services on September 30, 1965.

The C-130 with its versatile T56 has been flown off the Arctic and Antarctic ice with skis, out of desert airfields, and even off aircraft carriers. Hercules aircraft have flown into combat in the Falklands, and as a STOL High Technology Test Bed (HTTB) aircraft for Lockheed.[44] More than 2,050 C-130s have been built to date. Allison has signed a major agreement with Lockheed to supply a minimum of 100 Series III and Series IV T56 engines for the future C-130 aircraft program.[45]

Perhaps the most significant aspect of the T56 as installed in the Lockheed C-130 is that more than 90 percent of these aircraft have retained the same basic dimensions and appearance as the first YC-130, and that the gross weight and horsepower have increased by only 45 percent and 20 percent, respectively.[46] There have been five basic variants of the Hercules and over sixty-five different models of the C-130 in its forty-one-year history.[47] Lockheed has sold more than 700 C-130s to sixty nations.[48] In May 1992 Lockheed delivered its 2000th C-130 Hercules aircraft. The C-130 has become the world's most successful cargo aircraft with the longest production life in history, and with it the T56 has become the most successful turboprop in history.

## Development of the T56-A-100

In 1981 the Air Force and Navy began funding an upgrade of the T56, called the T56-A-100, under a new concept called the Engine Model Derivative Program (EMDP). Under EMDP, the Air Force/Navy propulsion establishments sought to improve current engines rapidly and incorporate new technology. The T56 was the first engine chosen for the new program. The EMDP goals for the T56 were a 25 percent increase in power at altitude and hot temperatures, and up to 12 percent reduction in specific fuel consumption. The first XT56-A-100 began testing in 1981. The T56-A-100 underwent a 700-hour Accelerated Mission Test, which was finished in 1983. Testing of this new variant of the T56 was conducted by the Air Force through 1984, when the testing program was transferred to the Navy.

## The Model 501 and the Lockheed Electra

Although the Convair Allison Turboliner was the first U.S. turboprop aircraft (powered by the Allison T40), the Lockheed Electra, with its 4,501 shaft-horsepower Allison T56 turboprop engines, was the first large aircraft designed from the start as a turboprop aircraft for carrying passengers and/or cargo.

Lockheed began design of what was to become the Electra in autumn 1954 at their California division. Although the Electra design started out as a company response to a specification from American Airlines for a small, high-wing transport, Lockheed soon evolved the design into a large four-engine, low-wing transport and passenger aircraft. By mid-1955 they had firm turboprop engine data from their use of the T56 on the Hercules.[49]

In the summer of 1955 Lockheed elected to go with the Allison commercial derivative of the same engine, the 3,750-shaft-horsepower Model 501-D13 for the new L-188 Electra (Figure 11-6). The primary requirement driver for the 501 was to become time between overhaul, or TBO, with a goal of 1000 hours. The first 501s had a 625-hour life. The biggest improvement in the engine's life came with the decision to replace the carbon seal between the hot-gas path and the oil system with labyrinth seals.

**Figure 11-6. Lockheed Electra**
*(Illustration courtesy of Allison)*

On May 20, 1955, the Civil Aviation Administration (CAA) announced its approval for commercial operation of the T56 with Type Certificate No. 282.[50] On June 9, American Airlines purchased 35 Lockheed Electras, the first four-engine turboprop commercial transport. On September 19, the airline also purchased Allison 501s for $12.5 million. On September 16, 1957, the CAA certified the 501-D13 for the Electra, and on December 27, 1957, Allison delivered the first production 501 engines to Lockheed.[51]

On October 23, 1957, Allison began a flight test program called Operation Hourglass to test the Model 501-D13 in a typical round-the-clock commercial schedule. The aircraft, one of the Air Force's YC-131C's used to test the T56 in 1955, was flown by a team of six Allison pilot-engineers. It was fitted with a few passenger seats for demonstration purposes, beds for crew rest, and extensive test instrumentation, including instruments for filming flight operations. Operation Hourglass put 1,057 flying hours on the YC-131C in 88 days, concluding on January 23, 1958.[52]

By 1958 Allison had major new models ready for production or coming on-line. They had the commercial Models 501-D22 and 501-D36 under development, and the D-13 undergoing constant improvement in terms of engine TBO. The Model 501-D22 and 501-D36 were used in both the CC-109 and the Lockheed commercial variant of the Air Force C-130, the L-382. On August 26, 1958, the CAA certified the Allison-powered Electra, the Electra aircraft having been certified on August 22, 1958.[53]

On September 5, 1958, the CAA approved 1,000 hours before overhaul for the 501-D13 on Electras. The 501 was officially certified for Eastern Airlines Electras on May 4, 1959.[54] On June 9, 1961, the FAA (successor to the CAA) approved the 501-D13 for 1,800 hours TBO on Pacific South West Airlines and Western Airlines. On October 13, 1961, the FAA approved the

501-D13 for 2,000 hours TBO on Eastern Airlines and Pacific South West Airlines.[55] On March 24, 1962, it approved the 501-D13 for 2,200 hours TBO,[56] and on May 3, 1963, it approved the 501-D13 cold sections for 3,200 hours TBO.[57] On May 12, 1965, Allison achieved a major goal for the T56/501 when American Airlines announced 5,000 hours TBO for 501-D13s.[58]

Only 170 Electras were ordered before the program was terminated in January 1961. Two factors led to the Electra's demise. First, the turbojet Boeing 707 surpassed it. The Boeing 707 began service in December 1958. Second, and perhaps more important, were public misgivings concerning the aircraft as the result of two very prominent aircraft accidents. A Braniff Airlines Electra disintegrated in midair over Texas in September 1959, and a Northwest Electra crashed near Tell City, Indiana. Both accidents were later attributed to a problem called "whirl mode." As related in *Allison: Power of Excellence*:

> Besieged by press and politicians to ground the Electra, FAA administrator Elwood Quesada instead imposed a speed limit of 295 mph on the planes while Lockheed, Allison, and the Civil Aeronautics Board sought to isolate the accidents' cause and devise a way to prevent recurrence.
>
> The accidents' cause was identified as progressive structural failure in turbulence of an airframe previously damaged as a result, for example, of a heavy landing. If the power plant structure had suffered slight damage in this way, not significant in itself, it was possible for subsequent turbulence to initiate an oscillation of the engine and propeller which did not damp out. Undamped, the motion led to nacelle vibrations which amplified to 'whirl mode,' and then to wing flexing and ultimate failure at the wing root. Careless press reports characterized the situation as "the wing came off."[59]

Paul Sonnenburg and William A. Schoneberger, the authors of *Allison: Power of Excellence,* go on to relate the experience of Allison engineer Wayne McIntire:

> In assessing what might happen if part of the engine mount system failed, our analysis revealed the so-called 'whirl mode' phenomenon. We took a T56 carcass to determine how many pounds of force the mounting structure had to absorb and in which direction. In the 'mine shaft' [test pit] under the tutelage of Lockheed, we tested the mount assembly to failure with hydraulic rams on all the structure to see what broke, to determine what had to be done to adapt the nacelle and mount to the wing. We ultimately added two mounts to the gearbox, one upper, one lower.
>
> Then we installed the new design on all four engines of a test airplane and the Lockheed crew flew it over the California mountains for several days of increasingly severe flying to find the right conditions of load and Mach number on the airplane and turbulence that might induce whirl mode to learn what would happen. [On that Saturday] in the Burbank hangar Lockheed had all four engines broken down for us to inspect to see what effect the flying with the new mounts might have had on the gear meshes. All four looked fine.[60]

The problem had been solved. But how was the fix to be applied, and who would pay for it? Allison and Lockheed came up with the Lockheed Electra Achievement Program, or LEAP. Both companies spent around $25 million to modify the entire Electra fleet, adding nacelle stiffeners and two additional gearbox mounts to each Electra, and replacing some wing skin with heavier-gauge panels. The program was completed by February 1961, at which time the FAA removed its speed restriction on the aircraft. But the damage had been done. Although the Model 501 had lost its Electra application, the engine still had a future in the commercial market with the L-100 commercial version of the C-130.

In September 1966 Delta Airlines became the first to operate the Lockheed 100 in domestic service.[61] By 1965 Allison had the 501-D22 model available in the A, C, and G variants. These powered the Convair Super 580, the Lockheed L-100, and the C-97. By September 1967 the Allison Model 501-D22A had been selected to power a stretch version of the Lockheed 100F[62] and by 1985 Allison had progressed to the Model 501-M71D series engines for commercial use.

## The T56 and the Lockheed P-3 Orion

Lockheed Aircraft and Allison teamed up again in the second major use of the T56 turbo-prop engine, their second major collaboration resulting in the Lockheed P-3 Orion antisubmarine warfare (ASW) patrol aircraft (Figure 11-7).

**Figure 11-7. Lockheed Orion**
*(Photo courtesy of U.S. Navy)*

Since the end of World War II, the last major naval war, the role of the antisubmarine warfare patrol aircraft had taken on a renewed emphasis. As submarines have evolved from the first primitive vessels of the pre-World War I era to the highly sophisticated nuclear attack submarines of today, so have their armaments. Whereas in World War II the major threat posed by submarines was mostly to shipping (with the occasional covert landing of raiding parties), today's submarines are strategic nuclear weapons systems poised to strike at any point of the enemy's heartland. They can deploy either conventional or nuclear torpedoes, nuclear-tipped ballistic missiles, or either conventional or nuclear subsurface-launched cruise missiles. Submarines represent an excellent investment for those countries which cannot afford large naval vessels or fleets, but which still want to project national power off their shores. They are cheaper now with the decline of the Soviet Union than they have ever been before. Even a relatively inexpensive, relatively primitive diesel-electric submarine, with skill and luck, can sink the largest and most sophisticated aircraft carrier with a well-placed torpedo. The major navies of the world (as well as countries that have no navy) have spent billions of dollars to counter the submarine threat with the development of antisubmarine technologies and specific antisubmarine doctrines. The cheapest and most effective antisubmarine weapon, however, remains the land-based antisubmarine warfare patrol aircraft. These aircraft are designed to patrol for long periods of time well off shore from their bases. They can strike with no warning with antisubmarine depth charges or homing torpedoes of their own.

The major U.S. long-range, land-based antisubmarine warfare patrol aircraft for the last twenty-five years has been the Lockheed P-3 Orion. The Orion is the primary weapon system for twenty-four front-line, two conversion, and thirteen reserve patrol squadrons of the Navy. Not only does the Orion serve the U.S. Navy and Coast Guard, but also the navies of Australia, Canada, Iran, Japan, Germany, New Zealand, The Netherlands, Portugal, Pakistan, South Korea, Turkey, Chile, Thailand, and Spain. By the end of 1992 over 720 P-3 Orions had been built in three major variants, the P-3A, P-3B, and P-3C. The P-3 is a four-engine fixed-wing aircraft with a maximum overload takeoff weight (TOW) of 142,000 pounds. It has a range of 2,070 nautical miles and a maximum operational ceiling of 28,300 feet. With a 3-hour time-on-station at 1,500 feet, the range of the P-3 is 1,550 miles.[63] Each and every variant has been powered by four T56 axial-flow turboprops.

The P-3 Orion originated in a Lockheed response to Navy Type Specification No. 146 in 1957 which called for a long-range patrol aircraft to replace the P2 Neptune. The Navy suggested that to save time and costs, manufacturers should strive to meet this requirement with an off-the-shelf aircraft already in production. Since Lockheed had the most experience building such aircraft, it easily won the competition on April 24, 1958, by adapting its commercial Electra airliner.[64] The Lockheed design (the Lockheed Model 185) retained the wings, tail unit, power plant (the Allison T56 turboprop) and other components of the Electra, as well as quite a bit of the fuselage structure. The fuselage itself was shortened by 7 feet, and Lockheed added a weapons bay and new electronics.[65]

In May 1958, Lockheed received an initial research and development contract from the Navy and the first prototype aircraft the YP-3V-1, flew on August 19, 1958. After an inspection of a production mock-up, a preproduction contract was awarded to Lockheed in February 1959. Lockheed flew the first production-standard aircraft on November 25, 1959.[66] On April 1, 1960, the Navy awarded Allison $11.6 million for T56 engines for GV-1, W2F-1, and P-3A aircraft.[67] After a very successful evaluation of the aircraft by the Navy, the first production contract for seven P-3V-1s was awarded in October 1960.[68] Later that year Lockheed gave the aircraft its Orion designation.

On April 5, 1961, the Navy announced that four Allison T56-A-10W turboprops, with an estimated shaft-horsepower of 4,500 would power the P-3V-1 aircraft.[69] The T56-A-10Ws were Series II engines incorporating water-methanol injection. The T56-A-10W also featured auxiliary engine mounts for P-3A installation and improved corrosion resistance. Allison ran the first T56-A-10W in March 1959 and it passed its 150-hour endurance test in July 1960.[70] The first flight of a preproduction P-3V-1 took place on April 15, 1961. On August 13, 1962, the first Navy unit, Patrol Squadron Eight (VP-8) at NAS Patuxent River, flew Orions. The first 157 P-3V-1 Orions, later designated P-3As, were powered by four Allison T56-A-10Ws.

On September 28, 1962, the Air Force and Navy awarded Allison a further $51.5 million contract for T56s to be used in C-130B and P-3A aircraft.[71] On January 3, 1964, Allison received a $17.5 million Navy contract for T56s for the P-3A.[72] On June 18, 1965, Allison was awarded $24.8 million by the Navy for T56-A-14s at 4,910 estimated shaft-horsepower to retrofit the P-3As, and to provide T56-A-8s for the E-2A Hawkeye.[73]

After entering Navy service beginning in 1962, the P-3As were later replaced in front-line units by P-3Bs and P-3Cs. The P-3As entered reserve service in July 1970 to equip the Naval Air Reserve Detachment (NARDET) at Naval Air Station Moffett Field, California.[74]

The second major variant of the Orion, the P-3B, incorporated an upgraded T56, the T56-A-14, at 4,910 estimated shaft-horsepower. The P-3As were later refitted with T56-A-14s as well. The Orion P-3B entered service with the Navy beginning in 1966.

The third-generation advanced Orion, designated the P-3C, first flew in September 1968 and entered service with the Navy in 1969. This model variant also used the T56-A-14.[75]

The T56-A-14s are considered by Allison to be Series III engines with Stage 1 turbine blade and vane cooling. This enabled the T56-A-14 models to operate at turbine inlet temperatures of 1,970°F, resulting in an improved estimated shaft-horsepower of 4,910. Specific fuel consumption was 0.50 at maximum power.[76]

The P-3 Orion and its subsequent models were very important to the Navy. P&W's Government Products Division estimated in 1981 that the P-3 and its mission used approximately 25 percent of all Navy aviation fuel. The 1981 annual fuel usage for this aircraft type was 233 million gallons.[77] Production of the P-3 totaled almost 300 aircraft up to 1990, when the Navy terminated the program in favor of the P-7, an improved derivative of the Orion.

## The T56 and the Grumman W2F and E-2 Hawkeye

On October 28, 1960, the Navy accepted the first T56-powered Grumman W2F-1 Hawkeye carrier-based early-warning (AWACS) aircraft.[78]

In 1985 Allison launched their Series IV T56 engine, the T56-A-427. This program to upgrade the T56 had been started in 1976 by an Allison team led by Frank Verkamp and Al Wilson in order to help launch a Navy engine upgrade program for the E-2C Hawkeye. Verkamp and Wilson incorporated a new compressor designed by Pete Tramm and Dick Alverson and achieved a 10 percent specific fuel consumption improvement in the T56. They won a follow-up contract under the Air Force's Engine Model Derivative Program (EMDP) for what was to become the T56 Series IV. Overall improvement of the T56's specific fuel consumption was 12.6 percent with an overall power improvement of 24 percent.[79] The Series IV model T56-A-427 also offers more corrosion protection.[80] The engine has been flight tested in a Lockheed C-130 test bed, and the Navy has purchased the engine for their E-2C Hawkeye and P-3 Orion aircraft.

Why has the T56 been produced for so long? There are several key reasons. The original design was conservative, thus permitting growth in engine power and use in new applications. The engine has been the power plant for several very successful aircraft, including the C-130, the P-3, and the E-2. The T56 has been exported to many different countries, including Japan, Israel, and Taiwan. Finally, there has been no real competitor for the T56 in its power range. That has ensured the engine the major marketshare for its applications. Allison has produced over 15,300 of the T56 turboprop engines since 1954, making the T56 one of the most popular and successful engines of all time.[81]

Allison now occupies an important niche in the aircraft gas turbine engine business. Their development of the T56 played an important role in helping Allison acquire the necessary engineering in-house expertise to design and develop engines as well as produce them. They have continued this tradition of building quality turboprops (as well as turbojets and turboshafts) to this day. Interestingly, the company was recently purchased in its entirety by Rolls-Royce of Great Britain. How this will impact its ability to continue as a force in the world engine market is yet to be seen.

## Design and Development of the Garrett AiResearch T76/TPE331 Small Turboprop Engine

The turboprop engine has, despite some early prognostications of obsolescence in the 1940s, survived the development and refinement of the turbojet and the turbofan quite well. This is particularly true of the small turboprop. The small turboprop has been quite successful in the areas of low and medium power requirements, especially with the application of new metal alloys. It has largely replaced piston engine technology in small military and business aircraft because of the ability of turboprop engines to deliver high power-to-weight ratios.[82]

The development of small-aircraft turboprop technology has been much different from its much bigger turboprop, turbojet, and turbofan cousins. Perhaps the most remarkable difference in the overall development of the small turboprop has been the lack of military involvement in its initiation. The military services in the middle and late 1940s were interested in large engines delivering ever-increasing power. The Air Force decision in the mid-1950s to forsake turboprop development completely left this technology in the hands of the Navy, which pursued the larger, higher-powered engines. The task of developing a smaller, lower-power application for aircraft gas turbine technology was left mostly to the private sector. Technological development of the small aircraft gas turbine engine took two basic forms, the small turboprop and the turboshaft. The turboshaft engine was examined in Chapter Ten. Development of the small turboprop will be discussed below.

Several companies are responsible for developing and delivering this increasingly utilized technology. One of the outstanding examples of the small aircraft gas turboprop engine has been the AlliedSignal (formerly the Garrett Corporation) T76/TPE331 turboprop engine. This remarkable engine program dramatically advanced aircraft gas turbine engine technology in two ways. First, it provided an ideal power plant for an emerging range of small business jets in the 1960s and 1970s. This ensured that the aircraft gas turbine engine would replace the piston engine as the propulsion system of choice in small business aircraft. Secondly, the T76/TPE331 provides an excellent example of how aircraft gas turbine engine technology can be "grown" to provide a wide range of desired power levels within the same relatively small engine size. In such an expensive field as aircraft gas turbine engine development, the ability to effect performance and reliability improvements within the same basic engine design and development program over a long period of time ensures reliability, diversification and, therefore, profitability.

The Garrett Corporation, under the leadership of its founder Cliff Garrett, began looking at gas turbines in the early 1940s. With initial research and development funding of $1 million of company funds, Garrett engineers looked at small gas turbines, commonly called auxiliary power units or APU's, for cabin pressurization, cabin cooling and heating, power for deicing, and for driving an alternator to provide electrical power for the aircraft.[83] An attempt in 1945 to develop a gas turbine APU with an axial compressor, called Project A or the "Black Box," failed, at an expense to the company of $800,000 and fifteen months of effort. But other research and development efforts, such as a 3-pound air expansion refrigeration turbine for the Lockheed P-80 Shooting Star jet, brought needed turbine expertise to the company's engineers.[84] Another more significant gas turbine development for the corporation was the ATS35 Air Turbine Starter, an adaptation of the P-80 air refrigeration turbine for aircraft starting. The requirement to produce air for the ATS35, in turn, brought about the development of the Garrett GTP50 small gas turbine.

Garrett received a contract from the Navy in the mid-1940s to develop and build a small 50 shaft-horsepower turbine for use in generating electrical power on-board aircraft carriers. This became the GTP50. GTP stood for gas turbine power. After developing this small power unit, the company decided to push the technology a bit further and designed a small gas turbine to start the main engines in new turbine-powered aircraft.[85]

Under Navy contract, Garrett began work in 1946 on two experimental units, the GTC43/44 (gas turbine compressor) and the GTP70 (gas turbine power). In 1947 they began their first gas turbine production contract with the Air Force, producing ground heaters that contained a gas turbine. Greatly assisting in the component research and development as well as in the GTC43/44's design were two key additions to the Garrett Corporation's engineering staff. Starting in 1951, Garrett obtained the services of two German turbomachinery experts through the Army Air Forces' "Operation Paperclip." Dr. Helmut Schelp and Dr. W.T. von der Nuell made significant contributions to the design of the turbine in the GTC43/44. They changed the "Black Box's" axial-flow compressor to a centrifugal design. Then they altered the design of the impeller and reversed the impeller's blades to make a radial-inflow turbine from the compressor wheel. Schelp and von der Nuell contributed as well to all other subsequent gas turbine designs in auxiliary power units and main propulsion aircraft gas turbine engines of the corporation.

The GTC43/44 was a gas turbine designed to produce pneumatic power (compressed air only). The GTP70 was a single-shaft engine designed to drive an aircraft-type alternator. The design concept of the Garrett design team, headed by Homer Wood, was to build a small gas turbine that would provide enough bleed air off the compressor to run a small air turbine starter which, in turn, would supply enough power to crank the propulsion turbine engines of the Navy. The GTC43/44 turned out to be the first successful small gas turbine. It incorporated a two-stage centrifugal compressor and a single-stage radial-inflow turbine, which had not been tried in the United States. The turbine, compressor, combustion chamber, and accessories sections were designed as separate, interchangeable subassemblies.

Although the GTC43/44 first ran in the fall of 1947, it took Garrett two more years to get the turbine to pass the Navy's 200-hour qualification test. Production began in 1950 and some 500 were built for the Navy. The GTC43/44 proved to be so successful that the Navy awarded the Garrett Corporation a $36 million production order for auxiliary gas turbines in October 1951.[86]

By the mid-1950s the Garrett Corporation claimed 80 percent of the United States and European market for industrial turbines and auxiliary power units in the 30-to-850-horsepower range. By 1958 they had developed the first commercial use of small gas turbines as ground power sources. They sold AiResearch GTCP85-91 turbines mounted in panel trucks to Eastern Airlines to provide pneumatic starting power for Eastern's fleet of Lockheed Electras and electric power for pre-flight radio, radar, and hydraulic systems checks.

Cliff Garrett was opposed to developing propulsion gas turbines, saying that he would be entering into competition with his customers for APUs and other components, but by 1959 he had retired from control over Garrett due to age and ill health. In 1959 the board of directors of Garrett's AiResearch Manufacturing Company and its vice president and general manager Harry Wetzel, along with the company's Phoenix Engineering Manager Ivan Speer, decided that it was time to take the company into the aircraft gas turbine propulsion engine market. Well aware of its potential for aviation main propulsion, the company had been looking at the small gas turbine market for some time, knowing that the small gas turbine was ready to be commercialized. They considered the helicopter the first area in which the small gas turbine was immediately useful, but they did not discount the potential of small gas turbines for the small aircraft market as well. Garrett's managers and officers decided to apply their small turbine expertise to the development of a main propulsion engine. Their director of research, retired Admiral Selden Spangler, assisted them in that decision. During his thirty-five-year career in the Navy, Spangler had served as director of the Navy's Power Plant Division of the Bureau of Aeronautics during World War II. He had been responsible for pushing Navy research into small gas turbines.[87]

For their first main propulsion engine, Garrett decided to combine two of their more successful programs. They had a successful compressor in the GTC43/44 auxiliary power unit, and a pretty good two-stage turbine in their GTP85. By combining the two the company would have two strengths to build on. Their first effort at designing and building a dedicated aircraft gas turbine engine for propulsion, the Model 331, began in March 1960. The turboshaft variant targeted for helicopter use was called the TSE331, and the turboprop variant was called the TPE331.

The goal of Garrett AiResearch was to enter the helicopter gas turbine engine market with a low-specific-fuel-consumption aircraft turboshaft engine (TSE) that would also be usable in military power units and industrial generator sets. The intended vehicle for introducing the TSE331 was to be the Lark helicopter, the American version of the Alouette, licensed from the French by Republic Aircraft. What proved even more significant for AiResearch was that market studies in 1960 also confirmed the need for a high power-to-weight ratio turboprop engine for a growing market for executive and utility aircraft. The company began designing a turboprop variant of the TSE331 design, the TPE331. The new engine's two variants were designed for inherent reliability and ruggedness. After signing the contract to develop the T76 variant of the TPE331, the company began concentrating on the turboprop.

Working toward a design that would have higher specific power and lower specific fuel consumption than any other turboprop, Garrett engineers focused on a fixed or single-shaft constant-speed engine design with a minimum frontal area. They also wanted ease of installation, and easy maintainability. The single-shaft, constant-speed configuration provided instantaneous power control response and made for a simpler bearing system. The initial design resulted in an engine that weighed 335 pounds, was 46 inches long, 21 inches wide, and 26 inches high.

The TPE331 design incorporated a propeller drive with a two-stage reduction gear, one helical spur and one planetary. The compressor was a tandem two-stage centrifugal forged from titanium. The design was taken wholly from AiResearch's 331 APU design, making the TPE331 the first aircraft gas turbine engine designed from an auxiliary power unit. Mass flow ranged from 5.78 pounds per second for the TPE331-25/61 to 7.8 pounds per second for the T76-G-3. Compressor pressure ratio ran from 8.0 in the TPE331-25/61 to 10.37 in the T76-G-3 and T76-G-5. The combustion system was annular with a capacitor discharge ignitor plug on the turbine plenum. The axial turbine had three stages, with an inlet gas temperature ranging from 987°C (1808°F) in the TPE331-25/61, to 993°C (1819°F) for the T76 models. Turbine speed was approximately 42,000 rpm.

The Model 331 was originally laid out as a 400 to 500 shaft-horsepower turboshaft, with growth potential to around 700 shaft-horsepower.[88] The turboprop version (TPE) first ran in early 1961. In October 1961, a 400 shaft-horsepower version of the TSE powered the Republic Lark helicopter on its first flight.

Although the TPE331 commercial aircraft engine was an important contribution to the advancement of aircraft gas turbine engine technology, the military version, the T76, became the most important engine program for the company in the 1960s and 1970s.

## T76 Military Turboprop Program

Garrett began the T76 turboprop program (Figure 11-8) in response to an anticipated military requirement for a counter-insurgency/spotter aircraft for service in Vietnam. They decided to use their TPE331 as the baseline for the new military engine, assigning the new designation G-10/12 to the military version. This engine was later designated the T76 by the Navy, who,

**Figure 11-8. Cutaway of T76-G-418 Engine**
*(Illustration courtesy of Garrett)*

when the requirement was formalized later in 1962, became the managing service for the $1.2 million new engine program for the Counter-insurgency Aircraft (COIN). The COIN program would result in the OV-10 Bronco aircraft by North American Aviation.

Requiring a slow- and low-flying STOL (short takeoff and landing) propeller-driven aircraft with extended range that could operate from unimproved runways in either mountains or lowlands, the COIN program offered some specific challenges to the Garrett design team. The aircraft would have to have extended range to either cover great stretches of territory or to have adequate loiter time over a particular target. This called for a fuel-efficient engine. In cases of intense ground fire from the enemy, it had to be able to get out of harm's way quickly. This meant a high thrust-to-weight turboprop engine with a very quick power response time.

In 1962 the 500 shaft-horsepower T76 development engine completed a 200-hour endurance run and in January 1963 Garrett initiated the 600 shaft-horsepower T76 program, which completed a 50-hour Preliminary Flight Ratings Test (PFRT) at 600 shaft-horsepower in June 1964. The T76 met all of the COIN requirements and had the advantage of lower specific fuel consumption and a fixed-shaft design over the P&W Canada PT6. It was capable of accelerating from flight idle to full military power within approximately one second, thus fulfilling the requirement to quickly elude ground fire. The 50-hour PFRT test completion was followed by a Navy contract for YT76 engines for the YOV-10 and for the COIN flight-test program, specifying a thrust level of 660 shaft horsepower. The T76 engine program for COIN was a fixed-price contract and was set up around the concept that the engine would be an off-the-shelf item with a 600 shaft-horsepower rating. In September 1964 a B-26 test bed aircraft with a YT76 engine installed completed its first flight from Phoenix.

Garrett achieved its thrust level goal of 660 shaft horsepower in a 50-hour PFRT in May 1965. On July 16 of that year, the YOV-10 made its maiden flight from Columbus, Ohio, with P&W YT74 turboprops.[89]

In January 1966 the Navy began test-pilot evaluation tests for the OV-10A and in February Garrett announced that they had received engine production go-ahead for the T76 and that the T76 was now uprated to 660 shaft-horsepower. Production machinery procurement for the T76, including special tooling and facility expansion at Garrett, dramatically increased.[90]. In August 1966 Garrett announced the start of a program to uprate the T76 to 715 shaft-horsepower, which was accomplished by December of that year, when it began Military Qualification Tests (MQT). This engine shaft-horsepower uprating program was in fact an emergency program initiated by Garrett to try to keep up with the constantly increasing weight of the OV-10.

In October 1966 North American Aviation was given a production contract to supply 157 OV-10As for the Air Force and 118 for the Navy and Marine Corps. Finally in December of that year, Garrett was awarded an $11.6 million production contract to provide 715 shaft-horsepower T76 engines to the Navy for the now-multiservice OV-10A. The 715 shaft-horsepower T76 completed its MQT 150-hour endurance test in April 1967.[91]

In June, 1967, the first 715 shaft-horsepower T76 was delivered to North American Aviation for the OV-10 Bronco (Figure 11-9), which first flew with T76 engines in July 1967. The first production OV-10A flew on August 6, 1967, and deliveries to the Air Force and Marine Corps began on February 23, 1968.[92] The OV-10A entered service in Vietnam in 1968 (with the Marines in July). Eventually, 128 Air Force and 114 Marine Corps OV-10As saw service in Vietnam.[93]

The T76 soon came to dominate AiResearch's Phoenix facility, occupying over one-third of the total effort. AiResearch began a comprehensive Power Up Program to provide additional models with increased horsepower to expand the range of aircraft applications and market op-

**Figure 11-9. North American OV-10 Bronco**
*(Photo courtesy of U.S. Air Force)*

portunities. This growth program was to ultimately provide engines with well over 2:1 power-to-weight ratios. In 1974 the Navy awarded Garrett a contract for growth of the TPE331 to 1,040 shaft-horsepower.

No engine ever escapes problems when first placed in the field, and the T76/TPE331 was no exception. One of the major problems encountered by the T76/TPE331 and Garrett's field maintenance engineers was that of foreign object ingestion (FOI). This problem was encountered both by the military users of the T76 in Southeast Asia and by civilian TPE331 users in Alaska, South America, Africa and elsewhere. The OV-10 Bronco was a STOL aircraft, and much of the utilization of the civilian TPE331 was in civilian STOL aircraft as well. The engine was ideally suited to short narrow approaches down narrow canyons to rugged airstrips. This also meant, however, that the engine "ran into the elements," so to speak. A flight into an unimproved, mountainous airfield in Southeast Asia is described by Garrett AiResearch engineers Howard Buckner and John Peach in a 1968 Society of Automotive Engineers paper. They also describe how the fixed-shaft T76 handled the mission requirements:

> The mountainside strip in Southeast Asia photographed from a (Pilatus) Turbo Porter on final approach, is at an elevation of 4,600 feet, is 600 feet long, is on a substantial incline, and has a hump halfway down the strip. The trees and rising terrain at the far end of the strip, together with the incline, make this a one-way strip with little or no go-around possibility.

> The ability to approach in beta mode and the instant response to power demand of the fixed-shaft turboprop engine are vital assets in this type of work. During approach, with the power lever at flight idle and the condition lever at full speed, the turboprop is in beta mode, which holds a constant propeller blade angle and approximately full engine speed. This provides the pilot with the capability of varying his angle of descent over a considerable range and of making changes quickly during approach as varying conditions dictate (without moving power lever); this is accomplished with only a small effect on airspeed. When the nose is lowered to steepen the approach, the propeller/engine provides an increased drag, thereby limiting the airspeed increase to a small amount. When the nose is raised to flatten the approach, the engine underspeed governor immediately supplies fuel to provide the power increase resulting from increased propeller blade angle of attack due to decreased airspeed, thereby limiting this airspeed decrease to a small value. The fixed-shaft engine excels in this regime as the engine (including compressor) is kept near full speed, and thus the time lag for engine acceleration upon power demand is eliminated. The fixed-shaft engine is also capable of absorbing more drag in the nose-down case because of the high engine rotational speed at flight idle.

> For landing strips similar to (this one), if an unexpected updraft or tailwind is encountered on the very last part of final, causing the aircraft to float past a safe touchdown point, the procedure is to put the propeller immediately into slight reverse thrust, which results in a very hard but otherwise safe landing. The ability to obtain full reverse thrust immediately upon touchdown is of obvious importance under such conditions.[94]

The requirement of takeoff from short, unimproved landing strips on mountainsides also required an engine like the T76 that could withstand high shock loads while delivering power at full speed.

The fine sand and dirt stirred up by repeated propeller reversing on steep landing strips caused severe problems with FOI. Although the TPE331/T76 turboprop design met the COIN requirements for FOI well, operation of the OV-10 and the T76 in the field in Southeast Asia showed far more problems due to FOI than the COIN requirements anticipated. Examination of a number of field engines, upon disassembly, revealed that while the T76 could ingest and then throw out a decent amount of sand and dust and rocks, there was significant erosion occurring near the discharge of the titanium second-stage compressor impeller. The dirt was collected by centrifuging into the fillet formed by the blade and hub where it produced a high-velocity scrubbing action, causing serious erosion of the blades. Adding particle separators to the engine would have helped alleviate the problem, but at serious cost to the engine and aircraft in terms of added weight, size and drag, complexity, cost, and of creating an icing hazard. The Garrett engineers, after testing both resilient and hard coatings on the centrifugal compressors settled on a hard tungsten carbide coating. This coating extended the life of the compressors up to 1,500 hours without excessive performance loss. Performance loss after 1,000 STOL hours was less than 5 percent.[95]

In summary, the AlliedSignal Aerospace/Garrett T76 has proven to be an effective small turboprop for the Bronco OV-10. Over 1,100 military T76s have been produced, logging over 7 million military service hours.

## The TPE331 Commercial Engine Program

In October 1963 Volpar decided on the TPE331 (Figure 11-10) for their Beech Super 18 Conversion business aircraft. This was the first commercial engine sale of the TPE331, but it would certainly not be the last.

**Figure 11-10. Cutaway of TPE331 Engine**
*(Illustration courtesy of Garrett)*

In July 1964 Mooney-Mitsubishi Aircraft selected the 331 for their MU-2B business aircraft. November 5, 1964, marked the first flight of the 331 in the Helio Stallion aircraft, and December marked the first flights of the 331 engine conversions for both the Volpar Beech (December 8) and the Turbo Commander (December 31) business aircraft. By mid-1964,

Garrett had accumulated nearly 13,000 hours of running time on the TPE331 turboprop.[96]

On February 25, 1965, the FAA awarded a Type Certificate to Garrett for the TPE331 Model I at 575 horsepower, followed by a production certificate in March. The Model I and Model II were called the Pre-Century Series because their 575 shaft-horsepower ratings were superseded in 1967 by the 715 shaft-horsepower TPE331-1 and TPE331-2 of the Century Series of engines. These events capped a four-year development program. Ivan Speer, AiResearch vice president and manager, stated that 186 TPE331 turboprop engines had been scheduled for production in 1965, with an additional 150 forecast for the remainder of the year. The engine had already found several new homes.

The Turbo II by Aero Commander was certified with the 331 on September 15, 1965, and the Japanese-built Mitsubishi MU-2B was certified by the FAA on November 4, 1965, the first flight of the aircraft with the 331 having taken place on February 11 of that year. The Volpar Corporation's Beech 18 modification was FAA-certified on February 17, 1966. The first flight of the Fairchild-Hiller Heli Porter with the 331 took place on October 25, 1965, and the aircraft was FAA-certified on April 21, 1966. Finally, 1966 saw the first flight of the Carstedt Jet-Liner with the TPE331.

AiResearch continued to broaden the use of the TPE331 in 1967. In that year the FAA certified the TPE331-1 and TPE331-2 versions of the Century Series at 715 shaft-horsepower, and the first flight of the Volpar Turboliner occurred in April. In May, Short Brothers and Harland Ltd. selected the TPE331 for their Skyvan aircraft and Air Parts Ltd. selected the TPE331 for their Fu-24 business jet. In August Swearingen Aircraft and Pilatus both selected the TPE331 for their Merlin II B and Turbo Porter, respectively. Of most importance to the future development of the TPE331, however, was the announcement by the company in 1967 of a "power-up" program to dramatically increase the shaft horsepower of the TPE331 family, while staying within the overall dimensions of the original model.

Garrett introduced the 840 Series of TPE331 engines in 1969 as the TPE331-3, TPE331-5, and TPE331-6 turboprop models. In 1969 the FAA certified the TPE331-3 840 shaft-horsepower version. The higher power of the 840 series was due to an improved gas generator, which provided higher airflow and higher pressure ratios. In 1970 the FAA certified flat-rated TPE331-5 and TPE331-6 840 shaft-horsepower versions. The TPE331-5 and TPE331-6 models matched a 715 shaft-horsepower gearbox to the improved compressor of the TPE331-3, therefore providing better high-altitude and hot-day performance. The TPE331-5 was different from the TPE331-6 only in terms of prop speed. More 840 Series engines are in operation than any other type of TPE331. A torque and temperature limiting system was introduced to production in 1971. This optional accessory greatly extended component life and also simplified pilot procedure by reducing the pilot's workload through the use of automatic monitoring procedures (thereby limiting potential over-limit power cycles).[97]

Garrett launched another program to uprate the TPE331 in early 1975. Four engine versions were to result from this program, and all four uprated versions were within the original TPE331 frame size. The first two uprated model versions were the TPE331-8 and TPE331-9 at 865 shaft-horsepower. This was 865 shaft-horsepower measured thermodynamically, but like the TPE331-5 and TPE331-6 models they were flat-rated at 715 shaft-horsepower up to 36°C (97°F) to improve performance on hot days. The TPE331-8 and TPE331-9 versions were FAA-certified in November 1976. They were followed three years later in 1978 by the TPE331-10 and TPE331-11 models at 940 and 1,100 thermodynamic shaft horsepower respectively. These models were civilian versions of the T76-G-420 and T76-G-421 military engines. The Navy certified both military versions in 1977. The FAA certified the TPE331-10 in 1978 and the TPE331-11 in 1979.

In 1980 Garrett announced that the official time between overhaul (TBO) for the TPE331 had been extended to 3,600 hours on the TPE331-1, -2, -3, -5, and -6 engines. The company also announced the development of the TPE331-14 and -15 growth versions in the 1,600 shaft-horsepower class. The TPE331-14A and TPE331-14B versions were type certified by the FAA on April 26, 1984. The certification included twenty-three separate engine tests, including rotor containment, 1.5-and 4.0-pound bird ingestion, over-temperature vibration, ice ingestion, and oil interruption tests. The most significant aspect of the testing was a precedent-setting 1,500-hour endurance run to verify the TPE331-14's initial maintenance period.[98]

The TPE331-14 and -15 models are actually slightly scaled-up models of the 331. Engine frame size was increased by only 20 percent. The TPE331-14F version was certified by the FAA on May 24, 1989, and the -14GR and -14HR versions were FAA certified on July 13, 1992. The GR and HR designations are for clockwise and counterclockwise versions of the engine.

To summarize, the TPE331/T76 was originally meant to be a growth engine in the 400-to-700 shaft-horsepower range; however, it has far exceeded that design goal. The basic design of the TPE331 encompasses 12,698 production units of seventeen different engine models ranging in power from 575 shaft-horsepower to over 1,760 shaft-horsepower. All engine variants of the TPE331 were within approximately the same engine size. Garrett TPE331 turboprops have accumulated over 70 million service hours.

---

## Endnotes

[1] NAL, "Turboprops Pay Off," Ryan Reporter, Vol. 15, No. 6, December 7, 1954, 9.

[2] Bowers, Peter M. and Swanborough, Gordon, United States Military Aircraft Since 1909, Washington, D.C.: Smithsonian Institution Press, 1989, 192.

[3] Schoneberger, William A. and Paul Sonnenburg, Allison Power of Excellence: 1915 - 1990, Indianapolis, IN: Allison Gas Turbine Division, General Motors Corporation, 1990, 104.

[4] NAL, Chronology of the Allison Gas Turbine Division of General Motors, unpublished manuscript, Indianapolis, IN: Allison Engine Company, no date, 11.

[5] Ibid, 6.

[6] Wegg, John, General Dynamics Aircraft and their Predecessors, Annapolis, MD: Naval Institute Press, 1990, 184.

[7] Schoneberger and Sonnenburg, Allison Power of Excellence, 108.

[8] Wegg, General Dynamics Aircraft and their Predecessors, 185.

[9] Ibid.

[10] The Navy subsequently canceled the R3Y program due to its high cost and the aircraft's instability in flight. Ibid, and NAL, Chronology of the Allison Gas Turbine Division of General Motors, 7.

[11] Schoneberger and Sonnenburg, Allison Power of Excellence, 108.

[12] Ibid.

[13] Wegg, General Dynamics Aircraft and their Predecessors, 185-186.

[14] NAL, Chronology of the Allison Gas Turbine Division of General Motors, 11.

[15] Schoneberger and Sonnenburg, Allison Power of Excellence, 106.

[16] Ibid, 130.

[17] Ibid, 138.

[18] Ibid, 137.

[19] Francillon, Rene J, Lockheed Aircraft Since 1913, Annapolis, MD: Naval Institute Press, 1987, 355.

[20] Ibid, and Schoneberger and Sonnenburg, Allison Power of Excellence, 127.

[21] NAL, Chronology of the Allison Gas Turbine Division of General Motors, 12.

[22] Dillard, James, Allison Engine Company, Indianapolis, Indiana, Interview, November 18, 1994.

[23] Francillon, Lockheed Aircraft Since 1913, 355.

[24] NAL, Chronology of the Allison Gas Turbine Division of General Motors, 15, and Francillon, Lockheed Aircraft Since 1913, 358.

[25] NAL, Chronology of the Allison Gas Turbine Division of General Motors, 16.

[26] Dillard, Interview, November 18, 1994.

[27] United States Navy Propulsion Characteristics Summary, Allison T56-A-8, -8A, -8B, -426, dated June 1984, 87.

28  NAL, Chronology of the Allison Gas Turbine Division of
    General Motors, 17.

29  Ibid, 361.

30  NAL, Chronology of the Allison Gas Turbine Division of
    General Motors, 22.

31  Ibid, 19.

32  Ibid, 20.

33  Francillon, Lockheed Aircraft Since 1913, 360.

34  NAL, Chronology of the Allison Gas Turbine Division of
    General Motors, 23.

35  Ibid.

36  Ibid.

37  Ibid, 27.

38  Ibid, 28.

39  Ibid, 25.

40  Dillard, Interview, November 18, 1994.

41  Ibid, 33.

42  Francillon, Lockheed Aircraft Since 1913, 364.

43  NAL, Chronology of the Allison Gas Turbine Division of
    General Motors, 56.

44  Francillon, Lockheed Aircraft Since 1913, 372.

45  Forecast International, Gas Turbine Forecast: Book One,
    Reports and Forecasts, Newtown, CT: Forecast International, 1993, 7.

46  Francillon, Lockheed Aircraft Since 1913, 383.

47  Ibid, 368.

48  Kolcum, Edward H, "Engine Competition Eyes Fuel Efficiency," Aviation Week and Space Technology, November 2, 1981, 43.

49  Bowers and Swanborough, United States Military Aircraft
    Since 1909, 383.

50  Ibid, 13.

51  Ibid, 15.

52  Ibid.

53  Ibid, 16.

54  Ibid.

55  Ibid, 21.

56  Ibid.

57  Ibid, 23.

58  Ibid, 27.

59  Schoneberger and Sonnenburg, Allison Power of Excellence, 145.

60  Ibid, 145-146.

61  NAL, Chronology of the Allison Gas Turbine Division of
    General Motors, 31.

62  Ibid, 34.

63  Bowers, Peter M. and Swanborough, Gordon, United
    States Navy Aircraft Since 1911, Annapolis, MD: Naval
    Institute Press, 1990, 309. [373]

64  NAL, Chronology of the Allison Gas Turbine Division of
    General Motors, 16.

65  Bowers and Swanborough, United States Navy Aircraft
    Since 1911, 306.

66  The Allison company chronology puts the first flight of the
    prototype P-3V-1 on November 30, 1959. NAL, Chronology of the Allison Gas Turbine Division of General Motors, 19.

67  Ibid.

68  Francillon, Lockheed Aircraft Since 1913, 408-409.

69  NAL, Chronology of the Allison Gas Turbine Division of
    General Motors, 21.

70  GE Company, Eight Decades of Progress: A Heritage of
    Aircraft Turbine Technology, Cincinnati, OH: GE Aircraft
    Engines, 1990, 91. [617]

71  NAL, Chronology of the Allison Gas Turbine Division of
    General Motors, 22.

72  Ibid, 25.

73  Ibid, 50.

74  Francillon, Lockheed Aircraft Since 1913, 417.

75  Forecast International, Gas Turbine Forecast, Allison
    T56/501, 5.

76  Ibid, 2.

77  Kolcum, "Engine Competition Eyes Fuel Efficiency,"
    Aviation Week and Space Technology, 41.

78  NAL, Chronology of the Allison Gas Turbine Division of
    General Motors, 20.

79  Fernberger, John M, "A Versatile Free Turbine," Interavia
    1 (1963), 141. [129]

80  Dillard, Interview, November 18, 1994.

81  Forecast International, Gas Turbine Forecast, Allison
    T56/501, 10.

82  Schiff, Barry, "The Compromisers" AOPA Pilot, 79. [563]

83  Buckner, Howard A. Jr. and Peach, John W, "Turboprop
    Engine Operational Experience in STOL Aircraft Operating from Rough Fields," SAE Paper No. 680228, presented at the Society of Automotive Engineers Business
    Aircraft Meeting, Wichita, Kansas, April 3-5, 1968, 80.
    [533]

84  Ibid, 81.

85  Ramsaur, W.R., "Twisting the Big Jet's Tail: The Story of
    the Small Gas Turbine," New Frontiers, The Garrett Corporation, Fall, 1959, National Air and Space Museum
    Document Control #BG-007-000-01, 3. [544]

86  Ibid, 6, and Scholl, Robert R. H. and Schoneberger, William A, Out of Thin Air: Garrett's First 50 Years, Los Angeles, CA: The Garrett Corporation, 1985, 100. [572]

87  Scholl and Schoneberger, Out of Thin Air, 122.

88  Garrett Corporation, TPE331/T76: The Garrett AiResearch Turboprop, Phoenix, AZ. [529]

89  Garrett Corporation, AiResearch TPE331/T76 Turboprop Engines, Phoenix, AZ: Garrett Corporation, AiResearch Manufacturing Company of Arizona, 1967. [531]

90  Garrett Corporation, TPE331/T76: The Garrett AiResearch Turboprop.

91  Garrett Corporation, The Garrett/AiResearch T76 Military Turboprop Engine, Phoenix, AZ:Garrett Corporation, AiResearch Manufacturing Company of Arizona, no date, 2 [534], and, Bowers and Swanborough, United States Military Aircraft Since 1909, 498-99.

92  Ibid, 498, Garrett Corporation. TPE331/T76: The Garrett AiResearch Turboprop, 3, and Bowers and Swanborough, United States Navy Aircraft Since 1911, 394-395.

93  Bowers and Swanborough, United States Military Aircraft Since 1909, 498-99, and Bowers and Swanborough, United States Navy Aircraft Since 1911, 394-395.

94  Buckner and Peach, "Turboprop Engine Operational Experience in STOL Aircraft Operating from Rough Fields," presented at the Society of Automotive Engineers Business Aircraft Meeting, 2.

95  Ibid, 5.

96  "Varied Applications for Light Turboprop," The Aeroplane and Commercial Aviation News, January 28, 1965, 20. [562]

97  Garrett Corporation, TPE331/T76: The Garrett AiResearch Turboprop.

98  Garrett Corporation, Garrett TPE331-14, Phoenix, AZ: Garrett Corporation, AiResearch Manufacturing Company of Arizona, 1984. [530]

Air Force SR-71, Powered by Two
Pratt & Whitney J58 Turbojets

# Chapter Twelve

# High-Mach Aircraft Gas Turbines

## The J93 and J58 Turbojet Engines

The raison d'être of the aircraft gas turbine engine has been to achieve greater power—power to fly faster, higher, and farther. The speed of sound, Mach 1, seemed an unbreakable goal in the early and mid-1930s. Rocket-powered aircraft first took man through that barrier, but aircraft gas turbines soon caught up and made supersonic flight a relatively common phenomenon. The mysterious barrier was broken in 1947. What was left to do? Why should aircraft and aircraft engine designers want to go beyond Mach 1.5 or Mach 2? When the "sound barrier" was broken, there were already plans for jet transport aircraft, and it was clear even then that jet transport or passenger aircraft did not have to fly faster than Mach 1 to bring about a revolution in transportation. All the new jet passenger aircraft had to do was approach the highest speeds of some World War II fighter aircraft to become economically viable. The maximum operating speed of the Boeing 747 is only Mach 0.92, that of the Airbus A320 Mach 0.82, and the McDonnell Douglas MD-11 Mach 0.87. But humans have flown in excess of Mach 3. Why the desire then, to fly faster yet? The answer lies in the Cold War era.

Although rooted in the economic, military, and diplomatic history of the Second World War, the Cold War was also a war of technology. Some of the amazing technological accomplishments in aircraft gas turbine engines have been logical outgrowths from preceding systems, but many of these accomplishments were spurred by real or perceived threats from the other superpower. There have been many obvious threats; e.g., the outbreak of the Korean War and the advent of the Chinese-flown MiG-15 over the Yalu River spurred the United States to develop the F-84 and F-86 jet fighters and sped up jet engine design, development, and production. Other less obvious but perceivable threats predicated on long-held assumptions of military necessity, which may or may not have been real, have driven the progress of aircraft gas turbine engine technology in this country. For example, one of the oldest assumptions of military necessity in this country has been the need for the long-range, strategic, intercontinental bomber. It is not the purpose here to determine the reality of this long-held assumption but only to relate its consequences on the technology of aircraft gas turbines.

Once held as primarily a defensive weapon to intercept and destroy hostile fleets far from U.S. shores, the strategic bomber evolved during the Second World War into an offensive weapon able to take high-explosive bombs into the enemy's country to ensure the destruction of industries, transportation systems, and then cities (to break the will to resist). The lessons of the Second World War in this respect were mixed. Planners of military strategy during that war had radically divergent thoughts on the efficacy of strategic bombing. How much strategic bombing was enough? At what point did it become wasted effort? How much did it really affect Germany's ability to make war? Strategic bombing's role in the overall formula for making war was the question. The arrival of the atomic bomb changed the military strategic planning formula dramatically.

The strategic bomber carrying an atomic bomb became the linchpin of military strategic planning. Even with the advent of the intercontinental ballistic missile, the intercontinental bomber remained a crucial third of the "triad" of U.S. strategic defense, along with ICBMs and nuclear submarines. Throughout the Cold War and beyond, the intercontinental strategic bomber has been a hallowed institution in the military-industrial complex, along with the

Navy's aircraft carriers and the Army's main battle tank. The intercontinental bomber is an intricate technological system, and technological systems tend to become more complex, not less. The technological advance of the intercontinental bomber has been historically limited by only two technological factors: the airframe and, more importantly, the gas turbine engine.

The first of the aircraft gas turbine engines to be examined is the General Electric J93 turbojet. When the B-70 Valkyrie bomber first flew, on September 21, 1964, the J93 was the fastest and most powerful engine in the world. The other engine considered in this chapter, the Pratt and Whitney J58, provided the world's first operational Mach 3 engine for the SR-71 Blackbird strategic reconnaissance aircraft. The design and development of these engines mark the end of a technological era in aircraft gas turbine engine development, when there were no limits to our technological horizon; when we were only held back by scientific and engineering barriers; and when the question "What can it do?" meant more than "How much does it cost?"

## The Design and Development of the General Electric J93 Turbojet Engine

In October 1954 the U.S. Air Force published General Operational Requirement (GOR) No. 38 entitled, General Operational Requirements for an Intercontinental Bombardment Weapon System Piloted Bomber. It specified the project as "Weapon System 110A" and established 1963 as the target date for the first wing of thirty operational aircraft.[1] The initial mission profile of the new bomber was that it would fly at Mach 2 to within striking range of its target, then fly at Mach 3 for a "dash" bombing run over the target, and fly back at speeds of Mach 0.9-2.[2] This program was in part meant to counteract the development of the B-58 Hustler supersonic bomber, a program that then-commander of the Air Force's Strategic Air Command, General Curtis LeMay, detested.[3]

GOR 38 was superseded on March 22, 1955, by GOR 82, and a revised Study Requirement No. 21, was issued, modifying the target speed of the aircraft.[4] Marcelle Size Knaack, in *Encyclopedia of U.S. Air Force Aircraft and Missile Systems, Volume II, Post-World War II Bombers: 1945-1973*, describes the new requirements:

> Study Requirement 21's performance objectives were Mach .9 for cruise speed and "maximum possible" speed during a 1,000-nautical mile penetration. Still, high speed was of less importance than the penetration altitude and radius. A revision of Study Requirement 21 on April 15 [1955] stipulated that the new weapon system's cruise speed should not be less than Mach .9, unless a lower speed would result in a significant range increase...[5]

In April 1955 the 110A Weapon System Project Office was formed as part of Headquarters Air Research & Development Command (ARDC) at Wright Patterson Air Force Base in Dayton, Ohio, and in June the Air Force deputy chief of staff for development directed that WS110A development be started as soon as possible with a multiple, competitive Phase I program.[6] The ARDC held to a target date of 1963 for the deployment of the first wing of thirty aircraft.[7]

In July the Air Force issued another GOR, this time for an intercontinental reconnaissance system having objectives similar to those of WS110A. This reconnaissance mission was later merged with that of WS110A, which became known as WS110A/L.[8] Also in July, a joint ARDC/Air Materiel Command (AMC) Source Selection Board proposed a list of six contractors eligible for consideration in the development of the WS110A/L airframe. Only Boeing and North American chose to submit proposals.[9]

On November 8, 1955, both Boeing and North American were awarded Phase I letter contracts as prime airframe contractors. The two letter contracts became definitive in 1956. Each contractor had to submit a design for the required weapon system and provide the Air Force with models, drawings, specifications, reports and other data. The contractor was also responsible for conducting wind tunnel tests and other studies, and constructing a mockup. The mockup of the WS110A/L was scheduled for November 1957, and first flight was scheduled for March 1960. The reconnaissance aspect of the WS110A's mission was later canceled by the Air Force.[10] Knaack describes the required operational characteristics of the new weapon system:

> With regard to operational characteristics, the new weapon system was to rely primarily on nuclear weapons to accomplish its mission, and the origin and termination of its operations were to be within the limits of the North American continent. The Air Force specified that weapon system 110A/L would have to be capable of performing during the day, at night, and in any kind of weather. A minimum unrefueled radius of 4,000 nautical miles and a desirable extended radius of 5,500 nautical miles were required, with aerial refueling allowed in the latter case. Finally, the minimum target altitude was to be 60,000 feet, and the contracts reiterated that cruise speed could not be less than Mach 0.9, with maximum supersonic dash speed in the combat zone.[11]

While this Air Force bomber was being developed in 1955, General Electric had been talking to North American about collaboration on a high-altitude, high-Mach interceptor aircraft for the U.S. Air Force Air Defense Command. In these discussions they had proposed a new engine system called the J79-X275. The -X275 stood for a proposed speed goal of Mach 2.75. The X275 Project was launched at General Electric Evendale in November 1955.[12] Dale Streid was named project manager. General Electric submitted the design to the Air Force in February 1956 for both the bomber (WS110A) and the high-altitude interceptor (WS202A). Mechanical design of the engine started in April 1956.[13]

The original design submitted in February 1956 called for Mach 3 capability. General Electric also proposed use of nickel-plated molybdenum turbine blades. The Air Force vetoed the use of molybdenum because of their real fear that any hole in the surface of the blade coating would cause the molybdenum blades to oxidize, therefore causing a catastrophic engine failure. William Travers describes GE's solution:

> GE engineers then decided that it was necessary to go to turbine blade air cooling in order to operate at the desired turbine temperatures. Thus, the so-called STEM [Sic Shaped Tube Electrolytic Machining] drilling process was developed and long radial cooling holes were designed into the turbine blades.[14]

On June 7, 1956, the Air Force's Power Plant Laboratory at Wright-Patterson AFB, Ohio, decided to launch an overall engine competition for the interceptor and the bomber. Both General Electric and the Allison Division of General Motors were asked to submit a proposal on September 14.[15]

In October 1955 the contractors involved in the WS110A program got a surprise when the Air Force directed that Phase I development of the WS110A be discontinued and that Boeing and North American Aircraft continue studies on a reduced research and development basis only. The Air Force also strongly suggested that the areas of high-energy fuels and boundary-layer control for improving range be investigated by the contractors.[16] This was not news to GE, which had been working on high-energy fuels, like boron hydrides, for a long time at the General Electric Project Zoom test station in Malta, New York, under a Navy contract for rocket fuels. When General Electric heard about the project redirection, they took their cue and reduced their X275 engine task force from 75 to 11 personnel.

On November 28, General Electric learned that they were unsuccessful in their X275 engine design proposal. North American Aircraft wanted the Allison engines because they felt the Allison engine was "far better at high altitude and high Mach (the area around Mach 3)."[17] The General Electric sales, marketing, and engineering teams, however, did not give up. They returned on December 19 and 21 to North American and the Air Force respectively, with an engine design, the X279, that offered improvements of 10 to 11 percent in thrust and 1 to 2 percent in specific fuel consumption at Mach 3 and 60,000 feet.[18]On December 27 they learned that their reengineering efforts had paid off. North American announced that they had changed their minds and that the engines in the 110A system would be General Electric engines. The competition, however, was not over. General Electric would still have to prove that their engine was the better engine and that it could be improved to stay ahead of the Allison engine. In fact the engine competition was just heating up. Both engine manufacturers stepped up their efforts to "sell" the Air Force on their engines. On December 31, General Electric delivered crucial technical substantiation data to the Air Force to back up their claims of increased performance for the X279A engine. To increase the momentum for selection of the X279A, General Electric released the engine to the public. Citing a 13 percent increase in thrust over previous designs at Mach 3 and 60,000 feet, General Electric went further and released data throughout January on several different proposed variants of the X279, including the F, G, H, J, and K engines. On January 29 the company released data for a Convair bomber variant of the X279 engine, the "M" variant. It was presented as a dry-growth version (without afterburning) of the X279 designs.[19]

North American Aviation was caught in the middle of this increased competition. It appeared to General Electric and North American that although North American had the best airframe proposal and supported the General Electric engine design, the Air Force still felt that the Allison engine was superior. On April 16, 1957, North American and Boeing (their competitor in the airframe competition) announced jointly that the General Electric X279E and Allison's engine were almost identical in performance and timing.[20]

On April 16, 1957, General Electric began two days of high-level presentations to the Air Force on the status and development projections of the X279 Program, working intensively to convince the Air Force that the X279 program was the best configuration for high-altitude, high-Mach flight.[21]

On May 1, 1957, Jack S. Parker of General Electric was notified by the Assistant Secretary of the U.S. Air Force that General Electric had won the 110A bomber engine competition. General Electric had won the battle. General Electric was also notified in May that they had been awarded the engine development contract for the WS202A interceptor, with North American receiving the airframe development contract.[22] Work statement negotiations among GE, North American, and the Air Force were complete on June 7.

On July 26 General Electric received a letter contract for a 50-hour Preliminary Flight Ratings Test (PFRT) development program for the X279E turbojet, and on August 23 they submitted a formal proposal for the X279E engine to the Air Force. On September 18, 1957, the Air Force gave Boeing and North American the new system characteristics established for the competition. These called for a speed of Mach 3 to Mach 3.2, a target altitude of 70,000 to 75,000 feet, a range of 6,100 to 10,500 miles, and a gross weight of between 475,000 and 490,000 pounds.[23] A week later, on September 25, the Air Force gave General Electric approval to start development of the X279E, now redesignated the XJ93-GE-1 turbojet. In October General Electric started detail drawings on the XJ93 design (Figure 12-1).[24]

On October 18, 1957, General Electric submitted data on the engine to both North American and Boeing for their bomber development competition. On December 23 North American won the competition for the 110A intercontinental bomber, to be designated the XB-70 Valkyrie.[25] They submitted the J93-GE-3 turbojet, a growth model of the J93-GE-1, in the proposal.

In December the Secretary of Defense directed the Air Force's ARDC and the Air Materiel Command (AMC) to determine the degree to which the B-70 bomber program could be accelerated to equip the first SAC wing at the earliest possible date. In January 1958 the ARDC and

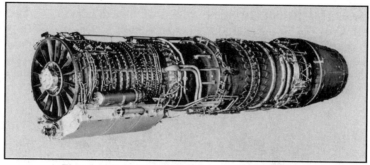

**Figure 12-1. General Electric XJ93 Engine**
*(Photo courtesy of GE)*

AMC, along with North American, found that an eighteen-month acceleration was possible. ARDC/AMC staff officers gave a briefing to Air Force Generals LeMay, Rawlings, Anderson, Putt, and Irvine recommending procurement of the entire weapons system. On January 13, 1958, General Electric submitted the J93-GE-3 Engine Proposal Supplement, showing eighteen-month accelerated development programs leading to PFRT and MQT, to the Air Force.

On February 21, General Electric submitted a formal Program Proposal and Preliminary Model Specification for the J93-GE-3 to the Air Force's AMC and the ARDC at Wright-Patterson Air Force Base.[26] By February 7 they had completed all layout drawings required for first engine build-up, and began testing of the full-scale combustor on March 1.

On April 17, 1958, the J93-GE-1 performance specifications were completed and approved by the Air Force for inclusion in the definitive contract for the engine. The definitive contract was signed between General Electric and the Air Force on May 15.[27]

On September 16, the first J93-GE-1 was delivered to the test cell, ready for first start-up. Start-up was accomplished on that same day, when the J93-GE-1 first ran self-sustaining. Six days later the J93-GE-1 was run up to 77.5 percent of full-speed, and ran self-sustaining for 5.49 hours. It ran in afterburner mode for the first time in March 1959 and in July it completed its first full engine cycle at Mach 3 conditions and 65,000 feet (in the Evendale Ram Test Facility).[28]

There were, however, some problems in developing the J93 turbojet. Travers describes the situation as follows:

> Through 1960, there were anxious days and weeks when the program was short on parts and long on problems. When a technical audit was made of the program, engineers concluded that the J93 "was not going to make it!" The first J93 engines to test had another deficiency. The compressor was stall-prone due principally to the unproven short-chord compressor blading. About that time, the engineers had become aware of compressor testing in Europe that indicated losses due to short chording and the need for additional blade width. It was difficult to face the Air Force and North American, for the compressor had to be redesigned to longer and heavier blades.[29]

## The J93-GE-3

On March 5, 1958, General Electric received the go-ahead to develop the J93-GE-3 model of the J93 (Figure 12-2). Preliminary design was completed in May. On July 15 General Electric received a letter from Air Materiel Command giving their approval to include development of a further growth version of the J93, the J93-GE-5. The combustor system of the J93-GE-5 would burn high-energy fuel. On July 30 General Electric submitted a proposal, which was subsequently approved by the Air Force in September, to use the J93-GE-3 in both the B-70 and the F-108.[30] In August, General Electric completed the basic gas generator layout for the J93-GE-3 and submitted a set of performance specifications for a version of the J93-GE-3 with a thrust reverser, the J93-GE-3R. The J93-GE-3 was sent to test in July 1959, becoming the first operational American air-cooled turbine engine to run.

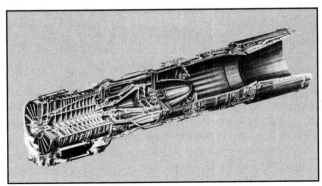

**Figure 12-2. Cutaway of J93-GE-3**
*(Illustration courtesy of GE)*

In the summer of 1959 the GE/North American effort was dealt a series of three blows by the Air Force. In August 1959 the High Energy Fuel (HEF) program was canceled. In September the North American F-108 "Rapier" program was canceled (this included the J93-GE-3R thrust reverser program as well).[31] The third blow came in December, when the B-70 procurement program was reduced from sixty-two aircraft to just two. Accordingly, the J93-GE-3 Military Qualification Test program was terminated. J93 development was continued on a minimum-cost Preliminary Flight Ratings Test basis, whose completion was extended for three months (from September to December 1960).[32]

In July 1960 General Electric instituted a compressor design change in the J93-GE-1, incorporating a new eleven-stage long chord compressor. This new compressor was introduced into the J93-GE-3 development program in August. The PFRT on the J93-GE-3 was also extended again by the Air Force from December 1960 to September 1961.[33]

On January 6, 1961, the J93-GE-3 MQT program was reinstated by the Air Force in another letter contract, but that decision itself was reversed on March 30, 1961, when the Air Force notified General Electric that the MQT program would be again terminated. This meant that there would be no flight program for the J93 beyond the XB-70. This was confirmed by official notice on April 7.

In September 1961 the J93 completed its official PRFT, totaling 96 hours with 22 hours at Mach 3. The Air Force, however, listed seventeen "penalty" items from the test which required subsequent requalification. These requalifications were finished by July of 1963. In April 1962 the first J93 was shipped for aircraft installation, and the first J93 was installed in the XB-70 in June of that year.[34] North American finished the installation of the sixth J93 turbojet in the Valkyrie in October 1962.[35] By December 1962 General Electric had accumulated 2,000 hours of test running on the J93, and had shipped the first prototype engine to Arnold Engineering Development Center in Tennessee for the North American Aircraft Inlet Duct Test Program.

The long-awaited first flight of the North American B-70 Valkyrie bomber (Figure 12-3) with six General Electric J93 turbojet engines took place on September 21, 1964, from Palmdale to Edwards Air Force Base in California. The flight lasted 1.1 hours.[36] The first Mach 3 flight of the B-70 was on October 24, 1965, with General Electric YJ93-GE-3 turbojets.

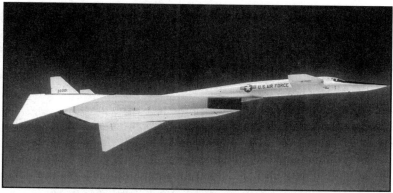

**Figure 12-3. North American B-70 Valkyrie**
*(Photo courtesy of U.S. Air Force)*

The second prototype of the XB-70A aircraft crashed on June 8, 1966, at Edwards Air Force Base in California when an F-104 photo chase-plane crashed into the tail of the prototype. The J93/XB-70 became a joint Air Force/NASA program in March 1967. The final flight of the first prototype from Edwards Air Force Base to Wright Patterson Air Force Base (WPAFB) took place on February 4, 1969. It is now on display at the Air Force Museum at WPAFB.

At a cruising speed of Mach 3.0, air temperatures at the face of the engine reach 623°F. To provide stall-free operation and high performance at this inlet temperature, the J93 compressor featured an advanced long-chord, low-solidity design using lightweight titanium in the first stage and stainless steel in the latter stages to accommodate the increasing temperatures. Other features of the compressor included positive blade retention, a structure independent of space rings for structural integrity, and a curvic coupling for increased stability.[37]

To provide high compressor efficiency and required engine/inlet compatibility over the wide flight operating range of the B-70, such as the high distortion and turbulence experienced with inlet duct unstart, the J93 featured two groups of variable stators in the compressor that operated independently. The forward group, comprised of the first three stages and the inlet guide vanes, provided stall margin for acceleration over the full range of operation, for high inlet distortion tolerance, and for low idle thrust. The variable stators in the rear of the compressor permitted increased airflow for improved performance at Mach 3 conditions.[38]

The J93 engine required high heat release to reach its 28,000 pounds of thrust. This was accomplished with a short, durable, film-cooled annular combustor incorporating thirty-two fuel nozzles. The annular design provided a single continuous compartment for combustion, unlike the separate flame tubes in the J79's cannular-type combustor. The J93's combustor also provided an operational capability at turbine inlet temperatures in excess of 2,000°F for takeoff, climb, acceleration, and Mach 3 cruise.[39]

The turbine rotor and blades of the J93 were designed for high-cycle operating temperatures above 2,000°F. General Electric achieved this through their advanced technology of air-cooled turbine blades and stators. Shaped Tube Electrolytic Machining (STEM), a process developed by GE, made it possible to drill small cooling holes in turbine blades without affecting the structure of the alloy. Air cooling of the turbine components permitted an increase of turbine inlet gas temperature of 300°F without increasing the basic metal temperature. In addition to STEM, use of long-shank turbine blades placed the turbine wheel rim out of the hot gas stream. The turbine material of choice was Udimet 700, a high-temperature, high-strength-but-forgeable material.[40]

The single rotor of the J93 series allowed for a three-main-bearing design. Travers describes this arrangement:

> The mechanical design of the J93 used three bearings with the number 1 bearing forward of the compressor rotor, the number 2 bearing aft of the compressor rotor, and the number 3 bearing aft of the turbine rotor. These bearings were installed in the front frame, compressor rear frame and the turbine frame, respectively. The number 1 and number 3 bearings were roller-type bearings while the number 2 bearing is a split inner race, ball bearing thrust type.[41]

This design was lightweight, enhanced the J93's reliability, and simplified assembly and maintenance.[42]

Jet nozzle thrust coefficient and augmentor efficiency are key factors in engine performance and fuel economy in that they provide the thrust for climb, acceleration and cruise over a wide range of Mach levels and altitudes, including Mach 3 and 65,000 feet (and including subsonic refueling).[43] To ensure a high degree of efficiency throughout this operating range, the J93 employed a fully modulating afterburner and exhaust nozzle system. The afterburner was designed to operate within a temperature range of 1,940°F and 3,240°F, with continuous operating capability. Catalytic ignitors were used to provide augmentor re-light capability. The J93 used a converging-diverging nozzle design with fully variable throat and discharge areas.[44]

The J93 employed a unique accessories capsule, which provided a fire-safe environment at Mach 3 by housing all controls and accessories in a sealed compartment vented to ambient pressure. The capsule acted as a heat shield and a secondary barrier against fluid that might leak from conventional fittings used within the capsule.[45]

## Summary of J93 Development

Although the XB-70/J93 development was ultimately reduced to a research and development program with only two prototypes (the third was canceled in March 1963), the General Electric Company did not come out of the program as a loser in any sense. The company had successfully developed a Mach 3 engine, tested and flown it at Mach 3. The J93 program provided General Electric with a sound technology base to later propose engines for the U.S. Supersonic Transport.

It is unfortunate that the B-70 program began in the same time frame as the intercontinental ballistic missile program. The B-70 program was downgraded during the Kennedy presidency at the same time that the McNamara tenure at the Department of Defense was focusing research and development dollars on missiles and space research. Was the B-70 a victim of "Sputnik" and the space race? The evidence is not very clear, but the intercontinental Mach 3 bomber has never again been attempted.

## Design and Development of the P&W J58 Turbojet Engine

The Lockheed SR-71 was first conceived in 1958 in response to intelligence reports that the Soviet Union was developing a new ground-to-air antiaircraft missile capable of reaching the operating ceiling of the current American reconnaissance aircraft, the U-2. The United States had to develop a strategic reconnaissance aircraft that could fly higher, faster, and farther than the U-2. This need was reemphasized in May 1960 when a U-2, piloted by Francis Gary Powers, was shot down.

The Pentagon wanted a new reconnaissance/fighter/interceptor that could fly over 2,000 mph at a ceiling of 100,000 feet and with a range of over 4,000 miles. All the U.S. aircraft manufacturers were called to Washington to see if they could design and develop an aircraft capable of meeting these criteria. One of the aircraft designers at the conference, Clarence L. "Kelly" Johnson of Lockheed, believed that such an advanced aircraft was feasible. Three major technological advances would be necessary for an aircraft of this type to be developed. First, an advanced airframe would have to be available. This condition had been met with the design and development of the North American X-15 rocket aircraft. Second, new lightweight metals capable of withstanding the heat and pressure of sustained high altitude, high Mach flight would be needed. This challenge was met by the development of a new titanium alloy by the Titanium Metals Corporation called Beta B-120, which was stronger than steel, lightweight, and resistant to temperatures higher than those encountered by the 4,000 mph X-15. These two advances were combined in an airframe that was unlike any other ever designed. Douglas J. Ingells, in *The L-1011 TriStar and the Lockheed Story*, described this new aircraft:

> Oddly, the Y-12A emerged as a biplane, two wings, but instead of being mounted one above the other the wings, shaped like arrow heads, were in tandem, one forward, one rearward on a long thin fuselage, virtually a flying fuel tank. The design was called a "double delta."
>
> The forward wing, which didn't look like a wing at all, was a narrow fairing with airfoil characteristics on each side of the fuselage like the eaves of a roof. The rear wing, a wide triangle in the tail, provided the main lift forces in subsonic and transonic flight.
>
> A pair of the high-thrust engines in long tube-like nacelles were mounted on this big "delta", faired to the airfoil like part of the wing, one on each side of the fuselage. Atop each nacelle was a large vertical fin and rudder...
>
> The "double delta" was a major innovation, and proved to be the answer to several problems. As the speed of the plane increased, particularly in the ultrasonic range, the forward "delta" generated an extra bonus in lift and provided desirable control stability, better than previous designs. At the same time, the big "delta" in the rear permitted excellent take-off and landing characteristics...[46]

The third advance was the most important. The propulsion system for sustained high-altitude, high-Mach flight would have to be an air-breathing system, not a rocket. The P&W J58 turbojet, then under development for a high-Mach-dash-capable Navy application was the answer.

The Air Force placed a contract with Lockheed in August 1959 for an unarmed reconnaissance aircraft to replace the U-2. Using Fiscal Year 1960 funds, the Air Force ordered twenty-five aircraft, of which nine were to be two-seaters. The contract was closely backed in terms of funding by the Central Intelligence Agency. The first flight of the A-12 (Figure 12-4) was on April 26, 1962, at Groom Lake, powered by two P&W J75 engines (as the first J58 engines had yet to be finished). The completed JT11D-20/J58s, powered by the new JP-7 fuel,

**Figure 12-4. Lockheed A-12**
*(Photo courtesy of Lockheed Aircraft)*

were installed by the end of 1962. Between 1963 and 1968, single-seat A-12s were used by the CIA for covert flights.[47]

In 1963 the Air Force issued a requirement for an advanced high-speed, high-altitude interceptor to replace the canceled North American XF-108 Rapier. Lockheed proposed a version of the A-12 designated the YF-12 to replace the XF-108. The first YF-12 was flown at Groom Lake on August 7, 1963, by Lockheed test pilot Louis W. Schalk to an altitude of 80,000 feet and at a speed of over 2,000 mph — Mach 3.[48]

On February 29, 1964, President Lyndon B. Johnson revealed the existence of the top-secret Lockheed A-12 experimental aircraft at a news conference. The aircraft designation was soon changed to the YF-12 because it was to be used as a fighter-interceptor as well as a reconnaissance aircraft.[49] However, no funds were made available to Lockheed for production of the YF-12, and this planned use was discontinued.[50]

The Air Force took up the A-12 under a new designation, the old CIA mission of strategic reconnaissance. The new SR-71 (Figure 12-5) was slightly heavier, slightly larger, and slightly slower than the A-12, but the new design incorporated more reconnaissance cameras and a second seat for a Reconnaissance Systems Officer behind the pilot. The first flight of the SR-71 (nicknamed the "Blackbird") was on December 22, 1964, at Palmdale, California. The SR-71A entered service in January 1966 with the 4200th Strategic Reconnaissance Wing at Beale Air Force Base in California.[51]

**Figure 12-5. Lockheed SR-71, Powered by Two
Pratt & Whitney J58 Turbojets**
*(Photo courtesy of U.S. Air Force)*

Lockheed built thirty-two SR-71 Blackbirds. Two were modified as two-seat trainers and the last Blackbird built, the SR-71C, also incorporated two seats. In September 1964 Clarence "Kelly" Johnson of Lockheed received the Collier Trophy for his design work on the Blackbird.[52] By 1988 the number of SR-71As in service had been reduced to only six, all with the 9th Strategic Reconnaissance Wing.[53]

As with almost all of the great technologically innovative aircraft gas turbine engine designs of the last half of this century, the P&W JT11D-20/J58 engine design was firmly grounded in the company's previous work. The first P&W engine designed for Mach 3 was the JT9 (J91) engine. This was a single-spool turbojet engine with an 8:1 pressure ratio and a total airflow of about 400 pounds per second. The massive JT9 was originally designed by the company anticipating the Air Force XB-70 bomber program.

The design of the JT9 was also based on two previously successful military turbojet programs. The first was the JT3/J57, which was designed for the North American F-100 Super Sabre and the Convair F-102 Delta Dagger jet fighters (among others). The second engine was the JT4/J75 turbojet, designed and developed for the Republic F-105 Thunderchief and the Convair F-106 Delta Dart jet fighters (among others). The JT4/J75 was rated at Mach 2 at 55,000 feet for a maximum of only 15 minutes. P&W felt confident in 1956 that they could build a Mach 3 engine. But they were also realistic about the job ahead of them. As quoted in *JT11D-20 Engine - A Successful Leap Into the Technical Unknown*:

> This background [for developing a high-speed engine] existed at P&W when the JT11D-20 design was initiated. Therefore, we knew enough to know we did not know how to design and manufacture an engine that would operate continuously at speeds over Mach 3.[54]

P&W laid down the centerline for the first JT11 engine, designated by the military as the J58-P2 (Figures 12-6 and 12-7), in late 1956. The J58-P2 was scaled down to about 80 percent of the JT9's size. The original military requirement for which the JT11 was designed was not the A-12 or SR-71, but for a Navy attack aircraft whose mission profile included Mach 3 dash capability.

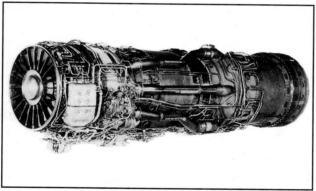

**Figure 12-6. P&W JT11/J58 Engine**
*(Photo courtesy of Pratt & Whitney)*

Design of the JT11/J58 began in the company's Connecticut engineering department. In 1956 P&W began construction of a new engineering facility on 7,000 acres northwest of West Palm Beach, Florida. This expansion was made to provide a remote test area for engine testing with liquid hydrogen and boron-doped jet fuels. JT11 development under W. H. Brown's direction was transferred to the Florida Research and Development Center in 1957. In September 1957 the first engine test in Florida was conducted on P&W's "304" engine, fueled by liquid hydrogen.

A highly classified Air Force project, the 304 was to be an afterburning turbofan operating at Mach 2 at extremely high altitude. Power to drive the fan was obtained by heating the liquid hydrogen with a heat exchanger at the fan discharge, then expanding the hydrogen through a twenty-four-stage turbine. The spent hydrogen was then all burned in the engine's airstream, some ahead of the heat exchanger, the rest in the afterburner. At Al Donovan's suggestion, this

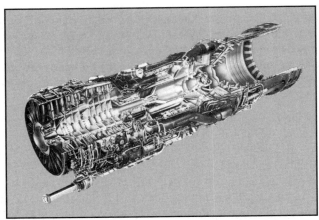

**Figure 12-7. Cutaway of JT11/J58 Engine**
*(Illustration courtesy of Pratt & Whitney)*

same cycle (substituting liquid oxygen for the 304's air oxidizer) was adapted to P&W's pioneering RL-10 rocket engine. Richard Mulready was the project engineer for the 304, and later for the RL-10. Air Force Plant 74 was built next to the P&W test site to manufacture liquid hydrogen. Initial test facilities at the Florida Research and Development Center included fuel pump and compressor test stands, and sea-level test stands for both the 304 and the J58, as well as Mach 3 endurance facilities and high-altitude engine test cells for the J58. A new metallurgy laboratory specialized in the problems of metal at extreme high and low temperatures. Here, Joseph Morre made major contributions by providing new alloys with higher temperature capability, and later pioneered the superplastic forging process that permitted turbine discs to be made of materials previously available only as castings.

The J58 was an afterburning turbojet rated at 26,000 pounds maximum takeoff thrust. By the time that P&W began to study the SR-71 requirements years later, the company already had about 700 full-scale testing hours on the J58-P2.[55]

The design requirements for the YF-12/SR-71 aircraft presented major challenges, or as the P&W engineers referred to them, "leaps into the technical unknown." The J58-P2 turbojet prototype revealed that a straight turbojet operating at the J57 and J75 turbine temperatures would not provide enough thrust to meet mission requirements. It also revealed some of the problems in overcoming the thermal environment at cruise speeds.

Twelve major design requirements for the engine would require overcoming "pockets of resistance" in current aircraft engine design (and in P&W's production engine experience to date). They were:

1. **Mach number:** P&W's previous high point in production engines was the J75, which could attain Mach 2.4 for about 15 minutes. The SR-71 required Mach 3+ continuously.

2. **Corrected airflow turndown ratio (cruise maximum):** Previous production experience achieved 90 percent; the SR-71 engine required 60 percent. This would lead P&W to develop a variable cycle for the J58, a bleed bypass engine.

3. **Altitude:** The SR-71 required an altitude ceiling of over 80,000 feet; previous P&W engines had achieved 55,000 feet.

4. **Compressor inlet temperature:** To fulfill its mission, the SR-71's engine would have to operate at a temperature range from -40°F to 800°F; previous engine designs at P&W had achieved a range of -40°F to 250°F.

5. **Combustor exit temperature:** Whereas P&W had been able to maintain a combustor exit temperature of 1,750°F on takeoff and 1,550°F continuous; the SR-71 required a combustor

exit temperature of 2,000°F continuously.

6. **Maximum fuel temperature:** Previous P&W engines had accommodated a fuel inlet temperature of between 110 and 130°F; the SR-71's engine would require a 350°F fuel inlet temperature capability.

7. **Maximum temperature of the lubricant inlet:** With previous engine designs a temperature of 250°F had been maintainable; with the SR-71's engine, 550°F would have to be maintained. At some points in the engine, lubricant temperatures would rise to 700°F or even 1000°F.

8. **Thrust/weight ratio:** P&W's previous engine programs had achieved a thrust/weight ratio of 4.0; the J58 program would have to achieve a ratio of 5.2.

9. **Military operation:** The normal amount of time in any one engine cycle for an engine to require full military power was usually 30 minutes or so; the SR-71 would require continuous full military power throughout its mission.

10. **Continuous temperatures at the turbine inlet:** Temperatures greater than the melting points of then state-of-the-art materials would be encountered at the turbine inlet. This would force P&W to develop a cooled turbine for the JT11D-20.

11. **Afterburner operation:** All previous military engines with afterburners required only intermittent afterburner operation (at takeoff and during short periods of the mission); the SR-71, however, required continuous full afterburner operation throughout its mission.

12. **Additional requirements for high temperatures:** The high temperatures would require, among other things, a fuel that would not "coke-up" at temperatures over 600°F; an engine lubricant that wouldn't break down at temperatures approaching 1,000°F; weldable engine sheet metal made from turbine blade materials; and an engine system that would operate without electrical power.[56]

## Inlet Development

The first JT11D-20 engines had permanently cambered guide vanes to give the best high-Mach-number performance. This design, however, suffered from less airflow capacity and less thrust during transonic flight. To achieve the maximum airflow at both transonic flight and high-Mach-number flight, the P&W engineers developed a two-position, variable-camber inlet guide vane. They ran tests on several "flap" configurations to determine the best subsonic airflow, supersonic flutter tolerance, and supersonic cruise efficiency and found that the best flap design was one that provided several degrees of pre-swirl at the tip and no swirl at the hub. The new design had a flap whose chord decreased toward its hub. It improved both compressor efficiency and surge margin, and eliminated blade flutter at low corrected speed.[57]

Providing up to 60 percent of the thrust above Mach 3, the inlets on the SR-71 were automatically programmed by the aircraft's Stability Augmentation System (SAS). The authors of JT11D-20 Engine relate how this system contributed both to the creation of a major flight test problem, inlet unstarts, and its solution. An inlet unstart was the movement and expulsion of the shock wave from the engine inlet.

> The most sensational and most confusing problem was inlet unstarts in supersonic flight. These occurred without warning and were seemingly inconsistent. To add to the confusion, the pilots consistently reported the unstart occurring on the wrong side of the airplane. This anomaly was solved rather quickly when Lockheed found that the Stability Augmentation System (SAS) slightly overcompensated for the sudden one-sided drag. This led the pilot to believe that the wrong side had unstarted, and consequently, his corrective action usually resulted in worsening the problem. Oddly enough, the engine did not blow out. It just sat there and overheated because the inlet airflow was so reduced that the engine minimum fuel flow was approximately twice that required. Worst of all, the inlet would not restart until the pilot came down to a much lower altitude and Mach number.[58]

Lou Drendel, in his analysis of the BlackBird entitled *SR-71 BlackBird in Action*, talked to SR-71 pilots and reported their thoughts on the unstarts:

One of the most dramatic occurrences in Mach 3 cruise flight is the expulsion of the supersonic shock wave from the engine inlet. This causes an "unstart", which is similar to a compressor stall. The system has been refined to such a high degree of reliability that unstarts are now a rarity. If an unstart should occur, the SAS would take immediate (within milliseconds) corrective action to counter the adverse yaw, while the inlets and spike were automatically being reprogrammed to recapture the shock wave within the inlet. Nevertheless, an unstart is a violent event, heralded by a series of shuddering bangs and head-snapping yaws. Crews have returned from unstart-punctuated missions with heavy, tinted visors on their helmets cracked from contact with the cockpit walls caused by this snapping yaw. One pilot described an unstart as '...like being in a train wreck!'[59]

Working together, the engineers from Lockheed and P&W finally found three main causes of the engine surge:

Manual trimming of the engine turbine temperature was not sufficiently fast or accurate to maintain the scheduled turbine temperature. If the turbine temperature dropped sufficiently, limits on engine jet area and inlet bleed caused mismatch between the inlet airflow supply and the engine airflow demand that resulted in an unstart.

...(There was) high, inconsistent nacelle leakage at the approximately 40:1 pressure ratio.

...(The) Alpha signal (angle of attack from nose boom) to inlet control (was) subject to G-loading.[60]

Lockheed and P&W incorporated five improvements to the SR-71 and its engine. They first improved the sealing of the inlet and bypass doors. Then they installed an auto-trimmer for turbine temperature. They increased the area of the inlet bypass doors and added an aft inlet bypass door which directed inlet air to the ejector. They added a "G" bias on the inlet control and they opened the bleed bypass and cambered the inlet guide vanes at a lower Mach number. Engineers from the two companies also made two changes to minimize the impact of an unstart. They automated the inlet restart procedure to include both inlets regardless of which one unstarted, and they added a solenoid valve to the engine fuel system that diverted fuel from the main burner if the exhaust gas temperature reading reached a level that indicated an unstart. This valve, called a de-richment valve, prevented turbine over-temperature during an unstart.

The foregoing seven items essentially eliminated inlet unstart as a problem. An additional benefit was also realized by the ability to use the aft inlet bypass door in normal flight instead of dumping all inlet bypass air overboard. This air becomes heated as it passes over the engine to the ejector and produces thrust instead of going overboard and creating drag. Better sealing of the nacelle also reduced drag.[61]

## JT11D-20 Cycle Selection

In selecting the optimum cycle for the JT11D-20 engine, P&W engineers had to attack several problems caused by high inlet temperatures at high supersonic speeds. The first problem was that a single-spool, fixed-geometry compressor runs out of surge margin. A second problem was that the small difference between high engine inlet temperature and turbine operating temperature limit results in low cycle efficiency, reducing thrust and increasing fuel consumption. A third problem is that compressor blades at high supersonic speeds may be subjected to high stress from the combination of high rotational speed and flutter from stall in the front stages. Finally, the combination of high turbine temperature and high temperature surrounding the engine results in cooling problems for the afterburner ducts. The P&W engine design team came up with a way of either eliminating these problems or reducing their impact; they developed the bleed bypass cycle for the JT11D-20. This cycle ducts a portion of the inlet air from part way through the compressor around the rear compressor stages and turbine, leaving most of the air to go through the core engine.[62]

The primary focus of the P&W engine design team was on how to achieve the increased thrust for the SR-71 necessary for sustained Mach 3 flight. They considered and rejected several approaches. The first approach would be simply to build a larger compressor and engine combination. The drawback and the reason for discarding this approach was that a larger engine is heavier and the extra frontal area of such an engine would result in severe drag penalties. Both of these reduce range or payload.[63] Another approach would be to precool the air entering the compressor by evaporating a liquid injected into the inlet, but this had three disadvantages. First, the liquid consumption of the engine, fuel plus coolant, was high and the takeoff weight of the aircraft would therefore be increased. Second, the front stage compressor blades and vanes would be subjected to the impact of the coolant droplets, eroding the blades. Finally, smoke is often produced as a combustion product. A third option would be to use variable-geometry stator vanes in the compressor, but the thrust increase due to variable stators was considered too limited. And, a fourth approach would be to bypass the entire turbojet and use the afterburner as a ramjet. A turboramjet, however, would have been too large and heavy because it would have had to pass an equal volume of air either through the turbojet or around it. In addition, the combustion efficiency of a turboramjet was low relative to a turbojet. Nevertheless, this fourth approach was partly used in the J58, with the adoption of the bleed bypass cycle.

## Compressor Design

Engines are designed to achieve a point of maximum efficiency and to maintain it over a wide range of operating conditions. Thus, the engine must be balanced between airflow conditions at different points in its operating range, usually a high corrected airflow condition that might occur at low speed and a high corrected airflow condition that corresponds to high speed at maximum power. The design point, or maximum efficiency condition of the engine, falls somewhere between the low-speed airflow condition and the high-speed, maximum-power airflow condition. At high speed, the front stages of the compressor cannot swallow all the air that wants to come in, so they choke. At low speeds on the other hand, the front stages want more air than the inlet can provide. This causes the blades to operate at a higher angle of incidence than desirable and they may stall; i.e., the air may separate from the suction surface of the blades. The overall difference between choke and stall incidence is less than 10 degrees for typical compressor airfoils. In a rotating stall, some airfoils reach stall incidence and a sector of the engine's flow path suffers reversed flow. In a more serious, violent type of airflow instability, the air in the entire compressor can begin flowing backwards in what is caused a compressor surge. The degree to which an engine can avoid this disturbance to the airflow is called the "surge margin." During a compressor surge, the entire engine passes the point of stable operation.

To overcome the high-speed/low-speed airflow problem, the P&W design team developed the bleed bypass cycle, adding a bypass door behind the fourth compressor rotor. Opening the door permitted more air to pass through the front stages, unstalling them at low speed. In consequence, the first four stages operated more efficiently and the compressor had more stall margin.[64]

The authors of *JT11D-20 - A Successful Leap Into the Technical Unknown* explain the cycle as follows:

> The bleed bypass cycle ducts air from the compressor middle stages into the afterburner, bypassing the flow restriction that exists in the rear compressor stages during supersonic flight, or subsonic flight at low power, and therefore improving airfoil incidence. This bleed air enters the afterburner at the same static pressure as the main flow and is heated in the afterburner during supersonic flight, so the bleed air produces almost as much thrust per pound of air as the main flow which passes through the rear compressor, burner and turbine...

> The JT11D-20 engine is an afterburning turbojet engine for takeoff and transonic flight, a low bypass ratio augmented turbofan for supersonic acceleration, it approximates a ramjet during high speed supersonic cruise and is a low bypass ratio turbofan during supersonic loiter...[65]

This remarkable engine addressed the mission profile requirements in several very important ways. Opening the bleeds raised the surge line due to more favorable incidence and lowered the operating line due to reduced mass flow through the rear stages, resulting in a 25 percent increase in surge margin during supersonic cruise. The bleed bypass cycle also gave 22 percent more airflow and a 19 percent increase in net thrust.

When drag is considered, which in this case means additive drag, spillage drag, and inlet bleed drag, the net result with the bleed bypass cycle was a dramatic 47 percent installed thrust advantage for the bleed bypass engine over the turbojet. At the installed thrust level required for cruise flight, the bypass bleed engine had a 20 percent advantage in fuel consumption.[66]

## Turbine Design

Looking at convection cooling, film cooling, transpiration cooling, and combinations of these techniques, P&W engineers explored several ways of cooling the turbine blades in the JT11D-20. They decided on convection cooling because, in the words of the authors of JT11D-20:

> Transpiration cooling, while theoretically giving higher degrees of cooling, presents many practical problems. Transpiration cooling requires built-up structures on which prior experience was limited to use in non-rotating parts. The welded or brazed joints in such a built-up structure could not be inspected with sufficient confidence to use this type of construction in turbine blades and assure the required degree of reliability. In addition, with both film and transpiration cooling, the mixing losses of the low-energy cooling air discharged on the airfoil surface into the high-energy main gas stream cause turbine efficiency loss. Burnout, caused by local cooling failure from impact damage or pore plugging, is an additional hazard.[67]

The engineers chose a convection-cooled, one-piece blade with tip discharge of cooling air.

Where previous turbine designs had incorporated tip shrouds to improve efficiency and act as vibration dampers, the JT11D-20 turbine design eliminated them. For this engine, tip shrouds caused too much centrifugal load. The JT11D-20 was the first engine to use root damping to prevent blade vibration.[68]

As W. Stanley Dees of P&W states in *JT11D-20*:

> The design of the JT11D-20 turbine and its blade and vane cooling were proved in the engine development test program. More that 14,000 hours of test operation at turbine inlet temperatures at or above 1,900°F, of which more than 7,300 hours have been at temperatures at or above 2,000°F, were accumulated. A large part of this test operation has been under conditions simulating Mach 3+ flight, which results in high turbine cooling air temperatures. These high cooling air temperatures present a very large obstacle in the development of reliable high temperature turbines, because all high temperature turbine materials exhibit greatly reduced ductility at metal temperatures in the 1,200-1,400°F range. This loss in ductility prevents proper stress distribution and results in premature failures unless special precautions are taken. From the completion of the initial 50-hour endurance test in a high Mach number environment at a turbine inlet temperature of 1,850°F, the turbine inlet temperature has been increased to the 2,000°F level employed for the current service engines.

> In the JT11D-20 development program over 200 configurations of compressor blading, compressor diffuser, burner cans, and transition duct were tested before the required stable (turbine inlet temperature) pattern could be achieved. The use of a burner can with a reasonably high-pressure loss helps to maintain this pattern under conditions of compressor inlet pressure distortion. Flight experience on the JT11D-20 has substantiated the choice of this design.

> In the JT11D-20 turbine development program, the principal problems were in the development of material processing techniques, parts quality control measures, and ductility of the turbine blade roots. It was necessary to develop adequate control of the grain size of the blade and vane castings of the new nickel base and cobalt base alloys in order to obtain consistent material characteristics in the engine parts.[69]

## Afterburner and Ejector Nozzle Development

The P&W engineers understood the key role the afterburner would play in the SR-71's mission. The JT11D-20's afterburner would be used continuously and would have to be extremely efficient. The bleed bypass cycle played an important role here. For subsonic operations all the air entering the afterburner was discharged directly from the turbine. When the bleed by-pass was opened above Mach 2.1, however, the bleed air entered in an annulus surrounding the turbine air discharge.[70] Part of the bleed air mixed with the turbine discharge air and was burned in the afterburner. The remainder passed behind the cooling liner and provided improved cooling at the high supersonic flight speed where the ambient temperature surrounding the afterburner was highest. The nozzle had a continuously variable throat area controlled to maintain constant airflow.

The authors of *JT11D-20: A Successful Leap Into the Technical Unknown* describe the J58's blow-in-door ejector nozzle:

> The term "ejector nozzle" was originally applied to nozzles that were used to induce secondary air into the nacelle for cooling. The secondary air was ejected through a cylindrical shroud. Ejector nozzles can operate in two ways (1) low flight speed pumping with an associated thrust loss compared to a convergent nozzle and (2) high flight speed thrust augmentation. At high flight speeds (high primary pressure ratio) the cylindrical shroud ejector restricts the flow of secondary air and produces thrust augmentation.

> The JT11D-20 ejector nozzle...bears little resemblance to the earlier cylindrical shroud ejectors. It is closer in appearance to a convergent-divergent nozzle. The cylindrical shroud has been replaced by a divergent shroud to improve thrust augmentation, and variable geometry has almost eliminated the low flight speed pumping characteristics of earlier ejectors.

> Originally, the blow-in door ejector nozzle was to be part of the engine. It was subsequently decided jointly by Lockheed and P&W that it would save weight if it was built as part of the airframe structure. This was deemed appropriate particularly as the main wing spar structure had to go around the throat of the ejector. P&W, however, would still be responsible for the ejector nozzle performance in conjunction with the engine's primary nozzle. In addition, we would perform all of the isolated wind tunnel testing. In exchange, P&W would develop the remote gearbox because Lockheed's gearbox vendor had no experience with gear materials or bearings or seals that would withstand the temperatures required. As a matter of fact neither did we, but we were already committed to learn.[71]

The first flight of the SR-71 BlackBird took place approximately nine months before P&W finished the Preliminary Flight Rating Test on the JT11. This was three years and four months after the company began work on the engine. The Engine Model Qualification Test was successfully completed in mid-1963.

Some intensive metallurgical development was required for successful continuous operation of the JT11 with a turbine inlet temperature of over 2000°F, with afterburning, and with air entering the compressor at 800°F, as may be seen in the following examples. To achieve the creep strength and bow resistance needed in the first-stage turbine nozzle guide vanes, directionally solidified castings with a new alloy, SM200, were used. This was the first application of this proprietary P&W invention. With no cold air to cool the engine exterior or the afterburner, the material once used for turbine blades (Waspaloy) had to be modified for weldability and fatigue strength so that it could be used for the main structural case and the afterburner shell. Afterburner fuel lines in a 1,500(F environment would be thermally shocked by fuel introduction, requiring particular attention to the problem of differential thermal expansion at mechanically assembled joints. A new brazing alloy (Ni-Au) was used for fabrication. For the turbine, precision-cast convection-cooled blades were used for the first time in a P&W engine. The blades were made of a new alloy, IN100, which had a consistent and predictable strength at high temperature. Waspaloy processing was also modified to permit forging of turbine discs from this intractable material.

As with most aircraft engine development programs, some problems cropped up in the aircraft/engine flight test program, which is the reason such programs exist. One such problem was "throttle creep."

The phenomenon was when engine power was set to that required for landing, engine power would sometimes increase and other times decrease. The pilot could reset the desired power but when he released the throttle it would move again. The cause was found to be due to the torque required to move the fuel control power lever. This change in torque could only be "felt" when the engine was operating without a standard throttle cable setup. P&W safety rules prevented anyone being near the engine when it was operating above idle, so the solution was to have the leader of the control group join the flight test group, on the west coast, to "feel" the problem. The "creepy" throttle was stabilized by incorporating an anti-torque device to hold torque change to no more than 5 in-pound/degree of movement.[72]

Other problems, such as the "unstart" problem, surfaced during flight testing but were handled by engineers from both Lockheed and P&W working together as a team. The major success of the J58/SR-71 program was probably due to the cohesiveness of the total effort and the willingness of both companies to work together to find solutions to problems.

For over thirty years the elegant, soaring SR-71s in the Air Force inventory represented the ultimate in high-altitude air-breathing propulsion. An SR-71 aircraft flying for NASA has contributed a great deal towards high-altitude and hypersonic flight. Why were these magnificent aircraft retired in 1991? One reason perhaps is that the aircraft and aircraft engine technology represented by the SR-71 and the J58 were superseded by more accurate and less-expensive unmanned reconnaissance satellites. Whatever the reason, the rapier-like SR-71 and its J58 will long remain the favorite combination of many aircraft historians.

## Endnotes

[1] Travers, William R, The General Electric Aircraft Engine Story, Cincinnati, OH: The General Electric Company, 1978, 2.

[2] GE Company Archives File on the J93 Turbojet Engine, Major Events of J93 Program History, 2.

[3] Knaack, Marcelle Size, Encyclopedia of U.S. Air Force Aircraft and Missile Systems, Volume II, Post-World War II Bombers: 1945-1973, Washington, DC: United States Government Printing Office, 1988, 351-396.

[4] Knaack, Post-World War II Bombers, 560.

[5] Ibid.

[6] GE Archives, Major Events of J93, 2.

[7] Knaack, Post-World War II Bombers, 560.

[8] GE Archives, Major Events of J93, 2, and Knaack, Post-World War II Bombers, 561.

[9] GE Archives, Major Events of J93, 2.

[10] Travers, General Electric Aircraft, 1.

[11] Knaack, Post-World War II Bombers, 562.

[12] GE Archives, Major Events of J93, 2.

[13] Ibid, 3.

[14] Travers, General Electric Aircraft, 2-4.

[15] Ibid, 1.

[16] GE Archives, Major Events of J93, 3.

[17] Travers, General Electric Aircraft, 4-5.

[18] GE Company Archives File on the J93 Turbojet Engine, Calendar of Significant Events in the History of the J93 Program, 1.

[19] Ibid.

[20] Ibid.

[21] Ibid.

[22] Ibid and General Electric Archives, Major Events of J93, 3.

[23] Knaack, Post-World War II Bombers, 564.

[24] GE Archives, Calendar, 1.

[25] Ibid and Wagner, Ray, American Combat Planes, Garden City, NY: Doubleday & Company, 1982, 437-438.

[26] GE Archives, Calendar, 1.

[27] Ibid.

[28] Ibid.

[29] Travers, General Electric Aircraft, 4-5.

[30] GE Archives, Calendar, 1 and General Electric Archives, Major Events of J93, 4.

[31] Ibid.

[32] Ibid.

[33] Ibid, 5.

[34] Ibid.

[35] Ibid, 6.

[36] Ibid, 7.

[37] Flight Propulsion Division, the General Electric Company, J93 Development and XB-70 Flight Test Results, Cincinnati, OH: Flight Propulsion Division, General Electric Company, 1966, 6.

[38] Ibid, 8

[39] Ibid, 12.

[40] Ibid, 14.

[41] Travers, General Electric Aircraft, 4.

[42] Flight Propulsion Division, General Electric Company, "YJ93-3 Turbojet," News Release No. FPD-064-366.1.5, Cincinnati, OH: Flight Propulsion Division, The General Electric Company, no date, 1.

[43] GE Company Archives File on the J93 Turbojet Engine, J93 Turbojet Engine Performance Demonstration, 1.

[44] Flight Propulsion Division, GE, J93 Development and XB-70 Flight Test Results, 16.

[45] Ibid.

[46] Ingells, Douglas J., L-1011 Tristar and The Lockheed Story, Fallbrook, CA: Aero Publishers, Inc., 1973, 148.

[47] Bowers, Peter M. and Swanborough, Gordon, United States Military Aircraft Since 1909, Washington, D.C.: Smithsonian Institution Press, 1989, 396 and Drendel, Lou, SR-71 BlackBird in Action, Aircraft Number 55, Carrollton, TX: Squadron/Signal Publications, 1982, 4.

[48] Hallion, Richard P, Designers and Test Pilots, Time-Life's "The Epic of Flight" Series, Alexandria, VA: Time-Life Books, 1983, 156 and 160.

[49] Ingells, L-1011 Tristar, 146.

[50] Bowers, and Swanborough, United States Military Aircraft, 396-397.

[51] Ibid, 397.

[52] Drendel, SR-71 BlackBird in Action, 5.

[53] Bowers and Swanborough, United States Military Aircraft, 397.

[54] Brown, William H., Dees, W. Stanley and Webb, William L. JT11D-20 Engine - A Successful Leap Into the Technical Unknown. Government Engine Business, P&W Group, United Technologies Corporation, no date, 1.

[55] Ibid.

[56] Ibid, 5 and 6.

[57] Ibid, 25.

[58] NAL, AW&ST (March 16, 1992), 110.

[59] Drendel, SR-71, 36, and Hallion, Designers and Test Pilots, 156.

[60] NAL, AW&ST (March 16, 1992), 111.

[61] Ibid, 112.

[62] Ibid, 29.

[63] Brown, Dees, and Webb, JT11D-20 Engine, 25.

[64] Ibid, 21.

[65] Ibid, 27.

[66] Ibid, 29.

[67] Ibid, 65.

[68] Ibid, 71.

[69] Ibid, 71.

[70] Ibid, 73.

[71] Ibid, 77.

[72] Brown, Dees, and Webb, JT11D-20 Engine, 109.

**Navy F-4A Phantom, Powered by
Two General Electric J79 Turbojets**

# Chapter Thirteen

# Variable Compressor Technology

## The J79 and TF34 Engines

High-pressure-ratio engines have posed many design problems, one of the greatest being the design of the compressor. The fundamental problem exists not at the design condition (high speed) but during off-design operation (low speed and acceleration) where excess inlet air tends to disrupt the smooth flow pattern and induce compressor stall. The designer's problem is to regulate airflow when the engine is operating off-design and yet still allow maximum flow at the peak speeds for which the engine is designed. Engine designers know of three practical ways to accomplish this. The first way is to dump excess air overboard by using interstage bleed valves. The second way is to reduce airflow through the front stages by using two rotors that rotate at different speeds—the dual-rotor technique. The third way is to reduce airflow through the front stages at off-design conditions by using variable compressor stators.[1]

This chapter discusses how General Electric dealt with the problem of off-design airflow by the application of variable geometry to the compressor system. Their variable-stator-compressor approach resulted in the J79 turbojet engine, the United States' first Mach 2 engine, and established a key technological breakthrough which permitted the development of supersonic turbojet and turbofan engines. The story of the development of the remarkable J79 turbojet engine and its adaptation to our country's most advanced operational aircraft is a piece of technological history in itself worth telling.

Although General Electric must have started work on the principle of applying variable geometry to compressors at an earlier date, the first official mention of the idea of using variable geometry in the compressor was the March 15, 1951, publication entitled Program of the Compressor Section of the Component Development Division, issued by W.G. Cornell.[2] Cornell says this program was first proposed by D.C. Prince, who filed a patent docket in mid-1951. Gerhard Neumann also filed a similar patent docket in 1951. Additionally, General Electric's R.E. Neitzel issued a technical report on the subject entitled, A Study of the J47-21 Compressor by Means of Stage Calculations, also on March 15, 1951. This report recommended a variable-stator program and advanced reasons for the recommendation.[3] Whatever the source, however, General Electric's Neumann is generally credited with advocating and designing the first application of variable geometry to a compressor design.

On June 15, 1951, Neumann and his preliminary design team were given approval to design a variable-stator compressor. Neumann was authorized to modify a fourteen-stage fixed-stator-blade research compressor into a variable-stator machine with the stator vanes of the first five stages variable. In November, testing of Neumann's preliminary design of the variable-stator compressor began. Three dummy wheels were used, resulting in an eleven-stage compressor, the V511.[4]

In December 1951, General Electric's engine development section began design of the GOL-1590 variable-stator demonstrator engine (Figure 13-1).[5] The project was called the Variable Stator Experimental Engine or VSXE Program.[6] In January 1952 the preliminary design team completed tests on the eleven-stage variable-stator compressor.[7] The tests had demonstrated that the unstable regions, typical for a high-pressure-ratio single-spool compressor, had disappeared in the variable-stator design.[8]

**Figure 13-1. General Electric GOL-1590
Demonstrator Engine**
*(Photo courtesy of GE)*

GE's Edward Woll had produced a series of studies for Division General Manager, C. W. LaPierre, beginning in 1949 for potential bomber propulsion. On April 25, 1952, General Electric issued a series of "Blue Letters" to the Air Force defining three series of dual-rotor engines for potential bomber application. The engines were designated the X24A (30-inch diameter, 9,292 pounds of thrust), the X35 (37-inch diameter, 14,820 pounds of thrust), and the X30 (46 inch diameter, 23,090 of pounds of thrust).[9] However, based on the preliminary success of Neumann's design team and their variable-stator compressor, on July 11, 1952, Woll sent the Air Force additional data on the X24A engine, which could be configured for either dual rotor or variable stators.[10] The X24A (later the J79) was ideal in cycle, weight, and airflow for what became the B-58 Hustler intercontinental bomber. Many at General Electric felt, however, that the design of the X24A was an overreaction to the serious overweight problem of the General Electric XJ53 turbojet.[11]

In May, General Electric completed tests on a fourteen-stage variable-stator version of the research compressor designed by Neumann's preliminary design team.[12] The success of these tests, however, set up an intense battle within General Electric to determine the future of compressor research. Russ Hall and Eugene Stoeckly advocated the dual-rotor concept. Gerhard Neumann and Dr. Chap Walker advocated variable stators. Engineers throughout General Electric lined up on either side of the issue. LaPierre intensified the conflict when he announced that the final decision would be based on a "winner-take-all" design competition, the results of which would be decided at a meeting in October at French Lick, Indiana.[13] On October 31, 1952, after intense discussion, General Electric decided to base their future family of turbojet engines on the variable-stator design of Neumann's preliminary design group.

William R. Travers quotes LaPierre as follows:

> I had a hard time to reconcile the different antagonistic views during debate. There were six task forces, manufacturing, cost, etc., all of which said the variable stator design was about 10% better and could be done, but the groups all recommended the dual rotor. The time came for the decision and I made it. The decision was highly controversial. I really did not have my mind made up prior to French Lick (although some thought so) but it was true that I wanted the variable stator idea to win as I did not want to say "me-too" to our competitors.[14]

Todd, in *History of General Electric J79 Turbojet Engine* states the resultant General Electric position on the question:

Interstage bleed was found least attractive for an engine of the thrust ratings the designers were considering.

The dual-rotor design presented the need for seven to nine bearings, coaxial shafts, and the resultant structural support and hardware necessary to hold them together. It was concluded that the heavy weight of the dual-rotor compressor design opposed the third design objective: reduced weight.

Use of the variable stator achieved the objectives of design speed efficiency and stall-free, low-speed operation and acceleration. It provided an inherent flexibility of adjustment not possible with the dual-rotor system; e.g., variable stator blade angles could easily be manually changed to a different setting by re-positioning or replacing certain external components of the linkage system

It permitted the use of the single-rotor design, requiring only three main bearings. This encouraged the use of lightweight construction throughout and decreased the necessary supporting lubrication hardware. Design of an actuation system for the variable stators utilizing fuel pressure from the fuel control, automatically scheduled as a function of engine speed and compressor inlet temperature, would relieve the pilot of any need to directly control the variable stator mechanism.[15]

While General Electric's Evendale engineers were busy deciding their future course of technological development, the Air Force was making up its mind on the next development program. It gave General Electric an initial Study Contract for the X-24A turbojet, which was officially redesignated by the Air Force on November 7, 1952, as the J79 (the General Electric designation was the MX2118 turbojet)[16] The Air Force requirements (and the subsequent General Electric design objectives) were: (1) efficient performance at Mach 0.9 cruise and at Mach 2 combat speeds; and (2) greater thrust for greater speeds with reduced fuel consumption and engine weight.[17]

The advanced J73 (GOL-1590) was authorized by General Electric as a demonstrator to support the design program for the MX2118 and to provide other supplemental design and test data.[18] The first run of the GOL-1590 test compressor took place in August and gave such outstanding results that the General Electric engineers thought their test instrumentation was faulty. (It was not.)[19] On December 3, 1952, General Electric formed the MX-2118 Project under Perry T. Egbert.[20] They began design of the YJ79-1 turbojet on January 1.[21] Travers writes of the J79 program design objectives:

In selecting the J79 design cycle, the engineers kept three carefully balanced objectives in mind: 1) excellent supersonic performance, 2) outstanding subsonic performance, and 3) lightweight design. As a result of all these considerations, the design pressure ratio selected was slightly greater than 12:1, and the turbine temperature selected was approximately 1700°F.[22]

## Design and Development of the General Electric J79 Turbojet Engine

On September 9, 1953, the Air Force approved contract AF33(600)-9956, Supp 3, for funding J79 development.[23] In October General Electric set up the J79 Project under Neil Burgess.[24]

During the entire period of time from design start to Model Test of the J79, General Electric had an average of 100 design engineers working on the project. At the peak of engineering activity for newer models in early 1956, 150 design engineers were assigned. Travers puts the total manpower assigned to the J79 Project during the 1956 period at 475 people.[25]

The first run of the GOL-1590 demonstrator engine was on December 16, 1953.[26] Bill Gunston relates:

Power was slowly brought up to the maximum; suddenly there was a deafening explosion and the front of the engine virtually disintegrated, the rest screeching to a stop. The cause: a faulty 'dog-bone' link holding the engine to the bed! Evidently the dog-bone, a test equipment part which had been fabricated in a local area shop, had been inadequately welded.[27]

By early February 1954, General Electric had successfully completed six runs on the GOL-1590.[28] June 8, 1954, marked the first run of the General Electric J79-GE-1 (MX-2118) turbojet with variable stators, the debut of the world's first production Mach 2 engine.[29]

The J79-GE-1 (Figure 13-2) was a single-rotor, axial-flow turbojet with seventeen compressor stages, three turbine stages, and a ten-flame tube cannular combustor. It had a maximum Mach capability of 2.4 with a maximum steady capability of Mach 2.0. Based on the result of a fourteen-stage research compressor, the compressor had variable stators and a low inlet-radius ratio along with high inlet airflow. Significantly, the weight of the J79 engine with afterburner was less than that of the basic J47. The J79 afterburner also had the highest augmentation ratio of any afterburner yet developed.[30]

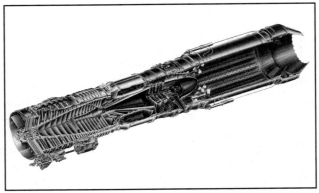

**Figure 13-2. Cutaway of General Electric J79**
*(Illustration courtesy of GE)*

From May 5 to May 6, General Electric began a series of meetings with engineers from Lockheed on development coordination of the J79 turbojet and F-104 jet fighter programs. On June 8, 1954, General Electric began testing of the first J79-GE-1, No. 030-001.[31] In April 1955, General Electric's Jack Parker asked Gerhard Neumann to head the company's Jet Engine Department.

The first flight of the J79 at General Electric/Schenectady was in a retractable pod under a B-45 flying test bed, on May 10, 1955.[32] The first engine run of the J79-GE-3 was also in May.[33] On August 25, 1955, the J79-GE-1 passed the military's 50-hour Preliminary Flight Ratings Test. This engine model did not run a 150-hour Military Qualification Test (MQT).[34]

The Air Force accepted the J79-GE-1 model with the understanding that...

> although the engine still had some imperfections, GE would improve the unsatisfactory parts and prove their reliability on the Preliminary Flight Ratings Test of the J79-GE-3 model. The company was to improve the performance of the J79-GE-1 model as soon as possible.[35]

In May 1956 the first production model of the General Electric J79-GE-1 turbojet was shipped to Convair for the B-58.[36]

The B-58 Hustler began as a 1946 study by Consolidated Vultee Aircraft Corporation (Convair), a contractor interested in delta-wing designs. The study was called the Generalized Bomber Study, or GEBO. The Air Force was looking for a supersonic bomber with low-aspect wings in general and delta wings in particular. The Convair response was a delta-wing design based on the recommendations of Dr. Alexander M. Lippisch, an eminent German scientist. The study got the Air Force's attention and the Air Force invited another contractor, Boeing, to also submit designs in response to a second GEBO study, called GEBO II. The Convair design called for a delta-winged, 100,000-pound bomber; the Boeing design (the XB-55) called for a conventional 200,000-pound bomber.[37] The decision as to which bomber design to build caused great consternation. Marcelle Size Knaack, in her history of Air Force bombers, describes the decision to select the Convair design:

Suggestive of the future B-58's tumultuous history, the two contractors followed totally different development approaches, and drastically opposed concepts emerged within the newly independent Air Force. United States Air Force engineers kept asking for realistic military requirements, but the Air Staff decided that instead of accepting technology as the determining factor against which a mission could be fitted, mission objectives would come first and technology would be developed to satisfy them.

In late 1952 believing it promised the best means of achieving supersonic speeds with a weapon system of minimum size, the Convair design, already altered several times, was selected over that of Boeing. The choice was not unexpected. In a recent study the Rand Corporation had clearly stated that by minimizing size, one reduced the radar reflectivity of a vehicle and, therefore, the probabilities of interception by surface-to-air missiles. Also, the Air Force's latest development directive had reemphasized the importance of minimum size, of high-speed and high-altitude performance and, finally, of the weapon system development technique, an objective with which Convair was familiar.[38]

Convair responded to GEBO II with a proposal to build a long-range supersonic reconnaissance bomber. The project was named Project MX-1626 by the Air Materiel Command. The specifications, under Air Force Letter Contract AF33(038)-21388, called for a 107,000-pound reconnaissance bomber, with a delta configuration and two-stage system (release and retrieval) based on the parasite principle, using the B-36 as the carrier. The parasite-carrier combination did not last very long, being dropped in favor of in-air refueling, and the aircraft's three non-afterburning engines (one was to have been located in the bomb pod and was to be jettisonable) were reduced to two afterburning engines. Subsequently (and inevitably), the gross takeoff weight was increased to 126,000 pounds, and the crew increased from two to three.[39] Knaack describes additional changes in the General Operational Requirements in the MX-1626's design:

> Concurrent with the elimination of flaws from the initial MX-1626 configuration, the Air Force further defined what would be generally expected of the future Supersonic Aircraft Bomber (SAB). United States Air Force planning culminated on February 1, 1952, with the publication of General Operational Requirement (GOR) SAB-51. This highly ambitious document called for a versatile, multi-mission strategic reconnaissance bomber capable of carrying 10,000 pounds of bombs, and of operating in daylight or darkness under "all-weather" conditions. Production should take place within five years. There were many other sophisticated requirements. The aircraft had to be able to cover almost 5,000 miles without refueling (4,000 nautical miles) both ways, with a single outbound in-flight refueling; about half that distance without refueling. It also needed supersonic speed at altitudes of 50,000 feet or more, and high subsonic speeds when flying at low levels. It was to be easy to fly, highly reliable, and should require few personnel for operation and maintenance. Although due to feature the best electronic countermeasures systems, "economy from the standpoint of cost to our national resources" was a must...[40]

This set of requirements was itself modified by a directive (No. 34, published on February 26, 1952) that dropped the low-altitude requirement for the now-redesignated MX-1964.[41] On March 20, 1953, the final design configuration was issued by the Air Force on transonic flight. The fuselage was redesigned to take the "area rule" effect into consideration, with the engines now housed in four staggered nacelles. A 10-degree trailing edge angle was added to the wing, increasing the wing area to 1,542 square feet. The wing's leading edge was also cambered and twisted to reduce drag at liftoff.[42] General Electric engineers informed the Air Force that the J79 engines for the B-58 could not be developed in less than four years (in those days the standard time frame for the development of a new engine was four to five years) from beginning of design to the completion of the 150-hour Military Qualification Test (MQT). The Air Force therefore made the decision to equip interim B-58 aircraft with Pratt and Whitney J57 engines. As events turned out, this proved unnecessary, as the B-58 development itself lagged behind sufficiently for the engine to "catch up" to the aircraft.[43]

The subsequent development of the aircraft, designated the B-58 "Hustler" in December 1952, was marked by controversy. By 1954 the B-58 had undergone four design reconfigurations. General Curtis LeMay of the Strategic Air Command fought the B-58 through every step of the aircraft's development and testing.[44] The Strategic Air Command tried to cancel it in early 1955, but the Air Force had already invested $200 million in the program. On June 2, 1955, after a B-58 review board had discussed the relative merits of keeping the program going or killing it, the Secretary of the Air Force decided to develop thirteen test aircraft. On August 22, 1955, the Air Force decided to put the B-58 into limited production, calling for a wing of the aircraft by mid-1960.[45]

Early in 1955 a slippage in Convair's production schedule of the B-58 prompted the Air Force to ask General Electric to elevate J79-GE-3 engine priority over the J79-GE-1 model and to speed up J79-GE-3 availability to Lockheed for the F-104 by 60 to 90 days.[46] General Electric had begun design of the J79-GE-3 on August 1, 1954.[47] On November 24, 1955, General Electric signed contract AF33(600)28812 with the Air Force, officially initiating the J79-GE-3 development program, although design and development were already well advanced.[48]

By December 1955 General Electric had resolved the difficulties in the J79-GE-1 testing and on December 1, 1955, the J79-GE-3 passed the 50-hour Preliminary Flight Ratings Test. The Air Force's only complaint was that the engines had failed to meet the specific fuel consumption guarantee.[49] On December 8, a Navy XF4D (Figure 13-3) made its first flight powered by the J79-GE-3 at Edwards Air Force Base.[50] General Electric shipped the first J79-GE-3 to Lockheed on December 31.

**Figure 13-3. Douglas F4D**
*(Photo courtesy of U.S. Navy)*

The Air Force was eager to get the F-104 and B-58 operational, which meant getting the J79 in a hurry. General Electric agreed to rush the J79 into production and to rapidly expand production facilities.

On November 11, 1956, the YB-58 Hustler (Figure 13-4), powered by four J79-GE-1 turbojets, made its first flight.[51] Subsequent flight testing revealed serious flaws in the prototype J79-GE-1 engines, which had been installed on the flight test aircraft pending certification of the J79-GE-5 engines.[52] Fuel system malfunctions caused the YB-58's fuel to slosh around when the aircraft accelerated or slowed down, causing aircraft instability. Yawing at supersonic speeds was traced to afterburner problems. Acoustic fatigue and vibration problems nagged the YJ79-GE-1 engines, affecting the aft section of the fuselage. Vibrational fatigue created cracks along rivet lines in the forward fuselage section causing testing restrictions until solved. The cracks appeared after less than 50 hours of flight, so replacing the J79-GE-1 engines with the more powerful J79-GE-5 engines would only worsen the problem because the J79-GE-5 produced sound levels 10 decibels above those of the J79-GE-1. The engines were not the only cause of the delay, as the YB-58 also suffered from brake and tire problems, and the bombing-navigation system was also behind schedule.[53]

**Figure 13-4. Convair B-58 Hustler**
*(Photo courtesy of U.S. Air Force)*

## The J79-GE-2

In January 1956 General Electric began design of the J79-GE-2, the J79-GE-5, and the J79-GE-7 turbojet engine models.[54] This codevelopment of three separate models was General Electric's effort to move the J79 along to accommodate Air Force and Navy aircraft programs.

In July 1955 General Electric's Neil Burgess, R.E. Small, and Jerard Pederson met with North American's Howard Evans. Their discussions led to the proposal of the J79 for the North American A3J Vigilante attack aircraft (Figure 13-5).[55]

**Figure 13-5. North American A3J Vigilante**
*(Photo courtesy of National Air & Space Museum)*

The J79-GE-2 first ran in March 1957 and passed the 50-hour Preliminary Flight Ratings Test (PFRT) in August.[56] It first flew in the A3J Vigilante on August 31, 1958,[57] passed its 150-hour MQT, and was awarded a commercial type certificate in August.[58] General Electric began producing YJ79-GE-2's in January 1958 for the Navy, shipping the pre-test Y version in that same month. Delivery of the first production J79-GE-2 began in October 1958.[59] The J79-GE-2 (and later the J79-GE-8) saw service in the Air Force's F4H1, in addition to the Navy's A3J (later redesignated the RA-5C) Vigilante.[60]

## The J79-GE-3

The Air Force was anxious to get the J79-GE-3 model turbojet, so they accepted the engine for flight testing before it passed its 150-hour MQT. This was normal in engine development; flight-testing can be done after the 50 hour, or YT Test. The J79-GE-3 first flew on February 17, 1956, in a Lockheed F-104 Starfighter (Figure 13-6).[61] Travers explains how the J79 was matched to the F-104:

> The F-104 had been tested with the Curtiss-Wright J65 (British Sapphire), which could power it slightly supersonic. The J79 offered Mach 2 capability for the first time.

> Back at the factory, the J79 team was busy refining the design. Testing at Tullahoma (an Air Force aircraft engine test facility located in Tennessee) indicated that the J79 was short of the design thrust at Mach 2 by 34%. GE was hesitant to tell Lockheed until they could say exactly what could be done to achieve the full Mach 2 thrust. GE related the problem to Lockheed at a management meeting in Washington, and showed how recovery could be made in phases which ultimately included a new turbine and somewhat larger afterburner. Lockheed was disappointed, expecting General Boyd to fly the F-104 in about two weeks, and after the news from GE, they thought the F-104 would be canceled.

> 1At the Washington meeting, GE had insisted on trying to fly to Mach 2, because Mach 1.2 represented a "bump" in the drag curve. Within two weeks, both Lockheed and GE had flown to Mach 2 and up to 60,000 feet! The Tullahoma tests had been incorrect! The J79 engine was only low in Mach 2 thrust by about 12% at that time and did have adequate thrust to power the F-104 to Mach 2.[62]

**Figure 13-6. Lockheed F-104**
*(Photo courtesy U.S. Air Force)*

On August 11, 1956, the J79-GE-3 completed its 150-hour endurance test required by MIL-E-5009A.[63] The first production shipment occurred in October 1957.[64]

## The J79-GE-5

The J79-GE-5 was the engine model selected by the Air Force and Convair for the B-58 Hustler intercontinental bomber. As such it was a very important military development program and the Air Force put a great deal of pressure on General Electric to deliver. The first run of the J79-GE-5 was in November 1956.[65] As with the J79-GE-3 model, the Air Force took delivery of the YJ79-GE-5 in June 1957 even before it passed the required Military Qualification Test, although the model had passed the 50-hour PFRT in April 1957. It passed the MQT in February 1958.[66] The first flight of the J79-GE-5 was in an F-104 Starfighter aircraft, on December 8, 1957.[67] Convair began production deliveries of B-58 Hustlers equipped with J79-GE-5s in August 1960.[68] Secretary of Defense Robert McNamara in December 1965 ordered the phase-out of the B-58 Hustler by the end of June 1970. A total of 116 B-58s were built, all at the Convair Fort Worth plant. Overall, the Air Force spent $1.4 billion on the research, development, testing, and evaluation of the B-58 weapon system.

## The J79-GE-7

The J79-GE-7 turbojet engine model was selected by the Air Force for installation in the F-104C, D, and F aircraft. [69] It first ran in February 1957 and completed its 50-hour PFRT on May 28. The first production model was shipped in October 1957. That month also saw the J79-GE-7 awarded a Commercial Type Certificate. The first flight of the J79-GE-7 was in an F-104A on November 26, 1957,[70] and it passed its 150-hour MQT in February 1958.

## The J79-GE-8

GE began design and development of the J79-GE-8 under Navy contract in April 1959. The engine first ran in December of 1959 and it passed its 150-hour MQT and was awarded a Commercial Type Certificate in July of 1960. Production shipments began in September. The first flight was on December 9, 1960, in a Navy F-4 Phantom (Figure 13-7). The J79-GE-8 also saw service in the Navy A3J Vigilante reconnaissance/attack aircraft.[71]

**Figure 13-7. McDonnell Douglas F-4A Phantom**
*(Photo courtesy of U.S. Air Force)*

## The J79-GE-11

The J79-GE-11 was developed for a growth version of the F-104 and was developed primarily for installation in F-104G aircraft of the Federal Republic of Germany and in the F-104J of Japan. It did not have to pass a PFRT as it was qualified on a "similarity basis" to previous J79 designs and, as an export, it also did not have to pass the MQT. Production engines were first shipped in May 1960.[72]

## The J79-GE-15

GE began design of the J79-GE-15 turbojet engine model in January 1962.[73] This version was an Air Force-contracted development and was the same as the J79-GE-8 turbojet built for the Navy, except for a modification made to the transfer gearbox to accommodate a cartridge-pneumatic starting system, a modification of the inlet gearbox to accommodate the alternator package, and the provision of a 28-volt ignition system.[74] The first engine run of the J79-GE-15 was in March 1962, it passed the 150-hour MQT in October 1962, and the first production shipments were made in February 1963. The first flight was on May 27, 1963, in an Air Force F-4C Phantom.[75]

## Summary of J79 Development

The J79 design and development program was absolutely crucial to the continued success of General Electric as a developer and producer of aircraft gas turbine engines. The high power of the J79 represented the company's dedication to staying competitive with all others in the field. The concurrent development of four different versions meant that General Electric was committed to fulfilling any and all engine production requirements that the military services could and would impose on the company.

The J79 is a good case study of why continuing development is required to fix service problems. It was shortchanged by the Air Force after qualification (by inadequate funds for continued development), and service was terrible. The Air Force finally stepped up funding for four to five years, and the J79 then matured rapidly.

On October 29, 1968, The Air Force accepted the 10,000th J79 turbojet engine for military aircraft. All U.S. military J79s were produced at General Electric's Evendale plant.[76] A total of 17,309 J79's were built, the second largest turbojet engine production program by the company. Aircraft powered by the J79 claimed thirty-four world records.[77] General Electric also developed the LM1500 for marine applications and the CJ805 for civil service with the Convair 880, both derivative versions of the J79.[78] Travers sums up what the J79 program meant to General Electric:

1) The J79 development made the most extensive use of stress, temperature, and pressure measurement devices and techniques ever used by GE up to that time in the design and development of an engine.

2) The J79 benefited from the valuable, timely, and noteworthy contributions by the demonstrator D-1 (or GOL-1590) engine.

3) The J79 made available a vast source of technical fund of data, as a result of the design and development by GE of the many and varied types of turbomachinery.

4) The J79 Project displayed a concentration of the total responsibilities and "tools" needed to accomplish such a program in a single closely integrated organization, personally identified with and dedicated to the success of the program.[79]

## Design and Development of the General Electric TF34 Turbofan Engine

We have seen how General Electric applied the variable-stator technology of the GOL-1590 first to the J79 turbojet and then to the T58 turboshaft. Another important application was to turbofan technology, in particular the General Electric TF39 and TF34 turbofan engines. The second part of this chapter will discuss the TF34 turbofan engine.

For two years, covering the period from 1966 to early 1967, General Electric engineers at the Aircraft Systems Analysis Unit at Lynn, Massachusetts had been conducting detailed mission systems studies. They consequently knew of an upcoming Navy competition for a new high-performance engine in the 9,000-pound-thrust class. The competition would have two distinct phases. The first phase would be a small competition to define the new engine, perform some initial component tests, and conduct some preliminary studies of aircraft applications for the new engine. The second phase would be the competition for the actual engine design and development program itself.

The Navy was looking for a high-thrust turbofan with especially good durability to incorporate into a carrier-based hunter-killer antisubmarine and marine patrol aircraft. Naval Air Systems Command studies from 1963 to 1965 indicated that a fixed-wing aircraft with a high bypass turbofan engine would be the best choice to succeed the current Grumman S-2E Tracker Antisubmarine Warfare aircraft (Figure 13-8).[80] The Navy mission profile called for a long flight over water; hence, good specific fuel consumption and durability were key requirements.[81]

**Figure 13-8. Grumman S-2E Tracker**
*(Photo courtesy of U.S. Navy)*

GE decided to propose the T64 gas generator with a high-bypass front fan, basically a scaled-down TF39 fan with a bypass ratio of 6:1 compared with 8:1 in the TF39 (see chapter 16 for the TF39 engine development story). They also made several minor changes in the fan to increase its ruggedness and maintainability.[82]

The TF34 engine was selected, as with all modern aircraft engine applications, on the basis of overall aircraft performance rather than isolated engine performance—the desired aircraft performance was defined, thereby challenging General Electric to design the best possible engine to meet the takeoff, climb, cruise, search, and loiter phases of a variety of missions. A prime Navy requirement was high reliability at the inception of engine service. To achieve this goal, the Navy considered only proven technologies and low-risk developments. Two General Electric engineers, P. Neiderer and R.E. Houlihan, described the General Electric methodology in a Society of Automotive Engineers paper in 1969:

> Repeated studies were conducted investigating the missions and their phases, such as catapult launch, climb, cruise and search, and wave-off to define the size and performance to best satisfy the application. Catapult launch and wave-off sized the engine. These sizing characteristics were in turn a function of the assumptions made concerning launch and arresting gear type and capability, aircraft aerodynamics and related requirements (ambient conditions, rate of climb, wind-over-deck, etc.) which had to be satisfied. The engine size obtained was then used in the missions to investigate the effect on overall mission capability of different climb path speed schedules, cruise and search altitudes and speeds and degree of detail used in the calculations themselves, (average values vs. successive small increments, etc.). This total effort enabled the company to respond to the official set of Propulsion System Requirements with speed and confidence.[83]

In a special ASW Weapons Specification, the Navy provided five missions which were used to demonstrate the capabilities of the selected engine cycle and to provide a basis for competitive engine evaluations.[84] General Electric won the preliminary design competition in January 1967.[85]

The second phase of the competition was more rigorous. If the General Electric proposal wasn't satisfactory, the Navy could reopen the first phase to one of General Electric's competitors, but General Electric won the second phase as well and was awarded a Navy engine development contract in March 1968. The first TF34-GE-2 engine (Figure 13-9) went to test in April 1969. It passed its PFRT in February 1971 and its MQT in August 1972.

The combustor on the TF34 was considered by Michael Yaffee of *Aviation Week and Space Technology* in an article in February 1972, to be the "newest and most unusual part of the engine:"

> Made from Hastelloy X nickel-based alloy, it is an annular combustor with the liner machined from a forging instead of being fabricated from sheet metal. This is the first time GE has used a forged combustor. Initial cost is higher than conventional combustors, but the TF34 combustor is expected to prove more cost-effective because its liner life will be much longer.[86]

Yaffee also provides details of the materials used in the turbine section of the TF34:

> Temperature of the gas entering the two-stage high-pressure turbine of the TF34 can go as high as 2,265°F, but the TF34-GE-2 is designed for a nominal turbine inlet temperature of 2,215°F. Rotors and

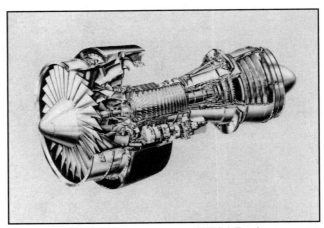

**Figure 13-9. Cutaway of TF34 Engine**
*(Illustration courtesy of GE)*

stators are convection- and film-cooled by compressor discharge air. The high-pressure turbine blades are machined from René 80 nickel-base alloy and are diffusion-coated with aluminum oxide. The first-stage turbine nozzle is fabricated from X-40 cobalt-based alloy, second stage nozzle vanes from René 80, and turbine wheels are made from Astroloy, another nickel-based alloy. Turbine nozzles are segmented — two vanes to a segment — so vanes can be replaced without discarding the entire nozzle.[87]

The TF34 series of turbofans was subjected to a very rigorous series of tests. In a water ingestion test, the TF34 demonstrated the capability of operating at throttle settings up to maximum power without performance loss while ingesting water at a rate of 120 gallons per minute. In the steam ingestion test, it was subjected to steam ingestion at a rate of 5.5 pounds per second. This test demonstrated suitability for steam-catapult launch. In the crosswind operations test, the engine withstood the flow from a portable wind machine placed crosswind to its operation. In the noise measurement test, fifty-seven microphones positioned at various distances and angles around the engine were used to measure noise during operation while fitted with an S-3A inlet. A B-47 flying test bed accumulated over 150 hours of engine operation at altitudes to 45,000 feet, and the engine underwent an additional 150 hours of altitude testing at the Trenton Naval Air Propulsion Test Center.[88] By 1971, the TF34 had completed 4,000 engine testing hours on schedule, as called for in the Navy contract.[89]

The first flight of the TF34-GE-2 model in the Lockheed S-3A Viking (Figure 13-10) was in January 1972, and the engine was cleared for quantity production on September 13, 1972. The first full-systems flight of the S-3A was in August 1973 and the first delivery to the Navy was in February 1974.[90]

**Figure 13-10. Lockheed S-3A Viking**
*(Photo courtesy of National Air & Space Museum)*

## The TF34-GE-100

The TF34-GE-100 (Figure 13-11) was an Air Force-sponsored program to develop a turbofan engine for the Air Force's AX close air support and attack aircraft. It was ultimately installed on the Fairchild Republic A-10 and A-10A Thunderbolt II (Figure 13-12).

Although using basically the same turbofan engine, the Air Force development program differed somewhat in orientation from that of the Navy. The Air Force's emphasis was on design for low cost, whereas this was not the first consideration in the Navy program. Both Fairchild and its AX competitor, Northrop, were designing to a "flyaway cost" goal of $1.4 million, based

**Figure 13-11. General Electric TF34-GE-100**
*(Photo courtesy of U.S. Air Force)*

**Figure 13-12. Fairchild A-10**
*(Photo courtesy of U.S. Air Force)*

on an expected purchase of 600 aircraft. General Electric was paired with Fairchild Republic and the A-10. The TF34 for the A-10 had basically the same technical requirements as the TF34-GE-2 in the S-3A — high thrust, in this case for short field takeoff, and low fuel consumption for long loiter time over the battlefield. The principal task was to reduce the engine cost, permitting the total weapons system to meet the overall flyaway cost goal. This philosophy became formalized as "design-to-cost" in 1971. Stephen J. Chamberlin, who was the general manager of the TF34/T58/T64 Projects Department, gave a presentation on how General Electric applied the concept. His description offers an excellent example of how an aircraft gas turbine manufacturer shifted its design emphasis from one military service to another, using a single engine program to meet both services' needs:

> We approached the trade-off study by investigating not only the technical performance of the engine such as thrust and efficiency, but also other important criteria including weight, subsystem features and the impact of deviating from a qualified design. The large investment already made in the development of the engine dictated that every effort be made to maintain commonality of critical design features.
>
> Trade-off studies involved evaluation of the combined effect of change on both the engine and airframe. It did not take long to realize that sacrifices in engine thrust would force Fairchild to design a more sophisticated airplane — clearly the wrong way to go.
>
> Similarly, early studies revealed that reductions in engine efficiency meant significantly more fuel was required. The increased operational costs made this alternative unattractive from a cost of ownership point of view. We also realized that a substantial departure from the qualified design would increase risk and development cost and erode the advantage of making larger quantities of common parts. As a result of our trade-off studies, we concluded that we should concentrate on maintaining as much commonality between the two engines as possible and trade weight and systems features to meet our cost goals.
>
> This resulted in a program more adequately described as 'modify-to-cost.' We channeled our efforts into reevaluation of the subsystems of the engine, and the mechanical execution of the basic design, made possible by relief in specification weight.[91]

GE combined parts, changed materials, and altered manufacturing processes and tolerances. They strove to maintain a commonality of parts between the Navy and Air Force engines. Starting in 1971 with a commonality of 88 percent, as the three years of the program developed, the commonality improved to 90 percent and added 35 pounds of weight to the engine, but it also substantially reduced the cost of the engine.

Some of the simplifications of the engine system were easily arrived at. When the engineers found that the TF34 had the ability to "swallow" large pieces of ice, they eliminated the anti-icing system in the engine. This in turn allowed them to eliminate valving, ducting, and manifolds worth $4,350 per engine. The complex, fabricated hollow airfoils required for convection heating were replaced by simple, one-piece solid forgings for a significant saving. A critical review of the fuel supply system achieved a combined saving of $3,000 per engine. A simplified gearbox meant an additional $1,200 per engine. As Chamberlin related:

> (When put all together,) ...reevaluation of the engine systems yielded nearly $30,000 savings per engine without reduction of the inherent capability of the A-10 weapon system. All the savings were due to elimination or simplification of parts, which in itself tends to improve the engine reliability and maintainability.[92]

Changes in design, process, and materials also saved an additional $10,000 per engine again with no degradation of inherent engine capability, durability, or maintainability.

The TF34-GE-100 program was initiated in September 1970, a development contract was awarded to General Electric in July 1972, and an experimental engine was ready in October 1973. The engine passed a 60-hour PFRT in February 1974, and passed its 300-hour MQT in December 1974. The Air Force configuration of the TF34-GE-100 first flew in the A-10 in May 1972.[93]

Based on the qualified TF34-GE-2 engine with modification to provide fire-resistant fuel lines, fireproof oil-system components, and modified performance ratings, the TF34-GE (AWACS) was developed to be the replacement growth model for the anticipated re-engining of the Boeing E-3A AWACS aircraft, with modifications and qualifications to be done under a Boeing contract. The Air Force, however, later decided to stay with the Pratt & Whitney TF33 turbofans on the E-3A.[94]

## TF34-GE-400, TF34-GE-400A, and TF34-GE-400B

The TF34-GE-400 series were growth models of the TF34-GE-2. All TF34-GE-2s were subsequently replaced with TF34-GE-400 series engines by 1977. A total of 472 Navy and 1,646 Air Force engines were in service by June 1984.

## Summary

Although the J79 and the TF34 were not the only variable-stator aircraft gas turbine engines produced, they both serve as examples of how the concept of varying the compressor stators produced two outstanding military service engines. The J79 was a large turbojet of outstanding power. The TF34 was a small turbofan of outstanding versatility. Together, they firmly established the principle of variable compressor stators in aircraft gas turbine engine technology. The following chapters will examine how General Electric applied this principle to both very-high-bypass turbofans and ducted turbofan developments.

### Endnotes

[1] Todd, D. M, "History of General Electric J79 Turbojet Engine," News Report from General Electric News Bureau in Schenectady, NY, 2.

[2] Cornell cited in Travers, William, History of General Electric, Unpublished manuscript, 122.

[3] Ibid.

[4] Ibid, 123.

[5] Ibid, 114.

[6] Gunston, Bill, The Encyclopedia of the World's Combat Aircraft: A Technical Directory of Major Warplanes from World War I to the Present Day, New York: Chartwell Books Inc., 1976, 65.

[7] Travers, William, History of General Electric, 123.

[8] Ibid, 124.

[9] Travers, History of General Electric, 126.

[10] Ibid.

[11] Travers, William R, The General Electric Aircraft Engine Story, Cincinnati, OH: The General Electric Company, 1978, 3-9.

[12] Travers, History of General Electric, 124.

[13] Ibid.

[14] Ibid.

[15] Todd, "History of General Electric J79," 2-3.

[16] Travers, History of General Electric, 130b, Gunston, The Encyclopedia, 65, and Eastman, James N. MACH II: A Case Study of the J79 Engine, Tinker Air Force Base, OK: Office of Information, Oklahoma City Air Materiel Area, Tinker Air Force Base, 1961, v.

[17] Todd, "History of General Electric J79," 1.

[18] Travers, History of General Electric, 126.

[19] Gunston, The Encyclopedia of the World's Combat Aircraft, 65, and Eastman, MACH II, v.

[20] Ibid, 127.

[21] Ibid, 130b, General Electric Company Archives File on the J79 turbojet engine, J79 Engine Milestones, and General Electric Company, Design and Development History of the J79 Engine, General Electric Company presentation, dated 1960, 14.

[22] Travers, William, The General Electric Aircraft Engine Story, Cincinnati, OH: The General Electric Company, 1978, 3-9.

[23] Ibid.

[24] Travers, History of General Electric, 128.

[25] Travers, The General Electric Aircraft Engine, 3-9.

[26] Gunston, The Encyclopedia of the World's Combat Aircraft, 65.

[27] Travers, The General Electric Aircraft Engine, 3-5.

[28] Travers, The General Electric Aircraft Engine Story, 3-5.

[29] Travers, History of General Electric, 130b.

[30] Ibid, Gunston, The Encyclopedia of the World's Combat Aircraft, 65, General Electric Company J79 Engine Milestones, and General Electric Company, Design and Development History of the J79 Engine, 14

[31] Ibid, v.

[32] Travers, History of General Electric, 131, General Electric Company, J79 Engine Milestones, General Electric Company, Design and Development, 14, and Eastman, MACH II, v.

[33] GE Company, J79 Engine Milestones.

[34] Ibid, General Electric Company, Design and Development, 14, and Eastman, MACH II, v.

35 Ibid, 13.

36 GE Company, J79 Engine Milestones.

37 Knaack, Marcelle Size, Encyclopedia of U.S. Air Force Aircraft and Missile Systems, Volume II, Post-World War II Bombers: 1945-1973, Washington, DC: United States Government Printing Office, 1988, 351-352 and 356.

38 Ibid, 352.

39 Ibid, 357.

40 Ibid, 358-359.

41 Ibid, 359.

42 Ibid, 367.

43 Ibid.

44 General LeMay was much more interested in the North American B-70 intercontinental bomber, which had it origins in May 1953. Boeing also received a contract in May 1953 to study the potential of a nuclear or chemical-powered bomber, Knaack, Post-World War II Bombers: 1945-1973, 372.

45 Ibid, 375

46 Eastman, MACH II, 14.

47 Ibid, v.

48 Ibid, vi.

49 Ibid, and General Electric Company, History of the J79 Project: 1952-1956. Five Volumes, Evendale, OH: General Electric Company, 1957, 102.

50 Travers, History of General Electric, 130b, General Electric Company. Design and Development, 14, and Eastman, MACH II, vi.

51 The first flight of the B-58, as well as the second, reached an altitude of 30,000 ft., while the maximum speed did not exceed Mach 0.9. Supersonic speeds of Mach 1.6 and Mach 1.35, at altitudes of 35,000 ft., were first reached in a third flight on December 4. Eastman, MACH II, vi, and Knaack, Post-World War II Bombers: 1945-1973, 376.

52 Knaack, Post-World War II Bombers: 1945-1973, 378.

53 Ibid, 379.

54 GE Company, J79 Engine Milestones, 1.

55 Ibid, 161.

56 Ibid.

57 Travers, History of General Electric, 130b.

58 GE Company J79 Engine Milestones, 1.

59 Travers, History of General Electric, 130b, and General Electric Company J79 Engine Milestones, 1.

60 GE Company Archives File on the J79 turbojet engine, The General Electric J79 Turbojet Performance and Specifications, 1.

61 Eastman, MACH II, vi.

62 Travers, The General Electric Aircraft Engine Story, 3-12.

63 Eastman, MACH II, vi, Travers, History of General Electric, 130b, General Electric Company, J79 Engine Milestones, 1, and General Electric Company. Design and Development History of the J79 Engine, 14.

64 GE Company J79 Engine Milestones, 1.

65 Ibid.

66 Ibid.

67 Ibid and Eastman, MACH II, viii.

68 Knaack, Post-World War II Bombers: 1945-1973, 385.

69 Ibid.

70 Travers, History of General Electric, 130b, and General Electric Company, J79 Engine Milestones, 1.

71 Travers, History of General Electric, 130b, and General Electric Company, J79 Engine Milestones, 1.

72 Ibid.

73 GE Company, J79 Engine Milestones, 1.

74 Air Force Propulsion Characteristics Summary, J93-GE Turbojet, 261.

75 GE Company J79 Engine Milestones, 1.

76 Falk, Eric and Stepp, Ernie, "GE Manufactures 10,000th J79 for U.S. Military Aircraft," News Report from General Electric Aircraft Engine Group, dated October 29, 1968, 1.

77 GE Company, The General Electric J79 Turbojet Performance and Specifications and General Electric Company, J79 Achievements History. Product Information Report, Evendale: Flight Propulsion Division, Large Jet Engine Department, June 1964.

78 Gunston, The Encyclopedia of the World's Combat Aircraft, 66.

79 Travers, The General Electric Aircraft Engine, 3-10.

80 Houlihan, R.E. and P. Niederer, "Design Considerations of the TF34-GE-2 High Bypass Turbofan Engine," SAE Paper No. 690688, given before the Society of Automotive Engineers National Aeronautic and Space Engineering and Manufacturing Meeting in Los Angeles, California, October 6-10, 1969, 1.

81 Angelucci, Enzo, Rand McNally Encyclopedia of Military Aircraft: 1914-1980. New York: Military Press, 1980, 463. [92]

82 Yaffee, Michael L, "Earlier Programs Spawned TF34," AW&ST February 5, 1972, 3.

83 Houlihan and Niederer, "Design Considerations," 4.

84 Ibid.

85 GE Company Flight Propulsion Division Management Communication Letter dated January 27, 1967, subject: "Lenherr Announces Development Contract," 1.

86 Yaffee, "Earlier Programs Spawned TF34," 3.

87 Ibid, 4.

88 GE Company Archives File on the TF34 turbofan engine, TF34 High Bypass Turbofan, 3.

[89] GE Company Aircraft Engine Group, "GE TF34 Turbofan Reaches Major Contractual Milestone," News Release No. AEG-171-4, 1.

[90] GE Company TF34 High Bypass Turbofan, 1, General Electric Company Aircraft Engine Group, TF34 Turbofan for the S-3A and A-10, Cincinnati, OH: Aircraft Engine Group, General Electric Company, no date, 4, and Naval Air Systems Command Public Affairs Office, "GE TF34 Engine for Lockheed S-3A Is Qualified by Navy," News Release dated 13 September 1972, 1.

[91] Chamberlin, Stephen J, "Designed-To-Cost...Lessons Learned," Presentation on the TF34 high bypass turbofan, no date, 4-5.

[92] Ibid, 7.

[93] Bowers, Peter M. and Swanborough, Gordon, United States Military Aircraft Since 1909, Washington, D.C.: Smithsonian Institution Press, 1989, 321.

[94] Ibid.

**Air Force F-5 Freedom Fighter, Powered by
Two General Electric J85 Turbojets**

# Chapter Fourteen

# The High Thrust-To-Weight Turbojet

## The General Electric J85

Although the technological advances in aircraft gas turbine engines have typically been driven by military requirements, there have also been occasions when a need in the commercial marketplace has coincided with a military requirement. When this happens, the engine developer must hope that the military engine will also produce a readily marketable commercial engine. Ideally, the government-sponsored research will result in multiple uses on the government side as well. Call it sound planning for the future or call it serendipity—sometimes in the aircraft engine business things just fall into place. The General Electric J85 was just such an engine. The J85's claim to fame is that it has the highest thrust-to-weight ratio of any U.S. engine ever built. Although built with no specific application in mind, the engine is also significant in that it came to power both unmanned and manned aircraft and, at the same time, served to fill a commercial need for an American engine in its thrust class. A truly remarkable engine, the J85 owes its origination and success to two men, Jack Parker and Edward Woll.

GE corporate management decided in October 1953 to reorganize the company's aircraft gas turbine projects. While "big engine" development was centralized at Evendale, Ohio, Jack Parker was directed in 1953 to organize a Small Aircraft Engine Department in Lynn, Massachusetts. Anticipating additional marketing opportunities for engines for small trainer and utility aircraft, Ed Woll, a member of the T58 design team (builders of GE's first small turboshaft engine), began studies in 1954 for small turbojets.[1]

Small turbojets, turbofans, and turboshafts need a high thrust-to-weight ratio. The British had already begun to design and build engines with a thrust-to-weight ratio of 6:1 in 1954. Parker and Woll felt GE could at least match anything the British were building and could probably go one better. Their staff concurred and in November 1954 Woll proposed to the Air Force a range of small turbojets of 10:1 thrust-to-weight ratio, with pressure ratios of 5, 7, and 12.[2] The initial engine layouts were done by Louis Lechthaler under Woll's supervision. Woll later became engineering manager of all small aircraft engine production at Lynn, managing the T58, T64, and J85 programs. The conception of GE's most powerful small engine is related in GE's *Eight Decades of Progress*:

> As it turned out, the Air Force was looking for a small turbojet for a new missile it was studying, the McDonnell GAM-72 Green Quail decoy to be used with the B-52 bomber. The "little" jet engine was the answer. An Air Force contract for $3.5 million for the 7-to-1 pressure ratio proposal was awarded to General Electric. The J85 engine became General Electric's second small engine in late 1954.
>
> The challenges of translating the technology of "large" gas turbines into an engine of the size of the J85 were to prove significant. The Air Force had selected the "middle" engine — a conservative choice — and the Lynn engineering team spent several years attempting to make the new engine achieve its performance rating, including making substantial compressor and turbine section changes.[3]

On November 4, 1954, GE received a design contract for a new missile engine, with a 10:1 thrust-to-weight ratio, 2,500 pounds of thrust, and a pressure ratio of 7:1. GE initially designated the program the MX-2273 Project.[4] This engine, designated the X104 by the Air Force, incorporated a six-stage compressor, a full annular combustor, a two-stage uncooled turbine, and two main rotor bearings. The compressor was cantilevered for the first four stages, and both turbine stages were overhung to the rear. Although submitted to the Air Force, this design was never constructed and tested.[5]

GE began the J85 project in December 1954 with the J85-GE-1 engine design. From 1954 to 1957 Joe Buechel was project manager, Sherman Crites was engine design manager, and Sherman Rosenthal was in charge of thermodynamic cycle design. Frank Lenherr was in charge of compressor design and Art Kohn was responsible for turbine design. The J85 compressor was based on a five-stage NASA experimental design. In February 1955 GE/Lynn began engine design and component development. The first component tests were in November. William Travers, in The GE Aircraft Engine Story, describes the first iterations of the engine:

> The J85 engine was originally designed with a short six-stage axial flow compressor. For light weight, the rotor was cantilevered, requiring no outward bearing. The first engine went to test eleven months after receipt of the contract, but would not self-sustain in operation. The original J85 compressor was a NASA five-stage design extended to 7:1 pressure ratio, so there were problems of matching air flow in the stage. Also the initial turbine was a little too small.
>
> At first the engine would not run. The pressure ratio and the air flow were both too low at design speed. At the time, the competitive engine, the Fairchild J83, would not work either. When General Electric finally succeeded with the more advanced engine, the Air Force stopped the other program. In May, 1956, the engine fired up and ran successfully for the first time. The J85 program finally got started when the engine could operate. The compressor had been redesigned to a seven-stage cantilevered rotor...[6]

This new configuration was the first pre-production configuration of the J85 (Figure 14-1), the YJ85-GE-1. It had a pressure ratio of 6:1, an airflow of 42.5 pounds per second, a turbine inlet temperature of 1,510°F, and a maximum thrust of 2,450 pounds at 16,500 rpm. The J85-GE-3 was configured similarly, but had a maximum thrust of 2,250 pounds at 16,050 rpm. The YJ85-GE-1 model was the man-rated version and the J85-GE-3 was the missile version.[7]

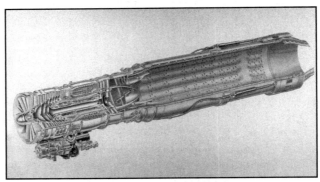

**Figure 14-1. Cutaway of J85 Engine**
*(Illustration courtesy of GE)*

The J85 development program was an example of GE's project/function matrixing, wherein each separate project was supported by division-wide functional organizations such as engineering and manufacturing. It is not readily known whether or not sufficient component testing was done on the J85's compressor. The Air Force, at any rate, felt that "engine stability/performance should be established with early component tests..." and that the GE "development program appears to have resorted to component tests after engine running did not yield progress at a fast enough rate."[8]

The YJ85-GE-1 engine first ran at GE/Lynn in January 1956, although as Travers states it would not self-sustain. In May the J85-GE-3 first ran self-sustaining. In June of that year GE received its first application contract for the J85-GE-3 model for the GAM-72 decoy missile. They also began design and development of piloted engine applications for both dry and afterburning models such as the YJ85-GE-5 (Figure 14-2). Former U.S. Air Force propulsion engineer

Marvin Schmidt, in *A Compendium of Quick Look Lessons Learned; Case Studies of Key Tur-bine Engine Programs*, has this to say about the seven-stage compressor models of the J85:

> The early seven-stage engine had vibration, performance and stall/surge problems. In November '56, General Electric had recorded 184 hours of full scale engine testing on the J85. The engine had reached 1,710 pounds of thrust at maximum engine speed. This represented 87% of the design thrust, a 22% shortfall. On December 11, 1956, the XJ85 was damaged, apparently by the surge of the engine which debladed the compressor. The 22% shortfall in thrust is thought (by the author) to be too great to attribute to efficiency discrepancies, particularly since the turbine was uncooled. If one assumes the various efficiencies were as-designed, the thrust discrepancy would be due to the compressor not pumping the desired airflow. This implies a 22% design shortfall in airflow. This is believed to be too high a value to have missed. The true answer is likely to have been a combination of missed efficiencies and airflow. Suffice it to say that the seven-stage compressor never performed to expectations in perfor-mance, stall margin, or durability. It was abandoned early and an eight-stage/three-bearing compressor was decided upon in July 1957.[9]

**Figure 14-2. J85-GE-5 Engine**
*(Photo courtesy of GE)*

In 1957 Harold T. Hokanson became project manager for the J85. The compressor for the engine was still giving the team trouble, as Travers reports:

> Very early, it was found that compressor blades, made by the large forging facility in Lynn, were not as accurate as necessary. The engineers took the compressor blades from a completed engine and gave them to die-makers to make the leading edge line an airfoil. Then, the engineers put the blades back in the engine and it "ran like a top." At the Ludlow Plant in Vermont the "pinch-and-roll" process was used to make these tiny blades with accuracy.
>
> By the summer of 1957, engineers realized that the seven-stage compressor was not going to per-form well. Based on engine application limitations and the results of a comprehensive design audit, a decision was made to switch to an eight-stage compressor, and by September 1957, the eight-stage re-design was well along, with hardware nearing test.[10]

Announced in July 1957, the new eight-stage compressor was designed to increase stall margin. That month also saw the first deliveries of the seven-stage J85-GE-3 engine model. The eight-stage compressor with three bearings had several variants and was to become the standard for the J85 until the design of the nine-stage J85-GE-21. It had variable inlet guide vanes and controlled interstage bleed. The J85-GE-4 delivered a pressure ratio of 6.8 at sea level static and an exhaust gas temperature of 1,350°F at a maximum of 16,700 rpm. The J85-GE-4 developed 2,950 pounds of thrust, had an airflow of 43.6 pounds per second, and weighed 415 pounds, for a thrust-to-weight ratio of 7.1:1. This engine was used in the T-2 "Buckeye" trainer.[11]

The J85 system was the first GE engine to have a center-bearing sump to relieve swings in axial thrust. The compressor showed the first use of the "pin-type" blade fastener, and used high stage loading technology from the NASA five-stage experimental compressor. The compressor also featured the first compressor dump diffuser and was the first engine to use bleed air for starting. And, as described above, the compressor blades were "pinch-rolled."

The J85's combustor system was an annular design based on the T58, with swirl cups to reduce smoke. At the time, it was the world's shortest combustor with the highest space rate (a combustor loading parameter—a function of heat release rate, pressure and combustor volume). The J85's two-stage turbine was also based on T58 technology.

By the end of January 1958, the J85 program had 2,000 factory, field, and flight hours under its belt. The J85-7 with its eight-stage compressor had completed its 15-hour qualification tests. The J85-GE-3 engine completed its 15-hour qualification tests in March, and deliveries of production J85-GE-3s began later that month.

August saw the J85-GE-3 pass a 50-hour PFRT and the man-rated YJ85-GE-1 (for the T-38) complete its 50-hour Preliminary Flight Test. The J85-GE-3 engine first flew in the GAM-72 in September 1958 (about five years after the engine's conception), although not without its share of development problems:

> The engine was particularly stall-prone. Fred MacFee, by then assigned to the J85 project, and his team determined that an engine start problem when the GAM-72 was dropped from the bomb bay of the B-52 was caused by the air currents within the bay of the giant bomber. The aircraft's air stream was turning the engine's compressor rotor in the reverse direction and the energy needed for starting was being used to stop the reverse rotation. The problem was soon solved and the GAM-72s performed as promised.[12]

In November 1958 the J85-GE-3 model completed its 15-hour Military Qualification Test (MQT) and the engine also received its FAA Certification.

The J85 was originally designed to be a "dry" or nonafterburning engine, but Ed Woll, who had considerable experience with afterburner development, realized that the extra thrust would considerably enhance the little engine. In 1959 Fred MacFee became project manager of the J85 and G.W. "Bill" Lawson was put in charge of afterburner design. The afterburner on the J85 had a burning length one foot shorter than the J79 and used a variable-area exhaust nozzle. This was the J85-GE-5 model, an "up-cycled" variant with after burner for the T-38A trainer. The J85-GE-5 had a pressure ratio of 7:1 and a turbine inlet temperature of 1,670°F, developing a sea level static thrust of 3,850 pounds with afterburner and a maximum "dry" (without afterburner) thrust of 2,860 pounds. It weighed 587 pounds for a thrust-to-weight ratio of 6.6:1.[13]

In California, Northrop Aircraft had begun in 1954 to design a new lightweight aircraft for the European and Asian markets. The company considered a single-engine design called the N-102 Fang powered by a single GE J79 turbojet, but later changed to a safer, more reliable twin-engine design. Northrop asked GE's top management to respond to their design, called the Northrop N-156. GE's engineers at Lynn felt that the J85, with the anticipated Lawson afterburner, could provide up to 40 percent more thrust than a dry J85. GE therefore embarked upon the design of the J85-GE-5 while continuing development of an afterburning model of the J85-GE-1. Northrop and GE proposed the N-156 with J85-GE-5's to the Air Force as a fighter, but there was no immediate requirement for a small combat aircraft. The Air Force did, however, need a small jet trainer to replace the aging T-33 , so the N-156 was reconfigured as the T-38 Talon supersonic trainer (Northrop model N-156T). Northrop redesigned the new configuration based on the use of two afterburning J85-GE-5s.[14]

In May 1958 the Department of Defense wanted a lightweight, low-cost, fighter aircraft to provide to approved nations as military assistance. Northrop had the design in hand and the engines to power it. Therefore, the Air Force signed a contract with Northrop to build an N-156F fighter derivative of the N-156 basic design.

The J85 suffered from continuing problems with the compressor and turbine. GE and the Air Force also continued to have major problems getting the J85-GE-5 to pass its 50-hour PFRT. From October 1958 through January 1959, the J85 suffered from factory engine endurance test failures, components that did not meet performance criteria, and other general problems including altitude performance. The Air Force, exasperated with delays, told GE and Northrop to fly the T-38 with the J85 afterburning engine by April 11, 1959, or lose the development contracts for both the aircraft and engine. GE had to produce or suffer a major defeat. Ed Woll was placed in charge of a task force that pressed to fix the problems.

After a concerted effort by GE and the Air Force, the J85-GE-1, with its seven-stage compressor and its afterburner, completed its PFRT in January 1959.[15] The first flight of the T-38 (Figure 14-3) with the J85-GE-1 engine was on April 10, 1959. Throughout 1960 the engine continued to require improvements in its control schedule, and in general it delivered poor altitude performance.[16]

**Figure 14-3. Northrop T-38 Talon Trainer**
*(Photo courtesy of GE)*

The YJ85-GE-5 completed its PFRT on November 3, 1959, to qualify the engine for flight in the Northrop T-38 Talon trainer, the Northrop N-156F prototype, and the Radioplane Q-4B target drone. Engines were shipped to Northrop on October 31 and to Radioplane in November. The YJ85-GE-5 engine, producing 3,600 pounds of thrust, first flew in the T-38 in November 1959. Production aircraft used the J85-GE-5, which produced 3,850 pounds of thrust.[17]

In July 1960 the J85-GE-5 production engine completed its 150-hour Military Qualification Test (MQT) and received its FAA Type Certificate. The T-38 established an Air Force record in

January 1962 by completing flight testing without a major accident, the first supersonic aircraft to do so.[18] The J85-GE-5A passed both its MQT and FAA Type Certification process in June 1962.[19] The first J85-GE-5 was shipped in December 1960 and the first J85-GE-5A was shipped in December 1962. Both the J85-GE-5 and -5A engines were afterburning models.[20] The first T-38A Talon Trainer was delivered to the Air Force's 3510th Flying Training Wing at Randolph Air Force Base, Texas, on March 17, 1961. Over 1,000 T-38 Talons were built, and for a while the T-38 was the Air Force's showcase aircraft used by the Thunderbird aerobatics team.[21]

## The J85-GE-7 and J85-GE-17

The J85-GE-7 was the first in the J85 series to incorporate the new eight-stage compressor. It completed its PFRT in 1958 and its MQT in 1959. The first production engines were shipped in November 1959, and the first flight of the J85-GE-7 model was in February 1960. The J85-GE-7 and J85-GE-17 models received their certification in February 1960. They were "dry" or nonafterburning engines. GE/Lynn shipped its 1,000th J85 engine in December 1961.[22]

The GAM-72B/J85-7 flight test program at Eglin Air Force Base, Florida, began in July 1962. The final research and development flight of the GAM-72B missile would take place in November of that year.[23]

The J85 program continued to have development problems, in part because the company continued to "stretch" the engine's growth potential. Another problem was that the engine's applications kept getting heavier. This problem, however, is suffered by virtually every new engine program that has been matched to a specific application from the early stage on. The application's mission requirements change, or the flight envelope is expanded, and both result in more weight added to the aircraft. Added weight means the engine must provide more thrust. The J85 engine was under continuous testing at the Arnold Engineering Development Center (AEDC) at Tullahoma, Tennessee. It was the only engine-testing program at Tullahoma to survive the launch of Sputnik and the subsequent Air Force priority reorientation to rockets. The J85 remained in testing when all other aircraft gas turbine engine testing programs were canceled. Its testing and "growing pains" resulted ultimately in an engine that produced almost 70 percent more thrust in its last iteration than it first delivered.

The J85 was the first engine used for the GE lift-fan engine/aircraft development program (Figure 14-4). Brian Rowe was a major contributor to the lift-fan engine program, coming to GE from deHavilland. GE later replaced the J85 engine with the bigger J79.

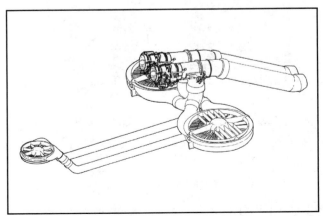

**Figure 14-4. Lift-Fan System**
*(Illustration courtesy of GE)*

## Commercial Variants of the J85: The CJ610 and the CF700

The first two commercial derivatives of the J85 were the CJ610, a commercialized dry J85; and the CF700, a J85 with a fan added for higher thrust. Both engines were meant for civil aviation use in small executive business jets. Travers recounts the origins of the commercial designs:

> Back in 1954, the Small Aircraft Engine Department made a comprehensive military and commercial product plan for the future. It indicated a market for the Napier Eland or Rolls-Royce RB109 type of turboprop engine. Further, this showed a sizable market for the "nonafterburner J85," which was to become the CJ610. But it was a little early, for General Electric was only starting the development of the J85 engine.
>
> The Aero Design and Engineering Company, located in Norman, Oklahoma, had been successful in developing an attractive propeller business aircraft called the Aero Commander. In 1961, General Electric's Dallas, Texas, representative persuaded the company to seriously study the possibility of "dry J85s" to power an all-new business jet aircraft called the Jet Commander. Aero Design and Engineering used a competitor engine in their studies. Then they changed their mind, and on December 6, 1961, General Electric accepted a contract for 100 CJ610 engines from the Vice President and General Manager of the Aero Commander Division of the Rockwell Corporation.[24]

The CJ610 (Figure 14-5) was a single-shaft, axial-flow, non-augmented turbojet engine with an eight-stage compressor, a single annular combustor and a two-stage, axial-flow turbine. It developed between 2,850 and 3,100 pounds of thrust. Two CJ610s also became the power plants for the Learjet, and the CJ610 was chosen to power the German HFB Hansa Jet, a unique forward-swept-wing business jet.

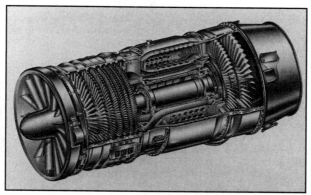

**Figure 14-5. Cutaway of CJ610 Engine**
*(Illustration courtesy of GE)*

The design of the CJ610-1 and CJ610-4 models began in 1959. The first run of the CJ610-1 was in April 1960, it received its FAA Certification in December 1961, and the first production engine was delivered in 1962.[25] In January 1962 it received FAA Production Certification, having previously received Type Certification in December 1961. July 1962 marked the first flight of the Fairchild C-123 with two CJ610-1 engines and the first flight of the Canadair CT-114, powered by the J85/CJ610-1, was in November 1962.[26] The first improved versions of the CJ610 were the CJ610-5 and CJ610-6 models. The FAA certified them in June 1966.[27] The second improved models of the CJ610 series were the CJ610-8 and CJ610-9 models, which were certified by the FAA in January 1968. The CJ610-8 was 45.4 inches long, had a maximum diameter of 17.7 inches, and weighed 411 pounds. In 1967 the CJ610, the CF700, the SST engine, the CJ805 engine, and the new CF6 engine program were all merged into a Commercial Engine Projects operation with Ed Hood as manager.[28]

The CJ610 powered the IAI Westwind 1121 and 1123 aircraft, the American Jet Industries Super Pinto, the Hansa HFB320, the Dassault Falcon 10 demonstrators, and the Gates Learjet 24E/F, 25D/F/G, and 28/29 model aircraft. GE delivered the last CJ610 in 1984, having produced about 2,100 engines.[29]

The CF700 (Figure 14-6) was a two-shaft turbofan version of the CJ610, producing between 4,150 and 4,500 pounds of thrust. It had a single-stage fan, based on the design used in GE's larger CJ805 airline turbofan, mounted aft of the main turbine. The engine was 53.6 inches long, 33.1 inches in diameter at the fan, and weighed 737 pounds. It was designed as an aft-fan for the Dassault Falcon 20C/D/E and F models with a twin jet configuration. Travers recounts how an adroit executive in the GE Small Aircraft Engine Division got the Air Force to help fund a commercial engine, with all parties satisfied:

> Pan American top management wanted a 4,000 pound thrust engine for their new Dassault business jet. General Electric decided that the best approach was to put an aft fan on the production J85 engine. The Fanjet Falcon was born. About the same time, General Electric officials visited Wright Field, and told the Air Force, "We want to build a 4,000 pound thrust engine." Air Force studies resulted in some enthusiasm for the aft fan J85, and it looked ideal for use on a Lunar Landing Training Vehicle proposed by Bell Aero Systems. General Electric engineers had worked closely with Bell Aero Systems in Buffalo, studying the suitability of the CJ700 fan jet for the Lunar Landing Trainer. Thus, the Air Force helped fund the development of the CF700. The vehicle was used to train astronauts for landing on the moon.[30]

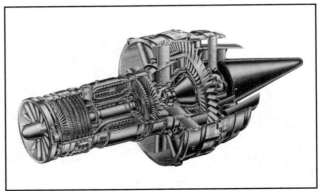

**Figure 14-6. Cutaway of CF700 Engine**
*(Illustration courtesy of GE)*

The fan gave the swift Falcon higher thrust while delivering better fuel efficiency. The engine incorporated numerous improvements from the CJ805-23 model, including the improved aft fan system, and these changes had to be scaled down for the CF700. A special GE/Evendale task force was dispatched to Lynn to assist in the effort, which took three months. The CF700-2B first ran in April 1960. In May 1961 the J85/CF700 completed its official 150-hour test (the J85/CJ610 engine completed its official 150-hour test a month later). The first flight of the CF700 was in July 1964, it received its FAA Certification in July 1964, and the first production engine was delivered in 1965.[31] The FAA certified the first improved version, the CF700-2D, in January 1968. A second improved version, the CF700-2D2, first flew in October 1973 and was certified by the FAA in October 1979. The first production engine was delivered in 1981. The CF700 was also selected by Rockwell to power the Sabre 75 version of their Sabreliner.[32] When production of the CF700 ended in 1982, about 1,200 had been manufactured, of which 1,030 had been built for the Dassault Falcon.

## The J85-GE-13, and the F-5A Freedom Fighter

In May 1962 GE and Northrop got very welcome news when the Department of Defense adopted the N-156F as the "Freedom Fighter," to be supplied to America's allies through the Military Assistance Program (MAP). This meant many more now-redesignated YF-5A aircraft and many more GE-built J85s.

The J85-GE-13, J85-GE-13A, and J85-GE-4 models passed their Military Qualification Tests in September 1963, although the first production shipments began in June 1962. On July 13, 1963, two J85-GE-13s, producing 4,090 pounds of thrust each, powered the first flight of the Northrop YF-5A Freedom Fighter (Figure 14-7). Northrop also produced the F-5 in an F-5B two-seater conversion trainer model, first flown in February 1964. Although the F-5A and F-5B were all intended for the MAP, the first F-5As were flown to the Air Force's 4441st Combat Crew Training Squadron at Williams Air Force Base in Arizona, in September 1964. The 4441st served as the training squadron for foreign buyers of the aircraft.

**Figure 14-7. Northrop F-5 Freedom Fighter**
*(Photo courtesy of U.S. Air Force)*

In 1965, with the large-scale American entry into the Vietnam War, twelve F-5As were "loaned" by the United States to South Vietnam. They were actually sent to South Vietnam to combat-test the aircraft under an operation called Skoshi Tir. These aircraft were designated F-5Cs and were flown by the 4503rd Tactical Fighter Squadron for more than 4,000 combat hours in 3,500-plus sorties. After the operation was over, the twelve aircraft were turned over to the South Vietnamese Air Force, who flew them until the war ended in April 1975.

## The J85-GE-21

In 1962, engineers at GE in Lynn, under the leadership of Ed Woll, began a major growth program for the J85 which was to result in the J85-GE-21. Frank Lenherr, and Art Adamson were the two leaders of the J85-GE-21 growth design program. Brian Rowe, Lee Fischer and Paul Setze led the design of the new model, which was started in early 1963.[33] The design improvements were paid for under an Air Force Component Improvement Program (CIP). Experimental tests of a new and larger compressor began in late 1962. Travers describes the growth of the engine:

> A zero stage (an additional stage on the front of the compressor) was designed for the J85 in early 1962. By November 1962, it was on test. One year later, November 1963, the new larger J85 compressor was operating on an engine. The engineers' goal was to reach 4,700 to 4,800 pounds thrust with the J85. The inlet blading was modified somewhat, and enabled the compressor to handle 50 pounds/second of airflow. A disagreement ensued at General Electric over whether the Company could or should quote 5,000 pounds thrust for this growth engine. Finally, all agreed that it was practical to do so.[34]

The J85-GE-21 (Figure 14-8) was a compact, high- thrust, lightweight, afterburning tur-bojet engine consisting of a nine-stage, lightweight, axial-flow compressor coupled directly to a high-performance, two-stage turbine. It incorporated a through-flow, annular-type combustion system, controlled variable-inlet guide vanes, plus three variable-stator stages and an after-burner with a variable-area exhaust nozzle. The J85-GE-21A designation was assigned to en-gines whose configuration met the requirements of 400-hour periodic inspection intervals.

**Figure 14-8. J85-GE-21 Engine**
*(Photo courtesy of GE)*

The J85-GE-21 first ran in December 1965, producing 5,000 pounds of thrust. The engine completed its PFRT in November 1967 and its first flight was in March 1969. GE's Eight De-cades vividly describes the preparations and that first flight:

> General Electric wanted to flight test the new, higher thrust J85. The Air Force agreed to the pro-posal. An F-5A (the basic F-5) was bailed by the Air Force to the company. Virgil Weaver's group at General Electric's Flight Test Center was again in the airframe modification business. The General Electric team at Edwards Air Force Base manufactured new engine bays for the airplane, extended the wings by about six inches and, in cooperation with Northrop's aerodynamicists, designed entirely new engine inlet ducts for the bailed F-5. Because the J85-GE-21 engine was the radical feature of this one-of-a-kind airplane, the prototype demonstrator was designated the F-5-21.

> John Fritz, the General Electric's chief of flight test, was to take the new "hot" little airplane aloft for the first time. The date scheduled was March 28, 1969. The time was 6 a.m. As the first flight of the advanced prototype airplane approached, the parallels between the J85 and its bigger brother, the J79, became evident. The J79 had first flown nearly fourteen years before at this same site in an airplane modified by General Electric's Flight Test personnel. The J85 and the J79 evidenced typical characteristics of General Electric turbojet design. And each engine was to go on to become a high point program that provided the production base for General Electric's two main aircraft engine facilities, Lynn and Evendale.

> Just as it had almost fourteen years before when Roy Pryor readied the XF4D for the first J79 flight, came the desert dawn on the scheduled F-5-21 flight day — and the airplane was not ready. Despite the frenzied efforts of the Flight Test crew, it was still up on jacks in the hangar that morning. But Weaver and company had committed to March 28. They were determined to achieve it. The crew worked fever-ishly all day and by 3 p.m., John Fritz, in his flight suit, climbed into the compact cockpit, shut the can-opy, and took the F-5-21 for its first high speed taxi run. The expected small problems surfaced and nearly two hours were spent fixing them. Finally, not unlike that day nearly fourteen years before when the J79 had powered an aircraft for the first time, the sun had all but disappeared behind the mountains when Fritz lifted the advanced J85-powered prototype into the desert sky for the first time. The flight lasted 40 minutes and when Fritz landed he signaled the traditional "thumbs up" that meant success. A new phase of J85 development and production had been launched that late March evening in 1969 in the California desert.[35]

In November 1970, Northrop and GE won the International Fighter Aircraft competition with the F-5A-21, powered by two J85-GE-21B turbojets. Single-seat versions of this aircraft were redesignated the F-5E (Figure 14-9) and dual-seat versions were designated F-5Fs. The name "Tiger II" was given the aircraft by the Air Force.

**Figure 14-9. Northrop F-5E**
*(Photo courtesy of U.S. Air Force)*

Early developmental problems with the J85-GE-21 model included fuel-pump failures and afterburner liner support failures. Both problems were eliminated through redesign and were subsequently verified during the 150-hour endurance portion of the Military Qualification Test, completed in February 1972. The J85-GE-21 completed its Military Qualification Test in May 1972. The first production engine was delivered in 1972 and the first flight of the F-5E was made on August 11, 1972. But the problems of the J85-GE-21 were not yet over. Marvin Schmidt, in *A Compendium of Quick Look Lessons Learned Case Studies of Key Turbine Engine Programs*, cites a Department of Defense Procurement Management Review dated February 1976:

> Between February 7 and August 6, 1973, the Dash 21 experienced 56 flameouts. Three types were generally identified, occurring during idle, cross feed fuel operation and combat maneuvers. A combined Air Force/contractor team directed its attention first to the field system and then looked at the engine's rigging and trimming procedures to determine if throttle movement was responsible for inadvertently shutting off the fuel supply. By December 1973 several changes had been devised and incorporated, including a modified pressure and drain valve, adjusted fuel control density setting, a rewired fuel boost pump, and additional inlet and vapor discharge valves.

> The modifications seemed to have resolved the problems. However, between April 8 and May 17, 1974, nine more J85-GE-21 flameouts occurred. A new investigation discovered quality control deficiencies in compressor blades and vane conformance and clearances. The contractor established a program to correct deficiencies, while United States Air Force officials undertook improvements to the fuel control system.[36]

The first flight of the F-5F was made on September 25, 1974.[37]

Production of the F-5E/F came to a close in late 1986, with around 1,500 aircraft produced. The last J85-GE-21 engine was delivered in 1988. In all GE/Lynn manufactured over 16,000 J85s.[38]

The J85-powered F-5 Freedom Fighter became the standard air defense fighter aircraft for over thirty allies of the United States during the 1960s, '70s, and part of the '80s. The engine's long production run funded other GE engine research and development at Lynn, while still producing a healthy profit for the company. Even more important for GE, the J85's engineers at Lynn used their experience gained from the J85's long development to design the next big step in GE's engine family, the YJ101, which became the F404.

What were the lessons learned from development of the J85 series engine? The government learned the value of demonstrating and verifying advanced engine features before development. GE and the government spent three years on the seven-stage compressor/two-bearing configuration of the J85, only to change the configuration to an eight-stage compressor and a three-bearing design.

The Air Force decided that handling characteristics need to be established in an altitude facility at an early stage. This would have addressed the J85's surge margin, performance lapse rates, combustor blow-out, AB blow-out and screech, and fuel control schedule and transfer problems much earlier in the development process.

The Air Force also learned that full pressure and temperature testing in a ground test facility would establish and document stress levels and vibration characteristics for the complete engine (blades, vanes, discs, cases, etc.) over the complete aircraft flight envelope.

In some ways the early J85 iterations fell victim to the early promise of the engine's designers. Higher thrust-to-weight is an ambitious goal and the GE engineers strove to deliver early on. The Air Force recognized the promise inherent in the J85 from the beginning and stayed with the engine, devoting over $110 million to its continuing development over twenty years. The J85 proved its initial promise. The J85 program was also very important because the engine's development spanned the Sputnik era for the Air Force. The promise inherent in the J85's design made the engine a high priority for funding and testing. During that era, when the Air Force was drastically trying to reorient its priorities to missiles and space, the J85 was the only air-breathing engine being tested at the Arnold Engineering Development Center.

## Endnotes

[1] GE Company, Eight Decades of Progress: A Heritage of Aircraft Turbine Technology, Cincinnati, OH: GE Aircraft Engines, 109.

[2] Gunston, Bill, World Encyclopedia of Aero Engines, Second Edition, England: Patrick Stephens Limited, 1989, 67.

[3] GE Company, Eight Decades of Progress, 109.

[4] Travers, William R, The GE Aircraft Engine Story, Cincinnati, OH: The GE Company, 1978, 3-16

[5] Schmidt, Marvin, "J85," from A Compendium of Quick Look Lessons Learned Case Studies of Key Turbine Engine Programs. David Hanson, editor, Report prepared by Universal Technology Corporation for the Turbine Engine Division, Aero Propulsion and Power Directorate, Wright Laboratory, Wright-Patterson AFB, Dayton, OH: Universal Technology Corporation, 1995.

[6] Ibid, 3-17.

[7] Schmidt, "J85," 24.

[8] Ibid, 27.

[9] Ibid, 25.

[10] Ibid.

[11] Schmidt, "J85," 26.

[12] GE Company, Eight Decades of Progress, 109.

[13] Schmidt, "J85," 26.

[14] Bowers, Peter M. and Swanborough, Gordon, United States Military Aircraft Since 1909, Washington, D.C.: Smithsonian Institution Press, 1989, 509, and GE Company, Eight Decades of Progress, 110.

[15] GE Company, J85 Significant Dates, Chart 1, GE Company Archives File on J85, Evendale, OH: GE Company, 1991.

[16] Bowers and Swanborough, United States Military Aircraft Since 1909, 510.

[17] Ibid, 509.

[18] GE Company, J85 Program - 1962 Highlights, GE Company Archives File on J85, Evendale, OH: GE Company, 3.

[19] Ibid, and GE Company Archives File, J85 Significant Dates, Chart 1.

[20] GE Company Archives File, J85 Program - 1962 Highlights, 4.

[21] Bowers and Swanborough, United States Military Aircraft Since 1909, 509, and GE Company, Eight Decades of Progress, 110.

[22] GE Company, J85 Program - 1961 Highlights, GE Company Archives File on J85, Evendale, OH: GE Company, 2., and GE Company Archives File, J85 Significant Dates, Chart 1.

[23] GE Company Archives File, J85 Program - 1962 Highlights, 4.

[24] Travers, The GE Aircraft Engine Story, 5-2.

25 GE Company Archives File, J85 Significant Dates, Chart 1.

26 GE Company Archives File, J85 Program - 1962 Highlights, 4.

27 GE Company Archives File, J85 Significant Dates, Chart 1.

28 GE Company, Eight Decades of Progress, 163.

29 Forecast International, Gas Turbine Forecast: Book One, Reports and Forecasts, Newtown, CT: Forecast International, 1993, Design, Preproduction and Inactive Programs, 6.

30 Travers, The GE Aircraft Engine Story, 5-4.

31 GE Company Archives File, J85 Significant Dates, Chart 1, and GE Company Archives File, J85 Program - 1961 Highlights.

32 GE Company, Eight Decades of Progress, 179.

33 GE Company, Eight Decades of Progress, 174.

34 Travers, The GE Aircraft Engine Story, 3-18.

35 GE Company, Eight Decades of Progress, 174-175.

36 Schmidt, "J85," 27

37 GE Company Archives File, J85 Significant Dates, Chart 1, and Bowers and Swanborough, United States Military Aircraft Since 1909, 510.

38 GE Company Archives File, J85 Significant Dates, Chart 1.

**Air Force F-15 Eagle, Powered
by Two Pratt & Whitney F100 Turbofans**

# Augmented Turbofan Engines

## The TF30, F100, F101, F110, and F404 Engines

A turbofan differs from a turbojet engine in two basic areas. The turbofan's specific fuel consumption is lower and its airflow is higher. The higher airflow results in a lower thrust per pound of airflow and hence in a lower equivalent jet velocity and a higher propulsive efficiency because the ratio of free stream to jet velocity is higher. The higher propulsive efficiency in turn increases the overall efficiency and thus decreases the specific fuel consumption, making the turbofan very attractive for certain applications.

This chapter examines the TF30, F100, F101, F110, and F404 high-speed turbofan engines. These are all fighter aircraft engines; high performance and high efficiency are blended to produce an aircraft gas turbine engine to match the rigorous requirements of America's current front-line fighter aircraft. These turbofan engines were designed to reflect the latest engine technology and were matched to comparable high-technology aircraft. As might be expected, matching advanced-technology engines and advanced-technology aircraft can sometimes cause unexpected challenges to those who must develop the integrated fighter aircraft system.

## Design and Development of the P&W TF30 Turbofan Engine

The Pratt & Whitney JTF10A, or TF30, is an excellent example of an advanced technology engine coming up against "the technology ceiling." This engine not only experienced more than the normal development growing pains (taking a full twelve years to develop, from the first version to the last), but also brought system developers up against the problem of aircraft inlet engine integration.

In 1956 P&W put together and ran a duct-burning turbofan, using the first three compressor stages of a J57 as a fan on a J57 core. This was done to investigate the practicality of this duct-burning augmentation scheme with the advantage of its short engine length for use in fighter aircraft. Satisfactory combustion stability and efficiency were not achieved in the limited testing accomplished. This cold-air combustion problem was ultimately solved ten years later by P&W's Florida Research & Development Center and was part of the P&W duct-burning turbofan entry in the U.S. supersonic transport (SST) engine competition. On June 14, 1960, the Air Force issued SOR 183. It called for an aircraft with four characteristics: good takeoff performance, low-level supersonic dash capability between Mach 0.92 and Mach 1.2, Mach 2.5 flight speed capability at high altitude, and unrefueled range across the Atlantic or Pacific.[1] P&W's response to these requirements became the JT10A (TF30), the first afterburning turbofan engine to see service.

The Air Force requirement coincided with a new Navy requirement to replace its aging F-4H Phantom fighter-bomber with a new Fleet Air Defense Fighter (FADF). The Navy's fighter requirement differed from the Air Force's in that the FADF program called for "a rather simple yet technologically advanced fighter/interceptor that was carrier-compatible and long-legged."[2] The FADF would carry a large, long-range radar and a substantial complement of air-to-air and air-to-surface missiles and have a sea-level speed capability of about Mach 0.90. To the dismay of both services, the Pentagon, in the person of the new Secretary of Defense Robert McNamara, decided to fill both services' requirement with the same aircraft. He instructed the two services on February 14, 1961, to consider a proposed multiservice fighter inevitable.

After several months of indecisive meetings between the Air Force and the Navy on the requirements for the new aircraft, McNamara decided to dictate the specifications himself. As a result of his decision, the new aircraft would be a fighter/ground attack type designed around the original Tactical Air Command SOR 183 requirement. Air Force desires would take precedence over those of the Navy, and the aircraft would favor Air Force specifications and performance criteria. Designated the TFX Program, it was fated to make neither service entirely happy.

In January 1962, Boeing (with General Electric) and General Dynamics/Grumman (with P&W) were selected as finalists in the design competition. Both designs featured variable sweep wings. For takeoff, landing, and subsonic cruise, the aircraft would fly with its wings extended forward, while at high-Mach-number dash, the aircraft's wings would be tucked back next to the fuselage. This was the first time that this feature was offered in a fighter aircraft. P&W's entry in this competition was the JTF10A, or TF30 (Figure 15-1).

**Figure 15-1. Cutaway of TF30 Turbofan**
*(Illustration courtesy of Pratt & Whitney)*

Although the Air Force and Navy evaluators recommended the Boeing design, McNamara and the Department of Defense selected the General Dynamics/Grumman design on November 24, 1962. The development contract between the Department of Defense and General Dynamics/Grumman for $5.4 billion was signed on December 21, 1962. This was, at the time, the largest single aircraft production contract ever awarded.[3] The first development batch was for twenty-three aircraft. The Air Force designation was F-111A (Figure 15-2) and the Navy designation was F-111B. Grumman produced six of the latter for the Navy,[4] who backed out of the joint program in April 1968 to develop their own aircraft under the VFX program.

**Figure 15-2. General Dynamics F-111 Aardvark**
*(Photo courtesy of U.S. Air Force)*

P&W began development of the JTF10A (TF30) in Connecticut, with a company engine order dated April 28, 1959, although the actual design of the TF30 began on April 1 of that year. The JTF10A-20 (TF30-P-1) engine was an axial-flow, dual-compressor, turbofan with a moderately high bypass ratio and a high compression ratio. The basic engine had a three-stage fan, six-stage low compressor, seven-stage high compressor, eight combustion chambers in a cannular arrangement, a single-stage high-pressure turbine, a three-stage low-pressure turbine and a mixed-flow afterburner system equipped with a fully modulating flap-type convergent primary nozzle and a blow-in-door ejector with variable inlet and exhaust areas. The TF30-P-6 and TF30-P-8 models were nonafterburning, while the TF30-P-1, TF30-P-3, TF30-P-7, TF30-P-9, TF30-P-12, TF30-P-12A, TF30-P-100, TF30-P-412, and TF30-P-414A were all afterburning models. Unlike the duct burning turbofan tested in 1956, the JTF10 (TF30) engine burned both fan and turbine exit air in a common duct, hence, a mixed-flow configuration.

The engine was released to the testing engineers on August 31 of 1959 and had its first run on December 10 of that year. The JTF10A underwent concurrent development and testing until March 14, 1961, when the first XJTF10A-1s were shipped for flight test. Their first flight test was on February 19, 1962.[5]

The then-redesignated YTF30-P-1 engine passed its PFRT on June 18, 1964, and was delivered to General Dynamics on July 28. The first flight of the F-111A with the YTF30-P-1 was on December 21, 1964, at Fort Worth, Texas. The initial Air Force plan was for 1,469 aircraft, but this was subsequently reduced to 520.[6]

While the development aircraft used the TF30-P-1 model, subsequent production aircraft used the updated TF30-P-3 model. The TF30-P-3 had three fan stages rotating with six low-pressure compressor stages and seven high-pressure stages, eight flame tubes, and 1 + 3 turbine stages. This engine swallowed 233 pounds per second airflow at a 17:1 pressure ratio, producing 10,750 pounds of thrust without afterburner and 18,500 pounds with afterburner.[7]

The biggest problem encountered by the development team was that of matching the aircraft's engine inlet with the turbofan engines. From the very first flight, the F-111A suffered from compressor stalling. This occurred near the outer edges of the F-111's performance envelope, at high Mach. At Mach 2 the stalling could be initiated by relatively abrupt high-g maneuvering; at Mach 2.35, it would occur without warning and without provocation, often in level flight conditions.

At high Mach, the F-111 suffered from inlet airflow distortion, where the airflow distribution across the face of the engine compression system was not uniform. The subsequent excessive airflow across some sections of the compression system and low airflow across other sections led to pressure pulses, which could blow out the combustion process inside the engine. Physical damage to the engine was common. The matching of the engine inlet to the F-111 airframe proved to be a difficult and expensive problem. The engine inlet configuration as initially designed for the F-111 worked fine at subsonic cruise, but at high altitude and high Mach flight conditions, the flow pattern around the nose, forward fuselage, and wing juncture was very different from that at low altitude at a lower Mach number. At high altitude the airflow pattern tended to have a more variable effect on the boundary layer air. Some separation of the boundary layer would occur and distortion and poor flow spread across the face of the turbofan's sensitive compression system. Soon thereafter the compression system would choke and stall (sometimes permanently).[8]

Air Force engineers, working with General Dynamics, developed a modified intake configuration for the F-111A called the Triple Plow 1. This modification did not completely solve the problem, however, so a further intake refinement called Triple Plow 2 was installed in the F-111D and F-111E.[9] This engine/inlet compatibility problem cost the government and General Dynamics over $100 million, and most F-111 models fly with serious performance restrictions to this day.

The F-111F used the uprated TF30-P-100 turbofan. This engine was rated at 25,100 pounds of thrust although it weighed somewhat less than the TF30-P-3's 4,022 pounds. P&W's model TF30-P-6s and TF30-P-8s powered early Navy A-7s, A-7Bs, and A-7C Corsair II aircraft and produced 11,350 to 13,400 pounds of unaugmented thrust.[10]

After backing off from the TFX program, the Navy started its own program called the VFX. This resulted in the Grumman F-14 Tomcat (Figure 15-3). The F-14 Tomcats also used the TF30 as their first power plant. In his World Encyclopedia of Aircraft Engines, Bill Gunston relates the Navy's experience with the P&W TF30-P-412 turbofan:

> In the F-14A, the P-412, with a different afterburner nozzle, suffered prolonged trouble requiring repeated redesign and various 'fixes' such as armor to contain burst compressors; after twelve years the TF30-P-414A appears to have solved the main problems, but this damaged Pratt & Whitney's reputation with the Navy and future F-14s are General Electric-powered.[11]

**Figure 15-3. Grumman F-14 Tomcat**
*(Photo courtesy of U.S. Navy)*

As described later in this chapter, the Navy entered into a Joint Engine Development Program (JEDP) with the Air Force to develop an engine for both the Air Force's F-15 and the Navy's F-14B. Later withdrawing from this joint program, the Navy, nonetheless stuck with the TF30 for many years before switching to the GE F110, a derivative of the F101DFE (Derivative Fighter Engine).[12]

There is no doubt that P&W's reputation suffered as a result of the TF30's long development problems. There is also no doubt that the company took the lessons learned from the TF30 to heart. The company won the subsequent competition for the F-15/F-16 based in large part on the expertise they gained fighting and overcoming the development and engine/inlet compatibility problems. Series production of the TF30 ended in 1987 with over 3,800 engines built.

## Design and Development of the P&W F100 Turbofan Engine

The next P&W augmented turbofan fighter engine not only produced a lot of headaches for the company, but ultimately resulted in perhaps the most closely contested, hardest-fought aircraft engine competition in history—the Great Aircraft Engine War. This competition between P&W and GE to provide the next generation of fighter aircraft engines has no parallel in U.S. aircraft engine development history. The effects of the war are still being felt and the struggle between these two aircraft engine giants can still engender strong feelings.

It all started with the failure of the Air Force and Navy to work together on the TFX program that resulted in the F-111. The Air Force and the Navy both wanted advanced fighters; the Air Force wanted a new F-X fighter, the Navy called their program the VFX. Both programs were considered crucial to upgrading each service's combat capability. The Air Force decided on the McDonnell Douglas F-15 Eagle. The Navy decided on the F-14 Tomcat. The Pentagon, acquiescing to the purchase of separate aircraft, mandated that the two aircraft development programs use the same engine core. Thus, the Advanced Technology Engine (ATE) program was born in December 1967, with the Air Force and Navy as its parents. It was to be a stormy and brief marriage.

The services embarked upon an Initial Engine Development Program (IEDP) to consider competing engine designs. The Air Force was selected as the supervising service for the Advanced Technology Engine (ATE) program, due to the role of the Aero Propulsion Laboratory in developing their Advanced Turbine Engine Gas Generator (ATEGG) program. Under the ATEGG program, advanced components had been brought together at GE, P&W, and the Allison Division of General Motors to see how effectively these components would work as a system. All three companies had developed portions of the engine capabilities needed for the F-X and VFX programs. The commanders of Air Force Systems Command and Naval Air Systems Command were designated as Source Selection Authorities for the IEDP.

On April 8, 1968, the Air Force sent Requests for Proposals (RFPs) to GE, P&W, and the Allison Division of General Motors. The Air Force would select two of the companies to build two prototype engines (one for the Air Force and one for the Navy). Then each of the two finalists would have eighteen months to prove their technologies. GE and P&W were chosen as the two finalists and entered their engines in the program. P&W won the IEDP on February 17, 1970, when the Air Force selected them to build the engine for the F-15. P&W was also to develop the marine version as the F401 for the Navy.

P&W began to design, develop, and test its JTF-22 engine design as the F100 engine (Figure 15-4) for the Air Force's F-15 and as the F401 for the Navy's F-14B on March 1, 1970. In *The Air Force and the Great Engine War,* author Robert Drewes quotes a history of the F-15 engine program:

> Basically it was felt that General Electric had a better engine structurally and control-wise but a higher risk fan in the stability area. The Pratt & Whitney aircraft engine was assessed to be considerably heavier and lacking a real control system but had a fan/compressor with more potential to meet specifications. Pratt & Whitney also demonstrated a greater understanding of engine/inlet compatibility phenomena.[13]

**Figure 15-4. Cutaway of F100 Turbofan**
*(Illustration courtesy of Pratt & Whitney)*

The F100 was an extremely innovative design incorporating a great deal of new materials technology, including the increased use of titanium to save weight and high-nickel alloys for increased temperatures. The F100 consists of three fan stages, a ten-stage high-pressure spool with three variable stators at the upstream end, an annular combustor, and 2 + 2 turbines with directionally solidified cast turbine blades. Airflow is 228 pounds per second at a 24.8:1 pressure ratio, and dry and augmented thrust ratings are 14,670 and 23,830 pounds respectively.

As development and component testing of the F100 began, problems began to emerge. Some of the technical problems encountered were first-stage fan-blade flutter, fan stator assembly flexing problems, titanium fires, fourth-stage turbine failures, and augmentor rumble.

Fan blades often fluttered, then broke under stresses generated during attempts to increase the engine's thrust. Rotor-to-stator rubbing caused titanium fires (or "ti-fires"). Titanium, when it burns, burns very hot and very fast, and can destroy an engine in seconds. The compressor stator was also unstable and tended to creep forward under stress, touching the titanium rotors and again touching off a ti-fire. This problem wrecked an F100 under test at Tullahoma, Tennessee, on March 14, 1973. P&W tried reinforced shields for the blades, ablative blankets for the blades, compressor stiffening, and fire dams to contain damage. The problem was that each of these fixes added weight to an engine that had to stay very lean to provide the necessary 3,000 pounds of thrust over and above previous generations of engines.

These and other fixes cost time and money, and under the contract with the Air Force and Navy, P&W had very little extra of either. Combined with differences in the testing schedules between the two services (the Air Force schedule being more time-constrained than the Navy's), the added technical difficulties in development boded ill for the F100's future. That future was to be dramatically altered by the decision of the Navy to drop its stake in the Joint Engine Program Office (JEPO).

The Navy began backing away from the joint engine development program in November 1970 and kept backing away until late June 1971. At that point, after spending over $300 million on the F401, the Navy informed the Air Force that it would not purchase the engine for the F-14. That left the Air Force with a substantial problem in continuing the F100 program. It was compelled to renegotiate the engine production contract with P&W under sole source conditions, which resulted in an increase in cost to the F-15/JEPO of $552 million. An already lean schedule and budget grew even leaner, because any renewed attempts by the Air Force or Pratt to get funding to devote to fixes above and beyond this half-billion dollar overrun were bound to be constrained. Without Navy funding to continue the F401, the Air Force dropped it.

Full-scale development of the F100 began in March 1970, and in spite of the development problems and testing problems, the F100-PW-100 was first flown in July 1972. Development costs had in the interim risen from $117.45 million in 1970 to $1 billion in 1975, and the F100 had entered production before being fully developed and tested. The engine entered service in November 1974, and as might be expected, service use of the F100 would produce even more problems.[14] Consequently, the rest of the development of the F100 had to be completed through Component Improvement Programs (CIPs). CIPs are post-production programs funded by the government to improve the components of an engine currently in service.

The F-15 (Figure 15-5) with its two F100 engines was a very "hot" fighter to fly. The power offered by the two F100s produced an aircraft that was highly maneuverable and offered a high rate of acceleration and high rate of climb. These new capabilities meant new air combat tactics, which meant pushing the aircraft's flight envelope. With the new maneuvers, new problems with the F100 engine emerged. One of the most dramatic of these problems was that of compressor stall.

**Figure 15-5. McDonnell Douglas F-15 Eagle**
*(Photo courtesy of U.S. Air Force)*

A stall is a momentary hesitation in engine operation caused by a disturbance in the air-flow through the compressor, which causes an aerodynamic stall in the compressor blades. The stall sometimes comes unstuck. A stagnation stall occurs when the stall in the compressor persists and the pilot must physically restart the engine to recover. The stagnation stall in the F100 occurred most often during operation of the afterburner (76 percent of the time). Some 223 stagnation stalls occurred with the F100 between 1974 and 1977. The engine team at P&W's Government Products Division in Florida felt that the engine was being asked to do too much by the pilots. The Air Force felt that the engine needed improvement. While this improvement process was going forward, the Air Force directed that the pilots try to restrict their operations in that part of the flight envelope where stalls and/or stall stagnations seemed to take place. That meant flying the engine, and not the aircraft, which made for very unhappy pilots. The Air Force became even more concerned when they considered the F100 for the single-engine F-16 Fighting Falcon (the F100-PW-200 model). While a stagnation stall on a two-engine aircraft could be dealt with by flying on one engine while attempting to restart the second, on the F-16 a stagnation stall could very well result in the loss of the engine, the aircraft, and its pilot.

Mechanics were also directed to "trim" or detune the engine (reduce its performance slightly) to provide more safety margin. The increased burden on maintenance crews also hurt the reputation of the engine. Also, the engines could be flown "trimmed" only in peacetime; wartime flying meant engines trimmed at top performance. Getting the stagnation stall problem fixed also meant renewed negotiations with Pratt's management, who felt they had delivered the engine that the original specification asked for, which they had. The Air Force wanted more than the original specification called for, so Pratt's management wanted more money. The problem also resulted in fixes being made while the engine was in manufacturing, so that necessary changes and new parts had to catch up with the engines already in the field.

The stall-stagnation problem was finally controlled by three changes, two having to do with the afterburner. Engine monitoring devices were installed that sensed when a pressure spike-causing stall-stagnation was building up. When that happened, the monitoring device automatically reduced afterburner flow to the minimum necessary, and opened the afterburner nozzle to the maximum possible, decreasing afterburner pressure pulses. A third change, which applied only to the F-16, was to install a proximate splitter that divided the airflow between the engine's bypass duct and the high-pressure compressor. This reduced the potential for a pressure disturbance from the fan duct blowing back into the engine core. These fixes greatly reduced the stall stagnation problem.

A second major problem with "growing" the F100's performance was turbine failures. Unlike a compressor stall-stagnation, which can be restarted, when a turbine fails it usually sheds its blades. Turbine failures, however, were linked directly to compressor stagnation stalls. When the compressor stalled, a lack of airflow caused the turbine inlet temperature to rise. This in turn resulted in very uneven temperature distribution, causing hot spots and some high local stresses on some parts of the turbine blades. This overstressing causes the blades to become brittle, at which point they could break and become projectiles, destroying the engine. And although many of these projectiles could be contained by the engine casing, many of them could not. For example, if even one of these projectiles penetrates a fuel tank, the results can be catastrophic. Part of the fix was to install new thermocouples in the engine to warn of overheat. In addition, the engine casing was strengthened with "belly bands," which wrapped around the engine to further impede broken blades from exiting the engine casing. Also, development of a flexible boroscope, which permitted a mechanic to inspect each section of the engine without removing the engine from the aircraft, greatly aided detection of cracked turbine and compressor blades. Even with the on-site, in-site boroscope inspection, however, the maintenance time required by the engine again increased.

The third major problem with the F100 was overcoming an aircraft gas turbine engine technology hurdle that had never been encountered before. Again, the problem was associated with the power provided by the F100 engine. Every engine is designed with a certain number of thermal cycles in mind. A thermal cycle is accomplished every time that an engine is started, run up to takeoff power, operated through the mission profile (including the use of afterburner), and shut down again. The number of thermal cycles imposed on the engine is determined by a variety of factors including aircraft mission profile, throttle transients, and sorties or flight mode.

With the enhanced power capability of the F100, pilots in the F-15 and F-16 (Figure 15-6) were operating the engine through more thermal cycles and more strenuous thermal cycles than the engine was designed and built to withstand, including rapid full-throttle transient cycles. The pilots were literally rewriting the book on fighter tactics, taking the engine where no engine had previously performed. The stress placed on the engine parts by protracted extremes of heating and cooling meant that parts wore out quicker than anticipated, creating a major maintainability, reliability, and support problem with the engine. Drewes cites the number of full-throttle transients that a typical engine designed for 2,000 hours of operational life would go through as 1,765 cycles; however, the F100 engines were being put through about 10,360 cycles.[15]

> The almost six-fold increase in full-throttle transients, or thermal cycles, stands out as the greatest single difference between the F100 design requirement and actual experience in operational use. Neither the Air Force nor Pratt anticipated this change in tactics and demands on the engine. Perhaps the change could not have been anticipated. Perhaps no one could have fully appreciated the capabilities and new opportunities provided by the F100 engine until fighter pilots could actually get behind the stick of production, not experimental, models and put them through their paces. In any case, as engine breakdowns occurred with increasing frequency, Pratt pointed out the growing gap between design goals and operational usage. Since Pratt had demonstrated through qualification tests that the F100 met the contractually required design specifications, changes to the design, now that the effect of thermal cycles was becoming better understood, would require additional Government funding to increase the scope of the contract.
>
> Although it's very doubtful that the increased volume and rate of accumulating thermal cycles could have been anticipated, the general impact of thermal cycles on engine life should have been known at the time the F100 was being developed. Perhaps it was. An Air Force engineer at Wright-Patterson Air Force Base recalls that when he was assigned to the F100 development program, he quickly noticed the absence of a requirement for achieving any specified structural life objectives or of criteria for measuring fatigue. Having had recent experience with airframe development techniques, he knew that the duty cycle (how the aircraft would be used on a typical mission) was a key factor in determining structural life. For an engine, duty cycle is the same as a thermal cycle. Consequently, the engineer believed it was important to test an engine as an airframe is tested, simulating actual usage.

Moreover, problems with other engines, such as the TF30 and TF41 in operational use at the time of F100 development, had detectable links to stress failures of component parts. Accordingly, the engineer urged the engine be required to achieve duty-cycle standards the same as those imposed on the airframe. Unfortunately for the Air Force, this engineer never succeeded in convincing management to change requirements and now believes some of his superiors may have felt that imposing a duty-cycle requirement would have required increasing engine weight to increase durability. Adding weight would have lowered the thrust-to-weight ratio of the engine and might have disrupted the schedule to meet the IOC.[16]

**Figure 15-6. General Dynamics F-16 Fighting Falcon**
*(Photo courtesy of U.S. Air Force)*

No one could have anticipated this growing gap between operational use and design goals, but it put the F100 program - already in a bad light — in a deeper hole than before. Other engine field problems included fuel pump and engine control system failures and a major problem with spare parts procurement.

The F100 has turned out over time to be an excellent engine. Its reliability and maintainability have improved dramatically. The Air Force has also been very supportive of Pratt's efforts to "grow" the engine to meet the performance of the GE F110, providing approximately $450 million for a very successful F100 Engine Model Derivative Program (EMDP). This program was designed to produce first the Increased Capability Engine (ICE) design and subsequently an Improved Performance Engine (IPE) design for Air Force service. The F100 engine program provided the basis for three derived engines, the PW1115, the PW1120, and the PW1129.

The PW1115 is an unaugmented F100 of about 15,000 pounds of thrust. The PW1120, or F100-PW-220, is an improved variant of the basic F100. It incorporates in its design a new fan and compressor boost stage, an uprated low-pressure turbine, improved augmentor, and dual augmentor ignition, yielding 20,500 pounds of thrust. This engine powered the now-canceled Israeli Lavi jet fighter prototype. The F100-PW-220E engine was an operational upgrade for previous F100s and was designed to provide performance, operability, and durability equal to the F100-PW-220 model to any existing F100.

Designed as the bolt-in replacement for the F100 in the F-15 and F-16 aircraft, the PW1129, or F100-PW-229, is a major growth version of the F100 developing over 29,000 pounds of thrust. Overall pressure ratio is 32:1 with a bypass ratio of 0.4:1. The engine features an improved efficiency core, an increased-airflow fan, a multizone augmentor, and a 2,000-hour gear-type fuel pump. An Air Force F-15E powered by twin F100-PW-229s first flew in April

1989. An F-16 powered by an F100-PW-229 first flew on May 16, 1989. The F100-PW-229 model entered service with the Air Force in the mid-1990s.

Although the stall stagnation problem and other problems of the F100 in the F-15 and the F-16 have been overcome, the pain and anxiety of finding the fixes as well as the problems encountered with Pratt's management caused the Air Force to have second thoughts about the desirability of having only one engine choice for the F-15 and F-16. Enter the General Electric Company with the XJ101/F404 and F101 DFE/F110!

## Design and Development of the GE YJ101/F101 Engine

GE's entry into the advanced technology fighter engine arena began in the late 1960s with two designs, the GE9 and GE1/10 demonstrator engines. These were derivatives from the GE "building block" program and were designed to fulfill the Air Force's requirements for both the Advanced Manned Strategic Aircraft (AMSA), and a new fighter aircraft. The Department of Defense had already decided that both the Air Force and Navy versions of a new fighter would share a common engine core, but with different accessories to meet the differing requirements of each service. Both P&W and GE entered their engines, P&W with the F100 and GE with the F101. As stated earlier, P&W was the winner of the original competition.

The F101 marked a slight shift in GE's philosophy of engine development. Most new military engine starts try to advance the technology to the greatest extent possible, thereby maximizing effort gained from government dollars spent on research and development. GE decided to start their new program with their own money and stress simplicity, reliability, and maintainability. They looked at the P&W F100 engine program and viewed it as too large a technology step to take at that time. The GE design called for a low-bypass engine with about 15,000 pounds of thrust. The GE9 demonstrator engine, developed under an Air Force Systems Command contract, was used as the baseline engine for the new program. GE teamed up with Northrop and that company's YF-17 in the Air Force's Light-Weight Fighter (later Air Combat Fighter) specification.

GE started design development of the XJ101 turbojet in June 1970 and moved to full-scale development in 1971. For the first year GE funded the development with its own money. Then in April 1972 the Air Force provided $20 million to complete development of the engine, flight-qualify the design, and produce six initial engines. The original designation for the engine was the YJ101. GE chose to proceed with a low bypass ratio of about 0.20:1 and an overall pressure ratio of over 20:1, providing 15,000 pounds of thrust. The engine featured a three-stage low-pressure and seven-stage high-pressure compressor section, an annular combustor, and single-stage high- and low-pressure turbines.

GE was also awarded an Air Force contract in April 1972 to develop and produce an augmented turbofan (F101) version of the J101 engine to power the North American Rockwell B-1 strategic bomber. From the F101 engine program stemmed both the F110 and the F101-GE-102 augmented turbofan for the Rockwell B-1B. The F101-GE-102 was a dual-rotor design with a bypass ratio close to 2. The GE design criteria were durability and operability, while maintaining high turbine temperatures for maximum performance and operating efficiency.[17] From its inception the F101 was designed to incorporate technology that would lessen the impact of exhaust emissions and noise and enhance fuel conservation. The engine was also virtually smokeless.

In 1976 GE and the Air Force instituted a continuing engineering development program for the F101-GE-102. The engine went through demonstrator testing from 1977 to 1978. The development program continued until 1981 with the objectives of accelerating engine maturity, extending component life, and reducing engine ownership costs. In June 1977 the Air Force canceled B-1 bomber production, so GE tried to sell the F101 as a replacement engine for the troublesome P&W F100 for the F-15 fighter. According to Air Force Major Tack Nix, the General Electric presenters said:

> Here's what we think are our goals; here's what we think it'll do; we have some data that proves it. We can show you one running in a test cell, and we'll go bang it around and show you that it doesn't have some of the throttle problems you're currently experiencing...

Nix remembered,

> The impression I got in three days in Evendale was that they had something that, perhaps from a durability standpoint, was dramatically different from what we were currently experiencing with the F100. Which meant it was probably worth looking at.[18]

The odds against a further development of the F101 with Air Force or Navy money were long at best. There was no money in fiscal year 1979 to fund an F101X demonstrator and there were good arguments for not spending money on a new engine. There was also reluctance to go through trauma similar to that experienced with the F100 program. A new engine would result in expensive logistical complications for the Air Force, and a new program would cost around $30 million to $40 million a year for a new demonstrator. Also, there was the implied commitment to a bigger "piece of the pie" in the future, if the engine actually entered production. Most Air Force propulsion people thought that at best the F101 would be a useful "card to play" against Pratt to get them to be more cooperative in fixing the F100.[19] Then the Air Force propulsion engineers came up with an idea. The Navy had been granted $41 million in funding by Congress to re-engine their F-14 aircraft, but the Navy, fearing the cost of new engines, declined to spend the money. The Air Force decided that this pool of dollars could be transferred to funding the F101X demonstrator program instead. General Alton D. Slay, then commander of Air Force Systems Command, was a leading advocate of funding the GE engine. The Navy was convinced to cooperate in the funding transfer, and after considerable maneuvering in Congress, the Air Force got the $41 million in fiscal year 1979. Both services signed a Memorandum of Understanding (MOU) in February 1979, entitled the "The Memorandum of Understanding Between the U.S. Air Force and the Navy for Cooperative Aircraft Engine Demonstrations and Development." The $41 million was split, with $33 million going to the Air Force and $8 million to the Navy. At this point the idea was still to maintain the F101 as a standby replacement for the F100. The Air Force was still interested in using the F101 to drive P&W to greater responsiveness on the F100 issues. However, a new directive from Congress was to change the scenario slightly.[20]

The "Joint Conference Report on the Fiscal Year 1979 Appropriation Bill" directed the Air Force and Navy to begin a joint competitive program to develop an alternative engine program for the F-14, the F-16, and other aircraft. In their response the services laid out a three-point strategy aimed at fixing immediate engine problems as well as providing a solid foundation for future engine development.

Under the joint strategy, Pratt continued to receive CIP funds to improve the F100 and TF30 engines (for the F-15 and F-14, respectively). Next, Engine Model Derivative Program (EMDP) funding would also go to Pratt to develop a higher-thrust model of the F100.[21] Engine Model Derivative Program was the designation for any program that would develop derivative models of an engine. EMDP money would also continue to go to GE for the F101 engine development. On March 5, 1979, the Air Force contracted with GE for initial development of an F101-derivative engine. The engine had recently completed preliminary Full Scale Development (FSD) testing, required for starting production of any engine. GE's task was to put the F101-derivative engine in the F-16 and fly it within thirty months. The overall funding split was about 90 percent to GE and 10 percent to P&W.

Skirmishing, politicking, and maneuvering in Congress between GE's and Pratt's advocates continued throughout 1980 with each side trying to gain some lasting advantage over the other. The Air Force tried to stay above the fray, but Pratt repeatedly succeeded in getting the Air Force called to Congress to justify funding an alternative engine program with GE. However, the Air Force could point to the success of the GE Derivative Fighter Engine (DFE, as it was now called) program. The reliability and maintainability of the F101 was better than that of the F100 at that time, and the GE F101 produced 28,000 pounds of thrust whereas the F100 produced 24,400 pounds. In the fiscal 1981 budget the Air Force sought an additional $25 million for the DFE program.

P&W thought that the Air Force was trying to get a higher-thrust engine out of GE as a direct competitor to the F100. Although, the Air Force did want the F100 developed to a higher thrust level, its bugs fixed, and issues of reliability and maintainability resolved, they also wanted the inherent promise of the F101 realized as well. As Drewes states:

> The Air Force was also legitimately concerned over the ownership costs of the F100 as well as the excessive combat-readiness vulnerability from dependence on a single source of supply for the propulsion of front-line fighters.[22]

General Electric got two major breaks when shortly after becoming President, Ronald Reagan restarted the B-1 bomber program. Then the Air Force announced that they were going to re-engine their KC-135 tanker fleet with GE/SNECMA CFM56 commercial turbofan engines.[23] As Drewes points out in his book "The Great Engine Wars," GE got a contract to provide the engines for 100 B-1 bombers, at four engines per plane (plus spares), for a total of 469 F101 engines. This provided important benefits to the F101 DFE program. The core of the bomber and fighter engine was the same as that of the CFM56 high-bypass engine, so depot repair facilities for the bombers and KC-135 tankers could also accommodate the fighter engines at a relatively small cost. The bomber engine production also spread GE's overhead over a larger business base, making the cost of the fighter engine less. This reduced cost in turn meant an easier "sell" to Congress.[24] In addition to the B-1 bomber news, the early flight tests of the F101 in the F-16 from December 1980 to May 1981 were very encouraging. The Air Force solved the problem of how to keep the F101 program going after flight-testing under EMDP by coming up with an EMDP program element called "transition to development."[25] The F101 engine completed a 2000-hour endurance test in June 1981.

## The GE F110 Turbofan Engine

At this point the F100 situation had begun to improve, and the Air Force was funding an additional engine for the future. The Air Force was at a crossroads when, in August 1981, circumstances took a strange turn.

> ...The propulsion program office issued a Request for Information (RFI) to industry to gather on a non-binding and strictly voluntary basis information about prices, product capabilities, schedules, and other pertinent terms and conditions. An RFI sort of says, "We are interested in this product. What might we expect from you, generally, if we were formally to ask for your competitive proposal at a later date?" The General Electric and Pratt replies were exciting; they provided strong support for proceeding with a formal competition. The industry inputs were irresistibly tantalizing. By the end of the year the Air Force, with General Skanze at the forefront, decided to compete. Even if circumstances were to change and make the competition infeasible (for example, if costs escalated unexpectedly), the competition could still be canceled with nothing lost.[26]

From July 1981 to March 1982 a developmental model of what later became the F110, the GE F101 derivative fighter engine, completed a 70-hour test in an F-14. From October 1982 to March 1982 the F110 was also flight tested in the F-16XL-2. GE was awarded a full-scale development contract for the F110 in October 1982. Throughout 1982 the engine companies worked to prepare for a Request For Proposal (RFP) from the Air Force. On December 15, 1982, the companies got a draft RFP.

A draft RFP states the requirements for an industry proposal. If the draft RFP does not differ too much from the final RFP, the companies can get their responses to the final RFP in to the Air Force in a relatively short time. This draft RFP began coming in to the Air Force in January 1983. The final RFP was sent out on May 18.[27]

> The RFP stated that contract award would be based on "an integrated assessment of offeror's capability and capacity." In descending order of importance the major assessment areas were overall engine capability, readiness and support, life cycle cost over a twenty-year period, and program adequacy and competition. The RFP further stated, "Consideration will be given to the effects of dual awards on acquisition and ownership costs, system readiness and availability, and the industrial mobilization base." Several unique Air Force requirements in the RFP reflected both a strong desire for contracting flexibility and a forceful reaction to controversy over spare parts acquisition policies and warranties.

> The Air Force asked contractors to submit proposals covering an estimated 2,000 engines for the F-15s and F-16s spanning fiscal years 1985-90. Asking for firm prices for each of several different contracting alternatives, the Air Force intended to select only one at the time of award. First the contractors were asked to offer their best prices if the Air Force chose to buy initially only the fiscal year 1985 requirements with priced options for the three years after that. Second, contractors were also asked for their best prices if the Air Force committed to a three- or five-year multi-year contract. Presumably, prices for the multi-year contract would be lower because of scale. However, a multi-year commitment would cost the Air Force the flexibility in future years to switch contractors based on changing needs of the Service. The Air Force might want to keep uncertainty and competition working by making annual buys through successive years to keep the contractors on their toes. Third, all proposals were to include not-to-exceed prices for the Navy, if the Navy were also to buy the selected engine.[28]

## The final decision on the competition

> ...would be made by the Secretary of the Air Force based on a careful analysis of the contractors' offers. As part of the process, though, contractors were also asked to submit their prices based on split award assumptions (75-25, 50-50, and 25-75) as well as a complete (100%) award.[29]

Much of the specificity in this RFP was due to a dispute between Pratt and the Air Force over what the Air Force considered the exorbitant cost of spare parts for the F100 engine. P&W was the single source for spare parts for their engine. Spare parts were in such short supply that the Air Force also believed P&W was giving its commercial customers priority in a time of limited manufacturing capacity. The parts pricing formula was the same as negotiated on previous military procurements. As prime contractor, P&W added overhead and profit margins to the costs of spare parts manufactured by subcontractors. This was normal pricing practice in previous procurements. The Air Force RFP was subsequently amended to include requirements for usable procurement data, dual sources of supply, unlimited rights of reprocurement data to be granted to the Government, options prices, and a warranty. This last requirement was the result of congressional legislation requiring the military to obtain warranty protection against faulty performance. The fiscal year 1983 Department of Defense Appropriation Act included specific language pertaining to engine competitions:

> None of the funds made available in the Act...shall be made available for the purchase of the alternate or new model fighter aircraft engine that does not have a written warranty or guarantee attesting that it will perform not less than 3,000 tactical cycles.[30]

## Drewes describes the details of the warranty clause:

> The RFP's warranty required three basic areas of coverage. First, for three years or 1,000 flight hours, the engine would be free from defects in material or workmanship. If defects were discovered, the contractor would fix them or pay the Air Force to do so. Second, the high-pressure turbine and combustor were covered for eight years or 3,000 tactical cycles. As its objective, the Air Force wanted coverage for long-term durability, the primary driver of depot overhaul workload. If an engine failed to retain 98% of its thrust or exceeded 105% of specified fuel consumption, the contractor was required to repair or replace it. Third, in order to prompt the contractor to design a reliable and durable product for the long term, the contractor had to guarantee a ceiling for engine removal rates from 1989 to 1995. The Air Force wanted to ease the workload on maintenance technicians. Obviously, the Air Force constructed each of these exacting requirements primarily to preclude anything even close to the nightmares experienced in maintaining the F100.[31]

The Alternate Fighter Engine (AFE) competition was on. The anticipated amount of the award was estimated at $10 billion. Best and final offers from the companies arrived on December 5, with GE proposing their F110 turbofan and Pratt proposing an enhanced F100 model, the F100-220.[32]

On February 3, 1984, Secretary of the Air Force Verne Orr announced a split award. Only the fiscal year 1985 quantity of 160 engines was awarded. Of that total, 120, or 75 percent, were contracted to GE for F-16s and the remaining forty, or 25 percent, were awarded to Pratt for F-15s. The Air Force rationale was that Orr wanted to wait a year and see what happened in the two engine programs. The official Air Force press release stated that GE had offered better (lower) overall support costs, ensured better procurement of spare parts, and offered an excellent warranty. Air Force Secretary Orr stated that the award would probably save the government between $2.5 billion and $3 billion in the engines' twenty-year life cycle, stating:

> We will actually have fighter aircraft engines with twice the life of today's engines at roughly the same projected unit cost.

He also said:

> Making this award ensures that we will continue to use competition to get the most for our limited resources as we procure these flight engines into at least the mid-1990s.[33]

Subsequent Air Force testimony before congressional hearings revealed that Pratt & Whitney had offered an all-or-nothing proposal.[34]

Several days after Secretary Orr's announcement of his decision, the Navy chose GE's F110 to re-engine the F-14. Navy Secretary John Lehman stated:

> We have begun negotiations now to put into contract form the price and options that were included in the Air Force proposal. We will participate with the Air Force to gain all the competitive benefits that the Air Force has achieved in its General Electric contract.

The award had an immediate impact on GE, both at their Lynn, Massachusetts, and Evendale, Ohio, facilities. On February 4, 1984, GE-Lynn announced the hiring of 300 new workers, with up to 600 more anticipated over the next two years.[35] The first production-qualified F110 engine (Figure 15-7) was delivered to the Air Force in January 1985.

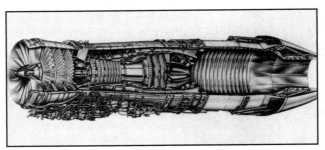

**Figure 15-7. Cutaway of F110 Engine**
*(Illustration courtesy of GE)*

In March 1989 the Air Force announced their final buy in the competition between GE and Pratt. GE received an order for thirty-nine F110-GE-100 engines (36 percent), while Pratt was given seventy of its F100-PW-200 engines to produce (64 percent). Overall, in the final tally of the six-year AFE race, GE received 50.4 percent of the orders. As the last order for AFE engines was made, the first order in a new, five-year Improved Performance Engine (IPE) competition was also announced. That order awarded fifty-four engines to GE and sixty-eight engines to P&W for a 44 to 56 percent split. Pratt's F100-PW-229 IPE engine was chosen for the F-15E aircraft, and the F110-GE-129 engines were slated for F-16s.

The GE F110-GE-129 was the growth version of the F110-GE-100. The engine completed altitude qualification testing in December 1988, endurance testing in June 1989, and all Air Force qualification testing by the end of 1989. GE delivered its first six production F110-GE-129s to the Air Force for flight-testing late that year. The engine completed flight-testing on the F-16 in December 1989, having finished its F-15 flight-testing in October.[36] On January 9, 1990, the Air Force selected the F110-GE-129 IPE engine to power about 75 percent of the F-16C aircraft purchased for fiscal year 1991.[37]

The Navy requested 18 F-14As in Fiscal 1986 and 18 more in fiscal 1987. The last five of the F-14As procured by the Navy were to be bought in Fiscal 1988, for a total of 41 additional aircraft. If the Navy's annual requests for new F-14As were to be approved, 29 F-14As already in the fleet would require engine retrofits. A larger retrofit program involving up to 300 additional F-14As also remained under consideration by the Navy. In July 1984, Navy Secretary John F. Lehman, Jr. expressed disappointment with the performance of the P&W TF30-P-414A installed in fleet F-14As. The decision by the Air Force to use increased numbers of F110s to power its McDonnell Douglas F-15s and General Dynamics F-16s had long-term cost benefits for the Navy.[38] Navy planners stated that the F110 had 30 percent more thrust at military and combat power than the TF30 and offered lower specific fuel consumption in both regimes. The difference was apparent in combat power ratings. Specific fuel consumption for the F110 was 1.98 pounds per hour per pound of thrust as opposed to 2.78 for the TF30. These figures translated into longer range and endurance for F-14s equipped with the F110. The increased thrust at military power, sufficient for single-engine positive rate of climb in the event of engine failure, allowed F-14s to launch from carriers without using their afterburners.[39]

## The GE F404 Turbofan Engine

The F404 (Figure 15-8) is the Navy version of the J101, proposed for the F/A-18 in 1975. Designed for simplicity and reliability, it was in the same thrust class (16,000 lb.) as the J79 of two decades earlier, but weighed only half as much, was about 2/3 as long, and had 7,700 fewer parts. The three-stage fan and seven-stage high compressor produced an overall pressure ratio of 25:1 and a bypass ratio of 0.34 (giving rise to the term "leaky turbojet") on an airflow of 142 pounds per second. The single-stage high-pressure turbine was film cooled to operate at temperatures in the 2500°F range. The low-pressure turbine, also a single stage, was convection cooled. Maximum diameter was 35 inches, length was 159 inches, and total weight was 2,167 pounds. The first flight was November 18, 1978.

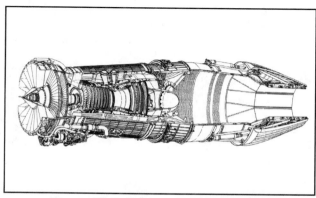

**Figure 15-8. Cutaway of F404 Engine**
*(Illustration courtesy of GE)*

The simple, compact design of the F404 enabled the use of a small, light frame and only five main bearings. Components in the gas path were designed to resist foreign object damage and corrosion, while modular design simplified maintenance. The design objectives were justified as the F404 compiled a maintenance and spare part cost of $44 per engine flight hour, compared to $75 for the J79.

In addition to the two F404-GE-400 engines in each F/A-18, a -400 powered the X-29 Advanced Technology Demonstrator aircraft with its forward-swept wing. The F404/RM12, developed in conjunction with Volvo Flygmotor, has five percent more airflow, putting it in the 18,000-pound thrust class. It powers the Swedish JAS 39 Gripen. The F404-GE-400D was a nonafterburning version of 10,800 pounds thrust for the Navy's A-6 Intruder, but was never produced. The F404 family has growth potential into the 20,000-pound thrust class.

It is very interesting to note that although GE won the Navy contract with its F404 design, P&W was named the second source for the F404-GE-400 engine design in October 1984. In 1985 the Navy cited P&W as the only other U.S. manufacturer with experience to make an exact copy of the power plant. Navy Secretary John Lehman, Jr. said that the widespread use of the F404 engine in the Navy's inventory of jet aircraft and the potential for its use in future aircraft necessitated a second source for mobilization and competitive acquisition. Lehman further stated:

> The fleet operational performance demonstrated by the F404-GE-400 engine has been outstanding measured against any standard. Furthermore, the logistic support elements are in place and are functioning smoothly. As a result, there is no requirement to improve or replace the F404 but rather to reproduce it to the same quality standards at a second manufacturing facility.

> The goal of the acquisition strategy for the F404 second source should be for the new manufacturer to produce an exact copy of the F404-GE-400. [40]

GE was required to transfer the technology required to manufacture the engine. P&W maintained their second source position until 1989, manufacturing approximately 125 engines.

The "Great Engine War" ended up a draw in terms of its final impact on both P&W and GE. Although neither company "won big" in terms of winning the entire fighter engine market, neither company lost all of their fighter engine business, either. Both companies still produce their respective engines and both are still steadily advancing their turbine engine technological bases. The Air Force got what they desired as well: a customer's respect from both companies and two relatively cost-effective and efficient products. The Navy got what they wanted, a totally separate fighter aircraft development program in the F-18.

## Endnotes

[1] Miller, Jay, General Dynamics F-111 "Aardvark," Fallbrook, CA: Aero Publishers, Inc., 1982, 11

[2] Ibid, 12.

[3] Ibid, 17

[4] Bowers, Peter M. and Swanborough, Gordon, United States Military Aircraft Since 1909, Washington, D.C.: Smithsonian Institution Press, 1989, 325.

[5] P&W Aircraft Engine Files, Resume of Engine Development Histories, East Hartford, CT: P&W Aircraft, Division of United Aircraft Corporation, 1975, 19-20.

[6] Bowers and Swanborough, United States Military Aircraft Since 1909, 325.

[7] Gunston, Bill, World Encyclopedia of Aero Engines, Second Edition, England: Patrick Stephens Limited, 1989, 162.

[8] Miller, General Dynamics F-111 "Aardvark", 44-47.

[9] Bowers and Swanborough, United States Military Aircraft Since 1909, 326.

[10] Gunston, Aero Engines, 126.

[11] Ibid.

[12] Bowers, Peter M. and Swanborough, Gordon, United States Navy Aircraft Since 1911, Annapolis, MD: Naval Institute Press, 1990, 276.

13 Westwood, Edward C, "The F-15 Engine Development," Professional Staff Study, Maxwell AFB, AL: Air War College, Maxwell Air Force Base, 1975, from Drewes, Robert W, The Air Force and the Great Engine War, Washington, D.C.: National Defense University Press, 1987, 31.

14 Drewes, The Air Force, 47.

15 Ibid, 60, and U.S. Congress, Senate, Committee on Armed Forces, F-15 and F-16 Engine Problems, Hearings, Washington, D.C.: 96th Congress, 1st Session, November 27, 1979.

16 Drewes, The Air Force..., 61-62.

17 NAL, Jane's All the World's Aircraft: 1986-87, Jane's Publishing, Incorporated, 1987, 943.

18 Kennedy, David M, The Great Engine War, Kennedy School of Government Case Program no. C16-85-629, Harvard University, MA: John F. Kennedy School of Government, 1985, 8.

19 Ibid, 9.

20 Drewes, The Air Force..., 98.

21 The F100 only had to show a higher thrust through ground tests. Ibid.

22 Ibid, 110.

23 Kennedy, The Great Engine War, 11.

24 Drewes, The Air Force..., 111.

25 Ibid, 112.

26 Ibid, 113.

27 Ibid, 116.

28 Ibid, 117.

29 Ibid, 118.

30 Ibid, 119.

31 Ibid, 120.

32 NAL, " 'The Great Engine War' That Is Splitting the Pentagon," Aviation Week (November 14, 1983).

33 Doe, Charles, "Pentagon's 'Great Engine War' Far From Over," New York Times (1984).

34 Drewes, The Air Force..., 126-127.

35 NAL, "GE Beats P&W in 'Jet Engine War,' " The Boston Herald (February 4, 1984), 18.

36 Weber, Dwight E., and Kennedy, Richard L., GE to Deliver F110-GE-129 Engines for USAF Field Service Evaluations, GE News Release No. GEAE-81E, December 7, 1989, 1-2.

37 Weber, Dwight E., and Kennedy, Richard L., GE F110-GE-129 Engine Selected To Power Majority of USAF F-16 Aircraft, GE News Release No. GEAE-01E, January 9, 1990.

38 Ibid, and AW&ST July 16, 1984, 26.

39 NAL, AW&ST (June 10, 1985), 151.

40 NAL, "Pratt Named GE F404 Second Source," Aviation Week & Space Technology, October 1, 1984, 20-21.

**Air Force C-5A Galaxy,
Powered by Four GE TF39 Turbofans**

# Chapter Sixteen

# High-Bypass and Very-High-Bypass Turbofan Engines

## The TF39, JT9D, and CF6 Engines

The evolution of the high-bypass and very-high-bypass turbofan engine has dramatically changed aviation. The huge transports of today owe their existence to the high-bypass engine's ability to produce very large amounts of thrust while keeping specific fuel consumption down to a minimum. The "jumbo jets" like the Airbus and the Boeing 747 can fly between continents much more quickly than they did before, making transatlantic and transpacific flights more efficient for the airlines and more affordable for the passenger. But these large diameter engines simply did not spring into being. All American companies who entered into the development of the high-bypass turbofan engine drew upon earlier work. Interestingly the first high bypass ratio (6/1) fan engine was the Lycoming PLF1A-2, Feb 13, 1964.

P&W was the first to exploit the advantages of jet transport on a large scale with its JT3 and JT4 turbojets. These early turbojets, while not as powerful or economical as their turbofan cousins, produced such large savings for the airlines that airframe manufacturers put pressure on both of the big American jet engine manufacturers (General Electric and Pratt & Whitney) to produce engines that were more fuel-efficient. In this chapter we will look at the highest bypass-ratio engine ever developed, the TF39, and its P&W counterpart, the JTF-14E. Both engines had their origin in the Air Force's Cargo Experimental-Heavy Logistics System (CX-HLS, later CXX).

## Design and Development of the GE TF39 Turbofan Engine

The success of the TF39 at GE owes a great deal to management foresight at Evendale. The Air Force had initiated an advanced planning project in 1962 called Operation Forecast, under the auspices of General Bernard A. Schriever. This program reviewed and established Air Force development priorities for the next decade. GE played a major role in that project, providing the Air Force with a great deal of data on the company's fan programs. The information was funneled through the Air Force's Cliff Simpson, then director of the Turbine Engine Division in the Aero Propulsion Laboratory. These fan programs were the XV-5A lift fan, the J79 and J85 cruise fans, and the CJ805 jetliner turbofan. GE believed that these programs could substantially improve the thrust output and reduce fuel consumption for the next generation of aircraft. Project Forecast produced, among others, the Air Force's requirement for the CXX large military transport with high-bypass turbofan engines. The Air Force set the target date for completed development at ten years later, 1972. GE's *Eight Decades of Progress* chronicles the origin of the GE design:

> With confidence in its fan experience, GE's management and engineers believed they could produce that engine right away.
>
> A major reason for the company's confidence—and its motivation—was the fact that group executive Jack Parker had exhorted the division to "get going on the next transport engine and don't be overshadowed by the competition." GE's advanced planners already had under way a series of studies on turbofans including engines with very high bypass ratios.
>
> The United States Air Force encouraged GE to "put up or shut up": submit an unsolicited proposal on the high bypass turbofan.[1]

This challenge came before the actual competition for the CXX in 1965. By getting involved with the Project Forecast planning in 1962, GE had gotten a huge jump on P&W.

In what had by then become GE aircraft engine management practice, competing design teams were established in late 1963 to determine optimum engine specifications. The race was on.

Within GE, a team headed by Don Berkey produced the winning design: an 8:1 bypass ratio fan, including a unique one-and-a-half stage fan (a full-size front fan plus an additional set of half-size fan blades) conceived by Lee Fischer, a very knowledgeable theorist and engineer who had contributed much to GE engines at both Lynn and Evendale. But it was just a paper design. In March 1964, the Air Force told GE, "You must have an engine running or you are out of the competition." (P&W, the other entry in the race, reportedly was in the process of demonstrating hardware for the CXX.).

With that message in hand, in his typical style, Gerhard Neumann turned on the heat.

Using the GE1 core engine as a basis (the building block concept was working well), the company laid out the design of the GE1/6 demonstrator: a turbofan engine with an 8-to-1 bypass ratio, a thrust output of 15,830 pounds and a specific fuel consumption (SFC) of only .336—a stunning reduction from the engines of the 1940s that had SFC rates of more than one. The GE1/6 was one-half the size of the planned large transport engine but it did the job.[2]

GE initiated the GE1/6 demonstrator program in April 1964 and a GE test team led by Marty Hemsworth successfully tested the demonstrator in December of that year.[3] The next step was to compile the formal proposal for the CXX's full-scale engine. The GE proposal filled ninety volumes, and the company had to provide fifty copies of each volume. This huge proposal was shipped by tractor-trailer to the CXX Systems Program Office at Wright-Patterson Air Force Base in Ohio.[4] The proposal was followed up by an oral presentation in April 1965 by a GE team composed of Jack Parker, Gerhard Neumann, Don Berkey, Jim Krebs, Marty Hemsworth, and Dave Shaw.

GE's hard work and experience with the Air Force paid off with the award of the CXX engine contract in August 1965. In October 1965 the Air Force and GE signed Air Force Contract AF 33(657)-15003 for the development of the TF39 (Figure 16-1), covering research and development, testing, and the production of three XTF engines, twenty-four YTF engines, and 440 TF39-GE-1 engines.[5] The 440 engines included thirty research and development engines, a Production A run of 228 engines, six engines for Air Force Logistics Command testing, and a Production B run of 176 engines. This contract was for $459 million, making it the largest single contract GE had ever received.

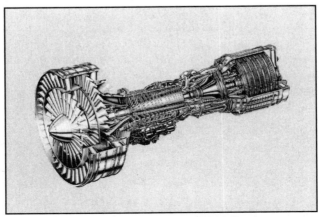

**Figure 16-1. Cutaway of TF39 Engine**
*(Illustration courtesy of GE)*

Twenty-six engines were designated to support the engine development program along with three core-engine cyclic-test vehicles that would be dedicated to low-cycle fatigue testing.[6]

The development program for the TF39 was laid out around four blocks of objectives. Block I consisted of four engines and concentrated on performance, simulated service, and environmental objectives. Block II consisted of seven engines and concentrated on performance, simulated service, environmental, and Preliminary Qualification Test (PQT) assurance objectives. Block III used six engines and focused on performance, simulated service, PQT assurance, PQT, and Formal Qualification Test (FQT) assurance objectives. The Block III designation covered the YTF39-GE-1 engine. Block IV used nine engines and focused on performance, simulated service, FQT assurance, FQT, and reliability assurance objectives. The Block IV designation covered the TF39-GE-1 engine.[7]

In December 1965 GE completed the first full-scale test of the compressor for the TF39. The company also brought the first engine to test in that same month.[8]

The TF39 Block II engine design was completed and released in March 1966. The full-scale fan test of the engine was started in February and completed in April 1966. The first Block II engine went to test in October 1966.[9] Through the end of 1966, the TF39 program was considered by the Air Force to be proceeding "on schedule."[10]

The first half of 1967, however, saw some major setbacks in the TF39 program. Ed Horn, at that time in the Air Force's Aero Propulsion Laboratory, remembers:

> During the first half of 1967 we had 7 premature engine failures and vendor problems were causing late delivery of hardware to test. PQT assurance testing also was impacted giving us less confidence that the official 60-hour PQT would be completed satisfactorily.[11]

In July 1967 the first Block III engine went to test. In August GE and the Air Force began climatic tests of the YTF39 in a special hanger at Eglin Air Force Base to prove the engine's environmental capability. The engine passed these tests. A YTF39 experimental engine was completed in September 1967 and the first ground-test engine was shipped to Lockheed. With the fabrication of the first YTF39, it was time for the PQT.

## The Preliminary Qualification Test

The Preliminary Qualification Program requirements for the YTF39-GE-1 consisted of a 60-hour official endurance test, fourteen component tests, performance tests, and demonstration of durability for flight test. The PQT then had to be approved by the Air Force. Edward Horn describes the requirement:

> What is not generally understood, particularly by the contractors who consider it 'double jeopardy,' is that we take into consideration all aspects and experiences of the development testing, good and bad, before granting approval.
>
> The primary results we expected from this program was [sic] the demonstration of adequate performance levels and satisfactory durability prior to the initiation and conduct of category I flight testing. Before the initiation of the official 60-hour endurance test we had negotiated a reduction in the performance requirements for the engine with Lockheed's concurrence. Instead of the engine being required to meet 40,805 pounds of thrust flat-rated at 89.5°F., the temperature requirement was reduced to 73°F.
>
> The 60-hour endurance test for the YTF39-GE-1 engine became quite a challenge to complete; but in retrospect [it] was identical to many programs we had experienced previously.[12]

The first attempt at the 60-hour endurance test on October 9, 1967, resulted in a failure in the high-pressure turbine section. A stage-two high-pressure turbine blade had failed in the shank below the platform, due to high cycle fatigue. Subsequent checks of YTF39 production engines revealed a similar flaw, and corrective measures were taken.

GE decided to use the first production YTF39 engine for the second attempt at the PQT. This second attempt, on October 20, ended with an engine seizure. A severe rub had occurred on the forward high-pressure turbine shaft. This rub was traced to the introduction of a performance improvement fix into the stationary seal.[13]

The third attempt, on November 2, 1967, resulted in turbine impact damage, which in turn caused moderate damage in stage 1 of the high-pressure turbine nozzle seal. This damage was determined to be foreign object damage (FOD) and was traced to the ingestion of a clip and rivet from the seal. As this failure had occurred in the sixth of ten scheduled cycles, parts were replaced in the engine and the test continued without further incident.

The fourth attempt began on November 10 and resulted in a partial run without incident. The engine was then torn down for inspection. Testing resumed on November 20 and was completed on November 25, 1967. The number of hours on this test engine totaled 129.[14] GE was cleared to deliver the first twenty-four YTF engines. The company did not finish PQT assurance testing and the last penalty tests until April 1968. The Air Force's Edward Horn describes the overall feeling of the Air Force for the PQT:

> Numerous minor failures and deficiencies were experienced; but all of those which were significant to the safe and effective operation of the YTF39 engine were corrected prior to engine shipment or were planned for retrofit prior to first flight.
>
> An additional 583 hours of PQT assurance and penalty testing was subsequently completed and based on this experience, we concluded that the YTF39 engine could be safely committed to flight in the first C-5A. Lockheed concurred in our decision and the PQT was officially approved on June 28, 1968.[15]

The TF39 fan was a high bypass (8:1) unit. The root section of the fan provided supercharged air for the compressor. The fan also incorporated mid-span shrouds. The compressor was a dual rotor type, providing an overall pressure ratio of 25:1. The combustor was an annular design, and the high-pressure turbine was designed to tolerate up to 2,500°F.

The first flight of the YTF39, in a B-52 flying test bed, was on June 9, 1967. No engine problems were reported.[16] The J57 engines in the number 3 position were removed and a special pylon was attached to support the Lockheed-supplied nacelle which supported the YTF39 and was identical to that to be installed on the C-5. The installation also included a cowl-mounted thrust reverser which was operable in flight. The nacelle pod also contained instrumentation capable of measuring performance parameters as well as strain gauges for in-flight fan stress.[17]

## Formal Qualification Test

In December 1967, General Electric and the Air Force started the Formal Qualification Test (FQT) of the YTF39 engine at the Arnold Engineering Development Center (AEDC). This test was a key point of the development process of the TF39. Both GE and the Air Force considered AEDC as the "Bureau of Standards" for the establishment of engine performance.[18]

GE delivered an installation-qualified TF39 in September 1968.[19] It passed the 150-hour FQT in October.[20] The first three XTF engines were delivered between September 1967 and January 1968, and the twenty-four YTF engines were delivered between November 1967 and June 1968.[21]

The first flight of the C-5A (Figure 16-2) with YTF engines was made on June 30, 1968. The first flight with the TF engines was made in March 1969, and the first flight of the engine on the C-5 was in April. The first C-5 with its TF39 engines was delivered to the Air Force in June 1969. Final FQT approval was given by the Air Force in October. Also in October, GE finished delivery of the first 160 production TF39s to Lockheed.[22]

In December 1969 the Air Force activated the first C-5 training squadron at Altus Air Force Base. In June 1970 the first Air Force operational wing at Charleston Air Force Base in

**Figure 16-2. Lockheed C-5A Galaxy**
*(Photo courtesy of U.S. Air Force)*

South Carolina began flying the C-5, with the first 1,000 flying hours being completed by July. A second operational wing was activated at Travis Air Force Base in California in October 1970, and a third wing was activated at Dover Air Force Base in Delaware in April 1971.[23]

Delivery of the TF39-GE-1 was completed in September 1971.[24] Retrofit of the TF39-GE-1 to an improved TF39-GE-1A configuration was begun in January 1972. Engineering responsibility for the TF39 was transferred to San Antonio Air Logistics Center in January 1973.

In the recollection of Ed Horn,

> ...the C-5A program is the first Air Force program where engine performance was not a controversial issue between the government and the system contractor. The pre-planning and the conduct of testing and resolution of the (testing) data was [sic] outstanding.[25]

GE built 464 TF39 engines before the program was completed in 1971, laying the foundation for future GE turbofan development. While the TF39 was doing yeoman service for the Air Force, GE started positioning itself for expansion into the commercial market. As in the mid '50s, Juan Trippe's Pan American Airways set off the next wave of evolution in jet transports. This was the competition for the first "jumbo jet." Boeing responded to the challenge with appropriate speed with their candidate for the CXX program. GE and P&W were asked to provide technical data, price, and delivery proposals to Boeing for its jumbo jet, to be called the 747.

Pan American wanted an aircraft with a significant speed increase at cruise altitudes of 35,000 to 40,000 feet. GE responded with the CTF39 turbofan, which was a commercialized version of the TF39. The CTF39, however, was about 10 percent too small for the 747, which would mean a costly development effort by GE with its own money. So GE withdrew from the 747 engine competition, leaving the field to P&W. This decision proved to be a serious mistake, and one that would cost GE a great deal of money to correct later.

GE did not walk away from commercial turbofan development, however. In 1967 GE created a Commercial Engine Projects operation with Ed Hood as its manager. The program included the SST engine, the CJ805 product support, the CJ610 and CF700 small business jets, and a new project, the CF6, under the direction of Brian Rowe. GE would be back in the commercial field soon.

## Design and Development of the P&W JT9D Turbofan Engine

P&W and GE had competed against each other in the competition for what became the C-5A Galaxy, the first high-bypass-ratio turbofan-powered aircraft. Both companies had submitted their best plans and GE had won. Where did that leave P&W? The company had invested massive amounts of funding for the CX-HLS program, with little or no payoff in sight. Many companies in the aircraft engine business had gone under after losing in such a gamble. P&W was more fortunate than that, however.

Pan American's Juan Trippe changed the jet transport scene dramatically with his decision to obtain a faster, bigger, and more powerful jet. He wanted a jumbo jet and when he went to Boeing, he got one.

Even before Boeing lost the CXX contract to Lockheed in mid-1965, the company's commercial market researchers had determined that a big step up in the capacity of long-range aircraft would be necessary by 1970 in order to cope with even normal growth in passenger and freight traffic. They felt that even if new advances in technology cut costs in the current airline fleets, brought down fares, and broadened air transport marketability, a totally new aircraft design was necessary. Attempts to "stretch" the 707 had barely kept up with growth, and competition was getting fierce. The introduction of the 250-seat Douglas DC-8 Super 63 had hit hard at Boeing's business. Boeing wanted a 300-seat, long-haul, fast (over 600-mph) advanced-technology aircraft.[26] They showed preliminary designs of the 747 to Trippe and he immediately ordered twenty-five aircraft. Trippe wanted this new aircraft right away before it would be superseded by the supersonic transport. This was enough to get Boeing moving. Trippe also wanted engines for the aircraft that could be fitted quickly, and he knew that P&W had been working for several years on a high-bypass engine for the CXX, the JTF-14E.[27] At that time P&W had begun work on a JTF-14E-derived JT9D turbofan engine (Figure 16-3) with a P&W engineering order dated September 13, 1965. Engine design started on January 12, 1966, with the engine's release to experimental testing on July 20, 1966. Trippe and Boeing decided that the P&W JT9Ds were what they needed.

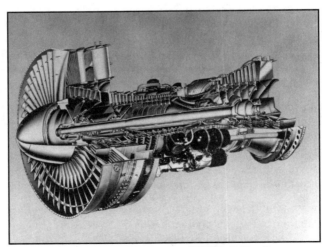

**Figure 16-3. Cutaway of JT9D-3 Engine**
*(Illustration courtesy of Pratt &Whitney)*

Throughout the winter of 1965-66, Boeing worked on the design and layout for the 747 (Figure 16-4). It became a formal Boeing project in March 1966. The principal question for the designers was whether the 747 was to have a single-deck or double-deck fuselage cross-section. They chose a single-deck layout so that it would accommodate "square-loaded" freight pallets up to the size of the 8-foot by 8-foot standard cargo container. The design capacity of the 747 was to rise quickly to between 363 and 400 passengers or 125 tons of cargo.[28] Boeing was so confident of future sales that it immediately began construction of a completely separate, massive new facility for 747 production at Everett, Washington.

**Figure 16-4. Boeing 747**
*(Photo courtesy of Boeing Co.)*

The JT9D was made of titanium, high-nickel alloys, stainless steel, and other advanced metals. Eventually the latest models incorporated single-crystal high-pressure turbine blades.[29] P&W built a special factory just to assemble the engine because of all the new tools and methods required to fit the parts together. The engine's 8-foot-diameter inlet was twice the size of the 707's long-range turbofans though it was only 128 inches long. The first test run of the JT9D-1A was on December 20, 1966. Meanwhile, as usual with new aircraft designs, the 747's gross weight had grown, requiring more thrust than provided by the JT9D-1A. Pratt uprated the engine and accelerated its development to higher thrust. Time did not permit a basic redesign. The first flight was in a B-52E test bed aircraft in June 1968 with a single JT9D taking the place of two J57s.

The production engine, the JT9D-3, had a single-stage fan that delivered 1,510 pounds per second airflow, three low-pressure stages, eleven high-pressure stages, an annular combustor, two high-pressure turbine stages and four low-pressure turbine stages. Its weight was 8,608 pounds and it produced 43,500 pounds of takeoff thrust.[30] Boeing accepted the first JT9D-3 prototype delivery on June 13, 1968. The maiden flight of the JT9D-powered Boeing 747 was on February 9, 1969.[31] On its debut the Boeing 747 was the largest and heaviest civil airplane ever built. The JT9D-3 passed its 150-hour endurance test for FAA clearance on April 25, 1969. The first production deliveries began on April 20, 1969, and the engine entered service on January 21, 1970.

On December 21, 1969, P&W began production deliveries of its first improved version of the JT9D, the JT9D-3A. This was an advanced-design, dual-spool, annular combustion chamber, axial-flow turbofan engine with a compression ratio of 21.5:1. The engine had a duct-to-gas generator bypass ratio of 5.1:1. The low-pressure compressor consisted of one fan stage and three compressor stages, and was driven by a four-stage turbine. A bleed valve assembly in the low-pressure compressor provided for inter-compressor bleed and was open during start, idle, low power conditions, and deceleration. The compact, high-pressure compressor was composed of eleven stages, and was driven by a two-stage turbine through concentric shafting. The JT9D-3A was identical to the JT9D-3 but due to its increased airflow and to the fact that the engine had been flat-rated to deliver its thrust at 80°F at sea level static, it could deliver 45,000 pounds of thrust.

Eighteen months after the first production deliveries of the JT9D-3A, on July 13, 1971, P&W began production delivery of its second improved model, the JT9D-7. This model had a higher overall compression ratio (22.3:1), delivered 47,000 pounds of takeoff thrust, and was flat-rated at 85°F. The JT9D-7 powered the 747-100, 747-200B, 747-C, and 747-F, models, and the 747SR. (A variant of the JT9D-7, the D-20, was also used in the Douglas DC-10-20 aircraft bought by Northwest Airlines.)

On March 19, 1973, P&W began production deliveries of its next improved model of the JT9D series, the JT9D-7A. This engine had been "grown" to 47,670 pounds of takeoff thrust. It powered the Boeing 747-100, 747-200B, 747-C, 747-F, 747SR, and 747SP aircraft.

Initial service reliability of the JT9D-3A and the JT9D-7 was poor, with many severe turbine failures. This stemmed directly from the earlier decision to propose an uncooled turbine for the C-5A competition. These problems were corrected by applying J58 materials and advanced cooling technology, but several years passed before the airline fleets were retrofitted. The JT9D then achieved JT3D levels of reliability.

October 15, 1974, saw the fifth improved version of the JT9D come off the production lines. This was the JT9D-7F, which delivered 50,000 pounds of takeoff thrust, largely due to its increased compression ratio of 22.8:1, its enhanced turbine cooling (impingement cooling was added to the second-stage turbine blades), and its use of directionally solidified materials for the first time in a commercial engine.

The JT9D-7F employed directionally solidified material to achieve the higher thrust ratings needed to power high-gross-weight versions of the Boeing 747. Directionally solidified material is the result of a casting process that produces a columnar, rather than randomly oriented, metal grain structure. It offers greater temperature resistance and longer life. Turbine blades of directionally solidified material were certified by the FAA after operational testing in the JT9D-7A engine. This new material permitted higher turbine-inlet temperatures, thus higher thrust. The JT9D-7F engine could therefore handle the 800,000-pound versions of the 747 while retaining a degree of commonality with the JT9D-7A. The JT9D-7F involved only nine changes from the JT9D-7A. In terms of aerodynamics it remained the same.[32]

The JT9D-7F was a response to the emergence of the Rolls-Royce RB211 and the GE CF6-50D engines. After an initial period of dominance of the 747 market, P&W's lead in providing the engine for these aircraft had diminished. Boeing became willing to power its 747s with whatever engine the customer wanted. Foreign airlines in Europe, Asia, and Africa sometimes chose the British RB211 or the GE product. Even more significantly, all major engine builders had to offer their large engines in variable sizes, as different 747 orders stressed adaptability to each customer's special needs. No longer would one or even two engines dominate the world jet aircraft market.

In the 1980s P&W responded to the emergence of the GE CF6 series with the JT9D-7R4 series of high-bypass-ratio turbofans for a wide thrust range in the large-aircraft engine market. The JT9D-7R4A delivered 44,300 pounds of thrust; the JT9D-7R4B, 46,100 pounds of thrust; the JT9D-7R4C, 46,900 pounds of thrust, and the JT9D-74RD, 48,000 pounds of thrust. These new engines introduced an important new turbine blade technology for P&W, single-crystal blades for the high-pressure turbine. While GE continued to use conventionally cast blades, P&W single-crystal blades could operate at higher metal temperatures and last longer than conventionally cast blades. Bill Sweetman, in the spring 1980 edition of Interavia, described the process by which the blades are produced:

The new plant produces blades which are unique in two related ways. First they are cast as one crystal: and this permits a second innovation, the casting of the blade in two halves, in the same mold from the same crystal...

The process works as follows: the wax matrix, around which the ceramic mold is built up, is poured around a thin ceramic plate called a "strongback" which splits the mold and carries the network of cooling tunnels. This remains in place when the wax is melted out by a microwave furnace.

Once the mold is filled it is carried automatically to a furnace from which it can be withdrawn vertically. This enables the blade to be solidified from root to tip.

This process was first used to produce directionally solidified blades, in which the grain boundaries between the crystals all run the same way. In a single-crystal blade casting, the first element to solidify is a 'starter block' attached to the root of the blade by a narrow helical passage in the mold. The helical passage obstructs the growth of multiple crystal boundaries, with the result that the blade is formed from a single crystal. This crystal propagates in two halves around the strongback. The two halves of the blade can then be joined by a process called 'transient liquid phase' bonding, in which the halves are mated around a foil 'gasket' of the same alloy as the blade—coated with boron to reduce its melting point—and joined under pressure. The gasket and the thin layer of metal immediately adjacent to it melt, the boron dissipates completely and the part solidifies while still under pressure. As far as can be ascertained, the join produced by this means in a single-crystal blade is effectively perfect...

P&W then uses this process to mold cooling passages into the blade rather than using time-consuming machining procedures.

The reason that single-crystal blades offer better performance and life is that some of the elements used to improve bonding can be removed from the alloy 'recipe'. This improves the life of the material at a given operating temperature and also appears to make the coating procedure more reliable. Offsetting the high investment in plant for the new blades and its sophisticated computer control are savings in alloying elements and lower rejection rates in production. Computer control means that an error need not affect an entire batch of blades. Cooling passages in the two-part blades can also be inspected more easily than the laser-machined or electrochemically drilled passages usually employed, and the design of the cooling system is less compromised by the limitations of the machining process.[33]

Into the late 1990s over 3,200 JT9D engines have been built, including 757 of the JT9D-7R4 series.

In December 1982, P&W announced the PW4000 turbofan engine series. Designed to be interchangeable with the JT9D, at first glance it would appear to be an upgraded JT9D, but it is in fact a near-complete redesign by P&W at company expense. They have reduced the total number of parts by half, improved the engine's economy, and promised longer engine life at lower engine cost. The first of this new series is the PW4052, at a thrust rating of 52,000 pounds. The PW4052 entered service in June 1987 on PanAm A310-300 Airbuses.[34]

## Design and Development of the GE CF6 Turbofan Engine

Although General Electric won the Air Force transport engine with the TF39 engine, P&W lost no time in making their JT9D a commercial success. GE was left with very little market share in the commercial engine business. Although their CJ805 small commercial engine was popular with small regional airlines like SwissAir, the large and very large commercial aircraft markets were where the major profits were to be made. GE was considerably behind P&W there, so they decided to launch a large-engine program, which was to become the CF6 family of engines. They announced their commitment to this new engine on September 11, 1967. The TF39 high bypass turbofan engine served as the base for the CF6 (Figure 16-5), which was oriented from the start as an airline transport engine.

The components of the two-shaft CF6 engine, particularly the hot section, were subjected early on to a comprehensive factory-testing program designed to simulate takeoffs and landings.[35] The hot section became a major feature of the CF6 design from the beginning. This component was designed, tested, redesigned, and refined, resulting in a design that was considered by many

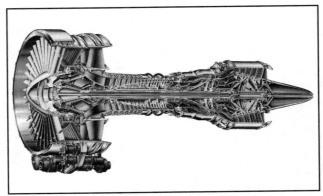

**Figure 16-5. Cutaway of CF6 Engine**
*(Illustration courtesy of GE)*

airline engineers to be several years ahead of the competition. The high-temperature turbine drew upon the design of the TF39.

The fan section of the CF6 consisted of a 38-bladed titanium single-stage fan with stator vanes arranged for reduced noise. The booster low-pressure compressor was a single (or quarter) stage for the CF6-6. The high-pressure compressor consisted of 16 stages (the same as the TF39).

The CF6 single annular combustor with 30 duplex-type fuel nozzles and swirler cups was designed to be smokeless. The axial-flow high-pressure turbine featured advanced film convection cooling for both the blades and vanes. The low-pressure turbine consisted of five stages. The engine's accessories and controls were located on the fan frame for better maintenance.

At 32,000 pounds of thrust the CF6 was considered too small for a twin-engine application in a large airliner. The engine did, however, fit nicely in a three-engine configuration, such as the McDonnell-Douglas DC-10 (Figure 16-6) or the Lockheed L-1011. Now the challenge facing GE was to get the CF6 into orders for the DC-10 or L-1011. Although Eastern Airlines and Trans World Airlines bought the Lockheed L-1011, they chose as the power plant the Rolls-Royce RB211 turbofan. However, on April 25, 1968, American Airlines chose the DC-10 and the CF6 engine. United Airlines also chose the DC-10/CF6 combination on the same date. By this time, GE had "grown" the engine to 40,000 pounds thrust. The first run of the CF6-6D engine was on October 21, 1968. Eighteen days later the engine attained 45,750 pounds of thrust in a test run. The engine was released for production in February 1969. The second CF6-6D, built to a production configuration, first ran in May 1969. A total of 30 engines had been shipped by December 1970. GE began delivery of flight-test engines to McDonnell Douglas in late 1969. The first flight of the CF-6D on the DC-10 was in September 1970.[36] William Travers, in *The GE Aircraft Engine Story*, describes the CF6-6 certification effort:

> A Project Hustle Manager was appointed to head an effort to get all necessary new parts together to meet the FAA certification test in June 1970. In March 1970, after 28 hours of the FAA Certification Test schedule, the turbine midframe liner collapsed and the low-pressure turbine section was badly overheated. In fact, the engine required more development, with the schedule date for completion of the test only three months away. A task force was formed to redesign the liner. The material thickness was increased and support beam stiffeners were added. In May 1970, there was another try at the Certification test. But the combustion liners were still inadequate. Engine Serial No. 009 was equipped with added reinforcements to the combustion liner and more cooling air added to the high-pressure turbine nozzle and it passed the test in June 1970. Actually, GE had already completed 6000 "C" cycles, which are severe engine tests duplicating each takeoff and landing of a fully loaded airplane.[37]

**Figure 16-6. McDonnell Douglas DC-10**
*(Photo courtesy of McDonnell Douglas)*

GE continued to have trouble with their combustion liners. The life of a combustion liner averaged less than 4,000 hours until 1974 when the company introduced a combustor package that included all the changes to the combustor up to the CF6-H model. This effectively ended the combustor problems (other than those that resulted from normally "growing" the engine). [38]

The engine entered airline service with the DC-10 in August 1971. A growth version, the CF6-6D1, was certified by the FAA in August 1971. The CF6-6D1's thrust rating was raised by 1,000 pounds to 41,000 pounds. In August 1971 GE launched another new version of the CF6-6, the CF6-6G, at 43,000 pounds of thrust.

The CF6-6G represented the first major change in the CF6 design. Developed under a TF39 engine Component Improvement Program (CIP) funded by the Air Force, the new engine incorporated a new high-pressure turbine and combustor that would enable it to operate at turbine inlet temperatures over 2,500°F while using about 15 percent less cooling air through the two air-cooled stages. This change was accomplished through major changes in the internal geometry of the blades and vanes in the turbine. The new turbine incorporated cast holes rather than drilled holes, which improved the heat transfer between the cooling air and the walls of the blades. GE engineers also added trip strips to create turbulence in the boundary layer within the coolant passage, enabling elimination of film cooling of the turbine blades as well. The new turbine was designed to be interchangeable with CF6-6D turbines. The CF6-6G also incorporated a new annular combustor, which featured a new cooling pattern to keep combustor metal temperatures down and a new fuel nozzle design to feed more fuel through the nozzles to increase operating temperatures. [39] The CF6-6K version of the engine, which featured decreased specific fuel consumption and improved performance retention and reliability, was certified in September 1981. By 1984, CF6-6 engines had logged over 10 million hours. [40]

While GE was trying to get the CF6 established with the major domestic airlines, they also looked to specific areas of the European airline market. Their target was a European airline consortium called KSSU, which consisted of KLM, SwissAir, SAS, and UTA airlines. KSSU was interested in an airplane that could fly from Copenhagen to New York in the summer heat. Their engineers felt that the engines in that type of airplane would have to have 50,000-pound-thrust capability. GE engineers proceeded to grow the CF6 again, committing the new growth version to KSSU in June 1969. KSSU agreed to purchase the McDonnell Douglas DC-10-30 with the new GE engine and announced their decision at the 1969 Paris Air Show.

The GE growth program resulted in the CF6-50 series of engines, the first of which, the CF6-50A, was announced in January 1969. The new engine series was designed to meet future airline requirements, and therefore GE developed several slightly different model variants. The CF6-50A engine model was designed for a takeoff thrust of 49,000 pounds at 86°F, although the engine went to 54,000 pounds during the first 9 hours of its testing. Reduction in bypass ratio from 5.9 to 4.4 increased airflow through the engine core from the CF6-6 engine's 180 pounds per second to 290 pounds per second while slightly decreasing turbine entry temperature.

A major change in the CF6-50 series was the introduction of two additional stages behind the single-stage LP compressor, with no change in the turbofan's external dimension. The engine was certified by the FAA in March 1972, and the CF6-50A engine entered service in the DC-10 Series 30 aircraft in December 1972. Further variants in the CF6-50 series were the 50,000-pound-thrust CF6-50B, the 51,000-pound-thrust CF6-50C (certified November 1973), the CF6-50C1/E1 at 52,500 pounds of thrust, and the CF6-50C2/E2 (certified in 1978) for the Air Force KC-10 and the Boeing E-4.[41] By 1984, the CF6-50 series had logged over 22 million hours in service.[42]

Not content with sales to KSSU, GE continued to aggressively market the CF6 and CF6-50. A second airline consortium, ATLAS, consisting of Alitalia, Air France, Lufthansa, and Sabena, also agreed to buy the DC-10-30 with the CF6-50 engine. GE and McDonnell Douglas were helped by GE's decision to select Air France in Paris as the overhaul shop for the CF6 engines in Europe. GE also won a key victory when Aerospatiale selected the CF6-50 engine for their A300 Airbus. Four factors were prominent in the Aerospatiale decision. First, the CF6 engine had thrust lapse rate characteristics that closely matched the requirements of the A300 airplane. Second, the CF6 was demonstrating an excellent record in the early airline service. Third, SNECMA of France and MTU of Germany were to participate in the manufacturing of CF6-50 engines for the A300. Fourth, GE provided the flight-test engines and associated support for Aerospatiale. GE also found a market for the CF6 in the Boeing 747. After a tough engine competition, the GE CF6-50 was selected for the Air Force Airborne Command Post (ACP) version of the Boeing 747. Foreign airlines were quick to see the value in the CF6-50-powered 747. KLM, Lufthansa, and then Air France bought it.[43]

In December 1977, General Electric launched a major new variant of the CF6 engine, the CF6-80 series. The company reduced the engine's weight and overall length by eliminating the midframe of the turbine and by reducing the length of the combustor and diffuser. The new engine series was designed to provide an average four percent improvement in specific fuel consumption. All the new engines used the same fan section, which featured airfoil changes and an aft movement of the blades' midspan shrouds, but retained the same number of blades and titanium alloy used in previous models. Improvements in the high-pressure compressor included optimized variable-stator schedules—changes in their angular settings for particular flight conditions—optimized clearances, better blade coatings and shrouds, more efficient airfoil shapes, reduced air leakage, better flow paths, and improvements in materials. The CF6-80 series of engines also included a new combustor featuring a machined ring in place of the previous sheet-metal combustor.[44] The CF6-80A/A1 model was rated at 48,000 pounds of thrust and the CF6-80A2/A3 model at 50,000 pounds. The first engine in the series first ran in October 1979, and GE obtained certification for the series in October 1981.[45] This engine design was further refined in the early 1980s into the CF6-80C2 engine. This engine first ran on May 27, 1982, and exceeded 60,000 pounds of thrust.

The early 1980s saw the beginning of an overall slump in aircraft and aircraft engine sales. The opportunities to sell new aircraft and new engines declined, although many in the industry believed that new models had to be developed to succeed the designs of the 1960s and 1970s. The 1980s proved to be a decade of variants of aircraft models and of aircraft engines, with two U.S. companies—P&W and GE—dominating the international aircraft engine market.

Rolls-Royce was a distant third with only about 13 percent of all orders in the large civil aircraft engine market. The three main contender engines remained the same as in the 1970s, with the P&W JT9D, the GE CF6 series, and the Rolls Royce RB211. P&W's market share still depended a great deal on JT8D engine orders, with the major market remaining with the Boeing 747. GE's primary market was the McDonnell Douglas DC-10. The Airbus market was split among American, British, and other European engine companies. Both P&W and GE's aircraft engine divisions were well supported by their parent companies. P&W was producing about 420 JT9Ds per year while GE was producing about 300 CF6s per year. Both companies had continued to follow their core engine development philosophies dating from the 1950s, with P&W successfully developing the twin-spool concept for the commercial market and GE continuing development of their variable-stator technology. Although the CF6 had dual spools, GE preferred to call its low-pressure compressor spool a "booster."[46]

In 1980 GE launched the CF6-80C program, a higher-thrust and reduced-weight design. GE's design motivation was to use the CF6-50 engine as the base line for a new model that would take full advantage of airline fuel burn, would reduce engine maintenance, increase thrust capability above the 60,000-pound range, and finally, could be optimally configured to very specific airline requirements. This new engine represented a marked advance in technology in terms of reduced length and weight, improved specific fuel consumption (an 11 to 13 percent improvement over the CF6-50 and five to eight percent over the CF6-80A), and enhanced performance retention. The front fan of the engine was replaced by a new 93-inch-diameter fan, marking the first time that the CF6's fan had outgrown the engine nacelle parameters. The engine had a redesigned four-stage low-pressure compressor and low-pressure turbine reduced aerodynamically with five and a half stages.[47] In the fall of 1982 the engine exceeded 62,000 pounds of thrust in a 75-hour test. This made the CF6-80C the most powerful civil turbofan yet produced. The first production engine was tested in March 1984. The engine was flight-tested between August and December 1984, and was certified by the FAA on June 28, 1985. In February 1984 GE began a technical collaboration with Rolls-Royce on the CF6-80C, complementing GE's prior building program agreements with SNECMA of France, MTU of Germany, Volvo Flygmotor of Sweden and Fiat Aviazione of Italy. The engine was certified at 60,200 pounds of thrust in September 1986. The applications for the CF6-80C included the Airbus A300-600, A310-200 and A310-300; the Boeing 767-200, 767-300ER, 747-300, and 747-400; and the McDonnell Douglas MD-11.[48] On June 12, 1987, GE announced a new model of the CF6-80C series, the CF6-80C2, at 64,000 pounds of thrust. The engine, installed in the new Airbus A330-300, was the first to receive joint U.S. FAA/European Joint Aviation Administration certification on October 21, 1993.

By 1991 GE had gained a considerable portion of the commercial large-engine business with the CF6 high-bypass engine. The U.S. military was flying with the CF6 in their E-4A, KC-10, and Boeing 7C-14 AMST prototype. The commercial market featured the CF6 in the DC-10-10, DC-10-30, A300, A310, 747-100, 747-200, 767, and 747SR. More than 400 CF6-powered aircraft and about 3,800 CF6 engines had been ordered. About 10 million CF6 engine flight hours had been logged.

---

### Endnotes

[1] GE Company, *Eight Decades of Progress*, 148.

[2] Ibid, 149.

[3] Horn, Edward, "Historical Analysis of the TF39 Development and Qualification Program for C-5A Heavy Logistic

Transport," United States Air Force Scientific Advisory Board Ad Hoc Committee on Engine Development Briefing, delivered at Wright Patterson Air Force Base, Ohio, on May 14-15, 1973, 77.

[4] GE Company, *Eight Decades of Progress*, 150.

[5]   Horn, "Historical Analysis of the TF39...," 77.

[6]   Ibid, 26.

[7]   Ibid, 30.

[8]   Ibid, 77.

[9]   Ibid.

[10]  Ibid, 32.

[11]  Ibid, 33.

[12]  Ibid, 37.

[13]  Ibid, 38.

[14]  Ibid, 39 and 77.

[15]  Ibid, 40.

[16]  Ibid.

[17]  Ibid, 29.

[18]  Ibid, 75.

[19]  Air Force Propulsion Characteristics Summary, GE TF39 Turbofan, 75.

[20]  Ibid, 75, and Horn, "Historical Analysis of the TF39...," 77.

[21]  Air Force Propulsion Characteristics Summary, GE TF39 Turbofan, 75.

[22]  Horn, "Historical Analysis of the TF39...," 77.

[23]  Ibid.

[24]  Air Force Propulsion Characteristics Summary, GE TF39 Turbofan, 75.

[25]  Horn, "Historical Analysis of the TF39...," 75.

[26]  Harrison, Neal, "Boeing 747," Flight International (December 12, 1968), 979.

[27]  NAL, "Powerplants for the Giant Jets - The New 40,000 lb. Thrust Class," Interavia (July 1966), 1033.

[28]  Harrison, Flight International, 980, and Bowers, Peter M, Boeing Aircraft Since 1916, Annapolis, MD: Naval Institute Press, 1989, 508.

[29]  Gunston, Aero Engines, 126-127.

[30]  Ibid, 128.

[31]  Ibid, 126.

[32]  NAL, "JT9D-7F Engine Developed for Heavier 747 Aircraft," AW&ST (January 28, 1974), 19.

[33]  Sweetman, Bill, "Big-fan Engines: A New U.S. Generation," Interavia, Spring 1980, 414.

[34]  Ibid.

[35]  Travers, William, History of GE Aircraft Engines, unpublished manuscript, 6-6.

[36]  NAL, Jane's All the Worlds Aircraft: 1986-87, Janes Publishing Company, Limited, London, UK, 941

[37]  Travers, History of GE, 6-8.

[38]  Yaffee, Michael L, "GE Continues CF6 Family Growth," Aviation Week & Space Technology, April 8, 1974, 42.

[39]  Yaffee, Michael L, "Uprated Versions of CF6 Developed," Aviation Week & Space Technology, August 2, 1971, 36-38

[40]  Jane's: 1986-87, 942.

[41]  Yaffee, "Uprated Versions of CF6," AVW&ST, 37.

[42]  Jane's:1986-87, 942.

[43]  Travers, History of GE, 6-10.

[44]  NAL, "Manufacturers Broaden Engine Families," Aviation Week & Space Technology, October 23, 1978, 62.

[45]  Jane's: 1986-87, 942.

[46]  Sweetman, Bill, "Big-fan Engines: A New U.S. Generation," Interavia, Spring 1980, 411-412.

[47]  NAL, "New Business in Reengining Transports Forecast," Aviation Week & Space Technology, November 9, 1981, 166-167

[48]  Jane's: 1986-87, 943.

**AV-8B Harrier, Powered by
One Rolls-Royce Pegasus 2 (F402) Turbofan**

# Vertical/Short Takeoff and Landing Aircraft Gas Turbine Engines

Ever since the first would-be fliers embarked into the air to emulate the birds, vertical takeoff and landing have been among their goals. The desire to take off vertically was partially satisfied by the development of the helicopter, but the goal of a practical vertical/short takeoff and landing (VSTOL) airplane eluded inventors and designers for many years.

Millions of dollars have been spent on lift-fan engines and miniature engines placed vertically in the fuselages of test aircraft, but no other design has been so successful as that exemplified by the Harrier aircraft and its vectored-thrust turbofan Pegasus (later designated the F402 by the U.S. Navy) engine. The Pegasus is included in this study of American aircraft gas turbine development both because it provides the power plant for the Marine Corps' primary ground-support aircraft, the Harrier, and also because the Pegasus represents the American ability to recognize and work effectively with foreign designs. The Pegasus continues the legacy of the Whittle engine, the Nene, Tay, Marbore, and other foreign designs that have been successfully imported by the United States.

## Development of the Orpheus Engine

To begin our examination of the evolution of the Pegasus engine, we must first look at the Bristol model BE.26 Orpheus axial turbojet engine, which provided the gas generator for the Pegasus. The Orpheus engine was developed expressly for the Folland Gnat, a lightweight fighter design by W.E.W. "Teddy" Petter, Folland's chief designer, who had earlier produced the Canberra jet bomber (U.S. Air Force's B-57, built by Martin from the original designs of the English Electric Team under Petter in the United Kingdom). Petter approached Dr. Stanley Hooker (later knighted by Queen Elizabeth II) and told him his requirements. Hooker, who was chief engineer of the Bristol Aero-Engine Company in England, was confident that he could design the engine needed:

> I knew from my calculations that there was no intrinsic difficulty in producing an engine weighing only 800 pounds yet able to give a thrust of 5,000 pounds. In keeping with the light-fighter concept, the engine needed to be simple, without any attempt to attain a high pressure-ratio, because for a short-range fighter the fuel saved would be more than outweighed by the greater engine weight. But it was apparent that providing an engine for the Gnat offered opportunities to rethink axial engine design and introduce a number of novel features.
>
> One was the elimination of the centre bearing. Previous UK axials, including the Avon, Sapphire and Olympus, had three main shaft bearings, one at each end of the compressor and the third at the turbine. According to Euclid a straight line is the shortest distance between two points, not three, and for this reason it is impossible to keep all three bearings absolutely in line. The main rotating assembly has to be split into front and rear sections joined by a coupling able to allow for small misalignments. In the design of the BE.26 Orpheus we adopted a short seven-stage compressor driven by a single-stage turbine, and it was desirable to eliminate the centre bearing. Doing this in ordinary engines would lead to the main drive shaft suffering from whirling, bending outwards and whipping around like a skipping rope. But we made the drive shaft in the form of a thin-walled tube more than 8 inches in diameter. It was surprisingly light, and had a critical whirling speed much higher than any possible excitation from the engine.[1]

By leaving out the center bearing and its coupling, the Bristol design team could also eliminate the accompanying supporting structure, the bearing lubrication system, a sealing system, and a bearing air-cooling system.

The Hooker team also came up with a novel method of constructing the compressor rotor. The rotor blades were slotted into aluminum disks, which were then separated by spacer rings. The whole compressor assembly was then doweled together for concentricity and fastened lengthwise by steel bolts.[2]

The team devised a new method of mounting the turbine on the large-diameter shaft. The disc was provided with precision-machined radial splines that engaged in similar splines on the face of the shaft. These radial splines ensured very accurate concentricity while allowing for the radial expansion of the disc and shaft due to temperature and centrifugal force. This was a most successful innovation, and for the first time it proved possible to remove and replace a turbine without having to rebalance the whole rotating assembly.

The combustion system was of the cannular type, a single outer casing containing seven flame tubes. These also broke new ground in that the downstream portion of each incorporated one-seventh of the turbine entry duct, complete with the stator vanes. This duct conveys the hot gas from the combustor to the turbine. Previously it had been made of a combination of steel castings and refractory sheet-metal parts fabricated by welding. Not only did this part of the engine often give a great deal of mechanical trouble, due to cracking and distortion, but it was also heavy, difficult to manufacture, expensive, and unreliable. The neat Orpheus design eliminated these troubles. The individual chambers were merely held together by a simple bolt, which allowed for expansion without stress.[3] Bristol designer Bernard Massey spearheaded the detailed design and development of the Orpheus.

The Gnat was the Folland Company's entrant in the NATO Light Attack Fighter design competition of 1954-55. Although the Gnat saw only very limited usage by the British, it was exported to Finland and was manufactured extensively under license by Hindustan Aeronautics Ltd. of India as the Ajeet fighter and the Kiran II trainer. Most importantly for this story, the Orpheus engine was the power plant of the winner of the NATO light-fighter competition, the Fiat G91.[4]

While the Massey team at Bristol was working on turning the Orpheus design into machinery, the Gnat had gained the attention of the U.S. Mutual Weapons Development Program (MWDP) office in Paris. At that time the aeronautics side of MWDP was headed by U.S. Air Force Colonel Johnnie Driscoll. MWDP picked up 75 percent of the development costs of the Orpheus engine, with Bristol adding the remainder.[5] Hooker recalls Driscoll and the MWDP:

> Johnnie had been a USAAF bomber pilot in the War, and was proud of his Irish descent. He was a keen, intelligent officer of great driving power, and poured millions into Orpheus and the Fiat G91 at a time when development funds in the United Kingdom had virtually dried up. The office of MWDP was an act of great generosity by the American people, and Johnnie and von Karman were great ambassadors for them. It was a stroke of good fortune for Bristol when the Orpheus was chosen, and I count myself as very fortunate in the friendship that I had with these two outstanding men.[6]

Theodore von Karman asked to serve as technical advisor to the Orpheus. (Hooker had been a star pupil of Professor von Karman during his studies in Germany before the outbreak of World War II). The first run of the Orpheus was in early 1955. Type-test (a mandatory test prior to the award of a civil Type Certificate for the engine) was in January 1956 at 4,000 pounds of thrust. In November 1956 the first Orpheus production series engine was type-tested at 4,250 pounds of thrust and in May 1957 the first Mk 800 series was type-tested at 4,850 pounds. The Orpheus ultimately gave almost 6 pounds of thrust per pound of weight.[7]

## Michel Wibault and the Role of the Mutual Weapons Development Program

The U.S. government in the early 1950s had conceived the Mutual Weapons Development Program as a sort of extension of the Marshal Plan. The program's mission was to seek out and financially support military research and development projects in Europe that would assist post-war technical-economic recovery. Its secondary mission was to augment the effectiveness of NATO without duplicating American ideas and programs. Among other projects, the MWDP sponsored both the Light Attack Fighter Requirement and the Orpheus development at Bristol. The MWDP was headquartered in Paris, and it was in Paris in 1956 that a new U.S. Air Force liaison officer for the MWDP, Colonel Willis Chapman, first examined a proposal for a new propulsion system designed by a leading French aeronautical engineer named Michel Wibault.[8]

Wibault was famous in France for his many years of aircraft designs, including the Wibault 7 (1925) and Wibault 72 (1926) fighters, and the Wibault 74 and 75 naval fighters. The Wibault 75 had seen 10 years of service. Between the first and second World Wars, Wibault ran his own aircraft factory. He escaped the Nazi occupation in 1940 and worked in the United States at Republic Aviation alongside Kurt Valli. He returned to France after the war and set himself up (with some financial support from the Rockefeller family) as a one-man think tank and aero-consultant.

In 1955-56, Wibault came up with the idea of an 8,000-horsepower Bristol Orion turboprop engine driving four centrifugal compressors in the sides of the aircraft fuselage (Figure 17-1). If the compressor outlets were turned downward, the thrust could provide direct lift as well as propulsion. The advantage in this proposal over all other previous VSTOL direct lift designs was that the engine and blowers could be placed behind the aircraft's center of gravity, and the four blower jets would produce a ground cushion of air for direct lift. Wibault called this new system and its aircraft the "Gyroptere."[9]

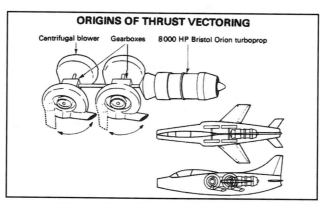

**Figure 17-1. Wibault Le Gyroptere**
*(Illustration courtesy of Rolls-Royce)*

Wibault submitted drawings and a proposal for a single-engine vectored-thrust turboshaft-driven propulsion system and fighter aircraft. After examining the proposal, Colonel Chapman turned to Dr. Stanley Hooker, the technical director of Bristol Aero Engine Limited (BAEL, the new name for Bristol), and a team of propulsion engineers from BAEL to examine the Wibault proposal and report on its practicality. Chapman also asked Hooker to meet in Paris with Wibault, which Hooker did in July 1956.

Although Chapman knew of other VSTOL proposals and the previous work on VSTOL that had been done in the United States and United Kingdom, he had not been particularly impressed with the practicality of previous designs. The Wibault proposal, though, intrigued him. If the Bristol group under Hooker could validate the concept, Wibault's proposal could be submitted to the MWDP's Technical Approval Board in Washington for funding of initial design studies at least.

## Gordon Lewis and the Evolution of the BE.53

After examining Wibault's proposal and meeting with him, Dr. Hooker gave the proposal to a young Bristol project engineer named Gordon Lewis, who determined the initial design of the Pegasus engine. Lewis and Hooker agreed that the major problem with the Wibault design was the heavy weight of the transmission shaft, gears, and volute casing. They agreed, however, that this new concept in VSTOL propulsion was cutting-edge engine technology, and they wanted BAEL in on that technology. Bristol would build the engine. Colonel Chapman of MWDP authorized 75 percent funding with Bristol providing the remaining 25 percent. The MWDP deal called for the development of two flight-cleared engines for Hawker Aircraft use.[10]

Lewis immediately began to revise the Wibault design. Instead of the four shaft-driven centrifugal compressors, he proposed a single multistage axial-flow fan, mounted directly ahead of the power generator, and driven by a reduction gearbox. The fan and turboshaft engine would have separate intakes, and the flow from the fan would be taken to two rotatable curved ducts in the sides of the aircraft. The turboshaft exhaust would flow aft like a conventional turbojet, producing horizontal thrust. This was a three-nozzle power plant with a limited STOL potential, but Bristol filed provisional patent application No. 881662 on January 29, 1957, naming Wibault and Lewis as joint inventors and listing the new design as the BE (Bristol Engine) .53 project.[11] Work began on the BE.53 project in 1957.[12]

From his first review of the Wibault proposal throughout the design evolution of the Pegasus, Lewis agreed with Hooker that any new VSTOL engine design would require strict control over three major design parameters: weight, reliability, and cost. Lewis also proposed using existing Bristol engine components wherever possible to lower the risk of developing the new engine design. The original Wibault proposal called for a Bristol Orion power plant driving a front fan through a reduction gearbox, designed originally for a propeller. Lewis, however, saw the weight penalty in the reduction gearbox and decided to drive the fan directly through a separate turbine and shaft. As the proposed separate shaft would not fit in the Orion engine, Lewis proposed the new Orpheus turbojet as the basis for the new engine design. The Orpheus engine had three things in its favor. First, the lightweight design of the Orpheus met the weight design parameter well, the thrust-to-weight ratio of the Orpheus being 5.8:1. Second, the engine was a solid, robust design with advanced aerodynamics. Finally, the Orpheus was a simple design with a two-bearing rotating assembly and a large-diameter shaft through which its fan drive shaft could pass (Figure 17-2).[13]

Lewis also configured the new engine to take a front-mounted overhung fan incorporating two low-pressure stages. This fan design was taken from the Bristol Olympus engine. The air from the fan was split; the inner annulus supercharged the gas generator, and the outer part discharged air through rotating, vectoring front nozzles.

It was in this configuration that the airplane designers under Sir Sydney Camm, a legend in British fighter aircraft development, first saw the BE.53 design proposed in a brochure in June 1957 (Figure 17-2). The creative engineering vision of Ralph S. Hooper, then a senior configuration designer in the Hawker Future Project Office, was responsible for a practical VSTOL airplane arrangement.

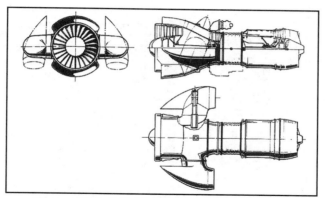

**Figure 17-2. Bristol BE.53 Orpheus in 1957**
*(Illustration courtesy of Rolls-Royce)*

Notwithstanding the Bristol Engine Company's patents and indeed ignorant of them at this time, Hooper "invented" the four-nozzle Pegasus and through the summer of 1957 pressed Bristol for this four-nozzle configuration. Hooper also repeatedly stressed the importance of the Pegasus shafts' counterrotating to minimize or eliminate gyroscopic cross coupling in hover flight.

At this point the two-stage fan was aluminum-bladed, and Hawker had to allay the nervousness of the Bristol team by offering to make the double compound-curved jet exhaust pipe. Bristol reckoned Hawker's skills in double-curved metal bashing to be much greater than their own. Sir Sidney Camm and his engineering team took this prospective task in their stride. After all, hundreds of Hawker Sea Hawks had been built using a Rolls Royce Nene power unit with a bifurcated exhaust pipe built by the Rolls Royce factory at Derby in England.

Hooker described later with benevolent hindsight how the four-nozzle concept was introduced:

> Camm, remembering his "birficated" [sic] jet pipe in the Sea Hawk, suggested bifurcating the jet pipe on the Pegasus and using a second pair of left/right nozzles rotating in unison with the first pair. A further desirable feature was to make the high-pressure and low-pressure spools rotate in opposite directions, thus almost eliminating the engine's gyroscopic couple. This is a very important objective for a VSTOL aircraft, enabling it to hover under perfect control.[14]

This later feature (counterrotation of the two spools) was not adopted until the Pegasus 2 design, the first version to be run on the test bench and the first to fly at about 11,000 pounds of VSTOL thrust.

The team decided for the sake of simplicity and weight to support the fan on just two bearings, making the fan an overhung fan. The engineers at Bristol also changed the high-pressure compressor blade material from aluminum to titanium to cope with higher operating temperatures and pressures. The new design was finished in August 1959, and was designated the BE53/1 by Bristol.[15] Figure 17-3 illustrates the derivation of the Pegasus design from the Orpheus.

## Center-of-Gravity and Vectored-Thrust Exhaust Considerations

The primary design constraint on both the engine and aircraft design when considering VSTOL is that the center of the engine's vertical thrust must coincide with the aircraft's center of gravity. In conventional aircraft the mass of the engine is placed well behind the thrust/lift center and the cockpit and accessories are forward of the center of gravity. Because the VSTOL engine must lie close to the center of gravity, the engine's intake duct is only about one diameter long, compared with a much longer duct in a conventional installation. The Pegasus installation required a short, high-curvature duct, which brought problems because the inlet had to deliver air

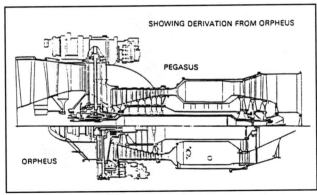

**Figure 17-3. Comparison of Pegasus and Orpheus**
*(Illustration courtesy of Rolls-Royce)*

to the engine fan face at a high level of pressure recovery. The engine responded to poor-quality air delivered by the intake at the rate of over 1 percent loss of gross thrust (i.e., lifting force in vertical takeoff and hover) per 1 percent loss of inlet air overall pressure recovery. The intake lip profile had also to be carefully shaped to minimize air intake spillage drag in cruise and other parts of the wingborne envelope.[16] The final inlet design delivered air to the engine entry face with moderate pressure loss but with a high level of static pressure distortion.

The jet exhaust beneath a VSTOL aircraft in the Vertical Takeoff (VTO) mode brings with it a unique set of problems, e.g., erosion of the ground surface, hot gas recirculation, lift force losses due to down-draft over the airframe caused by the pumping action of the ground jet sheets beneath the airframe, and rear-fuselage and tail surface buffeting and structure heating problems.

Ground erosion can occur when the surface is softened or dried by the jets so that particles are loosened and blown away by the jet flow. During taxiing with the lift-nozzles down, the jet exhaust impinges on the ground and can cause surface erosion. Although the erosion of the surface soil is not serious in itself, debris such as loose stones can be thrown up into the intake. The Pegasus and Harrier designers found that water-cured concrete is very resistant to erosion, but that asphalt or tarmac surfaces are not. The tar in asphalt or tarmac melts quickly, allowing the aggregate to blow away. Grassland was found to erode in less than one second's exposure at high power. They did, however, also find that practical lift jets have very short residence times on unprepared surfaces, and that vectored thrust minimizes ground exposure to jet blast. The Harrier has proved to be very successful operating from prepared and unprepared surfaces (grass, asphalt, wooden ship decks, etc.).

Hot-gas recirculation in VSTOL is primarily caused by jet exhaust "fountains," which are formed between pairs of jet exhausts. This gas can, under certain conditions, enter the intake and produce temperature rise and distortion effects, which reduce power and surge margin of the engine. The Pegasus has two sets of nozzles. The front pair exhausts cool air and the rear pair exhausts hot air. This arrangement produces two fountains, a longitudinal rising flow along the centerline of the fuselage and a transverse fountain between the front and rear pairs of exhaust streams. It was fortunate for the Harrier and Pegasus designers that the front nozzle exhaust produces a barrier of cool air that largely prevents the hot gases from the rear exhaust nozzles from reaching the engine intakes.

Vertical flight mode produces another effect that played a large role in the evolution of the Harrier and Pegasus design. That was lift in ground effect, the downward airflow induced by the jets in the air surrounding the aircraft producing a lift loss on the airframe. In the vertical mode close to the ground, this effect can produce a 10 percent loss in lift, though away from the ground it is much less. The Pegasus engines' exhaust fountains tend to equalize this effect when the Harrier is light, but when the Harrier has a war load, the effect is greater, and the subsequent lift loss is greater. The designers of the Harrier attached fences, called lift improvement devices (LIDS) or cushion augmentation devices (CADS), to the aircraft undersurface around the impingement area of the fountains to capture the fountain flow and deflect it downward, thereby increasing the air pressure under the fuselage.

Another VSTOL design complication that arose with the Pegasus/Harrier design was the problem of the effect of hot jet exhaust on the aircraft fuselage. Conventional jets exhaust their airflow at the rear of the aircraft. The Harrier, due to its center of gravity requirements affecting engine placement, exhausts its gases along the side of the aircraft in forward flight (although not in vertical takeoff or landing). The two front nozzles, exhausting cool air, do not present a problem to the aircraft. The two hot rear-nozzle flows, however, at 1,200°F, threaten to overheat the fuselage skin. The Harrier design team tried a triangular "pen nib" exhaust heat shield, but this proved inadequate. A later rectangular "spade" heat shield fixed the problem.[17]

## Thrust-Vectoring Nozzles, Plenum Chamber and Exhaust Ducting

The keys to vectored thrust are the nozzle arrangement and design. The Pegasus has two sets of nozzles, one pair carrying air directly from the fan and exhausting it forward of the Harrier's wing, and one pair of "hot" nozzles directing the turbine exhaust flows, located under the wing. The vectoring comes from the ability of each nozzle to direct the exhaust flow through an angular range of more than 90 degrees. Both front and rear nozzles are constructed of sheet metal and include two airfoil-section vanes equally spaced across the nozzle throat. The two front nozzles are airframe-mounted and the rear nozzles are engine-mounted. The nozzles were aerodynamically engineered to provide minimum internal pressure loss, minimum fan and turbine exit distortion, consistent thrust center locations, and acceptable flow characteristics. The nozzles are chain-actuated by the aircraft-mounted nozzle actuation system.

## Fan and Turbine Blade Excitation

In the Pegasus design the front fan vibration problems were a result of the short intakes of the Pegasus causing severe first- and second-mode flexural blade vibration. Pressure patterns in the Pegasus' plenum chamber also caused vibration in the back of the fan. The fan's blades had to be strengthened to account for these two factors, as neither the length of the intakes nor the design of the plenum chamber could be significantly altered. To strengthen the fan blades, the Bristol team "snubbed" the blades with titanium, introducing separators between the blades to absorb and damp out the vibration. From the Pegasus engine used in the XV-6A Kestrel, Bristol adopted much stiffer titanium alloy blading for all fan stages.

The blades of the turbine were not immune from development growing pains. The proximity of the rear nozzles to the turbine caused the development of pressure patterns that led the rear of the turbine, the low-pressure section, to vibrate. The high-aspect-ratio design of the turbine blades (to keep the engine short) made the problem worse. The engineers solved this problem by adding wire lacing to the turbine rotor blades. This damped the vibration to acceptable levels.

## Engine Rating Philosophy

The Pegasus engine, like any other VSTOL main propulsion system, is designed to deliver its maximum thrust in the vertical-lift mode, though only for relatively short times. The Pegasus engine's hot components must exhibit a very good heat-sink capacity to absorb the high temperatures required for vertical lift. Water injection helps this process. The engine must also be able to satisfy a varying air bleed demand for controlling the aircraft in powered-lift flight, and its throttle response must be rapid and very precise, because the Harrier's height during jet-borne flight is controlled entirely by engine thrust and in hover the throttle is the primary height control. Whereas the location of the throttle control is a relatively noncritical factor in a standard jet fighter, in the Harrier the throttle had to be located where the pilot could exercise very precise control over it during vertical takeoff and landing.

The collaboration between Hawker Aircraft Limited and Bristol to develop the Pegasus and P1127 was not driven by any corporate or governmental requirement or contract (from either side of the Atlantic). Although the Mutual Weapons Development Program underwrote most of the initial development (to 1961), there was in the United Kingdom no official military requirement for the aircraft or its engine. For that matter, the official British policy at that time was that the guided missile had made the manned airplane largely obsolete. The early collaboration between Bristol and Hawker later became very important because decisions were made to simply advance the state of the technology. Those decisions required great vision on the part of Sir Stanley Hooker, Sir Sidney Camm, and their teams. All were aware of the current state of VSTOL technology and all knew that a vectored-thrust design of such simplicity could finally bring about a fully functional, production aircraft. But it would take a great deal of money to do it, money that the two companies might have to provide themselves after the MWDP funding ran out. Hawker Aircraft did have a tradition of cutting-edge aircraft development and had been willing to gamble company funds on new aeronautical concepts in the past.

The Hawker P1127 design team included Roy Chaplin, Ralph Hooper, John Fozard, Harry Tuffen, and others. The Bristol team relied on Gordon Lewis, John Dale, Charles Marehant, and others who found Pegasus development equally challenging. Designing VSTOL aircraft did present some difficulties that the Hawker team had to overcome.

There is an inherent conflict between VSTOL and high-speed flight, and it comes from the configuration of the aircraft. Vertical takeoff and supersonic flight lie at two extremes of the aircraft speed spectrum. Most VSTOL designs—and the P1127 was no exception—tend to pay more attention to the zero-speed, powered-lift end of the spectrum. The vectored-thrust concept complicated the design even more for the aircraft designer. The Hawker engineers realized that the characteristics of the vectored-thrust power plant formed the foundation of the design, and that configuration and operation of any aircraft they designed would have to reflect that foundation. This realization marked the beginning of the very close design and development relationship between Bristol Siddeley engines and Hawker Aircraft.

## Problems Presented by the Vectored-Thrust Engine

From the perspective of the aircraft design team at Hawker Aircraft there were several features of the Pegasus engine that were of particular importance to the P1127 design. The first was that the engine required a large static air mass flow, thus requiring large intakes with the best possible pressure recovery in the VSTOL mode. The large intakes would also "spill" large quantities of air during cruise flight with the throttle back at low level. During these conditions the engine would be operating at less than one-fifth of its sea-level VSTOL power.

Another problem lay with the arrangement of the Pegasus engine and its nozzle vis-à-vis the aircraft fuselage. The rear of the P1127 fuselage was very narrow in the back, to allow passage of the exhaust of the rear nozzles. This took away from the aircraft designers those areas of the aircraft which could conceivably have been used for internal stores.

The multiple-nozzle approach of the Pegasus led the Hawker team to recognize that the thrust distribution of the four nozzles would impact on the design of the aircraft. They called the concept the "thrust center." The thrust center lay longitudinally about midway between the two pairs of exhaust nozzles, because each pair of nozzles provided about 50 percent of the engine's thrust. The problem was that during the aircraft's transition from direct lift to forward flight, the aircraft's thrust vector passed through the thrust center, which changed the thrust center over the VSTOL operating range of the aircraft. A further complication was that the thrust center and the aircraft's center of gravity had to remain as close as possible.

The final design of the P1127 came about because the design team had to keep the best possible relationship between the aircraft's thrust center and center of gravity, including during the all-important hover-to-forward flight transition. This relationship between the thrust center and center of gravity influenced all further development of the aircraft, from the initial P1127 to the design of the Kestrel and the subsequent Harrier design. Also affected by this thrust-center/center-of-gravity problem was the design of the forward and rear fuselage and the allocation of fuel tankage and equipment stowage.

As with the Pegasus engine, the Hawker design team "evolved" the aircraft design through the P1127 and the Kestrel to the Harrier. The specific problems encountered and the steps taken to address them (as were the details of the engine evolution described above) are detailed in the Rolls-Royce British Aerospace publication *Vectored Thrust Jet VSTOL: An Evaluation of the Harrier AV-8A and the Pegasus Engine*, written jointly with Hawker Siddeley Aviation. Bristol Siddeley Engines had become part of Rolls-Royce when they amalgamated in 1966. Hawker Aircraft Ltd. became a part of Hawker Siddeley Aviation in 1963 and by 1978 had become a division of British Aerospace.

## From P1127 to Kestrel

Ralph Hooper produced the first full design layout of the P1127 in August 1957, and it was shown to Colonel Bill Chapman of the MWDP office in Paris in September. Although impressed overall by the design, Chapman told Hooper that the aircraft needed double its designed range to be "sold." This was later achieved by the upgrading of the engine with the transonic fan. Hooper initially envisioned a "cropped-delta" wing for the P1127, similar to that of the very successful Douglas A-4 Skyhawk designed by Ed Heineman and first flown in 1954. The cropped-delta design was designated the P1127C and was shown to Chapman at MWDP on March 24, 1958.

As stated earlier, in June 1958 Chapman and the MWDP Technical Approval Group in Washington, D.C., decided to fund 75 percent of BE.53, with Bristol providing the remaining 25 percent. The British military, however, still refused to participate in the program unless a supersonic derivative could be developed. The Air Ministry's indifference to it led Hawker to cease working on the P1121, which had been the major design project of Hawker Aircraft up to that time. This left the field open, so to speak, for the P1127. The British Ministry of Supply also issued GOR 345, an official requirement for the development of an aircraft to replace the Hawker Hunter in the ground attack and reconnaissance roles from 1965 on. This requirement was open to all British aircraft manufacturers. Hawker, therefore, decided to authorize the company's experimental drawing office to begin work on the P1127 under company funding. In March 1959 the Hawker Siddeley Board officially authorized the building of two P1127 prototypes and the company issued the first drawings for manufacture of the first two demonstrator aircraft.[18]

In July 1959 Hooper and Bob Marsh, another senior Hawker engineer, visited the Bell Aircraft Company and the NASA Langley facility at Hampton, Virginia, to inspect the American vectored-thrust Bell X-14 aircraft. NASA Langley's director, John Stack, offered to build and test a one-sixth scale free-flight model of the P1127. The work on this model (and an additional transonic model with jets represented by steam produced from hydrogen peroxide) was funded by the U.S. Air Force. Indeed, NASA's Marion "Mack" McKinney was responsible for validating (with the free-flight model in the NASA Langley full-scale tunnel) the P1127's ability to make the transition from hovering to forward flight without auto-stabilization.[19]

While work continued on the P1127 prototypes, the BE.53.2 or Pegasus 1 (Figure 17-4) of 9,000 pounds of thrust made its first run in September 1959.[20] In October the unexpected happened when the British Ministry of Supply (MOS) awarded Hawker a £75,000 holding contract to cover the airframe work then in progress (although Hawker wasn't to see the first money until June the next year). The Ministry assigned the building of the two prototype airframes under Specification ER 204D. Funding for the BE.53 engine was still left in the hands of Bristol and the MWDP but with the Ministry exercising a very loose supervisory role.

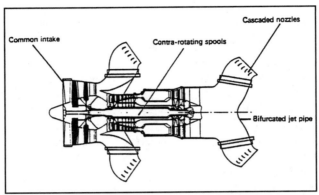

**Figure 17-4. BE.53.2 or Pegasus 1**
*(Illustration courtesy of Rolls-Royce)*

In March 1960 Hawker dispatched Chief Test Pilot A.W. "Bill" Bedford and his assistant, Hugh Merewether, to get some background experience in VSTOL from NASA and the U.S. Air Force. They gained valuable experience on both the NASA variable-stability Sikorsky S-51 helicopter and the X-14 before they returned to England excited about the upcoming trials of the P1127.

On July 15, 1960, Hawker delivered the first P1127 prototype to the Hawker airfield at Dunsfold. The first flight engine (recently named the Pegasus) was a Pegasus 2.

## Evolution of the Pegasus from Development to Production

Once the basic design concepts had been set and the configuration of the Pegasus engine had been decided, the engine enjoyed a steady growth in thrust, not as a luxury but a necessity, because all aircraft designs tend to become heavier over their development time and the customer wants more performance. Through changes in the engine's main performance parameters and within the engine's overall fuselage envelope, the Pegasus design and development team took an incremental approach to the engine's development. The overall thrust of the Pegasus engine during its evolution increased about 60 percent. The Pegasus 2, the first of the definitive series, had been designed by Hooker's team with counterrotating spools.

## Pegasus 2

The Pegasus 2 first ran in February 1960 on the test bed. Its takeoff thrust was 11,000 pounds with a turbine inlet temperature (TIT) of 1,810°F. The Pegasus 2, the first variant to fly, had arrived from Bristol in September 1960. The 11,000 pounds of thrust of the Pegasus 2 was so marginal compared to the weight of the first P1127 aircraft that "in order to get off the ground at all the aircraft had to be stripped of 700 pounds of electrical equipment, etc., and carry fuel for only three minutes' flight."[21]

The first tethered flight (prototype aircraft serial XP831) took place on October 21, 1960. After twenty-one tethered hops, the first untethered flights began on November 19, 1960. The first conventional flight was made on March 13, 1961. After a second redesign of the reaction control system, the first complete transition from jet to wingborne flight and back again were made on September 12, 1961. These tests were crucial in that Hawker and Bristol were able to completely prove the single-engine vectored-thrust concept. It did not matter that the engine could barely lift a stripped-down P1127 off the runway, or that the P1127's wing aerodynamics was impractical, or that the engine consumed fuel at an alarming rate during vertical takeoff. Those areas could be and were improved with subsequent models and flights. The important point is that the Pegasus and P1127 delivered a successful, practical aircraft from the drawing board to the airfield. The British Ministry of Supply was impressed to the point that they not only funded the development of four more P1127 aircraft, but they also began funding part of the Pegasus engine development program as the MWDP sources of cash were drying up.[22]

## Pegasus 3

The Pegasus 3 was a flight-development engine that produced 13,500 pounds of thrust with a TIT of 1,865°F. The Bristol team increased the pressure ratio by adding an extra stage to the high-pressure compressor and added a second stage to the high-pressure turbine. This model had an operating life of about 30 hours.[23]

Short takeoff (STO) testing, beginning in October 1961, confirmed that a relatively short ground run made it possible to lift much heavier loads than with vertical takeoff (VTO). This was of course due to the combination of jet and wing lift. This period also saw the redesign of the aircraft's wing and the change to a 'drooped' tailplane. And in the midst of continuing improvement in both engine and aircraft, government attitudes towards the value of jet VSTOL, spurred by NATO, were changing dramatically in VSTOL's favor.

Between 1959 and 1960 the Royal Air Force and the British Ministry of Supply had developed an Operational Requirement (OR.345) around a projected service version of the P1127. While the government admitted that the P1127 could conceivably do the job, the debate on full development funding of both the Hawker and Bristol programs continued until late 1961. At that point NATO had published its Basic Military Requirement No. 3, calling for the development of a supersonic VSTOL attack fighter. The British government withdrew OR.345 in favor of the new NATO requirement. Hawker Aircraft and Bristol quickly proposed a supersonic VSTOL aircraft based on the P1127. Called the P1154, the new design immediately took first priority at Hawker, although factory work and flight testing continued on the four P1127D development aircraft. This commitment toward P1127 development would prove crucial in the next several years.

The first half of the 1960s saw many developments and refinements in both the Pegasus engine and the P1127 aircraft. The Bristol engineers encountered and overcame many of the problems that pushing the engine technology had caused. The use of titanium in the Pegasus 2 and 3 models was reevaluated after rubbing between the stator and rotor blades in the high-pressure compressor under high temperature and high G forces caused a titanium fire, which in turn caused the crash of the first of the government-funded prototypes (XP972). Although the decision was made to continue the use of titanium, the stators were cut back to compensate for "creep" under high temperatures. Current Pegasus engines are comprised of some 20 percent titanium. The Pegasus 3 and 5 models each increased the thrust of the engine as well as its operational life, from 13,000 pounds to the Kestrel's 15,500-pound Pegasus 5.[24]

The P1127 aircraft was also being tested, modified, and re-tested. Conventional flight and high speed testing had shown inadequacies in the aircraft's flying qualities. The third, fourth, and fifth P1127 aircraft first flew in the period between April 1962 and February 1963. The third in the series incorporated an improved wing design in which the protruding outrigger/reaction control valve fairing was suppressed to give a smooth streamwise wingtip form. The tailplane was also given a sharp downward pitch and an increased span to counter transonic pitch-up.

## The Tripartite Squadron, Trials, and the Pegasus 5

On January 16, 1963, the British government, along with the governments of the Federal Republic of Germany and the United States, signed the Tripartite Agreement to jointly fund procurement of nine P1127s. Their purpose was to form a multinational Tripartite Evaluation Squadron to judge the merits of VSTOL operations in the field. The British government's Ministry of Supply issued Specification FGA 236 D&P for the production of the aircraft.

During 1963, while preparations were underway for the production of the nine P1127s for the Tripartite Squadron, the sixth production P1127 was being modified and fitted with a new swept wing. This aircraft was to be the prototype for the Evaluation Squadron aircraft and was officially designated the Kestrel F.G.A. (Fighter, Ground Attack) Mk1 by the RAF. It first flew in February 1964 powered by a Pegasus 5 engine rated at 15,200 pounds of thrust.

The Tripartite Squadron began forming up in late 1964, and on April 1, 1965, began operations from RAF West Raynham, Norfolk in England. The squadron was commanded by Wing Commander (now Air Commodore Retired) David Scrimgeour and had on its roster three other RAF pilots, two pilots from the German Luftwaffe, one from the U.S. Navy, two from the U.S. Army, and one from the U.S. Air Force. All the U.S. aircrew were qualified test pilots. The RAF and the Luffwaffe assigned regular squadron pilots.

The trials lasted nine months, and the squadron flew 938 sorties for a total of over 600 hours in the United Kingdom. These sorties were mainly to test the feasibility of dispersed operations from grass fields, but the Kestrels also operated from Army battle training areas, roads, disused runways, and meadows. The pilots found out that rolling vertical landings (around 40 knots) best avoided the ground erosion problems. The rolling vertical landing made little use of the wing's lifting power; it was initiated by the Hawker test pilot as a means of keeping the air intakes and cockpit in front of the jet/ground disturbance. The standard mission cycle was a Short Takeoff (STO), a standard reconnaissance or attack profile, followed by a Vertical Landing (VL). These STOVL missions essentially validated the Kestrel as a concept. As an effective military aircraft, however, the Kestrel still had some serious shortcomings, including limited capability and high cost of operation, largely due to the short (50-hour) life of the Pegasus 5 engine (discussed below). Both Hawker and Bristol, as well as the governments involved, knew that although the Vertical/Short Takeoff and Landing (VSTOL) vectored-thrust concept had been proved, future military sales would necessitate more power from the engine and, overall, a more cost-effective next-generation aircraft.

## Pegasus 5

First run in June 1962, the Pegasus 5 was the engine in the Kestrels flown by the Tripartite Squadron. It was a redesigned engine with a new three-stage titanium fan, an annular combustion chamber, variable inlet guide vanes (IGVs) in the compressor and air-cooled blades for the first turbine stage. The takeoff thrust was now up to 15,500 pounds with a turbine inlet temperature of 1,990°F. By 1965 and the Kestrel trials, the Pegasus 5 had a life of 50 hours.[25]

## From Kestrel to Harrier

The crucial year for the start of the vectored-thrust jet VSTOL aircraft was 1965. During that year, the Tripartite Squadron staff field-tested and validated the aircraft, providing important data for further development. But would the Kestrel go any further in its development, especially with the supersonic P1154 VSTOL fighter being pushed by Hawker and, particularly by the RAF Air Staff? The P1154 (to which it was intended to give the name Harrier) was the cowinner of the third National Basic Military Requirement (NBMR-3) competition, along with the Mirage III, but in 1964 Britain changed governments, with Labour replacing the Conservatives. In 1965 the Labour government closed out the P1154 program and that of its engine, the Bristol B5100.

The P1127's originator, Ralph Hooper, became assistant chief designer for projects at Hawker's Kingston facilities, and John Fozard was made chief designer for the Kestrel projects newly renamed Harrier. In 1968 Hooper was appointed an executive director of Hawker Siddeley Aircraft and became chief engineer of the Kingston fighter design team. Fozard became deputy chief engineer in 1971 and in 1978, after British Aerospace had been formed, director of marketing for Harrier and Hawk.

The cancellation of the supersonic P1154 was a major blow to Hawker, but it meant new life for the P1127. At the same time that the British Ministry of Aviation canceled the P1154, they announced that the Royal Air Force would be permitted to acquire an advanced version of the Kestrel for a subsonic VSTOL attack/close-support aircraft.

Thus, in February 1965 the Hawker team at Kingston was invited to redesign the Kestrel to provide a P1154-like capability (in almost all respects except payload/radius and supersonic speed, but including the Harrier name). This redesign involved a complete rework of the airframe and systems, the introduction of a very large part of the P1154's avionics and armament capability, and the fitting of a higher-thrust version of the Pegasus engine. Specific requirements were laid down for maintainability and reliability based in part on the operating experience at that date with the Kestrel and including the assessments of the P1154 made by the engineering staff of the Ministry of Defense.[26]

## Pegasus 6

The Pegasus 6 engine (designated by the RAF when in production as the Pegasus Mk 101) first ran in March 1965. It was the first production engine for the first Harrier GR.Is to enter RAF service. The Pegasus 6 developed 19,000 pounds of thrust with a turbine inlet temperature of 2,160°F. The Bristol-Hawker team introduced the concept of short-lift rating with the addition of a revised combustion system using water injection for thrust restoration. They also changed the front fan to an all-titanium design; introduced cooling to both stages of the high-pressure turbine; incorporated two-vane exhaust nozzles; provided additional fuel system controls for high-pressure spool temperature and pressure-ratio limitation; and added an engine-life recorder for creep monitoring. This engine entered service with the RAF in April 1969. Its operational life was much improved to over 300 hours.[27]

In 1965, Bristol, with John Dale as Chief Engineer of Pegasus, also began design of a new version of the Pegasus with more VSTOL thrust, 2,500 pounds more than the Pegasus 6. They began design of a new fan with transonic blading and more airflow capacity in late 1965. The new airflow requirements in turn required redesign of the Harrier's engine intakes, a change incorporated in the last of the original six prototype Harriers.

In late 1968, however, the new fan was still not forthcoming from Bristol for the next anticipated Pegasus version, the Model 11. The Harrier airframes meanwhile had been progressing and were currently in flight testing. Bristol and the RAF decided therefore to use an uprated Pegasus 6 engine, accomplished by overspeeding. Bristol meanwhile continued work on the transonic fan for the Pegasus 11.

## Pegasus 10

The Pegasus 10 (designated by the United States as the F402-RR-400 and by the Royal Air Force as the Mk.102) was the engine in the first Harriers to enter U.S. Marine Corps service. This model developed 20,500 pounds of thrust when introduced in early 1971. Bristol achieved the extra thrust by increasing the water flow to the engine by 32 percent and increasing turbine inlet temperature by 30°F. John Fozard relates:

Much flight development effort went into proving the Pegasus Mk.102 in the period 1969 and 1970. Because it was a 'stretched' engine, surge problems at high positive incidence in wingborne flight (and in inverted flight) had to be solved. Because the Mk.102 obtained its thrust by overspeed, the hovering thrust centre was further aft than in any earlier or later Harrier, and in the effects of this feature on VSTOL performance and flying qualities needed careful assessment. Fortunately no insuperable problems were found. With both the Mk.102 and Mk.103 engines, increased thrust was available only in the VSTOL ratings, these engines being rated in wingborne flight (nozzles aft) at the same performance levels as the Mk.101.[28]

## Pegasus 11

For the Pegasus 11, the Bristol designers added a titanium rebladed low-pressure compressor to increase mass flow, an improved combustion chamber, increased high-pressure turbine cooling, and a manual reversionary fuel system. These improvements increased the operational life of the engine to over 400 hours.[29] The current Pegasus 11/F402 (Figure 17-5) has a three-stage titanium fan with part-supersonic blades, a design airflow of 432 pounds per second, a titanium eight-stage high-pressure compressor with an overall pressure ratio of 14, an annular combustor with low-pressure vaporizing burners, a two-stage high-pressure turbine using air-cooled rotor stages and cast first-stage blades, a two-stage low-pressure turbine, and four exhaust nozzles (the front nozzles in steel and the rear nozzles in Nimonic, a nickel alloy).[30]

## The Harrier Comes to the U.S. Marine Corps

Early in the 1960s, the U.S. Marine Corps had expressed some interest in purchasing the P1127 as a replacement for the OV-10 Bronco as a close-support aircraft. The Marines, who have been interested in VSTOL since the development of helicopters, have a distinct need for close-support aircraft in their division operations, since they lack the same degree of artillery firepower as a U.S. Army division. Marine air and ground units work very closely together. Their experience in World War II, operating on islands sometimes far from land-based or carrier-based aviation, and their post-war evolution into an expeditionary force, gave the Marine Corps a strong incentive to base their tactical air support as close to the front lines as possible. The Corps had led the way in developing an "expeditionary airfield," made from aluminum matting. This matting could be quickly transported ashore and assembled in the absence of fixed airfields. The Corps had also subsequently laid down a requirement that all Marine tactical aircraft had to be able to take off with a useful combat load within 4,000 feet. In 1958 the Corps called for a fixed-wing high performance VSTOL aircraft.[31] Although they had not taken part in the Tripartite VSTOL evaluation squadron, the Marines had watched the trials very carefully. The Kestrel was judged to be too limited in payload to be of immediate use to the Corps, but they maintained their interest in the aircraft's development. The goal of the Marine Corps was to purchase their VSTOL aircraft "off the shelf," thus saving the development cost, so they bided their time. In 1968, with the Vietnam War at its height, a group of Marine Corps senior staff, including Major General Keith B. McCutcheon, viewed a promotional film of the then-Harrier. McCutcheon was at that time the chief of Marine Corps Aviation. He was very impressed.

**Figure 17-5. Cutaway of Pegasus 11/F402**
*(Illustration courtesy of U.S. Air Force)*

McCutcheon dispatched Colonel Tom Miller, Deputy Chief of Staff for Air, and Lieutenant Colonel Bud Baker to the United Kingdom to look at the Harrier aircraft performing at the International Farnborough Air Show near London. Bruce Myles recounts the events that led up to the first flight of the Harrier by a Marine pilot:

> The United States Navy is responsible for procurement, research and development of Marine Corps aircraft, and for obvious reasons they have always been anxious to get as much "commonality" between the two services as possible. The Marines anticipated trouble from their "big brother," if and when they finally decided to ask the Navy to procure this new airplane for them. After all, the Navy at that time had no requirement for VSTOL, and the inclusion of the Harrier into the Navy/Marines inventory could not be further from the concept of commonality particularly as the Harrier was a 'foreign airplane'. Thus, there was considerable secrecy in the run up to the 1968 Farnborough Air Show. It was not underhanded, but the Marines wanted to have "all their ducks lined up" before they asked for budget approval. So they did not even tell Vice Admiral Tom Connolly, the Deputy chief of Naval Operations for Air Warfare. Ironically, Connolly was to turn out to be a consistent champion of the Marines' request for the aircraft. They did not want Hawker Siddeley, the manufacturers, to know how intense their interest was. British Embassy officials in Washington passed back to UK technical questions on the Harrier and fed back the answers off the record to people like Colonel Miller and General McCutcheon. Although Hawker Siddeley knew the Marines would be at Farnborough, the intensity of their interest came as a shock. The two colonels and a Marine Corps one star general (Johnson) walked into the aircraft company's chalet and said, "We want to fly the Harrier." Tom Miller asked for a set of pilot's notes, and on the last day of the show, the Ministry of Defense gave permission for the two Marines to have ten flights each. They spent many hours discussing the aircraft with people like Fozard, Hooper, Merewether and Bedford. At the start of the second week, they were at Dunsfold Hawkers' test and development airfield deep in rural Surrey to start flying.[32]

The pilots put the Harrier through the normal flight test procedures, starting with taxiing at low and high speeds, then limited hovering, then wingborne flights, and then practice attacks (including using the nozzles to slow the aircraft down in their attacks). Then the Marines asked the British for something unusual. What they proceeded to do would cause the British and Americans to reexamine the way they looked at the Harrier. The Marines had discovered Vectoring in Forward Flight (VIFF). Myles recounts:

> They also asked Hawker to provide them with a flight envelope within which they could experiment with putting the nozzles down in conventional flight, to try to improve their maneuverability in air combat. From the reaction the American pilots got, they assumed they were the first ever to ask permission to use the airplane in this way. The manufacturer computed speed and engine ranges, and at around 25,000 feet and 300 knots, Miller and Baker made the first hesitant steps towards Thrust Vectoring in Forward Flight—a facility which the Marine Corps pilots have since developed into a potent dog-fighting weapon.[33]

In self-defense, the Hawker team pointed out that the RAF Harrier was not intended to be a fighter. Therefore, no bonus would be awarded for drawing attention to the use of nozzles in combat wingborne flight, so no part of the Harrier flight test program would be devoted to investigating VIFF. The RAF repeatedly emphasized the Harrier as Ground Attack/Reconnaissance Design (Ground Based) and not as an F (Fighter).

The two Marine pilots came back to the United States convinced that the Harrier was the best aircraft for the Marine Corps, who then launched a stealth campaign to procure it. The Corps did not manage to get their request into the Marine Corps' portion of the defense budget request for 1970 before the budget left the Department of the Navy in July 1969, and the Department of Defense in September, and went to the Office of Management and Budget in October. However, the Marine Corps headquarters staff maneuvered the proposal through all three agencies and into the budget before Congress as a special amendment.

The battle to get the Marine Corps' request for Harriers approved by Congress was a tough campaign, commencing in March 1969. There were two major battles to win involving companies with major allies in Congress. First there was the Ryan Aircraft Corporation, which had invested millions in the development of the XV-5 VSTOL aircraft.[34] The second company was McDonnell Douglas, which had a more immediate stake in the fight, for the Marine Corps had been forced to eliminate an order for seventeen new McDonnell Douglas Phantoms in order to save $56 million for its first twelve Harriers. Colonel Tom Miller of the Marine Corps knew the top management of McDonnell Douglas well, having been part of the team on the development of the Phantom, and Miller convinced the company that their financial sacrifice would not be wasted. This later proved to be very advantageous to McDonnell Douglas.[35]

The Corps' efforts in Congress were also well served in 1969 by the presence of RAF Harriers in the United States. The two aircraft had recently arrived from Britain, having just won the London Daily Mail Transatlantic Air Race. A Harrier, using in-flight refueling en route, achieved pad-to-pad times of 5 hours, 57 minutes westbound and 5 hours, 31 minutes eastbound between the London G.P.O. tower and the Empire State Building in New York, a distance of 3,030 nautical miles.[36] The Marine Corps and Hawker decided to put on a demonstration for Congressmen and Senators, who were flown to Andrews Air Force Base, then ferried with senior military officers out to an aircraft carrier off Norfolk, Virginia. Nearby was the U.S.S. La Salle, a landing platform dock ship, with an aft helicopter platform. Hawker Siddeley's Harrier test pilot, John Farley, took off from Andrews Air Force Base, landed vertically on the La Salle, shut off the engine, and then loaded rocket pods and fuel tanks on the Harrier and took off vertically again. The test had a dramatic effect on the observers. The Marine Corps got their Harriers.

On October 22, 1969, the Naval Air Systems Command and the United Kingdom executed a Memorandum of Agreement whereby the Hawker Siddeley Harrier could be purchased. A subsequent letter of offer covered procurement of twelve aircraft with initial delivery in January 1971. The contract was between the U.S. government and the British Ministry of Defense. Hawker Siddeley Aviation, in turn, was a subcontractor to the British government. The Harrier was given the U.S. designation AV-8A.[37] The first flight of an AV-8A Harrier was on November 20, 1970. On January 6, 1971, the Marine Corps/Navy's first AV-8 Harrier was accepted by Marine Corps' Major General Homer S. Hill at Dunsfold, England. The Harrier was the first Vertical Takeoff and Landing (VSTOL) fixed-wing aircraft ever accepted for use as a combat aircraft by U.S. armed forces.[38]

## Thrust Vectoring in Forward Flight (VIFF)

Although the Marines are first credited with developing Thrust Vectoring in Forward Flight, or VIFF, the Air Force was the first to consider optimizing the use of VIFF with the Harrier. Dr. John Attinello was the first scientist outside the expertise exhibited by Hawker Siddeley Aviation and a few Ministry of Defense individuals in the United Kingdom to actually consider using the engine's thrust in flight for more than just propulsion. In the early 1950s, Attinello was a designer of U.S. Navy aircraft, working on the problems associated with landing and taking off from aircraft carriers. Having to design aircraft small enough to be stored on and fly off carriers convinced Attinello of the attractiveness of VSTOL aircraft. He first discussed his VSTOL ideas with Hawker Siddeley in 1961, when making a VSTOL research visit to Britain. Although the Kestrel/Pegasus combination was already well underway, the designers at Hawker were not much interested in Attinello's data and arguments for thrust vectoring to increase maneuverability. They were designing a ground-attack and reconnaissance aircraft and not a highly maneuverable air-superiority fighter. Besides, the British government had not allocated any budget to explore Thrust Vectoring in Forward Flight.[39]

Attinello bided his time. In 1967, with the Vietnam War raging, his work at the Institute of Defense Analysis gave him the opportunity to try to advance his theories again. General A.J. Beck of the Air Force gave Attinello the chance to prove his VIFF theories by carrying out a study on air combat maneuverability called "Project Red Baron," on American aircraft in Vietnam. Attinello found that American pilots were flying high-wing-loading Phantoms against low-wing-loading MiGs. In some flight regimes the high-wing-loading airplane had the advantage, and in some situations it did not. Attinello decided it would be nice for a fighter pilot to have his cake and eat it too. This meant the high-wing-loading aircraft could engage the low-wing-loading plane whenever the pilot chose. This concept brought him straight back to VIFF. Wing loading is a major factor in an aircraft's maneuverability. In simple terms it is the weight of the aircraft divided by the square footage of the wing. Low wing loading helps reduce the radius of a turn and also augments an aircraft's ability to pull sustained G's. The Harrier is a high-wing-loading airplane at about 100 pounds per square foot. It seemed to Attinello that by using thrust vectoring in the high-wing-loading Harrier, one could exploit the aircraft's characteristics to a point approaching the ideal.[40]

General Beck, although impressed by Attinello's results, wanted to test the theories against the experience of Air Force pilots who had already flown the Kestrel in England. Beck sent Colonel J.M. Broughton to assess the Air Force pilots' experience with nozzle deflections when flying the Kestrel. That experience, in the one operational instance when nozzle deflection was accidentally encountered, was wholly negative.[41] That assessment seemed to be the end of VIFF, at least until 1968. In that year Attinello got the chance to talk to the Marine Corps pilots who had tested the Harrier. In a briefing by Marine Colonel Miller, Attinello was able to ask his questions directly. Tom Miller told Attinello that he had indeed tried purposefully deflecting the nozzles in flight and that it worked well. Attinello went home and wrote up his conclusions to his study and delivered them in October 1969. That Institute of Defense Analysis report was read by the Marine Corps and particularly by Lieutenant Colonel Bud Baker, who was to become the first commanding officer of the first Marine Corps Harrier squadron. The pilots of the Marine Corps have been in the forefront of using VIFF ever since.[42]

On January 26, 1971, the first AV-8A Harrier arrived at the Naval Air Test Center for commencement of Board of Inspection and Survey trials. This date marks the official entry of the Harrier into U.S. Marine Corps service. All of the new Harriers (110 for the U.S. Marine Corps, thirteen for the Spanish Navy) including the two-seat version, were built in Britain with McDonnell-Douglas providing support from its St. Louis facilities. McDonnell-Douglas also provided the upgrade package for an additional 47 AV-8As to be converted to AV-8Cs.[43] On April 16, 1971, Squadron VMA-513 at Marine Corps Aviation Station Beaufort, in South Carolina, took delivery of three AV-8A Harrier aircraft, thereby becoming the first operational high performance VSTOL squadron in the United States.[44]

On October 29, 1971, HS-15, the first sea-control ship squadron, was commissioned at Naval Air Station Lakehurst, in New Jersey. The squadron was made responsible for protecting convoys and vessels not operating with or within the protective range of carriers. Tests along these lines were subsequently conducted aboard the U.S.S. Guam utilizing the SH-3H Sea King helicopters of HS-15 and Marine Corps AV-8 Harriers of VMA-513. Tests included VSTOL and helicopter compatibility, antisnooper and antisurface tactics, bow and cross-axial deck landings, night operations and shipboard control of airborne intercepts.[45]

In 1972 the Harrier program for the Marine Corps came under scrutiny from the Pentagon, in the person of Deputy Secretary of Defense David Packard. Packard had reviewed three major weapons programs, the Harrier for the Marines, the AX (later named the A-10) aircraft for the Air Force, and the Cheyenne helicopter for the Army. Packard felt there were weaknesses in all three programs. Before he would authorize further procurement of the Harrier, Packard wanted to validate the aircraft's development. The Marine Corps, in their procurement requests, had claimed that the Harrier's sortie rate would be four per day. During the Vietnam War, the Air Force had averaged a rate of one sortie per day per plane, and the Marine Corps had averaged between 1.2 and 1.5 per airplane. During the Six-Day War the Israelis had achieved sortie rates of six and seven a day during "surge" periods. The Marines claimed four sorties a day for the Harrier at a sustained rate, and six sorties during a surge. Packard called upon the Marine Corps to prove this claim under the auspices of the Weapons System Advisory Group (WESAG). The sortie evaluation tests were scheduled at Camp Lejeune in North Carolina during March of 1972. The test was called the Harrier WESAG Sortie Rate Validation Trial.

On March 23, 1972, Squadron VMA-513 completed the Harrier WESAG Sortie Rate Validation and demonstrated the capability of the AV-8A to respond rapidly and repeatedly to requests for close air support while operating from austere forward bases. During the ten-day test the squadron flew 376 sorties with a complement of six aircraft, averaging six sorties a day and a surge of ten.[46]

On October 6, 1976, Squadron VMA-231, equipped with the AV-8 Harrier, was assigned to the U.S.S. Franklin D. Roosevelt, en route to the Mediterranean Sea for a Sixth Fleet deployment. This was the first overseas operational commitment on a carrier for the AV-8 aircraft.[47] On January 13, 1977, Naval Air Station Jacksonville announced that two AV-8A Harrier aircraft had made a bow-on approach and landing aboard U.S.S. Franklin D. Roosevelt. This may have been the first time in naval aviation history that a fixed-wing aircraft made a bow-on, downwind landing aboard a carrier at sea. This landing, with the aircraft facing aft, demonstrated that VSTOL aircraft could be landed aboard a carrier without many of the ship constraints necessary for operating fixed-wing, non-VSTOL aircraft.[48]

On March 26, 1979, the AV-8A Harrier was used at the Naval Air Training Center (NATC) Patuxent River in Maryland to test a new ski-jump ramp developed by the British to cut down the takeoff distance for the Harrier. The ramp was designed with a 12-degree angle of elevation and was 130 feet long. A 12-degree exit angle ski jump enabled a Harrier to launch in about one-third the distance needed for the same weight Harrier launching from a flat deck. NATC Patuxent River was evaluating the ramp for possible use in the fleet.[49]

On March 6, 1980, the U.S.S. Nassau began a month-long cruise to the Caribbean to demonstrate U.S. capability to defend the Panama Canal in accordance with the 1979 treaty with Panama. The Nassau carried a 400-man Marine detachment, CH-46 Sea Knight and CH-53 Sea Stallion helicopters, and AV-8A Harriers.[50]

## Development of the Harrier AV-8B

On May 10, 1972, the commander of Naval Air Systems Command promulgated a plan for management of advanced prototype development and demonstration of a thrust-augmented wing attack plane-fighter VSTOL aircraft. A prototype development manager was to be established under the deputy commander for plans and programs and was to be assisted by a small cadre of management and technical personnel located in the office of the assistant commander for research and technology and at the contractor's facility.[51]

On April 13, 1973, the Secretary of the Navy announced that an agreement with the United Kingdom had been signed providing for an eight-month joint study of an advanced VSTOL Harrier involving participation by Hawker Siddeley, Rolls Royce, McDonnell Douglas, and Pratt & Whitney. The overall aim was to determine the feasibility of joint development of an advanced concept VSTOL aircraft incorporating a Pegasus 15 engine and an advanced wing.[52] Known as the AV-16A, this advanced Harrier failed to win support owing chiefly to the estimates of the alarming cost of upgrading and Americanizing the Pegasus from the then-current Pegasus 11 with 21,500 pounds of VSTOL thrust to the Pegasus 15 rating of 25,000 pounds of VSTOL thrust. The AV-16 program collapsed in 1974.

The British went away separately to study an updated Harrier airframe with a new wing known as the "Big Wing Harrier" as well as the Sea Harrier for the Royal Navy. McDonnell Douglas put together a proposal for a revised AV-8A airframe, also with a larger wing, aimed at providing twice the payload radius of the AV-8A without engine development. In May 1975, they completed their studies on the AV-8B, a new version of the Harrier to meet the requirements of the Marine Corps for an advanced STOVL aircraft for light attack close-in ground support.[53]

On July 27, 1976, the Marine Corps announced approval for development of the AV-8B advanced Harrier. The new development called for engine improvements to bring the Harrier's thrust up to 22,000 pounds with the improved Pegasus 11 Mark 103 vectored-thrust turbofans and to increase the Harrier's range, payload, reliability and maintainability.[54] U.S. designation for the engine is F402-RR-401. The Hawker Siddeley Aviation Company became part of British Aerospace (BAe) in April 1977 as a result of the Aircraft and Shipbuilding Industries Act of 1977.[55]

On November 9, 1978, a prototype of the Marine Corps' newest light attack aircraft, the YAV-8B, piloted by McDonnell's Charles Plummer, flew for the first time at McDonnell Douglas Corporation in St. Louis. The AV-8B Harrier had more than double the payload and radius of its predecessor, the AV-8A.[56] On January 25, 1979, the Harrier prototype arrived at the Naval Air Test Center to test its aerodynamic improvements. Improvements built into this aircraft over the AV-8A included a new UHF radio, a chaff and flare dispensing system, lift improvement devices, a radar warning system, secure voice equipment, and extended life for the rear fuselage. From October 1-8, 1979, Harrier shipboard trials were conducted aboard the U.S.S. Saipan. Testing consisted of thirty-three flights involving short takeoffs, vertical takeoffs and vertical landings.[57]

On August 29, 1979, the first flight of a pilot-production AV-8B (Figure 17-6) took place at Patuxent River. Subsequent operational evaluation flights revealed that the AV-8B Harrier exhibited a significant gain in performance, range, war load capacity and war load range.[58]

In January 1984 the first deliveries of the AV-8B Harrier were made to the VM(T)-203 at Marine Corps Air Station Cherry Point. Subsequent production of Harrier AV-8Bs was split between McDonnell Douglas (60 percent) and British Aero Engines (40 percent). A total of 252 AV-8Bs have been built through FY1991. Early production aircraft incorporated the F402-RR-406, and aircraft delivered since March 1987 have been powered by the F402-RR-406 turbofan with digital fuel control.[59]

**Figure 17-6. McDonnell Douglas AV-8B Harrier**
*(Photo courtesy of McDonnell Douglas)*

## Summary

The Harrier program is a remarkable example of international collaboration. Although it was totally British in technical origin and production until the late 1960s, without U.S. support and intervention at several crucial points in the history of the P1127/Kestrel/Harrier enterprise, the aircraft and its unique engine would not have survived.

1.  U.S. funding support through NATO Mutual Weapons Development Programs in 1958-61 sustained Bristol Aero Engines in early Pegasus development.

2.  John Stark, deputy director of NASA Langley, lent support from 1958-60 with free-flight and transonic tunnel models.

3.  Jack Reeder and Fred Drinkwater of NASA Langley became the first non-British pilots to fly the P1127 in mid-1962 in England. It was their report that enabled U.S. funding to be made available for the XV-6A Kestrel Evaluation Squadron from 1963.

4.  U.S. Marine Corps interest in and orders for the AV-8A variant from 1969 to 1975 enabled Harrier production to continue in the United Kingdom at a time when the RAF might have been forced by budget paring to close the program when only sixty Harriers had been delivered.

5.  AV-8B initiatives by McDonnell Douglas with British Aerospace as a major subcontractor led to the AV-8B Harrier II entering service with Marine Aviation in 1984 and, as the Harrier II GR Mk5, serving with the RAF from 1987. By the end of the century, the Harrier II international program will have produced some 400 aircraft for the U.S. Marine Corps, the RAF, and several export customers.

6.  If deliveries of the Harrier I are included, the grand total for Harrier production in 27 years encompasses over 800 jet VSTOL attack fighters for six military air arms.

Alone among over twenty jet VSTOL programs in Great Britain, the United States, and Europe since the mid-1950s, the vectored-thrust jet VSTOL single-engine configuration has survived.

The factors contributing to the success of the Harrier and its Pegasus engine are, most importantly:

1. A single engine providing both powered lift and wingborne propulsion for unmatched basic simplicity and reliability in the design.

2. The techniques and procedures needed to operate in the powered lift parts of the envelope required only simple extension of current fighter pilot skills.

3. The design allows all the installed thrust to be deployed in the optimum direction for all the VSTOL or STOVL launch and recovery procedures.

4. Short takeoff loaded at weights up to 40 percent greater than can be lifted vertically can be performed from a wide variety of sites and surfaces ashore as well as from the decks of moderate-size flat-top ships at sea.

5. The Harrier is the only jet VSTOL vehicle which can fully exploit the ski-jump launch technique, ashore or (most advantageously) afloat.

6. The Harrier can be flown and recovered in the powered lift flight modes without auto-control or added artificial stability. Throughout its extensive flight envelope the Harrier has pilot-friendly flying qualities that would be remarkable in a non-VSTOL airplane.

7. The Harrier/Pegasus combination allowed use to be made in combat of Thrust Vectoring in Forward Flight (VIFF), providing Harrier pilots with a remarkable additional arrow in their quiver.

8. The Harrier paved the way for use of thrust vectoring in combat in the latest generation of fighters. In the Harrier, VIFF comes for no penalty since the VSTOL systems (reaction controls and nozzle actuation) are already present in the airplane for the powered-lift flight modes at a price which adds well under 1 percent to the operating weight empty.

9. By its example during more than 1 million flight hours in six fighting services, the Harrier has proved that multiple engines in a small attack/fighter airframe are delusory in terms of safety of flight.

10. The Harrier has survived and succeeded because of its basic engineering simplicity and its operational flexibility. All other jet VSTOL configurations are penalized by their inevitable greater complexity and reduced flexibility.

## Endnotes

[1] Hooker, Sir Stanley, Not Much of an Engineer: An Autobiography, Shrewsbury, England: Airlife Publishing Ltd., 1984, 162.

[2] Ibid, 163.

[3] Ibid.

[4] Ibid, 167.

[5] Ibid, 164.

[6] Ibid, 166.

[7] Ibid, 165.

[8] Fozard, John W, "Vertical Heroes," Air Power History, Fall 1990, 56, and Hooker, Not Much of an Engineer, 162.

[9] Rolls-Royce, Vectored Thrust Jet V/STOL, 2.4-2.5.

[10] Hooker, Not Much of an Engineer, 172.

[11] Ibid, 142-143.

[12] Ibid, 171.

[13] Fozard, "Vertical Heroes," 18.

[14] Hooker, Not Much of an Engineer, 172.

[15] Ibid, 172.

[16] Rolls-Royce, Vectored Thrust Jet V/STOL, 3.2.

[17] Ibid, 3.4-3.9.

[18] Braybrook, Roy, British Aerospace Harrier and Sea Harrier, London, UK: Osprey Publishing Limited, 1984, 52.

[19] Ibid, 53.

[20] Hooker, Not Much of an Engineer, 229.

[21] Rolls-Royce, Vectored Thrust Jet V/STOL, 6.4.

[22] Fozard, John W., The British Aerospace Harrier: Case Study in Aircraft Design. AIAA Professional Study Series, Kingston upon Thames, UK: Kingston-Brough Division, Aircraft Group, British Aerospace, 1978, 1.

[23] Braybrook, British Aerospace Harrier and Sea Harrier, London, UK: Osprey Publishing Limited, 1984, 60.

[24] Ibid, 60, and Fozard, The British Aerospace Harrier, 1.

[25] Braybrook, British Aerospace Harrier and Sea Harrier, 60.

[26] Fozard, The British Aerospace Harrier, 1978, 7.

[27] Braybrook, British Aerospace Harrier and Sea Harrier, 72.

[28] Fozard, The British Aerospace, 9.

[29] Rolls-Royce, Vectored Thrust Jet V/STOL, 6.4.

[30] Gunston, Bill, World Encyclopedia of Aero Engines, Second Edition, England: Patrick Stephens Limited, 1989, 38.

[31] Myles, Bruce, Jump Jet: The Revolutionary V/STOL Fighter, San Rafael, CA: Presidio Press, 1978, 128-129.

[32] Myles, Jump Jet, 131-132.

[33] Ibid, 133-134.

[34] The XV5 had lift fan engines in the wings and had already undergone considerable test flight time. Myles, Jump Jet, 136.

[35] Ibid, 137.

[36] Ibid, 139.

[37] Francillon, Rene J., McDonnell Douglas Aircraft Since 1920: Volume II, Annapolis, MD: Naval Institute Press, 1990, 329.

[38] Pearson, Lee M., Van Vleet, Clarke, and Adrian Van Wyen, United States Naval Aviation, Washington DC: Deputy Chief of Naval Operations (Air Warfare), Naval Air Systems Command, 1981, 282.

[39] Myles, Jump Jet, 187.

[40] Ibid, 188.

[41] Ibid, 188-189.

[42] Ibid, 189.

[43] Pearson, Van Vleet, and Van Wyen, United States Naval Aviation, 283, and Francillon, McDonnell Douglas Aircraft, 333.

[44] Pearson, Van Vleet, and Van Wyen, United States Naval Aviation, 284.

[45] Ibid, 287.

[46] Myles, Jump Jet, 149-150, and Pearson, Van Vleet, and Van Wyen, United States Naval Aviation, 290.

[47] Ibid, 313.

[48] Ibid, 314.

[49] Ibid, 319.

[50] Ibid, 323.

[51] Ibid, 294.

[52] Ibid, 302.

[53] Francillon, McDonnell Douglas Aircraft, 1990, 330.

[54] Ibid, and Pearson, Van Vleet, and Van Wyen, United States Naval Aviation, 313.

[55] Francillon, McDonnell Douglas Aircraft, 329.

[56] Ibid, 332, and Pearson, Van Vleet, and Van Wyen, United States Naval Aviation, 317.

[57] Ibid, 319 and 321.

[58] Francillon, McDonnell Douglas Aircraft, 332.

[59] Ibid.

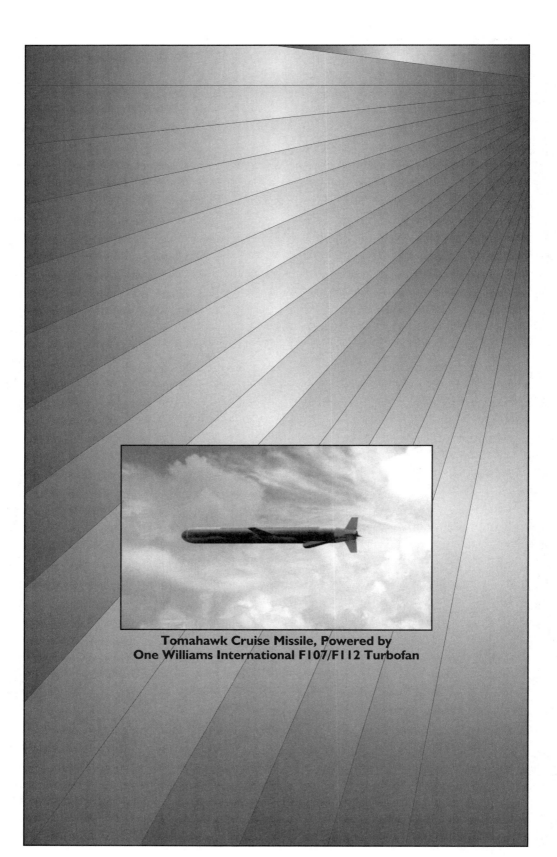

**Tomahawk Cruise Missile, Powered by
One Williams International F107/F112 Turbofan**

# Chapter Eighteen

# The Development of Cruise Missile Propulsion

## The J69, J402 and F107 Engines

Certain technological advances in the history of warfare have changed the way that military and civilian leadership view war making. The stirrup, the crossbow, the longbow, gunpowder, ironclad warships, the tank, and the airplane have all not only displaced existing armaments, but also have changed the way that we look at organizing and practicing war. As it has been with warfare in general, so has it been with air power.

Technological developments such as lighter-than-air aircraft, the airplane itself, bombs, the synchronized machine gun, mono-wing technology, all-metal aircraft, radio and radar, the jet engine, rocketry, nuclear armaments, and tactical and ballistic missiles have each, in turn, forced air power managers to rethink strategies and tactics. Cruise missile technology is the latest of these pivotal technologies to change the nature of both air power and the nature of warfare itself. The cruise missile concept has been around since man first considered the aircraft as a war machine, and the military establishments of all major powers have sought to develop a pilotless aerial weapon since man's first heavier-than-air flight. Some form of cruise missile has been used in all major wars since World War I, in both guided and unguided applications.

World War II first saw the practical deployment and operation of unguided cruise missiles, the pulsejet-powered V-1, by the Germans. Although there have been various forms of guided drones and Remotely Piloted Vehicles (RPVs) since then, a practical strategic cruise missile has only been possible for the last thirty years. In fact, the cruise missile was an effective contributor to aerial warfare in only the most recent conflict, the Persian Gulf War/Operation Desert Storm, where it performed beyond expectations. The two most crucial technological advances to the development of this new factor in warfare have been guidance/targeting technology and the development of a compact, cost-effective, off-the-shelf propulsion system.

There has been an ongoing struggle in the military establishment of the United States over the desire for and value of a pilotless aerial weapon. Although the military aviation establishment has always recognized the need for drones (both reconnaissance and target), there has been historically a deep resistance to any use of pilotless aircraft as strategic weapons replacing the manned bomber. Both the aviation establishments of the Air Force and Navy have at one time or another fought the idea of an unmanned bomber.

Another obstacle to the development of the cruise missile in the United States has been the struggle over who would develop, and ultimately command, this new weapon. Was the missile (and by extension the cruise missile) an artillery weapon belonging to the Army, or was it an inherently aerial weapon properly belonging to the Air Force? The Navy also viewed any form of missile as a tactical and strategic weapon capable of being fired from surface ships or submarines, and therefore a potential extension of naval force. The services followed a path typical of weapons development in the United States; they each developed their own programs, which thereafter competed with one another for funding.

A third major factor affecting cruise missile development has been the concurrent development of the ballistic missile, in both tactical and strategic warfare applications. While the history of the cruise missile has been beset by problems in propulsion, airframe, and especially guidance, the strategic ballistic missile was quickly developed and refined for short, intermediate, and intercontinental applications. In fact, the intercontinental ballistic missile, or ICBM, has become the major factor in national strategic defensive and offensive calculations.

The predecessors to the present-day family of cruise missiles from the Army Air Force's side were the Banshee, the Hound Dog, the Northrop Snark, the North American Navaho, and the Martin Matador. The Navy's side of the cruise missile family is represented by the Regulus I, Rigel, Regulus II, and Triton.

We are going to look at two of the most successful of the world's cruise missile engine programs, the Teledyne CAE J402 turbojet engine for the Harpoon cruise missile and the Williams International F107/F112 turbofan engine for the Tomahawk cruise missile. However, before looking at the Teledyne CAE J402 we must first examine how Teledyne got into this business, and that story begins with the J69 turbojet.

## The Teledyne J69 Turbojet Engine

Continental Motors, subsequently known as Teledyne CAE, is one of the oldest engine manufacturers in America, producing auto and aircraft engines since 1902. They have manufactured aircraft engines and parts for the U.S. military through the two world wars, Korea, Vietnam, and up to the present. Shortly after the end of World War II, Continental set out to examine its role in the postwar aircraft engine market. The company began stressing research and development work on turbine engines, compound engines, and piston engines for helicopters. All of this research was sponsored either completely or in part by the U.S. Army. In 1945 Continental Motors received a substantial contract from the Army Air Forces to study German "pulse-jet" turbine engine developments during the war.

Teledyne CAE owes its current role in the aircraft gas turbine engine business to an engineer recruited by Continental in 1927, Carl F. Bachle. A graduate of the University of Michigan, Bachle led Continental's efforts to seek out new technology for fifty years. It is his foresight and timing that enabled Continental to make the transition from reciprocating engines to turbine engines. As he told William Wagner in *Continental Motors and Its People: The Eight Decades of Teledyne Continental Motors*:

> At the time, 1951, CAE had only one experimental turbine. Large turbines for jet transports and military planes were coming into their own, but small turbine development was lagging because in that era it was considered they would pay too serious a penalty on fuel consumption.
>
> When I was in England, I dropped in to see my friend Air Commodore Francis Rodwell Banks, Director of Engine Research and Development during World War II for the British Air Ministry. "Rod," I said, "what is the best way for a small aircraft company to get into the turbine business?" "Carl," he replied, "why don't you try Turbomeca?"
>
> So I did.[1]

Societe Turbomeca S.A., located in Bordes, France, had developed a series of small and medium-sized gas turbine engines in conjunction with the French Air Ministry. The driving force behind Turbomeca was a Polish engineer named Josef Szydlowski. Bachle remembers Szydlowski as follows:

> He was...the most envied man I ever saw because he was the owner, the chief engineer, the head of sales, the director of manufacturing and the sole patent owner of Turbomeca. In 1980, at age 83, he is still around and still performing as usual.
>
> Turbomeca was so attractive to Continental because they had vastly reduced the previous serious penalty small turbines had to pay in fuel consumption to the point you could say it was almost break-even with the big turbines.[2]

Other reasons for Continental's interest in the Turbomeca engines were their long service life, their absence of reciprocating parts, their ability to use a wide range of fuels, their favorable power-to-weight ratio, and the interchangeability of parts among various models. Among the Turbomeca designs that Continental was interested in were the Artouste turboshaft, the Aspin ducted turbofan, the Palouste compressed air generator, the Palas turbojet, and the Marbore turbojet (Figure 18-1). Continental managed to obtain the license to all five engines for production and application in the United States.

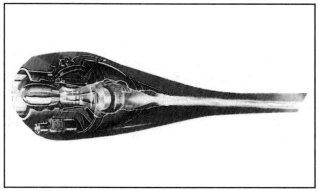

**Figure 18-1. Cutaway of Turbomeca Marbore**
*(Illustration courtesy of Teledyne Continental Motors Turbine Engines)*

The Marbore I and II engine models were the most successful for Continental right from the start. Continental teamed up with Cessna Aircraft to win an Air Force competition for a small side-by-side twin-engine jet trainer (the subsequent T-37), powered by two Marbore turbojets.[3] The first flight of the T-37 (Figure 18-2) was in October 1954. Production of it ended in 1977.

**Figure 18-2. Cessna T-37 Jet Trainer**
*(Photo courtesy of Cessna)*

Winning the T-37 competition meant that Continental had to bring the Marbore I turbojet up to Air Force standards, so they started modifying it. Bachle and the company also made what turned out to be a momentous decision; they started considering the Marbore for use as a drone engine. They targeted the Ryan Aeronautical Company whose "Firebee" target drones were just starting production for all three military services. As Bachle relates the story:

Ryan had the Fairchild J44 engine already installed in its first production "Firebee" targets. The J44 was touted as the best and cheapest available. It was sponsored and financed by the Navy, and everything was in favor of Fairchild continuing as the supplier.

How were we going to get into that job?

At that time Ryan was making exhaust manifolds in large volume for the Continental 1790 tank engines. On a routine trip to the Ryan plant, I went in to chat with Claude Ryan as I usually did. I hinted that we'd better get a little more serious attention on the Marbore engine for the Air Force Q-2A drones or something might happen to "that good old exhaust manifold contract that is producing a pretty good profit for you."

Claude got the message; we got better attention after that!

Because our Marbore engine was far more fuel efficient we were able to give Ryan twice as much time on the target range as they could get with the Fairchild J44. That was a proper and convincing argument.[4]

The first Continental Marbore II arrived at Ryan in June 1952 and was designated the J69 turbojet by the Air Force. A turbojet engine producing 880 pounds of thrust, the J69-T-3 (Figure 18-3) had a direct annular intake with fixed inlet guide vanes, a single-stage centrifugal compressor of one-piece light alloy casing with aluminum alloy impellers. It incorporated a single annular combustor with a one-piece steel casing, a centrifugal fuel-distribution system, and a single-stage axial turbine with individually replaceable, uncooled blades, hollow nozzles, and a stainless steel casing.[5] Bachle says of the Marbore and its growth:

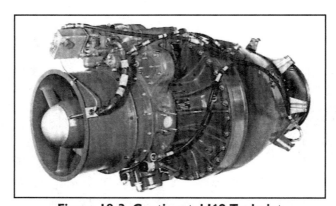

**Figure 18-3. Continental J69 Turbojet**
*(Photo courtesy of Teledyne Continental Motors Turbine Engines)*

As we received the prototype turbine from Turbomeca, it had a thrust rating of 880 pounds. That was the J69-T-3 engine we called "Marbore II" which went into the Ryan XQ-2A target drone in 1952.

In the course of negotiations with Cessna, it turned out they needed 920 pounds of thrust to meet Air Force performance guarantees. We said, "Why, sure, we can give you 920 pounds just as well as we can 880."

Then we spent millions of dollars and two years of heart-breaking development getting to 920 pounds thrust.

However, it was no great problem in conversion between inches and metric measure because we had been through that before with the British Rolls-Royce Merlin engine during World War II. We minimized the problem for ourselves and our customers because we didn't convert everything. Only what we had to: for example, studs, so we could use nuts which were common in this system. The starter was completely American. The fuel control was metric, but we had no problem.[6]

The first improved model of the J69 was the J69-T-9. The prototype Firebee first flew in December 1958. The T-9 developed the 920 pounds of thrust that Cessna was looking for and powered the Cessna T-37A. The second improved model of the J69 was the J-19 model, which produced 1,000 pounds of thrust for the Ryan Q-2A production drones, and the third was the J69-T-25 at 1,025 pounds of thrust. This engine was cleared to 50,000 feet maximum and an operational altitude of 45,000 feet. The J69-T-29 (Figure 18-4) was the engine for several models of the Ryan AQM/BQM/BGM-34 Firebee subsonic target drones, the first of which flew in January 1960.[7] The T-29 was an uprated model featuring an added single-stage axial compressor forward of the centrifugal stage, and was rated at 1,700 pounds of thrust up to 60,000 feet. This remarkable engine model delivered 60 percent more thrust with only a 6 percent increase in weight. This engine is still in production today.[8]

**Figure 18-4. Cutaway of Continental J69 Engine**
*(Illustration courtesy of Teledyne Continental Motors Turbine Engines)*

The next improved version of the J69 was the J-41A model. It featured a transonic compressor and revised centrifugal-stage aerodynamics to operate at 70,000 feet. This engine was rated to 1,920 pounds of thrust. It powered drones and other special-purpose tactical subsonic remotely piloted vehicles of the AQM/BGM/BQM-34 Firebee Series.

The last of the J69 series was the J69-T-406. It incorporated an added advanced axial compressor stage and an afterburner to attain supersonic performance at high altitude. Rated at 1,920 pounds of thrust, it powered the Teledyne Ryan BQM-34E/F and T versions of the Firebee II target drones. Over 11,000 J69 turbojets have been produced to date.[9]

In 1968 Teledyne Inc. bought Continental for $128 million and renamed it Teledyne CAE. The purchase became effective on January 2, 1969. Teledyne Inc. was the 1960 creation of Dr. Henry Singleton, a brilliant MIT engineer with industry experience at Hughes Aircraft, North American Aviation, and Litton Industries.

In 1970 the Air Force persuaded Teledyne CAE to become involved in the Air Force's Advanced Turbine Engine Gas Generator (ATEGG) program. This program was aimed at developing "core" technology to which could be added other components to make complete turbojet, turboshaft, and turbofan engines.

In November 1970 Teledyne CAE received another contract, this time from the Navy, to develop a low-cost expendable small turbojet engine for a naval cruise missile application. This was to become the J402 engine for the Harpoon missile. The program was destined for the "fast track." The United States was behind the Soviet Union in cruise missile development and needed to catch up.

In October 1967, during the Arab-Israeli "Six-Day War," the western military establishments had been stunned when an Israeli destroyer, the Elath, was sunk by Egyptian patrol boats using a new Russian-developed antiship surface-launched missile called the "Styx" (Figure 18-5). The race to counter the new threat and develop our own antiship cruise missiles was on.

**Figure 18-5. Russian "Styx" Cruise Missile**
*(Photo courtesy of U.S. Department of Defense)*

This pattern of response-to-threat as a motivator to develop technology has been a familiar one in aircraft gas turbine engine history, indeed, in all military history. The Allies pushed for the development of the Meteor and the P-59 in response to the threat posed by the German Me 262. The United States launched new programs after first encountering Soviet MiG-15s over Korean skies. The pattern has been maintained up to the present day with F-14, F-15, F-16, and F-18 fighters designed after and in response to the development of the MiG-27 and MiG-29.

## The Teledyne J402 Turbojet Engine

Between November 1970 and July 1974, Teledyne CAE designed and developed the J402 expendable turbojet engine (Figures 18-6 and 18-7). The J402 design was a scaled-down variant of the J69-T-406 turbojet engine of the BQM-34 Firebee program. Through the use of extensive computer design, the J402 engine was ultimately reduced to 32 percent of the original J69 size, but the company improved on the J69's low thrust-to-weight ratio by the use of invest-

**Figure 18-6. Teledyne J402 Turbojet**
*(Photo courtesy of Teledyne Continental Motors Turbine Engines)*

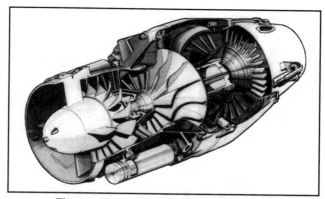

**Figure 18-7. Cutaway of J402 Engine**
*(Illustration courtesy of Teledyne Continental Motors Turbine Engines)*

ment castings. These castings resulted in much lower parts counts in the J402 than the J69. For example, the J402 rotor has only sixteen parts as opposed to the 149 parts in the J69 rotor.

The intake of the J402 is annular, with a bullet-dome that acts as a bearing housing for the compressor shaft. A new metal alloy called C355 is used for the air inlet housing. The J402 compressor is a single-stage transonic axial-flow unit, followed by a single centrifugal compressor. This provides a pressure ratio of 5.6:1 at a compressor air mass flow of nearly 9.6 pounds per second. The J402 is 29.44 inches long, has a 12.52-inch diameter, and weighs 100 pounds (dry).

The engine (Teledyne CAE Model 370) was designed with simplicity in mind. Along with reduced parts count, the J402 was developed with a "pot" lubricated bearing and a grease-packed rear roller bearing instead of a circulating lubrication system, thus saving weight, complexity, and cost. The engine's flight limit is approximately 40,000 feet, and engine life is about 1 hour.

Teledyne CAE teamed the J402 with the McDonnell Douglas Harpoon (Figure 18-8) design in the competition for a Navy antiship missile. The Harpoon is a turbine-powered, low-flying, all-weather, over-the-horizon, antiship cruise missile weighing between 1,140 and 1,500 pounds with a range of about 54 nautical miles. It can be fired from submarines, surface ships, and coastal launchers on land, or air-launched from a wide range of aircraft, including the Air Force's B-52 (using the AGM-84D variant). The Harpoon uses a small digital computer for guidance and control, relying upon a radar altimeter and attitude reference system to fly a sea-hugging profile, and an onboard radar to search out and destroy enemy ships.

The J402/Harpoon technical evaluation was completed in July 1974. In June 1977 McDonnell Douglas was awarded an initial production contract for the Harpoon. The company began full production in October 1977, an incredible turnaround time for any weapon system.

The first improved version of the J402 was the J402-CA-401 (or Model 370-1). This was a derivative engine featuring a longer-life turbine, external oil supply, and a coated combustor. These changes were made to permit additional tactical use of the missile. Its electronic fuel control was also upgraded to allow more complex mission profiles.

The second improved version of the J402 was the J402-CA-700 (or Model 372-2). This variant was used for the MQM-107A Streaker variable-speed training target (VSTT) missile. Although similar to the J-401, this variant was designed for an engine life of up to 15 hours, with repeated use. The engine is rated at a maximum of 640 pounds of thrust and weighs 113 pounds.

**Figure 18-8. McDonnell Douglas "Harpoon"
Antiship Cruise Missile**
*(Photo courtesy of McDonnell Douglas)*

The next variant of the J402 was the J-701 model (or Model 372-11A). Rated at 725 pounds of thrust, this engine was designed for use in a target missile.

The most powerful version of the J402 series is the J402-CA-702 (or Model 373-8), which develops 960 pounds of thrust at a total weight of 138 pounds. Airflow for this overachieving engine is 13.7 pounds per second. Rated at 50 hours between overhaul, it powers the MQM-107D Streaker VSTT and the Northrop NV-144/NV-151 recoverable target drones. The J402-CA-702 also powers the Teledyne Ryan Model 324 and Model 350 Scarab high-speed, long-range RPVs to be used for surveillance, targeting and reconnaissance missions.

The first combat use of the Harpoon by the United States came in 1986 in the campaign against Khadaffi in Libya. It served again in the Gulf War. In the mid-'80s McDonnell Douglas developed a special Harpoon land-attack variant for use by carrier-based aircraft against land targets and ships in port. Richard P. Hallion, in Storm Over Iraq, describes the new missile:

> The new missile, the AGM-84D SLAM, used the same 500-pound warhead and propulsion as the Harpoon, but had different guidance and control, consisting of an inertial navigation system using Global Positioning System (GPS) updates for midcourse guidance, a data-link system adopted from the earlier Walleye missile program for terminal "man-in-the-loop" aim point control, and an imaging infrared (IIR) seeker adopted from the Maverick program. SLAM, the newest weapon in the Navy's inventory at the time the Gulf war broke out, made its combat debut against Iraq when an A-6E fired two against an Iraqi hydroelectric plant, with GPS and an accompanying A-7E controlling them into the target during the final phase of the attack.[10]

The J402 continues to be a very successful engine program for Teledyne CAE. The Harpoon antiship missile is currently in the inventory of twenty-six nations worldwide.

## The Williams International F107 Turbofan Engine

In 1954, with $3,500, Dr. Sam Williams founded Williams Research Corporation in Walled Lake, Michigan, to work on small turbojet applications. Williams had previously worked at Chrysler on turbine engine research and development, mostly automotive applications. From 1954 to 1964, Williams Research developed several small turboshaft and turbojet engines for automotive, aircraft, marine, and industrial applications. Among these were the WR9-7 and WR27-1 auxiliary power units for the de Havilland Buffalo and S-3A.[11]

In 1957, Williams International (formerly Williams Research) also began development of a miniature, limited-life turbojet engine producing 200 pounds or less of thrust for unmanned applications. The prototype engine in this series was the WR1, a 70-horsepower regenerative free-turbine engine for marine use. In 1957 Williams International repackaged this engine as a jet engine, the WR2. The WR2 consisted of a single-stage centrifugal compressor, annular burner, centrifugally fed atomizing fuel nozzles, and a single-stage axial turbine. It achieved about 60 pounds of thrust. Shortly after the WR2 was revealed to the public, the engine captured the interest of Canadair Limited, which was searching for a propulsion system for a small, highly sophisticated reconnaissance drone. The two companies got together in 1960 and began work on integrating the engine and the drone.[12]

Development of the WR2 proceeded from the WR2-1 prototype through three design models to flight test in 1964-65. Two additional model changes were made, culminating in the WR-5 and WR-6. The WR-6 (Figure 18-9) was rated at 125 pounds of thrust but weighed only 29 pounds. It was the production engine for the CL89 reconnaissance drone built by Canadair and used in Canada, the United Kingdom, West Germany, and Italy.[13]

**Figure 18-9. Williams International
WR 2-6 Turbojet**
*(Photo courtesy of Williams International)*

Concurrent with the latter stages of the work with Canadair, Williams International teamed with the Ventura Division of the Northrop Corporation in the design and production of a naval target drone. The design requirements for the new engine, designated the WR24, were substantially more challenging than those of the WR2-6. The WR24 required a 1-hour flight duration whereas the WR2 required only 10 minutes per flight, it had to fly at 20,000 feet versus only 10,000 feet altitude for the WR2; it had to be capable of variable flight speeds; and perhaps most importantly, it had to be capable of reuse twenty times after sea-water recovery.[14]

Richard J. Mandle, an engineer at Williams International, described the sea immersion requirement and testing process in a paper delivered to the Society of Automotive Engineers Aerospace Meeting in 1977:

> Navy targets are generally recovered in the sea. The engine was required to be reusable after a maximum of 19 sea-water immersions, each of which could last up to 3 hours. Selection of corrosion resistant materials and protective coatings as previously discussed were [sic] only part of the job. Withstanding thermal shocks and developing an acceptable decontamination and maintenance procedure still remained.
>
> The small size of the engine permitted immersion tests to be conducted in the engine test cell. An overhead trolley was installed to lift the hot engine from the test stand and immerse it into a tank full of "sea water" (simulated by use of ASTM-D-1141-52 sea salt and tap water). Development tests to assess thermal shock effects and locate water trap areas were first conducted using fresh water. Except for a lot of hissing, the engine was not effected [sic] by its plunge into the water.
>
> An immersion test cycle consisted of an engine run to full power for 5 minutes followed by a 5-minute run at flight idle prior to shutdown. Immersion was made within 65 seconds after fuel shutoff. To simulate an actual flight condition, the engine was immersed completely within 2 seconds from first contact at a 30 degree nose down attitude. The engine soaked in the salt water for 2 hours then was lifted and allowed to air dry for 1 hour before proceeding with decontamination and maintenance.
>
> To determine the extent of maintenance necessary, it was planned to conduct as many immersion cycles as possible without disassembly. After a total of 19 test cycles were completed, the parts were disassembled and inspected. Evidence of contaminated generator bearings were [sic] found and traced to a faulty generator cavity seal. The seal was designed to operate only when the engine was stopped so that the grease-packed generator bearings could be protected from sea-water. Modifications to the seal proved successful so ten more immersion cycles were conducted to verify its operation.
>
> The tests did establish that the engine was capable of 20 reuses after the specified immersion time, provided the decontamination and maintenance procedures were followed. These procedures were essentially a fresh water flush, internally and externally, followed by drainage of contaminated fuel, lube and internal areas of the engine with a water displacement and corrosion resistant oil (RUST-LICK 606), and finally a 5-minute drying-out run using normal fuel and oil supplies. Disassembly for inspection was required only after every tenth immersion. The validity of these tests were [sic] proven during field and ship board use of about 2,000 engines.[15]

The WR24-6 turbojet passed its qualification tests in 1968, successfully demonstrating operation without surge or over-temperature throughout its flight envelope of sea level up to 20,000 feet and zero to 0.8 Mach number, and was thus cleared for production for the Northrop MQM-74A target drone. By adapting successful components from its family of auxiliary power units and by quickly redesigning in response to development and testing problems, Williams International was able to announce the release to production of both the WR24-6 and the WR2-6 at about the same time. But Williams and his company did not stop there. They knew that more thrust could be produced from their engine.[16]

While the development phase of the WR24-6 was winding down with the beginning of the qualification tests, Williams International design engineers began work on getting higher thrust out of the engine. The corporation put up its own money for further research, enabling development to proceed without having to request funding from the government. Williams International is a privately held company and has on many occasions spent corporation funds for developments that would have had to wait for government support.

In the redesign, which was completed in 1967, the team added a single-stage axial compressor ahead of the existing centrifugal compressor. This added stage promised a 40 percent increase in thrust. The two-stage design passed its compressor rig tests and two prototype engines, designated the WR24-7, were built. In the fall of 1973 the Navy's MQM-74C target drone successfully completed its flight-testing program using the Williams WR24-7.

Williams International began the development of a small turbofan engine variant of its WR2/WR24 production turbojet engine. The basic concept involved adding a two-stage fan and a two-stage intermediate pressure section ahead of the centrifugal stage of a WR24 turbojet. This four-stage assembly was driven with a concentric shaft and a two-stage axial turbine located behind the original single-stage turbine, thus creating a counterrotating, two-spool fan engine. A by-pass ratio of approximately 1.0 was selected for the engine, which was designated the WR19.[17]

First use of the WR19 was with the Bell/ARPA Jet Flying Belt in September 1968. The engine design had been modified to permit inlet-down (vertical) operation and to keep weight to a minimum. The result was a fan jet engine weighing only 67 pounds and producing 425 pounds of thrust. The Air Force immediately took an interest in the WR19 as a possible new system for missile propulsion.[18]

The first development test of the WR19-A2 Cruise Missile engine prototype took place in 1970.[19] In 1971 a prototype Navy pilot rescue autogyro powered by the WR19 turbofan made its first flight.[20] The Air Force awarded Williams International a competitive demonstration program for development of the WR19 turbofan engine in 1972.[21]

In the summer of 1973, Williams, with its WR19-A7D turbofan engine, was selected by the Air Force as the single contractor to continue with development and testing of engines for the Subsonic Cruise Armed Decoy (SCAD) program. The SCAD was designed to assist strategic bombers in penetrating enemy defenses by confusing radar after being launched from a mother ship (a B-52). The competition included tunnel testing and an evaluation of Williams International's capability and management. The company then proceeded to build an engine for Preliminary Flight Rating Test (PFRT). The engine was designated the F107-WR-100 (Figure 18-10) by the Air Force, but the SCAD program was terminated in late July 1973, before this test could be completed.[22]

**Figure 18-10. Cutaway of F107 Engine**
*(Photo courtesy of Williams International)*

The design of the F107-WR-100 at this time included the two-rotor counterrotating design, mixed-flow exhaust, integral lubrication system, fuel pump, control system, and special provisions for high-altitude starting (cartridge and gaseous oxygen injection). Its thrust rating had been increased to 630 pounds. The engine also featured a cast aluminum interstage compressor housing. The four compressor stators were made in a casting process involving integrally cast steel vanes in the aluminum housing. The low-cost bimetal casting process had been developed by the company.[23]

In 1974 the Air Force SCAD program became the Air Launched Cruise Missile (ALCM). The F107-WR-100 engine was designated the ALCM propulsion system.[24] That same year, the WR19 turbofan powered the two-man version of the Williams Aerial Systems Program, or WASP, in tethered flight. The F107 for the ALCM also completed its first test run.[25]

In 1975 the F107 engine was successfully tested for air-start capability in Air Force wind tunnel tests. The F107-powered ALCM was designed to start operating after the missile was dropped from the weapons bay of a strategic bomber. In October of that year Williams delivered the first F107 for the Air Force flight test program. The F107 completed the ALCM Engine Preliminary Flight Test on November 18, 1975, and subsequently passed the Air Force Propulsion Review Board.[26]

The first test run of the F107 for the Navy's Tomahawk Cruise Missile was in late 1975. That year also saw all four airframe bidders on the Tomahawk cruise missile choose the F107 engine, but the Navy required two competing engine bidders on the two selected airframes. By the end of 1975 Boeing's ALCM was in the final stages of its Advanced Development Program. The first run of the Tomahawk version of the F107 was completed in late 1975. This version was designated the F107-WR-400 engine.[27]

The F107-WR-400 is a low-bypass-ratio turbofan with mixed exhaust. The low-pressure spool consists of a two-stage axial fan, followed by two additional axial-compressor stages in the gas generator flow path, all driven by two axial turbines. The high-pressure spool consists of a single-stage centrifugal compressor driven by an axial turbine. The engine uses an annular burner with rotary fuel injection, and is started by impingement of solid propellant gases on the turbine blades. The lubrication system is self-contained.

The F107-100 and F107-400 versions have the same gas-flow paths, rotating elements, and combustors, and they share most static structures. The gear-case, lube and scavenge pumps, compressor inter-stage castings, and engine mounts are different to meet the installation requirements in the two different airframes.[28]

In 1976 the Navy selected the General Dynamics/Convair airframe and the F107 engine for the Tomahawk program after fly-off competition and competing engine tunnel tests.[29] The first flight of the Air Force's F107-powered ALCM was in 1976. Later that year the F107 engine completed the Demonstration Flight Rating Test (DFRT) for the Navy Tomahawk cruise missile, and the Tomahawk completed its first flight.[30]

Williams International also announced the expansion of engine production facilities in Utah in 1977. The new plant became operational on June 18, 1978, and was formally dedicated on October 16, 1978. The Utah facility delivered its first F107 cruise missile engine in March 1981, three months ahead of schedule.[31]

In 1977, after completion of separate advanced development phases for both the Navy Tomahawk and the Air Force ALCM, Williams International was awarded contracts covering both programs under the oversight of the Air Force-run Joint Cruise Missile Project Office for full development of the F107 engine. The company entered full-scale engineering development for F107 engines in March 1977, and in March 1980, a DSARC decision resulted in a production go-ahead.[32]

In the next year, 1978, the Williams team initiated studies to improve the performance of the F107. Also in 1978, the Navy Tomahawk Cruise Missile was ground-launched from a tube launcher mounted on a truck bed using an F107 engine.[33] In 1979 the company started testing the F107-WR-101 Air Launched Cruise Missile engine.

Dr. Williams was awarded the 1978 Collier Trophy for conceiving and developing the world's smallest high-efficiency turbofan for the U.S. cruise missile programs. Also in that year, Dr. Williams was awarded the French Federation Aeronautique Internationale award, which recognized the F107 engine as a major contributor to the advancement of aeronautics.[34]

Throughout 1979, a fly-off competition of ten flights each between Boeing and General Dynamics, under the auspices of the Joint Cruise Missile Project Office, took place. All the cruise missiles used were powered by Williams F107 engines. Also in that year, Williams International began a technology transfer effort to Teledyne CAE for manufacturing the F107.[35]

In 1980 Williams International was given the production go-ahead for the F107 following successful cruise-missile engine qualification. Also in 1980 Boeing won the Cruise Missile fly-off competition with its design for the AGM-86 ALCM. Williams began production deliveries of ALCM engines to Boeing three months ahead of contract requirements in 1981.[36]

In 1982 Teledyne CAE began licensed production and deliveries of F107 engines as the official second source for the engine. Also in 1982 Williams began full-scale development of an F107-derivative engine, the F112-WR-100, for an advanced cruise missile.[37]

In 1983 Williams International became the first cruise-missile contractor to receive the Tomahawk "E" flag for excellence. Williams also started production deliveries of F107 engines for ground-launched cruise missiles (GLCM). The Navy also began funding for Tomahawk Technical Modernization Programs (TMPs). This Navy funding was followed in 1984 by Air Force funding for TMPs.[38]

The F107 program passed a significant milestone in 1984 by successfully demonstrating operation after thirty-six months of storage. In 1985 the F107 had exceeded all Air Force and Navy reliability goals. That year also saw the first ALCM launch from a rotary launcher.[39]

In 1986 Williams International completed deliveries of ALCM engines and completed a successful demonstration of a requirement for the F107 engine to operate within specification requirements after sixty months of storage.[40] The company began development of an upgraded, extended storage life engine for the Tomahawk program in 1987. Williams International also delivered its 3000th cruise missile engine that year, with all deliveries ahead of schedule. That year also saw the first ALCM launch from a B-1B bomber.[41]

---

## Endnotes

[1] Wagner, William, *Continental Motors And Its People: The Eight Decades of Teledyne Continental Motors*, Fallbrook, CA: Armed Forces Journal International in cooperation with Aero Publishers, Inc., 1983. 138.

[2] Ibid, 138-139.

[3] Ibid.

[4] Ibid, 140.

[5] Forecast International, *Gas Turbine Forecast: Book One, Reports and Forecasts*. Newtown, CT: Forecast International, 1993, Teledyne CAE J69, 1.

[6] Wagner, Continental Motors, 154-155.

[7] Specific models included the BQM-34A/S, MQM-34D, AQM-34G/H/J/V, and the BGM-34A. Forecast International, Teledyne CAE J69, 2.

[8] Wagner, Continental Motors, 155.

[9] Forecast International, Teledyne CAE J69, 2.

[10] Hallion, Richard P, *Storm Over Iraq: Air Power and the Gulf War*, Washington, D.C.: Smithsonian Institution Press, 1992, 296.

[11] Williams International, *History and Evolution of the Williams International F107 Cruise Missile Turbofan Engine*, Covers years 1955 through 1988, Walled Lake, MI, no date, 1, Williams International, Fact sheet stating history with point of contact Mr. David C. Jolivette, 313-624-5200, ext. 1206, Williams International, Walled Lake, MI, no date.

[12] Mandle, Richard J., Williams Research Corp., "Twenty Year Evolution of the WR2/WR24 Series of Small Turbojet Engines," No. 770998, presented at the Society of Au-

tomotive Engineers Aerospace Meeting, November 14-17, 1977, 1.

[13] Ibid, 9-10.

[14] Ibid, 10.

[15] Ibid, 13-14.

[16] Ibid, 14.

[17] Williams International, History and production of the F107 engine produced by organization, Williams International, Walled Lake, MI, no date, 1.

[18] Williams International, History and Evolution of the F107, 1, and Williams International, History and production of the F107, 1.

[19] Williams International, History and Evolution of the F107, 1.

[20] Ibid.

[21] Ibid.

[22] Ibid, 2, and Williams International, History and production of the F107, 1.

[23] Williams International, History and production of the F107, 1.

[24] Williams International, History and Evolution of the F107, 2.

[25] Ibid, and Williams International, Fact sheet summarizing history and capabilities of organization, Williams International, Walled Lake, MI, no date.

[26] Williams International, History and Evolution of the F107, 9.

[27] Williams International, History and Evolution of the F107, 2, and Williams International, History and production of the F107, 1.

[28] Williams International, History and production of the F107, 2.

[29] Williams International, History and Evolution of the F107, 2.

[30] Ibid.

[31] Ibid, and Williams International, Fact sheet.

[32] Williams International, History and Evolution of the F107, 2, and Williams International, History and production of the F107, 2.

[33] Williams International, History and Evolution of the F107, 3, and Williams International, Factsheet.

[34] Ibid.

[35] Williams International, Factsheet, and Williams International, History and production of the F107, 2.

[36] Williams International, History and Evolution of the F107, 3, and Wills, T.K., USAF ASD/AFSC and Wise, E.P., Williams Research Corp., "Development of a New Class of Engine - The Small Turbofan," AIAA Paper No. 76-618, Presented at the AIAA/SAE 12th Propulsion Conference, Palo Alto, CA, July 26-29, 1976, 1.

[37] Williams International, History and Evolution of the F107, 3.

[38] Ibid.

[39] Ibid.

[40] Ibid.

[41] Ibid.

**IHPTET LOGO**

# Research and Technology Focus

The previous 18 chapters focused primarily on engine development and application. This chapter shifts to the research and technology that precedes development and is crucial to the successful fielding of a product. This stage is especially important for improving industry's design system and includes the following key elements: 1) research to better understand the basics physics; 2) development of light-weight, high strength, high-temperature material systems; 3) experimental validation of analytical methods and design codes; and 4) component/engine technology demonstration. The federal government has had a significant role in developing gas turbine engines. The responsible government establishments are DOD for military applications; NASA for commercial applications; and DOE for ground power applications. Although this chapter concentrates on aircraft-engine technology needs and enabling improvements to the design system, some technology has multiple applications that affect all three establishments.

This chapter indicates what research is being conducted on 1) the basic engine components and 2) technologies that have pervasive applications throughout the engine system. Because DOD is the customer for its military aircraft, its turbopropulsion research and technology development activity is managed under the Integrated High Performance Turbine Engine Technology (IHPTET) program, a program with a very broad charter to research and develop all engine components, and one that demonstrates technology maturity through engine testing. NASA, principally NASA Glenn Research Center in Cleveland, Ohio, also researches many engine component and pervasive technologies; however, the agency's charter does not emphasize full-scale demonstration testing. Thus, the NASA discussions in this chapter focus instead on concerns that are primarily commercial with respect to durability, modeling, high-temperature materials and structures, and reducing emissions, noise, and fuel burned. Of these concerns, the most critical is making the engine more energy efficient (that is, reducing fuel burned).

In 1988 the Department of Defense started an aggressive technology development plan to leapfrog technical barriers and deliver twice the propulsion capability of the current military aircraft propulsion systems by around the turn of the century. Dubbed the Integrated High Performance Turbine Engine Technology (IHPTET) Program, it was started by the Air Force's Aero Propulsion Laboratory at Wright-Patterson Air Force Base in Ohio.

IHPTET began as the High Performance Turbine Engine Technology Program (HPTET) of the Air Force's Aero Propulsion Laboratory in 1984. Although the program began as a strictly in-house program, it quickly expanded when the Materials Laboratory at Wright-Patterson became involved. Materials Lab and Propulsion Lab cooperative efforts soon began yielding impressive results. Former Materials Lab engineer Dr. John Henderson remarked on the new cooperation between the laboratories:

> What happened in the Materials Area was a lot of good decision-making on what the Navy was doing and what we were doing and eventually what NASA was doing. The other positive thing that happened was the cooperation...we got truly interactive programs going as a result of this interaction in propulsion. We had...not been talking to each other. The Materials Lab had been working on propulsion materials [and the] Propulsion Lab was putting new materials into their demonstrators and frequently having failures but never pulling back for Materials Lab analysis, ...so I think those kind of interfaces were recognized as being important as we got IHPTET.[1]

In March 1985 Dr. James Petty of the Turbine Engine Division of the Aero Propulsion and Power Laboratory became HPTET manager. Dr. Robert Barthelemy, deputy director of the laboratory, asked Petty to prepare a briefing on HPTET for General Skanze, then commander of the Air Force Systems Command. Upon hearing the presentation, Skanze proposed that the labs involve industry in the HPTET program. In the summer of that year six engine companies, General Electric, Pratt & Whitney, Garrett Aircraft Engines, Williams International, Teledyne CAE, and Allison Division of General Motors were brought into the HPTET program. Each company was asked to develop its own advanced turbo-propulsion plans. The program began to roll. Textron Lycoming joined after the program became multiservice.

In February 1986 Dr. Petty and Mr. Tom Sims of the Propulsion Laboratory's Turbine Engine Division put together an HPTET briefing for Dr. Donald Dix of the Office of the Deputy Director for Research and Engineering in the Pentagon.[2] Dr. Dix was very impressed and passed the briefing up to the Deputy Director, who was so impressed with the program that he ordered the integration of the Army and the Navy into HPTET, which therefore became the Integrated High Performance Turbine Engine Technology Program. NASA and the Defense Advanced Research Projects Agency (DARPA) were also invited to join in the program. A steering committee was formed, with Tom Sims as the Aeropropulsion Lab representative (Figure 19-1). All participants were encouraged to put together an integrated government plan for advanced air-breathing propulsion, which was then presented to Dr. Dix. With Dix's enthusiastic endorsement, Undersecretary of Defense Taft signed the IHPTET program plan on November 12, 1987.

Richard Hill, chief of technology in the Turbine Engine Division of the Wright Laboratory's Aero Propulsion and Power Directorate, explains the purpose of the program:

> The IHPTET program was established during the middle 1980's to be the "technology springboard" for the next century's high performance military turbine engines. The main thrust of IHPTET was focused during this time period on a wide spectrum of new systems, and success in IHPTET would assure continued United States air superiority over any new aggressor system.

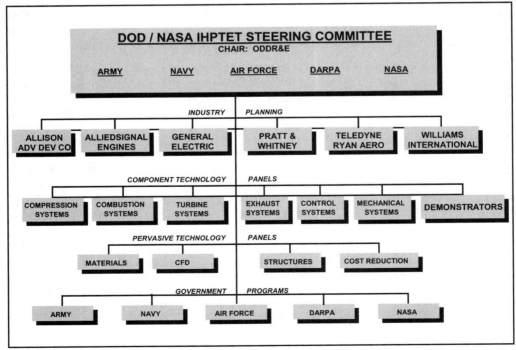

**Figure 19-1. IHPTET Organizational Structure**
*(Illustration courtesy of U.S. Air Force)*

IHPTET's purpose is to integrate government and corporate efforts to develop long-range turbine engine technology goals and programs beyond the next ten years timeframe. IHPTET developed technologies are being applied to both military and commercial turbine engines—both new engines and fleet modernizations. IHPTET is the technology base for all future military systems and the springboard for many new commercial engines.[3]

Hill goes on to explain this unprecedented change in the way that the United States has approached aircraft gas turbine development.

IHPTET is a coordinated, three-phase, Government and Industry visionary initiative. Formally initiated in 1987, IHPTET includes virtually all government and industry sponsored propulsion Research and Development (R&D) activities devoted to advancing technology for military turbine engines. The goal of IHPTET is to develop and demonstrate technologies by the turn of the century that, when applied, will double a 1985 level of turbopropulsion capability. The technologies of IHPTET offer significant payoff when applied to any turbine propulsion system.[4]

Under IHPTET there exists one IHPTET government plan and seven individual industry plans, coordinated among the Department of Defense (DOD) Military Services — Army, Navy, Air Force; the Defense Advanced Research Projects Agency (DARPA); and the National Aeronautics and Space Administration (NASA).[5]

A DOD-chaired steering committee provides overall IHPTET guidance. Each aircraft gas turbine technology area is addressed by a technology panel which has representatives from all the government agencies as well as from Pratt & Whitney, Allison, Williams International, Teledyne Ryan Aeronautical, GE, and AlliedSignal Aerospace (which includes Textron Lycoming as the result of a company merger). Furthermore, these panels may be organized as either a component technology panel or a pervasive technology panel. The component technology panels focus on key engine components such as fans/compressors, combustors/augmentors, turbines, nozzles, mechanical systems, controls and instrumentation, and demonstrator engines.

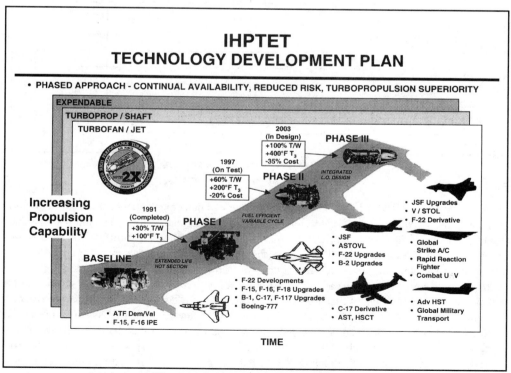

**Figure 19-2. IHPTET Time Phases**
*(Illustration courtesy of U.S. Air Force)*

The pervasive technology panels focus on innovative structures, computational fluid dynamics, materials, and cost reduction. Other areas covered within the panels include manufacturing processes, analysis and design, test facilities, and maintainability.[6] Hill talks about the development process within IHPTET:

> Payoffs from IHPTET come from increasing propulsion system performance and affordability with no compromises in system life, reliability and maintainability. To focus the initiative on these payoffs, IHPTET management established specific goals as a function of time for each of the three aircraft turbine engine classes— turbofan/turbojet, turboshaft/turboprop, and expendable. Shown in Figure 19-2 are the time phases of IHPTET. These goals were chosen as having the highest effect in maximizing payoff to military systems. The three IHPTET phases shown in Figure 19-3 were created to provide milestones against which to assess progress, and, most importantly, to provide opportunity for transition to current, upgrade, derivative and new engines.

> The IHPTET goals for each of the three phases are based on a 1985 technology level. They are "typical" technology goals for each class of engine (do not interpret them as a specific "engine cycle" description). Through the achievement of these goals, IHPTET will provide technology for propulsion systems that are lower cost, lighter weight and easier to maintain than today's systems, yet can fly faster, higher, and with increased maneuverability.[7]

| | PHASE I | PHASE II | PHASE III |
|---|---|---|---|
| **TURBOFAN/TURBOJET** | | | |
| THRUST/WEIGHT | +30% | +60% | +100% |
| COMBUSTION INLET TEMP | +100°F | +200°F | +400°F |
| PRODUCTION COST | | -20% | -35% |
| MAINTENANCE COST | | -20% | -35% |
| **TURBOSHAFT/TURBOPROP** | | | |
| SFC | -20% | -30% | -40% |
| POWER/WEIGHT RATIO | +40% | +80% | +120% |
| PRODUCTION COST | | -20% | -35% |
| MAINTENANCE COST | | -20% | -35% |
| **EXPENDABLE** | | | |
| SFC (STRATEGIC) | -20% | -30% | -40% |
| THRUST/AIRFLOW (TACTICAL SUPERSONIC) | +35% | +70% | +100% |
| COST (TACTICAL) | -30% | -45% | -60% |

**Figure 19-3. IHPTET Goals by Phase**
*(Illustration courtesy of U.S. Air Force)*

Since 1988, IHPTET has produced revolutionary advancements in turbine engine technologies due to the synergistic effect of combining advanced material developments, innovative structural designs and improved aerothermodynamics. The committee accomplished this through implementation of an aggressive three-phase plan. The plan targets three areas for specific technology improvements and provides clear goals for implementation. The first area is fighter/attack/transport aircraft, such as the YF-22 Advanced Tactical Fighter (Figure 19-4), bombers, transports, or other aircraft that use turbojet or turbofan engines. The second area is devoted to missile/Unmanned Air Vehicle (UAV) aircraft, such as the Tomahawk Cruise Missile (Figure 19-5), or other expendable turbine engines and the third area addresses subsonic patrol/rotary-wing aircraft, such as the AH-64 Apache Attack Helicopter (Figure 19-6), or other turboshaft or turboprop aircraft. The plan is to minimize technology development risks, provide continuous technology transition to both military and commercial users, and define interim technology goals against

**Figure 19-4. YF-22 Advanced Tactical Fighter**
*(Photo courtesy of U.S. Air Force)*

**Figure 19-5. Tomahawk Cruise Missile**
*(Photo courtesy of U.S. Air Force)*

**Figure 19-6. AH-64 Apache Attack Helicopter**
*(Photo courtesy of U.S. Air Force)*

which progress can be measured. Hill describes the payoffs to military systems:

> Through the development and validation of IHPTET technologies, major payoffs to military sys-
> tems will occur. These modernized high performance military aircraft will supply the affordable battle
> field advantage — low fuel burn allowing longer missions; high thrust-to-weight allowing larger pay-
> loads; low maintenance and support in the field yielding higher sortie rates; and excess specific power
> during critical flight maneuvers — the air superiority advantage![8]

The Phase I goal of the IHPTET plan was to provide a 30 percent increase in propulsion
capability. In the fighter/attack aircraft area IHPTET reached its goal of increasing engine
thrust/weight by 30 percent. In the missile/UAV area, the specific goals were to increase
thrust-to-airflow by 35 percent, reduce specific fuel consumption by 20 percent, and reduce cost
by 30 percent. In the area of subsonic patrol/rotary-wing aircraft, the specific goals were to increase horsepower/weight ratio by 40 percent and decrease specific fuel consumption by 20 percent. These goals were achieved by 1994.

Richard Hill describes the IHPTET progress under Phase I (Figure 19-7):

> The goals are achieved for expendable engine and turboprop/-turboshaft engine classes; but for the
> turbofan/turbojet, more work is needed. The technology that slowed the achievement of the turbo-
> fan/turbojet goal centers on material maturity for the high temperature rotating structure at the dis-
> charge end of the compressor. What is lacking is final development of a full life, low density material
> system capable of enduring the high combustor inlet temperature goal conditions. Significant progress
> is being made on the class of materials that will meet this need and once the material is fully character-
> ized, the turbofan/turbojet goals will be achieved. The goals of Phase I for turbofan/turbojet will be met
> in the next engine test. Wisely, IHPTET management did not wait for all of Phase I to be completed
> prior to initiating the long-lead critical path technologies of Phase II. As a result, the Phase II technolo-
> gies are becoming well established and on schedule for demonstration by 1997.[9]

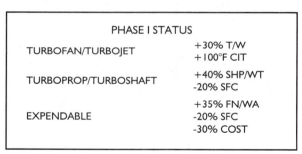

**Figure 19-7. IHPTET Phase I Status**
*(Illustration courtesy of U.S. Air Force)*

As of 1997, IHPTET Phase II goals in the fighter/attack aircraft area were to increase the
thrust-to-weight ratio by 30 percent over Phase I and decrease fuel-burn ratio by an additional 10
percent. In the subsonic patrol/rotary-wing area, goals are to further increase power-to-weight
ratio another 40 percent and decrease specific fuel consumption by an additional 10 percent over
Phase I levels. In the missile/UAV area, goals are to increase specific thrust by another 35 percent, decrease specific fuel consumption by an additional 10 percent, and decrease overall cost
by another 15 percent relative to Phase I levels. The IHPTET Committee expects to achieve
these goals by 1997. Hill discusses some of the difficulties in achieving these goals:

> The major problem now being faced is keeping industry centered on early acceptance and applica-
> tion of these newer IHPTET advancements in an affordability driven market economy. The difficulty
> stems from the Government's need to keep an industrial defense base alive over a long period of declin-
> ing budgets and low levels of production and yet capable of short notice, full-scale production of
> IHPTET materials and innovative designs.[10]

The year 2003 is the target for the IHPTET Phase III goals. In the fighter/attack area the goals are to again increase thrust-to-weight engine ratios by another 40 percent or 100% above the pre-Phase I baseline engine technology level and to decrease engine fuel burn rates by a further 10 percent over Phase II (Figure 19-8). In the subsonic patrol/rotary-wing area, the goals are to achieve another 40 percent improvement in engine power-to-weight ratio and attain a further 10 percent reduction in specific fuel consumption beyond Phase II levels. In the missile/UAV area the goals are to increase engine thrust-to-airflow ratio another 30 percent over Phase II levels, achieve a further 10 percent decrease in specific fuel consumption and an additional 15 percent decrease in cost over Phase II levels.

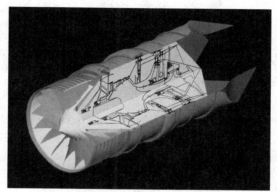

**Figure 19-8. Conceptual IHPTET
Phase III Engine**
*(Illustration courtesy of U.S. Air Force)*

The U.S. Air Force provides approximately 70 percent of IHPTET funding and the Navy provides about 15 percent. The Army provides about 7 percent, NASA about 7 percent, and DARPA about 1 percent. Of that funding, 70 percent goes into the fighter/attack area, 20 percent goes into the subsonic patrol/rotary-wing area, and the remaining 10 percent is allocated to the missile/UAV area.[11]

IHPTET emphasizes the concept of teaming, not only with other services, but also with academia, via consortia (Figure 19-9).

The current IHPTET consortia are focused on (1) forced response prediction methods and (2) fiber development for advanced MMC and CMC material....

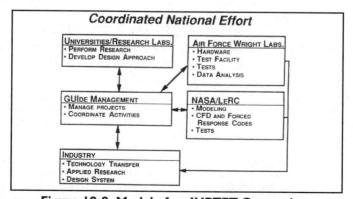

**Figure 19-9. Model of an IHPTET Consortium**
*(Photo courtesy of Allison)*

**Figure 19-10. Pratt & Whitney Phase I ATEGG**
*(Photo courtesy of Pratt & Whitney)*

> IHPTET consortia are structured with an organization (in this case, Carnegie Mellon and Purdue Universities) as the integrating subcontractor. Each member of the consortium contributes resources at varying levels (funds, facilities or data) and technical expertise to help meet the consortium goals. In addition, the Government contributes funds, expertise and in some cases, rig testing to the consortium. Contracts are then let to chosen organizations to actually conduct the research and report the findings. The Forced Response Consortium…is focused on the establishment of standard industry assessment methods of structural damping and understanding structural response to engine/inlet induced aerodynamic forcing functions. The, like the Forced Response Consortium, is a jointly funded effort by all the seven engine Materials Consortium companies, DOD, DARPA, and NASA. The objective is to develop affordable high temperature fibers for use as reinforcement in both CMC and MMC material. These will be developed as "industry fibers"—well understood, documented and ready for production use by each of the participants…. The consortium is unique and acts as an impetus for industry to work together on other common IHPTET technology problems resulting in cost benefits and market opportunity to all.[12]

Four joint service technology demonstrator engine programs, the Advanced Turbine Engine Gas Generator (ATEGG, Figures 19-10, 19-11, and 19-12); the Joint Technology Demonstrator Engine (JTDE, Figures 19-13 and 19-14); the Joint Turbine Advanced Gas Generator (JTAGG, Figures 19-15 through 19-18); and the Joint Expendable Turbine Engine Concept (JETEC, Figures 19-19 through 19-22) form the heart of IHPTET. These programs validate new technologies for multi-role fighters, special operations aircraft, transports, advanced rotorcraft, and cruise missiles of the future. The ATEGG program dates back to 1963. The JTAGG program was started in 1987 and was integrated into IHPTET upon IHPTET's startup in 1988. In each of these programs demonstrated technologies are transferred to all three classes of gas turbine engines which address the critical military needs of propulsion development of the next two decades. Hill describes the importance of the demonstrator concept:

> It should be noted that the IHPTET goals are not considered to be achieved until the enabling technologies have been assembled and tested under actual engine conditions in an engine demonstrator (core or full engine configuration) — commonly called a "Tech Demo" under IHPTET sponsorship, technologies mature at a component level until ready for evaluation in dedicated rig testing. The primary IHPTET compressor test facility is the Air Force's Compressor Research Facility (CRF). The newest IHPTET test facility, the Advanced Turbine Aerothermal Research Rig (ATARR), is dedicated to turbine research and also belongs to the Air Force. The best and most promising technologies that successfully complete testing in rigs like CRF and ATARR are further assembled into Tech Demos and evaluated for synergistic problems. All Tech Demo testing is done with significant amounts of instrumentation. Typically over 1,000 pieces of instrumentation are

**Figure 19-11. GE Phase I ATEGG**
*(Photo courtesy of GE)*

**Figure 19-12. Allison Phase II ATEGG**
*(Photo courtesy of Allison)*

**Figure 19-13. Pratt & Whitney
Phase I JTDE**
*(Photo courtesy of Pratt & Whitney)*

**Figure 19-14. GE Phase I
Variable-Cycle JTDE**
*(Photo courtesy of GE)*

**Figure 19-15. Textron Lycoming Phase I JTAGG Rotor**
*(Photo courtesy of Textron Lycoming)*

**Figure 19-16. GE Phase I
JTAGG Core Engine**
*(Photo courtesy of GE)*

**Figure 19-17. AlliedSignal
Phase I JTAGG**

*(Photo courtesy of AlliedSignal)*

used on a single Tech Demo test with the majority of the testing done at sea level conditions. The major work-horse demonstrators for turbofan/jet engines are the Advanced Turbine Engine Gas Generator (ATEGG) cores and Joint Technology Demonstrator Engine (JTDE). For turboshaft/prop engines, the demonstrators are the Joint Turbine Advanced Gas Generator (JTAGG) cores. Missile engine technology is demonstrated in the Joint Expendable Turbine Engine Concept (JETEC) engines. Upon successful completion of Tech Demo evaluation, technologies are typically matured to the level necessary for system transition. Many times, technologies that are tested in the Tech Demo are found to be lacking the qualities necessary to continue further development and are returned to a component rig for further evaluation and correction. Thus the progression of testing can be cyclic in nature between rig evaluation and Tech Demo testing.[13]

Industry contributes up to 40 percent of the funding for these demonstrator programs. This teaming of funding and expertise between the government and industry is unique in American turbine engine development experience.

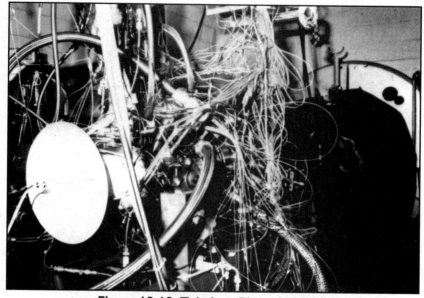

**Figure 19-18. Teledyne Phase I JTAGG**

*(Photo courtesy of Teledyne Continental Motors Turbine Engines)*

Hill talks about the importance of the demonstrator concept in IHPTET, even as it applies to subcomponent technology:

> Historically, risk, viewed in terms of level of "readiness," is the reason given for the nonuse of advanced technology. In choosing technologies for systems, "better" technology has always been, and remains the enemy of "good enough" technology when budgets are tight. This is due to the manager's dilemma of always having to trade part of the desired capability to meet schedule and budget constraints. Historically, the newer and better technology has always had a lower readiness value and higher risk. The same is true for current IHPTET technologies.
>
> Technology readiness is difficult to quantify and understand. However, in IHPTET, a joint industry/government task is underway to both define criteria for assessing readiness of technology and put in place the effort to increase the readiness when a low value is determined. The considerations being used to determine the readiness of IHPTET technology center on the extent of design and test experience with the new technology; the amount of extension beyond known values for manufacturing and production; and the degree of similarity to known design methods, materials processing and manufacturing. Readiness assessment is judgmental and varies from company to company for the same class of material or application of similar technology advancements. Effort to increase readiness has taken different forms in IHPTET. One such form in the Air Force is the formulation of additional Tech Demo tests for specific technology items. This new effort is termed Advanced Technology Transition Demonstrations (ATTDs). These IHPTET programs are short duration, low cost and directed at removing the last remaining risk barriers on a technology — the ones preventing immediate transition of the technology to a product application. Currently, IHPTET is sponsoring ATTDs for the Air Force's F100, F110 and F119 fighter engines. The completion of these ATTDs will result in significant performance improvements while producing major life cycle cost savings.[14]

The aircraft gas turbine engine is a nearly mature technology. As such, future technology advances will not come cheaply. In order to lower costs associated with research and development, teaming between companies has become more popular in the United States. Richard Hill describes the IHPTET focus on teaming between the IHPTET industry participants:

> In the area of contractor-teamed Tech Demo testing, significant progress has been achieved. Currently, GE and AlliedSignal Propulsion Engines are teamed in JTAGG to develop and share in the technology payoff of the small to medium class of turboprop/shaft engines. This takes the form of testing each company's technologies in several builds of a common JTAGG Tech Demo.
>
> Considerable synergistic benefit and technology innovation have resulted from this union. A second team of GE, Pratt & Whitney and Allison is working on a joint structural Tech Demo focused on advanced intermetallic titanium aluminide compressor blade development, innovative turbine cooling designs and reduced engine weight concepts. This program is called Component and Engine Structural Assessment Research (CAESAR). It is becoming a successful program as well as business concept. The first test of CAESAR will be in 1995 and will help reduce the risk of these technologies.[15]

**Figure 19-19. AlliedSignal Phase I JETEC**
*(Photo courtesy of AlliedSignal)*

**Figure 19-20. Allison Phase I JETEC**
*(Photo courtesy of Allison)*

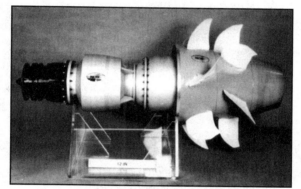

**Figure 19-21. Teledyne Phase II JETEC**
*(Photo courtesy of Teledyne Continental Motors Turbine Engines)*

**Figure 19-22. Williams Phase II JETEC**
*(Photo courtesy of William International)*

Complementing the industry teaming described above is the DOD-NASA government teaming under IHPTET. Many technologies emerge with dual use potential in both military and commercial sectors, but their application design criteria often diverge. Hence, the following discussions will highlight the differences in military and commercial research and technology development focus or emphasis. Although NASA works with the IHPTET program, its primary mission is to interact with industry in the development of commercially applicable engine components and systems. More specifically, NASA has three roles within the IHPTET program: 1) development of key high temperature, high strength materials; 2) development of advanced design analysis capability; and 3) to provide unique test evaluation facilities.

## Fan Technology

During the past 30+ years, major advances in the area of fan technology have been realized for both military and commercial applications. The military has focused on reducing the number of fan stages to make the fan lighter and more reliable while the primary commercial emphasis for fan technology has been on reducing noise.

### Military Focus

The goal of the fan technology programs in IHPTET is to improve pressure ratio with fewer fan stages. To do this, improvements in "enabling technologies" such as sweep and other three-dimensional blading, high tip speeds, mixed airflow concepts, and increased use of computational fluid dynamics are necessary.

Hollow fan blades (Figure 19-23), integrally-bladed rotors (Figure 19-24), and organic and metal matrix composite materials have led to additional weight savings, critical for lower takeoff gross weight aircraft and mission fuel burn. For example, using titanium technology in hollow fan blades can reduce weight by 50 pounds.

Three-dimensional bowed stators increase efficiency and diminish aeromechanical interactions with the rotating blades. New "splittered" rotor fan designs (Figure 19-25) offer higher single-stage pressure ratios, more efficient operation, and stall-free operation over conventional fans while eliminating a stage in the compressor rotor.

**19-23. Hollow Bladed Fan**
*(Photo courtesy of U.S. Navy)*

**Figure 19-24. Integrally Bladed Rotor (IBR)**
*(Photo courtesy of U. S. Air Force)*

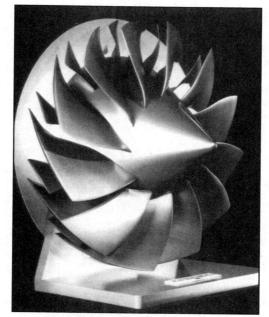

**Figure 19-25. Splittered Rotor Technology**
*(Photo courtesy of U.S. Air Force)*

**Figure 19-26. Core-Driven Fan Stage**
*(Photo courtesy of U.S. Air Force)*

A new core-driven fan stage used in variable-cycle engines translates into dramatic performance improvements for multiple-design-point aircraft (Figure 19-26). The core-driven fan permits the variable-cycle engine to operate either as a turbofan or turbojet. This new stage replaces two high-pressure compressor stages, reducing engine weight by approximately 150 pounds. Computational fluid dynamics (CFD) software has been key to developing these new technologies.[16]

## Commercial Focus

The military's interest in high performance has led primarily to the development of low-bypass-ratio engines. On the other hand, NASA has concentrated on fuel efficiency with a focus on developing high-bypass-ratio engines. While these engines reduce fuel burned, they also aggravate noise problems. Beyond gaseous and particulate atmospheric pollutants, noise ("emissions") became a public concern in the 1960s[17]. In late 1966, NASA began testing to determine how turbofan-cycle characteristics affect engine noise levels, size, and performance. Researchers found [18] that the fan in turbofan engines generated the most noise—forward from the inlet and aft from fan discharge ducts. Then in 1969 the Federal Aviation Administration (FAA) began responding to legislation calling for reduced aircraft noise.

NASA significantly influenced how to retrofit 1960s- and early-1970s-vintage commercial aircraft to reduce fan noise levels, developing technology that markedly reduced Boeing 707 and Douglas DC-8 aircraft engine noise. This work laid the foundation for acoustic treatment in today's new engine nacelles.

Industry's move toward and acceptance of the more powerful, higher-bypass-ratio fan designs prompted NASA to initiate the Quiet Clean Short-Haul Experimental Engine (QCSEE) Program in the early 1970s.[19] It also investigated new concepts that reduced fan tip speed, optimized rotor/stator ratio, and developed acoustic lining/treatment techniques. These design concepts reduced both high-frequency fan and turbine noise and low-frequency combustor noise.

The 1973 energy crisis prompted NASA's largest and broadest noise effort: the Energy Efficient Engine Project (E[3], 1976-1984).[20, 21] Both P&W and GE participated in this technology development program resulting in the competing engine configurations illustrated in Figures 19-27 and 19-28 . The E[3] technologies developed under this program paved the way in 1993 for the GE 90 and PW4084 high-bypass engines—currently the largest, most powerful engines, which power the Boeing 777 commercial aircraft.

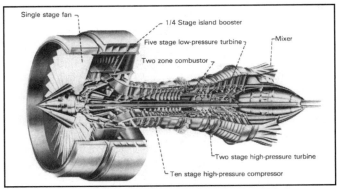

**Figure 19-27. E[3] Engine Cutaway, GE**
*(Illustration courtesy of NASA/GRC)*

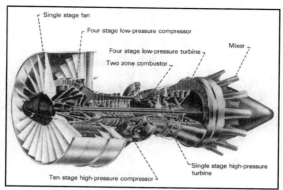

**Figure 19-28. E³ Engine Cutaway,
Pratt & Whitney**
*(Illustration courtesy of NASA/GRC)*

# Advanced Compressor Technology

## Military Focus

Advanced compressor concepts have played a major role in revolutionizing conventional engines and their applications. IHPTET is seeking compact, high-pressure-ratio compression systems that will produce in a few stages the same pressure ratios that required over a dozen stages a few years ago (Figure 19-29). This means that the new compression systems will be more affordable and maintainable, with fewer parts and lower weight. A compressor design concept that leads the way in IHPTET is the enhanced-flow compressor. This design doubles engine Mach number capability by maintaining high flow levels across the Mach number range. The Enhanced-Flow Compressor (Figure 19-30) will provide common compressor technology for missions ranging from transport to supercruise to intercept.

Both the core-driven fan and the enhanced-flow compressor concepts have been successfully tested at the Wright Laboratory. Also, emerging centrifugal compressor technology will lead to single-stage high-pressure compressors for some applications.[22]

**Figure 19-29. High-Stage-Loading,
Three-Stage Axial Compressor**
*(Photo courtesy of U.S. Air Force)*

**Figure 19-30. Enhanced-Flow Compressor**
*(Photo courtesy of U.S. Air Force)*

## Commercial Focus

For decades both the military and commercial sectors have developed (and continue to evolve) the technology for centrifugal (small engine), axial-centrifugal, and axial (large engine) compressors. Although some early turbojet engines incorporated the centrifugal compressor, today most designs for large engines—especially for high-speed and long-range applications—use the more efficient axial-flow type that NACA began investigating shortly after the laboratory opened in 1941and continues developing today. A significant summary report that focused on compressor design and operation fundamentals documents the NACA work prior to 1965.[23]

## Advanced Combustor Technology

### Military Focus

In the technology field of combustors, IHPTET aims at developing new, affordable, robust, lightweight and compact combustor systems with improved reliability. This is no simple task. Higher compressor exit temperatures and through flow velocities as well as near-stoichiometric combustion temperatures at the ever-widening high and low power engine operation conditions also present a challenge to the way in which combustors have been designed in the past.

Single-dome, minimum-volume combustors are a key to weight and volume savings. Front-end dome aerodynamics for enhanced fuel/air mixing are very important considerations for improving low-power stability while simultaneously increasing high-power temperature rise. Single-dome combustor designs require innovative swirler technology, advanced concepts for ignition/flame stabilization, and improved 3-D steady and unsteady computational codes. The tri-wall air swirler (Figure 19-31) has demonstrated the capability to expand the combustor operating envelope and may allow a return to simpler, more affordable single-annular combustors in Phase III.

IHPTET also seeks to develop reduced liner cooling concepts to maintain combustor exit temperature control and meet longer life requirements. New tri-passage diffuser technology (Figure 19-32) allows operation at high-Mach compressor exit conditions with greatly improved airflow distribution.

Floatwall® panels with $Si_3N_4$ tiles embedded in Compglas® (Figure 19-33) improve liner cooling flow reduction by 30 percent at Phase II combustor temperatures. Ceramic

**Figure 19-31. Tri-Wall Air Swirler**
*(Photo courtesy of U.S. Air Force)*

**Figure 19-32. Tri-Passage Diffuser**
*(Photo courtesy of U.S. Air Force)*

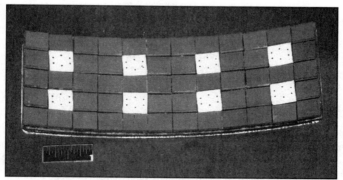

**Figure 19-33. Floatwall Panels with $Si_3N_4$ Tiles**
*(Photo courtesy of U.S. Air Force)*

Matrix Composite (CMC) effusion cooled liner technology (Figure 19-34) enables high heat release rates, reduced liner cooling, reduced pattern factor, and improved hot-section durability while achieving JTAGG II temperature goals. Multihole cooled combustion domes (Figure 19-35) applied to high-speed civil transport engines resulted in both the elimination of splash plates and a 30 percent reduction in cooling air, which could then be used to enhance combustion.[24]

**Figure 19-34. CMC Effu-
sion-Cooled Liner**
*(Photo courtesy of U.S. Air Force)*

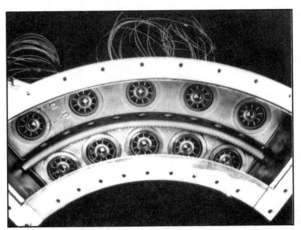

**Figure 19-35. Multihole Cooled
Combustor Dome**
*(Photo courtesy of U.S. Air Force)*

## Commercial Focus

Military and commercial combustor design criteria differ significantly in several respects:  operating temperatures, emissions, and hardware life/durability. In response to public concern during the 1960s and 70s over aircraft engine exhaust emission levels of carbon monoxide (CO), total unburned hydrocarbons (THC), oxides of nitrogen ($NO_X$), and smoke, NASA initiated a number of in-house and contracted efforts to address this issue, the largest and most influential of which was aimed at turbofan engines – the Experimental Clean Combustor Program (ECCP).[25,26] Both GE and P&W were major participants in this program, developing the two-stage combustion process – a pilot zone that controls the low-power engine emissions of CO and THC, while a main zone controls the high-power NOx emissions. GE's "double annular" approach offered both stages in an axially parallel arrangement resulting in a very short combustor, while Pratt & Whitney's "Vorbix" approach provided both stages in an axially series design. In October 1973, while these combustor efforts were underway, the global energy crisis occurred. With Congressional encouragement, NASA, in 1976, initiated the $E^3$ project as the ECCP neared completion. As a result, the $E^3$ combustor efforts built upon the foundation of the ECCP's two-stage combustor designs (Figure 19-36), providing further reduced emission levels under even more challenging operating conditions.[27, 28]

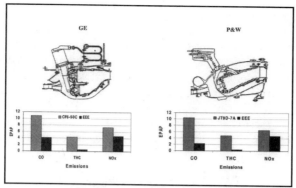

**Figure 19-36. GE and P&W Two-Stage,
Reduced-Emission Combustor
Designs and Results**
*(Illustration courtesy of NASA/GRC)*

## Advanced Turbine Technology

IHPTET turbine technology goals stress maintaining a balance among high performance, affordability, and design robustness. Such a balance is necessary in order to make the most of engine investment. It requires low initial part cost as well as a substantial improvement in life-cycle cost. To accomplish these goals, IHPTET seeks to significantly enhance manufacturing techniques, develop strong, low density and affordable materials, and encourage the use of concurrent engineering practices from initial concept to fielding of the part. IHPTET also seeks to develop parts with improved fatigue behavior, such as the advanced high-work turbine blade with CastCool® blade tip and abrasive tip-rub material (Figure 19-37), for more robust components with longer life between inspections and overhauls.

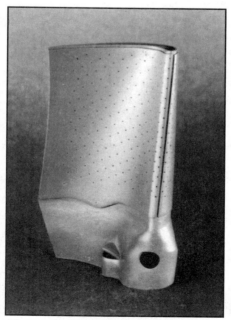

**Figure 19-37. Advanced High-Work
Turbine Blade with CastCool® Blade
Tip and Abrasive Tip-Rub Material**
*(Photo courtesy of U.S. Air Force)*

New IHPTET high performance cooling technologies will make the most of the effectiveness of reduced cooling flows while improving life through the application of novel structural designs, such as the turbine nozzles with advanced shower head and trailing edge cooling. IHPTET also places emphasis on performance, which requires reduced total cooling flow and revolutionary materials to improve cooling effectiveness. A good example of this technology is the CastCool® advanced high-work turbine vane with airfoil and end walls (Figure 19-38) and the internal-convection-enhanced (ICE) advanced cooling scheme (Figure 19-39). Enhanced analysis techniques, including 3-D steady and unsteady computational codes, provide better understanding of the aerodynamic and heat transfer mechanisms occurring in extremely complex airfoils.[29]

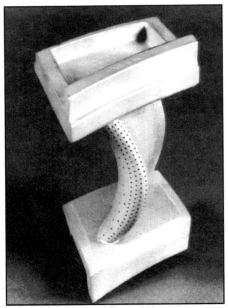

**Figure 19-38. CastCool© Advanced
High-Work Turbine Vane
Airfoil and End Walls**
*(Photo courtesy of U.S. Air Force)*

**Figure 19-39. Internal Convection Enhanced
(ICE) Cooling Scheme**
*(Illustration courtesy of U.S. Air Force)*

## Mechanical Systems Technology

The mechanical systems technology area is focused on providing substantial improvements in lubrication, seal, shaft and bearing systems.

**1. Advanced Lubricants:** One specific goal is to develop a high-temperature liquid lubricant with a bulk oil capability of 625°F, more than double the durability of previous high temperature lubricants. In the area of advanced expendable limited-life engines, development of solid-film and vapor-phase lubrication technologies is crucial. Vapor-phase lubrication will reduce engine cost and improve SFC compared to a conventional oil or fuel lubrication system. An Air Force high-temperature bearing-test rig (Figure 19-40) demonstrated the feasibility of vapor-phase lubrication at 47,000 rpm and 700°F bearing temperature.[30]

**Figure 19-40. Air Force High-Temperature
Bearing Rig Test**
*(Photo courtesy of U.S. Air Force)*

**2. Air Leakage Control:** IHPTET seeks to reduce air leakage by more than 50 percent, thereby improving specific fuel consumption and life-cycle cost through the development of advanced high-speed counterrotating intershaft carbon seals. Similarly, brush seals also offer a 50 percent reduction in air leakage compared to the more conventional labyrinth seals Figure 19-41).

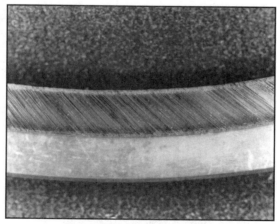

**Figure 19-41. Brush Seals**
*(Photo courtesy of U.S. Air Force)*

**3. Composite Shafts:** Titanium matrix composite engine shafts (Figure 19-42) are lighter weight and can achieve reduced dynamic loads and improved clearance control. This means a 30 percent weight reduction from INCO shafts or a 40 percent increase in stiffness over titanium shafts can be achieved.

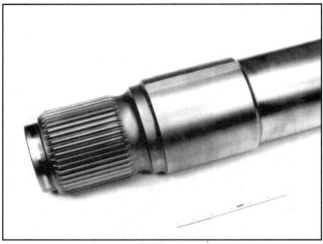

**Figure 19-42. Titanium Matrix Composites
Engine Shaft**
*(Photo courtesy of U.S. Air Force)*

**4. Bearings:** IHPTET-sponsored development of corrosion-resistant bearing materials with improved fatigue life and fracture toughness, such as Pyrowear 675, Cronidor 15, and silicon nitride, will result in a significant improvement in engine durability and life-cycle cost.

During Phase III, development of magnetic bearings and an integral starter generator will result in a 16 percent reduction in engine weight through elimination of the conventional liquid lubrication system (pumps and associated plumbing) and gearbox. Newly developed tilting pad, fluid film thrust bearings (Figure 19-43) eliminate the need to use secondary air for rotor thrust control, resulting in an improvement in specific fuel consumption.

**Figure 19-43. Tilting Pad, Fluid Film
Thrust Bearing**
*(Photo courtesy of U.S. Air Force)*

## Controls Technology

IHPTET has focused control system development technology on reducing system weight and cost while improving engine performance throughout the flight envelope. Organic and metal matrix composites are being applied in place of stainless steel and titanium to reduce the weigh of control components while increasing temperature capability. New nozzle actuator technology can reduce weight by 35 percent through the use of high-temperature Organic Matrix Composites (OMCs).

Smart sensor and actuator development under IHPTET will enable the technology to move to a more affordable and robust distributed processing architecture than existing conventional control architectures. This will reduce full authority digital electronic control (FADEC) acquisition cost up to 60 percent by reducing design and manufacturing complexities. Increased engine robustness can also be gained by spreading control authority across the engine, thereby eliminating the FADEC as a single-point failure. High-temperature silicon carbide (SiC) electronics are also being developed to operate at 660°F (Figure 19-44), significantly expanding the operating temperature capability of solid-state electronics.

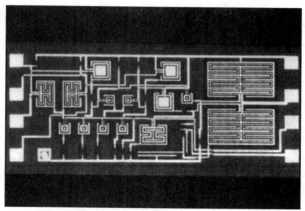

**Figure 19-44. High-Temperature Silicon Carbide (SiC) Electronics**
*(Photo courtesy of U.S. Air Force)*

A flame-detector circuit and the world's first SiC integrated circuit, an operational amplifier, have been demonstrated. An ongoing effort will also employ SiC circuits in smart sensors and actuators for distributed control.

IHPTET-sponsored electric actuation and pumping technologies will reduce weight and improve supportability via the elimination of engine gearboxes and hydraulic systems. Multimode, model-based controls will optimize engine performance and operability while tracking engine health in real time. Advanced IHPTET engine health management modes will provide support personnel with instant feedback on remaining component life, in-flight failures, and recommended maintenance procedures.[31]

## Innovative Structures Technology

IHPTET has radically changed the way engine components are designed and manufactured. To take full advantage of the advanced materials under development, you need structural design innovation. The challenge is to produce affordable structures that maintain their strength while operating at increased temperatures. IHPTET is meeting these new challenges with aluminides and new alloys that extend the operating temperatures of metallics, along with ad-

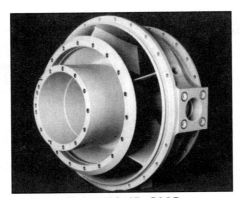

**Figure 19-45. OMC
Intermediate Case**
*(Photo courtesy of U.S. Air Force)*

**Figure 19-46. JETEC Titanium Aluminide Axial
Stage & Carbon/Carbon HPT Rotor**
*(Photo courtesy of U.S. Air Force)*

**Figure 19-47. Bypass Ducts of Titanium
Metal Matrix Composites**
*(Photo courtesy of U.S. Air Force)*

vanced composite and nonmetallic materials. Some examples of innovative designs with the potential to reduce life-cycle cost include the Organic Matrix Composite (OMC) intermediate case (Figure 19-45) and the JETEC titanium-aluminide axial-stage and carbon/carbon HPT Rotor (Figure 19-46). The titanium metal matrix composite (MMC) bypass duct (Figure 19-47) offers a 40 percent greater stiffness and a 50 percent weight reduction over current titanium structures.[32]

## Exhaust System Technologies

### Military Focus

IHPTET has been active in developing new exhaust technologies, including pitch and yaw thrust vectoring, thrust reversing, and low observable designs (Figure 19-48). To support these new designs, IHPTET technology is being developed in low-density, high-temperature materials, cooling technologies, and innovative multifunction exhaust nozzle design concepts. The spherical-convergent-flap nozzle (Figure 19-49) will provide pitch/yaw vectoring and reversing with a 20 percent weight saving over current two-dimensional nozzles having similar functions. These new technologies can be applied to current as well as next-generation affordable, high-performance fighter aircraft. Low-observable-axis nozzles are retrofittable to existing tactical aircraft such as the F-15, F-16, and F-18, as well as the emerging generation of fighters. They provide benefits such as reduced signatures and potential for fleet size reduction.

These new technologies also have to be integrated, which requires innovative mechanical designs that reduce complexity and take advantage of the capabilities of advanced metallic and composite materials. These materials are the keys to providing multifunction capability at high temperatures and pressures. Hence, efficient aerothermodynamic designs which incorporate multifunctional capabilities with fixed geometries will result in over 60 percent reduction in nozzle weight and cost. The requirements for future practicable advanced nozzle design approaches will be affordability, reliability, and improved survivability.[33]

**Figure 19-48. Low-Observable Axi-Nozzle**
*(Photo courtesy of U.S. Air Force)*

**Figure 19-49. Spherical Convergent
Flap Nozzle**
*(Photo courtesy of U.S. Air Force)*

## Commercial Focus

Here again, while the chief military focus is on thrust vectoring/reversing and low observables, NASA emphasis is primarily on reducing that engine noise generally attributed to the fan and jet. Consequently, the commercial focus for this section will be on exhaust jet noise reduction (fan noise reduction was covered in the "Fan" section of this chapter).

Under the NASA AST and HSR programs, flow mixer technologies were developed to ameliorate jet noise caused by the very high velocity gas flow from the core engine and the relatively slower air from the fan bypass duct. The technology consists primarily of a multi-lobe mixer design that mixes the two flows, thereby reducing the final jet velocity and noise.[34] Alternative techniques consider acoustic wall treatment and separate flow nozzles. The HSR program also developed exhaust noise-reduction technology for the proposed supersonic commercial aircraft.

**Figure 19-50. Laser Doppler Velocimeter (LDV)**
*(Photo courtesy of U.S. Air Force)*

## Instrumentation Technology

New IHPTET engines, with their high temperatures and new materials, require more durability and greater accuracy from engine test instrumentation. To monitor the structural integrity of engine components, one needs to measure surface temperature, heat flux, and strain. IHPTET is fostering the development of optical systems and thin-film sensors to make accurate measurements in the harsh environment of engine operation without disturbing the structural component or internal engine flows. For example, non-invasive combustion diagnostic systems are now used to provide data on combustion processes and efficiency in combustors. The Laser Doppler velocimeter (LDV) has been developed to measure velocity profiles in a jet-in-crossflow at simulated engine operating conditions (Figure 19-50). Rayleigh-scattering-based optical diagnostic systems (Figure 19-51) can provide data on fuel mixing and temperature pattern factor for the development of very high temperature combustors, where incomplete mixing and "hot spots" must be avoided.

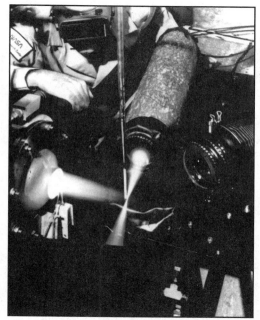

**Figure 19-51. Rayleigh-Scattering-Based Optical Diagnostic System**
*(Photo courtesy of U.S. Air Force)*

The noninvasive optical vibration analysis system (Figure 19-52) has been developed to determine blade-tip deflection by using case-mounted optical probes. Tip deflection data can then be analyzed to provide dynamic stress and strain data over the entire surface of the blade. Laser-induced fluorescence of thermographic phosphors (Figure 19-53) is also being developed to optically measure surface temperatures beyond the range of conventional thermocouples.

Lastly, flight-weight fiber optic turbine inlet temperature sensors have also been developed that use ceramic components and a novel intermetallic blackbody to directly monitor the record-setting IHPTET Phase I gas temperatures demonstrated in ATEGG. Additionally, thin-film thermocouples have been developed to measure ceramic surface temperatures of more than 2700°F.[35]

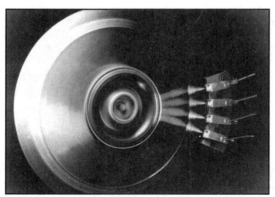

**Figure 19-52. Noninvasive Optical
Vibration Analysis System**
*(Photo courtesy of U.S. Air Force)*

**Figure 19-53. Laser-Induced
Fluorescence of Thermographic Phosphors**
*(Photo courtesy of U.S. Air Force)*

## Advanced Materials Technology

### Military Focus

Providing improved and advanced materials has always been a key goal of IHPTET. New advanced low-density, high-temperature materials are crucial to achieving IHPTET's Phase III milestones. Research in the development of new materials, in materials processing, and in the understanding of materials behavior and life prediction have all made rapid progress. Richard Hill discusses the importance of materials technology advancement:

> The benefits of several new IHPTET innovations can be seen in Figures 19-54, 55, 56, 57 and 58. As shown in Figure 19-54, the application of innovative designs and advanced high strength, low density material is key to IHPTET long-term success. These advancements offer, for example, the potential

to reduce a compressor rotor's weight 70 percent. This is accomplished through the application of advanced materials and innovative structural designs including Integral Blade/Disk Rotors (IBR or BLISK), hollow airfoils, composite spacer rings (Figure 19-55) and ring rotors. The final Phase III compressor is envisioned to be made entirely of advanced Metal Matrix Composite (MMC) materials and be only composed of ring-type structures (Figure 19-56). The primary need for these new materials and innovative designs is centered on the compressor's need for high rotational speeds to take full advantage of the advancements in IHPTET aerodynamics in the blade rows. If the rotor had to be constructed of conventional materials, the design would require full webs and bores on each rotor stage. This would result in a heavy and lengthy rotor. For comparison, a conventional rotor was designed to meet the rotational speed requirements of an IHPTET configuration, but constructed from conventional nickel-based alloys. The result of this design effort is the Baseline 1985 Technology Compressor (Figure 19-57). Using this base design, the major IHPTET compressor technologies cited above were added to the design with the results as shown in Figure 19-58.[36]

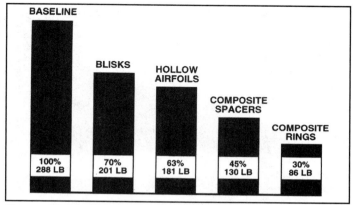

**Figure 19-54. Benefits of Innovative Design and Advanced
Materials to a Compressor Rotor**
*(Illustration courtesy of U.S. Air Force)*

Hence, the technologies shown in Figure 19-54 can be used independently or bundled together to increase the performance attributes of a chosen design application—resulting in either a new or upgraded component or engine. Each of the technologies of Figures 19-54 through 19-57 has been tested successfully in a Technology Demonstrator Engine. Figure 19-58, for example, shows the IHPTET ring rotor that was tested successfully in a recent advanced technology core engine.[37]

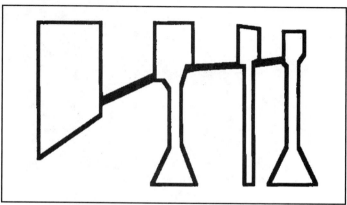

**Figure 19-55. Addition of Composite Spacers**
*(Illustration courtesy of U.S. Air Force)*

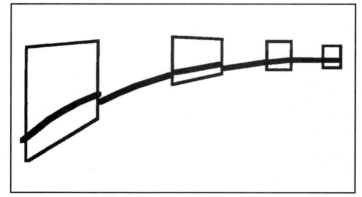

**Figure 19-56. Addition of MMC Rings to Rotors**
*(Illustration courtesy of U.S. Air Force)*

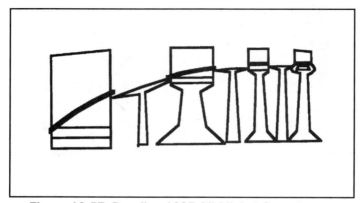

**Figure 19-57. Baseline 1985 All-Nickel Compressor**
*(Illustration courtesy of U.S. Air Force)*

**Figure 19-58. Advanced MMC Fiber
Reinforced-Ring Rotor**
*(Photo courtesy of U.S. Air Force)*

Titanium aluminides, specifically gamma TiAl, provide a high-temperature, noncombustible gas flow-path material for the last stages of the compressor. In addition, the resulting density of half that of nickel-base superalloys promises dramatic weight savings in large static structures such as combustor inlet diffusers and engine cases (Figure 19-59).

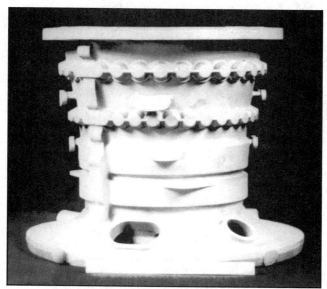

**Figure 19-59. Titanium Aluminide
Combustor Diffuser**
*(Photo courtesy of U.S. Air Force)*

Ceramic matrix composites using creep-resistant ceramic fibers are the enabling technology for reaching the highest temperatures in components such as the combustor, turbine, augmentor, and nozzle. Organic matrix composites satisfy the need for lightweight structures at temperatures up to 700°F for components such as fan frames, inlet guide vanes, stator vanes, cases, and control housings.

High-temperature intermetallics, such as single-crystal nickel aluminides, extend the use temperature of metallic materials beyond that of current superalloys and reduce weight by one-third, making them ideal candidates for turbine airfoils. Metal matrix composites provide high specific strength and stiffness in structures such as compressor rotors and spacers, impellers, shafts, fan blades, cases and frames.

Higher-temperature matrix materials and processing methods such as foil-fiber-foil, plasma spraying, and powder-based tape casting are also being developed. Materials characterization of new intermetallic lightweight, high-temperature metals and alloys, and organic, metal, and ceramic matrix composites will require the use of advanced diagnostic and analysis tools such as the scanning electron microscope pictured in Figure 19-60.

These new materials are crucial to the design and construction of innovative structures that reduce parts count while increasing component efficiency. Advanced monolithic and composite materials, in conjunction with innovative designs, could provide for reduced SFC and 60 to 70 percent thrust-to-weight increase if applied to today's engines. Advanced materials in these more efficient high-performance engines will also result in enhanced durability and reduced life-cycle costs.[38]

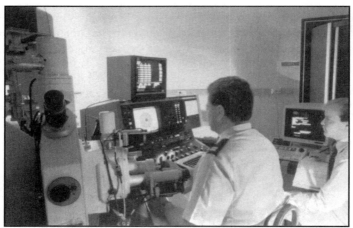

**Figure 19-60. Scanning Electron Microscope**
*(Photo courtesy of U.S. Air Force)*

## Commercial Focus

For highly reliable, long-life commercial technologies, NASA has focused primarily on developing light-weight, high-strength, high-temperature materials for engine cold and hot sections. Specifically, NASA has made advances in polymer matrix composites, superalloys, structural ceramics and ceramic matrix composites, and thermal barrier coatings. Many of these materials are dual use, applicable to military engines as well, and provide direct support to the IHPTET component material needs (Figure 19-61).

### Polymer Matrix Composites (PMCs; temperature range 600-800°F)

Lightweight polymers and fiber reinforced polymer matrix composites have become attractive for energy-efficiency engine component applications because they significantly reduce vehicle weight, decrease fuel consumption and related pollutants, and increase aircraft passenger and payload capacity. In the mid-70s, NASA was instrumental in the development of a family of high-temperature polymers called Polymerization of Monomer Reactants or PMR polyimides offering good processability and high-temperature performance.[39] The principal polyimide in this family, PMR-15, offers long-term use (10,000 hours) at 550°F and can be processed into components having void contents below 3%. PMR-15 is widely used in both military and commercial engine components including the F-404 outer bypass duct, the E-90 center vent tube, and the F-100-229 exit flaps. Later, PMR formulations to even higher temperature capabilities, such as PMR-II-50, which handle temperatures up to 650 °F.[40, 41, 42] In cooperative programs with industry, NASA researchers have demonstrated higher-temperature PMR formulations for an F-110 aft fairing and a compressor case for a JTDE Phase I demonstrator.

### Superalloys (temperature range 1200-1400°F for turbine disks and 1900-2100°F for turbine blades)

During the early 1960s, NASA initiated the development of Oxide Dispersion Strengthened (ODS) materials. NASA contributed especially to the understanding of complex thermomechanical processing of this alloy class and to elucidating their unique failure modes.[43] This research with International Nickel Company and several universities ultimately yielded iron-base MA956 and nickel-base MA754 alloys—popular sheet and bar alloys.

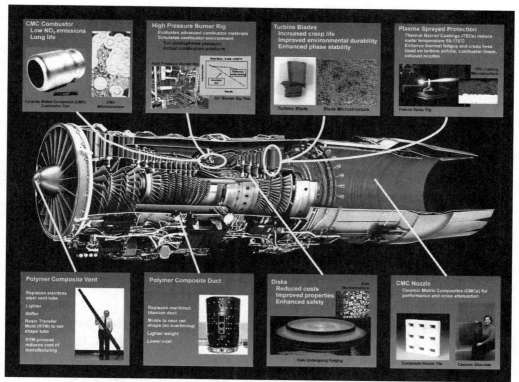

**Figure 19-61. Turbofan Engine Advance Materials Applications**
*(Photo courtesy of NASA/GRC)*

Early work was in process and alloy development during which important contributions were made to the problem of "sigma phase instability", and pioneering alloys containing tantalum were introduced for turbine blade applications.[44] Moreover, NASA's fundamental work on strengthening alloys by adding refractory metals has become the industry standard and is now flying in virtually *all* commercial turbine engines today. Additionally, Pratt & Whitney and GE are incorporating single-crystal orientation and gamma prime "rafting" behaviors in their next-generation, turbine-blade alloys.[45]

### Structural Ceramics (temperature range 2000-3000°F)

*Monolithic Ceramics:* Major NASA aerospace ceramics efforts began in the late 1970s and early 1980s as researchers improved the understanding and processing of reaction bonded silicon nitride (RBSN) and sintered RBSN (SRBSN), both of which contributed to commercial uses. During the 1980s, researchers made great strides in understanding sintered silicon nitride, especially processing of sintered and HIP'ed silicon nitride ($Si_3N_4$) via NASA's Improved $Si_3N_4$ for Heat Engines contract. During this period and extending into the early 1990s, NASA/DOE's Advanced Gas Turbine (AGT) and Advanced Turbine Technology Applications Program (ATTAP) led to many advances in material development (properties and fabrication) and the ability to design with ceramics. [46, 47]

*Ceramic Matrix Composites:* NASA has studied many aspects of SiC (fiber) and SiC (matrix) and $SiC/Si_3N_4$ CMCs, developing and examining fibers, interfaces, and matrices, and composite processing and thermomechanical testing.[48] NASA has also completed preliminary rig testing of a SiC/SiC combustor liner as part of the Enabling Propulsion Materials (EPM) effort within the HSR Program. The technology has been applied to the CMC combustor for the

GE/Allison ATEGG core engine demonstrator to be tested under the IHPTET program. Researchers chose this liner to reduce cooling flows and increase engine efficiency.

### Thermal Barrier Coatings (TBC)

In the mid-70s, NASA developed a TBC to extend airfoil life. Researchers eventually optimized the composition that has now become the industry standard (6-8 wt % $Y_2O_3$ -$ZrO_2$).[49] Early efforts in life prediction, however, identified bond coat oxidation and thermal cycling as key failure elements.[50] Recently, researchers developed a unique TBC laser thermal shock test to reproduce the high thermal gradients and heat fluxes exhibited in an actual engine, significantly contributing to the understanding of metallic coatings. Popular pack aluminide (NiAl) coatings were first modeled with a thermodynamic and kinetic deposition model and shown to degrade primarily by substrate interdiffusion. Researchers later modeled this in a life prediction program.[51, 52]

## Manufacturing Technology

New materials contain expensive fibers and require new processing and manufacturing methods. Microwave chemical vapor infiltration (CVI) is a very promising technique for producing ceramic composites. These materials and associated CVI processes will find applications in IHPTET, hypersonics, high-speed civil transport, and energy conservation.

In a significant step toward rapid prototyping, stereolithography and solid free-forming can produce solid geometric shapes directly from digitized data. A laser creates the shapes in resins or metal and ceramic powders. Although the shapes are limited in size and dimensional accuracy, continuing advancements are assured.

Improvements in manufacturing processes for engine components are resulting from a strong alliance among component designers, advanced materials specialists, and the manufacturing community. Nickel-based super-alloy compressor blades (Figure 19-62), such as those for the F119 sixth stage, can now be forge-joined to the disk rim in an air environment, reducing production costs (Figure 19-63).

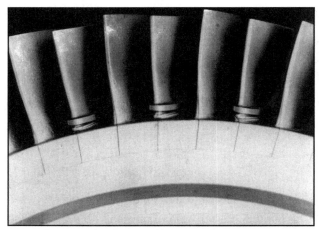

**Figure 19-62. Nickel-Based Super-Alloy
Compressor Blades**
*(Photo courtesy of U.S. Air Force)*

**Figure 19-63. Forge Joining**
*(Photo courtesy of U.S. Air Force)*

## Analysis and Design Technology

Engine manufacturer design systems are generally applicable to both military and commercial engines. Recently, CFD has become a critical design system element, the results of which are often shared by both sectors. Since developing CFD codes is one of NASA's core competencies, NASA heads the CFD technology-development panel within IHPTET and contributes significantly to the program's CFD capability.

### Military Focus

The use of CFD is a key to design. Geometric concepts being investigated include swept fans, multistage compressors, highly loaded turbines, annular combustors, and advanced thrust-vectoring nozzles. Two- and three-dimensional inviscid and viscous codes are being used to gain insight into airflow through the components, driving design changes and improvements. CFD has been used to investigate the effectiveness of dilution hole patterns on combustor performance; shock-boundary layer interactions; and velocity, pressure, and temperature distributions to determine regions of separated flow and vortex development. CFD is a critical and enabling technology in the endeavor to double turbine engine performance capabilities. DOD has worked closely with NASA to develop advanced CFD tools for military applications.

The role of structural analysis in IHPTET is becoming increasingly important. As described earlier, advanced structural designs and advanced materials have been identified as critical technologies in meeting the aggressive IHPTET goals. Engine structures have a direct impact on thrust-to-weight, which drives the requirements for lighter, stronger, and more durable components. These requirements emphasize the need for innovative designs, advanced materials development, and powerful analysis techniques to create the structurally optimal and most affordable designs for engine components.

Additionally, a probabilistic design approach (Figure 19-64) makes full use of the known statistical distribution of all design parameters, as opposed to a deterministic design practice which uses single values for material properties, manufacturing tolerances, mission usage, and other parameters. The probabilistic approach reduces conservatism to a known and acceptable level, allowing component designs to be optimized for weight, performance, life, cost, and any other criterion.[53]

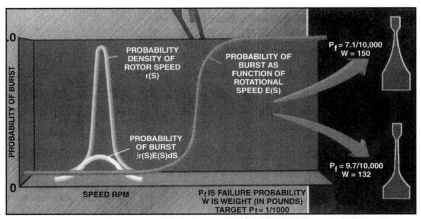

**Figure 19-64. Probabilistic Design**
*(Illustration courtesy of U.S. Air Force)*

## Commercial Focus

For many years, design and analysis of advanced components[54] were based on relatively simple analytical methods and large volumes of experimental data. During the 1970s and early 80s, improvements in modeling, later in Computational Fluid Dynamics (CFD), and in high-speed, supercomputer CFD applications allowed researchers to reduce their dependence on experiment-based engine design and to adopt modeling and code-guided design. An initial, significant focused-research effort, the Hot Section Technology (HOST) Project (1981-1987[55]), developed new or improved codes and benchmark-quality data sets to enhance the understanding of the physics needed to develop and validate more accurate design analysis codes—all leading to more accurate, deterministic life prediction capability. The HOST Program helped stimulate NASA's CFD programs and led to the National Propulsion System Simulator (NPSS), a major element of IHPTET's focus on reducing the cost of development testing. Later, programs in multi-stage aero-structure analysis, probabilistic structural design, and life-prediction methods followed.

### Multistage Aero-Structural Analysis

In the early 1990s, NASA embarked on an effort to develop CFD codes for simulating multi-stage turbomachinery flows. The first, known as Average Passage NASA (APNASA),[56] used a flow model that governed the time-average flow field in a typical passage of a blade row embedded in a multi-stage turbomachine. This code explicitly accounts for the unsteady flow environment in multi-stage turbomachinery – within computer resource requirements compatible with the design environment.

As part of NASA's AST program, the U.S. industry transformed the APNASA into a fully integrated, turbomachinery production design code. APNASA seriously advances beyond codes that simply represented the flow in each blade as steady-state. Using the APNASA code in aeronautics design led to hardware that achieved its aerodynamic goals in the first build, radically reducing both development cost and time.

### Numerical Propulsion System Simulation (NPSS)

Finally, NASA is developing a numerical engine simulation platform under its High Performance Computing and Communications (HPCC) program. The NPSS project will link APNASA, MSU-TURBO and other aeronautics and heat transfer codes, thereby providing a numerical engine testbed that simulates an engine over its entire operating range. This capability will allow designers to address engine problems long before they fabricate hardware, which will, again, significantly reduce engine-development cost and cycle time. The goals are to reduce the engine design and development time by a factor of two and also help improve engine performance and durability. Major advances are being made to go beyond the axisymmetric full engine simulation. Additional system features include:

*High Speed Computing:* A 200:1 reduction in the time to simulate a 3-D reacting flow for a gas turbine combustor on a cluster of SGI Origin 2000 processors – allowing the designer to solve large-scale combustor problems (1 Million+ grid points) in <15 hours.

*Common Thermodynamic Analysis:* In 1998, NASA released NPSS software (to industry) that can significantly increase productivity in the preliminary design of propulsion systems and its integration with airframes. The advanced software design and object-oriented structure provide a framework to extend modeling capabilities to include collaborative, high-fidelity, multidisciplinary system analysis.

### Life Prediction Methodologies

Predicting component durability and hardware life expectation is crucial for lowering costs and improving safety. NASA has developed pioneering computer-based tools for predicting gas turbine engine component life using experimentally verified deterministic and probabilistic analytical methods. These codes predict fatigue, creep, and crack initiation. Life prediction work divides into two basic methods: deterministic (using extensive testing to characterize material behavior) and probabilistic (using computer codes that researchers validate with limited experimental testing).

*Deterministic:* NASA focused its deterministic work on the following approaches.

Traditional fatigue life estimation methods—strain-based methods for low-cycle fatigue and stress-based for high-cycle fatigue for applicability to metallic materials in hot section components

Models—for assessing fatigue crack initiation lives of metallic materials subjected to isothermal and nonisothermal uniaxial and multiaxial cyclic loading conditions

Crack-growth codes—to predict damage tolerance under time-dependent *and* cyclic loading

*Probabilistic:* During the early 1980s, NASA initiated a major effort in the Space Shuttle Main Engine (SSME) program (rocket engine with turbopumps) to develop probabilistic methods for accurately evaluating how design variable uncertainties affect required structural responses. Industry has since adopted many cutting-edge probabilistic life-prediction technologies/techniques and is beginning to apply them to turbine engine components.

## Test Facilities Technology

IHPTET goals are demonstrated and validated at government facilities including those at the Air Force Research Laboratory at Wright-Patterson Air Force Base in Ohio, the Arnold Engineering Development Center in Tullahoma, Tennessee, the Naval Air Warfare Development and Engineering Center, at Patuxent River, Maryland, the NASA Glenn Research Center in Cleveland, Ohio, and at various contractor facilities. These facilities can be used by more that one project at the same time and can operate at one-fourth to one-half the cost of duplicated independent facilities. They allow designers the ability to verify their theories quickly and comprehensively. For example, the mission of the Air Force Turbine Research Facility (Figure 19-65) is to validate the heat transfer and cooling designs of advanced turbine hardware, gain knowledge in turbine fluid mechanics, and make turbine aerodynamic performance measurement possible. Operating for only one or two seconds and applying similarity principles to matching engine conditions results in a major cost saving over conventional facilities and in the rapid verification of flow field aerothermal behavior.

**Figure 19-65. Air Force Turbine Engine
Research Facility**
*(Photo courtesy of U.S. Air Force)*


The Air Force Compressor Research Facility (Figure 19-66) at Wright-Patterson Air Force Base is used to provide accurate, detailed mapping of the aeromechanical and aerodynamic interactions of advanced fans and compressors, leading to more rugged component designs. For example, the CRF has conducted in-depth fan evaluations for the F119 engine, which reduced the number of design iterations and development costs for the F-22 fighter program. The Navy Rotor Spin Facility (Figure 19-67) validates rotating component vigor in such areas as rotor stress distribution, low-cycle fatigue, new material evaluation, crack-growth phenomena, burst characterization, and containment studies. Lastly, the Small Engine Component Test Facility (Figure 19-68) at NASA Glenn Research Center in Cleveland provides a large test envelope through its broad speed and temperature capabilities. It can test either axial or radial turbines at conditions similar to actual small engines, and it can be modified to allow for the use of nonintrusive instrumentation.

**Figure 19-66. Air Force Compressor
Research Facility (CRF)**
*(Photo courtesy of U.S. Air Force)*

**Figure 19-67. Navy Rotor Spin Facility**
*(Photo courtesy of U.S. Navy)*

**Figure 19-68. NASA Small-Engine
Component Test Facility**
*(Photo courtesy of NASA)*

Additionally, the industry's extensive sea level and altitude test facilities are continually upgraded to enable development of turbine engine technology.

Test facilities for commercial components and systems are equally impressive. Supporting gas turbine engine testing with unique, world-class facilities since the laboratory's inception, NASA/GRC has ten premiere testing facilities: five wind tunnels (1x1, 8x6, 9x15, 10x10, hypersonic), an Icing Research Tunnel, a Propulsion Systems Laboratory, an Aero-Acoustic Facility, an Advanced Subsonic Combustion Research Facility, and the Engineering Research Building facilities.

## IHPTET Maintainability Issues

Military and commercial turbine engine users have different airborne requirements, but on the ground, ease of maintenance is of paramount importance to both (Figures 19-69 and 19-70). There is a concerted effort within IHPTET to improve the time between maintenance intervals by developing robust, long-lived components. The development of enhanced field maintenance procedures has significantly increased the percentage of repairs accomplished in the field without the need to return to depot. These procedures provide both faster turnaround times and fewer depot returns. Additionally, solutions to military turbine engine problems ultimately enhance the maintainability of commercial turbine engines as well. Hence, as IHPTET advances the technology state-of-the-art of military turbine engines and the public benefits by having access to a more reliable and affordable transportation mode.[57]

**Figure 19-69. Fighter Engine Removal**
*(Photo courtesy of U.S. Air Force)*

**Figure 19-70. Field Maintenance**
*(Photo courtesy of U.S. Air Force)*

According to Hill the future of IHPTET will include both cooperation with NASA and an emphasis on the dual-use applicability of the technologies developed:

> The major areas of focus for technology application under IHPTET started as and continues [*sic*] to be the achievement of affordable thrust-to-weight and power-to-weight growth, lower fuel consumption, decreased (low observable) engine signature, increased repairability, operability and maintainability and decreased acquisition, operation and support costs. In the man-rated turbofan/turbojet arena for example, the payoff gained by the achievement of the IHPTET goals is providing the technologies for upgrade and growth F-15 and F-16 aircraft engines (F100 and F110 engine families), as well as providing the technology base for the new F-22 Advanced Tactical Fighter (ATF) engine (F119), and ever more recently, the Joint Strike Fighter propulsion system.

The dismantling of the Warsaw Pact, however, created the need to rethink many of the U.S. military Science and Technology (S&T) plans, including IHPTET. What is seen now by top command officials is a diminishing need to develop new high performance aircraft to overcome new aggressor advancements and an increasing need to modernize the fleet of current systems. The focus of S&T is now changing to be more evenly split between creating new systems and that of upgrading existing systems. The new systems, when needed, will be developed in minimum numbers and will be replacements for near-obsolete aircraft. They will be based on the best, affordable technology available at key points in the development process. The second focus, that of modernizing the current fleets, will also use the best, affordable technology but will be directed at specific engine components combined to form "upgrade kits." The new U.S. military force structure will rely on a combination of these high-quality, technologically advanced systems to cope with regional threats. The major objective of this new trend is to continue a high quality, high readiness force to perform regional operations, like Desert Storm, at a minimum cost. The Gulf War proved that air superiority is a result of superior training and technologically advanced propulsion, aircraft, and weapons. The long-term view of IHPTET will produce the technology to equip the next century peacekeeping force with affordable, superior systems. As defense drawdown continues and weapon system acquisition becomes based on selective upgrades and new engine low-rate production, with a continual insertion of advanced technology, the application of IHPTET technology will increase proportionately. [58]

## IHPTET and Dual Use

Significant profit losses, undelivered products and declining sales have forced a major restructuring of the U.S. aerospace industry. Total U.S. engine production value is down by nearly one-third since 1991. Since the IHPTET initiative represents a major investment by industry (nearly 53 percent of all money from 1988 through 2003 will come from industry), this problem becomes a significant concern to managers within the Federal government. The national approach to this situation is the expansion of so-called dual-use technology. Under this idea, commercial and military applications become of relatively equal importance. Thus, every dollar spent on technology development should be leveraged for use by both government and industry sectors. Such an idea is presented in the Aeronautical Technology Consortium Act of 1993 (Aerotech). Without straying from its basic purpose of pursuing high-payoff military goals in aeronautical technology, IHPTET will also support initiatives like Aerotech.

IHPTET management recognized early that technology modernization and application are key to increased productivity in the aerospace industry. Numerous IHPTET - developed technologies have made the transition into commercial engines so far, and over 100 technologies now being developed under IHPTET have the potential for dual use. In fact, nearly 80 percent of IHPTET has commercial spin-off potential.

The concept of dual use is but one aspect of the new national policy relating to defense reinvestment, diversification, and conversion. This new congressional policy has inspired new initiatives in the areas of advanced subsonic propulsion and HSR for civil air transportation by NASA. IHPTET will be a major springboard for the new NASA initiatives; and together NASA and DOD will work on advanced technologies for both military critical and commercial critical applications. IHPTET will continue with technology development through the 1990s, focusing on the high-payoff military goals, but will do so in concert with all new national technology development and application initiatives. For example, IHPTET will work on the military unique technologies of stealth, expendable engines, and thrust vectoring for STOVL applications, while NASA will work on commercial unique technologies—pollution control, noise suppression, universal fuels, and novel regenerative cycles. Together IHPTET and NASA will work on the more common dual-use technologies such as advanced materials, CFD design codes, advanced engine controls and logic, advanced turbine cooling concepts, bearings, and structures. Technology success in this common area will be applied to both military and commercial critical needs, as necessary. For example, success in advanced turbine blade-cooling technology may be applied in military engines to increase the allowable gas temperature at constant turbine blade life and thereby increase the engine's specific thrust. In a commercial application, this technology may be used to lower the turbine blade bulk metal temperature at constant gas temperature (constant thrust) and thus increase the life of the component—the same technology but applied differently.

As America approaches the next century and beyond, the programs of IHPTET and NASA, working together will provide a strong national technology base. Through the NASA efforts the American civil aviation industry will sustain its dominance of the global aviation market. Through IHPTET the military will continue to achieve affordable national defense without sacrificing global reach or global power.

It appears that IHPTET has a promising future, at least until 2010. The organization's ideas and methodology for developing new technology, however, may be its most lasting contribution to history. Given the ever-increasing cost of developing new aircraft gas turbine technology, the IHPTET approach to industry-government cooperation is a very attractive business philosophy. But there are other questions looming in the near and far term for IHPTET. For example, now that Rolls-Royce has acquired the Allison Engine Company, how can IHPTET retain the advanced technology in America? How can IHPTET's participants sell the advanced technology in aircraft without restricting that technology from being then exported to countries from whom the United States wants to withhold technology? Can the technological advances from IHPTET be licensed to foreign companies? These are but some of the questions that the government will have to address in the next two decades as we enter the 21st century.

## Endnotes

1 Henderson, Jack, Universal Technology Inc., Beavercreek, Ohio, Interview, August 18, 1995. [626]

2 Ibid.

3 Ibid.

4 Hill, Richard J., *"Progress and Purpose of IHPTET Program,"* Wright-Patterson AFB, OH: Chief of Technology, Turbine Engine Division, Aero Propulsion and Power Directorate, Wright Laboratory, 1995, 1. [631]

5 Ibid.

6 Air Force Aeropropulsion and Power Directorate, *IHPTET: Technology Teams in Action*, Wright-Patterson AFB, Dayton, OH: Turbine Engine Division, Air Force Aeropropulsion and Power Directorate, 1995. [624] I owe much of the information about IHPTET to an excellent brochure prepared by Chris Lykins and Kathleen Watson of the Turbine Engine Division of the Air Force's Aeropropulsion and Power Directorate.

7 Ibid.

8 Ibid, 2A.

9 Ibid, 3

10 Ibid, 3.

11 Thayler, Rich, Telephone interview, August 16, 1995. [625]

12 Hill, *"Progress..."*, 6.

13 Hill, *"Progress..."*, 2B.

14 Ibid.

15 Ibid

16 Air Force Aeropropulsion and Power Directorate, *IHPTET: Technology Teams in Action*, 5-6.

17 First Federal Aircraft Noise Abatement Plan: FY 1969-70, U. S. Government Printing Office, 1970 O - 378-996, 1970.

18 Progress of NASA Research Relating to Noise Alleviation of Large Subsonic Jet Aircraft, NASA SP 189, 1968.

19 *Aircraft Engine Noise Reduction*, NASA SP 311, 1972.

20 *"Aircraft Fuel Conservation Technology,"* NASA Office of Aeronautics and Space Technology Task Force Report, September 10, 1975.

21 Chamberlin, Roger and Miller, Brent, *Energy Efficient Aircraft Engines*, NASA TM79204, 1979.

22 Air Force Aeropropulsion and Power Directorate, *IHPTET: Technology Teams in Action*, 7-8.

23 Johnsen, I.A. and Bullock, R.O., eds., *Aerodynamic Design of Axial-Flow Compressors Revised*, NASA SP 36, 1965.

24 Air Force Aeropropulsion and Power Directorate, *IHPTET: Technology Teams in Action*, 9-10.

25 Niedzwiecki, Richard W., *The Experimental Clean Combustor Program – Description and Status to November 1975*, NASA TM X-71849

[26] Jones, R.E., Diehl, L.A., Petrash, D.A., and Grobman, J., *Results and Status of the NASA Aircraft Engine Emission Reduction Technology Programs*, NASA TM79009, 1978.

[27] Sokolowski, Daniel E. and Rohde, John E., *The E³ Combustors: Status and Challenges*, NASA TM82684, 1981.

[28] Greene, W, Tanrikut, S., and Sokolowski, D., *Development and Operating Characteristics of an Advanced Two-Stage Combustor*, AIAA-82-0191, 1982.

[29] Air Force Aeropropulsion and Power Directorate, *IHPTET: Technology Teams in Action*, 11-12.

[30] Ibid, 13-14.

[31] Ibid, 15-16.

[32] Ibid, 17-18.

[33] Ibid, 19.

[34] Povinelli, L.A. and Anderson, B.H., *"Investigation of Mixing in a Turbofan Exhaust Duct, Computer Code Application and Verification"*, AIAA Journal 22, 4 (April 1984), 518-525.

[35] Air Force Aeropropulsion and Power Directorate, *IHPTET: Technology Teams in Action*, 20.

[36] Hill, *"Progress..."*, 3.

[37] Ibid.

[38] Air Force Aeropropulsion and Power Directorate, *IHPTET: Technology Teams in Action*, 21-22.

[39] Serafini, T.T., Delvigs, P.D., Lightsey, G.R., *"Thermally Stable Polyimides from Solutions of Monomeric Reactants,"* Journal of Applied Polymer Science 16 (1992), 905-915.

[40] Chung KC, *"Polymides Based on 2,2',6,6'-Tetra-methylbenzidine,"* High Performance Polymers 7 (1995), 81-92.

[41] Meador, M.A. , *"High Temperature Polymer Matrix Carbon Fiber Composites Critical Degradation Mechanisms and Test Methodologies,"* Proceedings of the 40th International SAMP Symposium 40 (1995), 268-276.

[42] Meador, M.A. , *"Recent Advances in the Development of Processable High Temperature Polymers,"* Annual Reviews of Materials Science 28 (1998), 599-630.

[43] Alexander, G.B. and Glasgow, T.K., *"A Brief History of Oxide Dispersion-Strengthened Alloys,"* Mechanical Properties of Metallic Composites, Ed. S. Ochai, Marcel Dekker, 1994, 5-23.

[44] Freche, J.C. and Waters, W.J., *"Continued Investigation of An Advanced-Temperature Tantalum-Modified, Nickel-Base Alloy,"* NASA TN D-1531, 1963.

[45] MacKay, R.A. and Nathal, M.V. *MiCon 86: Optimization of Processing, Properties, and Service Performance through Microstructural Control*, ASTM STP979, Ed. B.L. Bramfitt et al., 1988, 202.

[46] Levine, S.R., Duffy, S., Vary, A., Nathal, M.V., Miner, R.V., Arnold, S.M., Castelli, M.G., Hopkins, D.A., and Meador, M.A., *"Composites Research at NASA Lewis Research Center,"* Composites Engineering 4, 8 (1994), 787-810.

[47] Herbell, T.P. and Sanders, W.A. *"Monolithic Ceramics,"* Ceramics and Ceramic Matrix Composites, Ed. S.R. Levine. Vol. 3 in Flight-Vehicle Materials, Structures and Dynamics Assessment and Future Directions, Ed. A. K. Noor and S. L. Venneri, New York: American Society of Mechanical Engineers, 1992.

[48] Levine, S.R., and Herbell, T.P., *"Structural Applications for Technical, Engineering, and Advanced Ceramics: Aerospace Applications"* Engineered Materials Handbook, Vol. 4, *Ceramics and Glasses*, S.J. Schneider, Ed., ASM International, 1991, pp. 1003-1006.

[49] Stecura, S. *"Two Layer Thermal Barrier Coating for High Temperature Components."* Amer. Ceram. Soc. Bull., 56 (1997), 1082-1085.

[50] Sokolowski, D.E., ed., *Toward Improved Durability in Advanced Aircraft Engine Hot Sections*, ASME I00268, IGTI1-V2, 1988.

[51] Jacobson, N.S. Smialek, J.L., and Fox, D.S. *"Molten Salt Corrosion of Ceramics."* Corrosion of Advanced Ceramics Measurement and Modelling. Ed. K.G. Nickel, Dordrecht: Kluwer Academic Publishers, 1994, 205-222.

[52] Lee, K.N. and Miller, R.A. *"Development and Environmental Durability of Mullite and Mullite/YSZ Dual Layer Coatings for SiC and $Si_3N_4$ Ceramics."* Surface and Coatings Technology, 1996 Special Issue.

[53] Air Force Aeropropulsion and Power Directorate, *IHPTET: Technology Teams in Action*, 25-26.

[54] Glassman, A. J. NASA SP-290, Vol. 1 (January 1972), 2 (January 1973), 3 (January 1975).

[55] Sokolowski, D.E., ed., *"Toward Improved Durability in Advanced Aircraft Engine Hot Sections,"* ASME I00268, IGTI1-V2, 1988.

[56] Adamczyk, J.J., Hathaway, M.D., Shabbir, A., and Wellborn, S.R., *"Numerical Simulation of Multi-Stage Turbomachinery Flows,"* AGARD conference presentation, Toulouse, France, May 11-15, 1998.

[57] Air Force Aeropropulsion and Power Directorate, *IHPTET: Technology Teams in Action*, 29.

[58] Hill, *"Progress..."*, 3.

# Engine Features and Specifications
# for Selected Models
## (Alphabetical by Engine Designation)

**Unless otherwise indicated, all photos and engine data contained within this Addendum were extracted from multiple sources, courtesy of the U.S. Department of Defense.**

# ATF3

**Garrett**

## Comments

The ATF3-6A engine incorporates an annular inlet without inlet guide vanes and an aft-mounted high-pressure gas generator featuring a reverse-flow annular combustion chamber. An aft-mounted accessory gearbox, driven from the high-pressure spool, provides shaft power. The ATF3 and ATF3-6 are earlier versions of the engine.

## Features

| | |
|---|---|
| Compressor . . . . . . . . . . . . . . . . . . . . . . . . . . . . 3-Rotor | Turbine. . . . . . . . . . . . . . . . . . . . . . . . . . . . . . . . . . 3-Rotor |
|   Fan Rotor. . . . . . . . . . . . . . . . . . . . . . . . Axial, 1-stage |   LP Rotor . . . . . . . . . . . . . . . . . . . . . . . . . Axial 2-stage |
|   LP Rotor . . . . . . . . . . . . . . . . . . . . . . . . Axial, 5-stage |   HP Rotor . . . . . . . . . . . . . . . . . . . . . . . . Axial 1-stage |
|   HP Rotor . . . . . . . . . . . . . . . . . . . . . . . Radial, 1-stage |   Fan Rotor . . . . . . . . . . . . . . . . . . . . . . . . Axial 3-stage |
| Max Design Pressure Ratio/SLS: | Exhaust Nozzle . . . . . . . . . . . . . . . . . Fixed, 396 sq in. |
|   Fan . . . . . . . . . . . . . . . . . . . . . . . . . . . . . . . . . 1.61:1 | Thrust to Weight Ratio . . . . . . . . . . . . . . . . . . . 4.86:1 |
|   LP Rotor. . . . . . . . . . . . . . . . . . . . . . . . . . . . . 5.71:1 | Bypass Airflow Ratio . . . . . . . . . . . . . . . . . . . . . 2.82:1 |
|   HP Rotor . . . . . . . . . . . . . . . . . . . . . . . . . . . 2.60:1 | Max Allowable Air Bleed . . . . . . . . . . . . . . . . . . 8.5% |

## Performance

Performance Ratings at Standard Sea Level Static Conditions for ATF3-6A

| RATING | THRUST (lb) | RPM (Fan) | SFC (lb/hr/lb) | MEAS. GAS TEMP (°F) | AIRFLOW (lb/sec) |
|---|---|---|---|---|---|
| Takeoff, 59° F (5 min) | 5,440 | 9,765 | 0.506 | 1,850 | 163 |
| Takeoff, 86° F (5 min) | 5,050 | | 0.512 | 1,850 | 158 |
| Max Continuous 86° F | 4,312 | | 0.504 | 1,750 | 147 |
| Max Climb 86° F | 3,854 | | 0.505 | 1,710 | 139 |
| Max Cruise 86° F | 3,217 | | 0.506 | 1,650 | 128 |

## Size and Weight

| | |
|---|---|
| Length, Overall. . . . . . . . . . . . . . . . . . . . . . . 101.97 in | Weight, Dry . . . . . . . . . . . . . . . . . . . . . . . . . 1124.9 lb |
| Diameter, Nominal . . . . . . . . . . . . . . . . . . . . 33.77 in | Weight, Wet. . . . . . . . . . . . . . . . . . . . . . . . . 1154.3 lb |

## Applications

Used in the Dassault Falcon 200 and the USAF Tacit Blue

**Dassault Falcon 200**

**Tacit Blue**
*(Photo courtesy of U.S. Air Force Museum)*

# ATF3

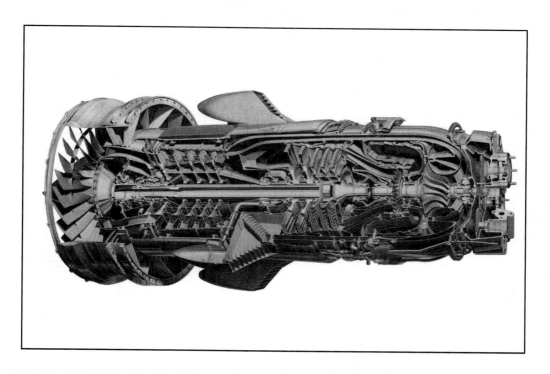

# F100

**Pratt & Whitney**

## Comments

The F100 engine development program has been described as the most successful in history. Technology was drawn from the J58 engine and from demonstrator engine programs for the supersonic transport and the VSTOL fighter. Advanced technology was also developed in such areas as turbine durability, where a nickel-based alloy was incorporated for blade material, and in lightweight materials, where some engine parts were formed from powdered metal. F100 versions include the F100-100,-200, -220, -220E, -220+, -220E+, and the -229. The following data represent F100-200.

## Features

| | | | |
|---|---|---|---|
| Compressor . . . . . . . . . . . . . . . . . . . . . . . Dual Rotor | Combustion Chamber . . . . . . . . . . . . . . Single, annular |
| LP Rotor(Fan) . . . . . . . . . . . . . . . . . . . Axial, 3-stage | Turbine. . . . . . . . . . . . . . . . . . . . . . . . . . . . Dual rotor |
| HP Rotor . . . . . . . . . . . . . . . . . . . . . . Axial, 10-stage | LP Rotor . . . . . . . . . . . . . . . . . . . . . . . Axial, 2-stage |
| Max Design Pressure Ratio/SLS: | HP Rotor . . . . . . . . . . . . . . . . . . . . . . . Axial, 2-stage |
| LP Rotor (Fan) . . . . . . . . . . . . . . . . . . . . . . . 3.12:1 | Exhaust Nozzle . . . . . . . . . . . . . . . C-D variable area: |
| HP Rotor . . . . . . . . . . . . . . . . . . . . . . . . . . . 8.02:1 | 2.7 to 6.4 sq ft; |
| Overall . . . . . . . . . . . . . . . . . . . . . . . . . . . . 24.9:1 | 1.06 to 1.61 area ratio |
| Bypass Airflow Ratio. . . . . . . . . . . . . . . . . . . . 0.63:1 | Thrust to Weight Ratio . . . . . . . . . . . . . . . . . . . 7.7:1 |

## Performance

### Performance Ratings at Standard Sea Level Static Conditions for F100-200

| RATING | THRUST (lb) | RPM | SFC (lb/hr/lb) | MEAS. GAS Temp(°F) | AIRFLOW ((lb/sec) |
|---|---|---|---|---|---|
| Max (5 minutes) | 23,840 | 12,960 | 2.170 | 1,710 | 228 |
| Maximum Cont. | 12,410 | 12,570 | 0.690 | 1,555 | |
| 90% Max Cont. | 11,170 | 12,360 | 0.680 | 1,040 | |
| 75% Max Cont. | 9,300 | 12,020 | 0.670 | | |
| Ground Idle (max) | 400 | 9,130 | | | |

## Size and Weight

| | |
|---|---|
| Length, Overall. . . . . . . . . . . . . . . . . . . . . . . . . 198.0 in | Weight, Dry. . . . . . . . . . . . . . . . . . . . . . . . . . . 3185 lb |
| Diameter, Nominal . . . . . . . . . . . . . . . . . . . . . 46.5 in | Weight, Wet . . . . . . . . . . . . . . . . . . . . . . . . . . 3264 lb |
| Max Radial Projection. . . . . . . . . . . . . . . . . . 27.39 in | |

## Applications

Twin-engine installation in the USAF F-15 Eagle. Used (1 engine each) in the USAF F-16A/B Lightweight fighter.

**F-15 Eagle**

**F-16A/B Fighting Falcon**

# F100

# F101

**General Electric**

## Comments

The F101-GE-102 is an augmented mixed flow turbofan engine. The 2-stage axial low-pressure compressor (fan) has fixed geometry and variable inlet guide vanes. It has heavier (than the F101-GE-100) 1-piece milled sheet and stringer design fan ducts to reduce cost and improve fan duct durability. No acceleration air bleed is required. Customer bleed is provided at interstage and compressor discharge, and power take-off is provided for customer power extraction. The high-pressure turbine is air cooled and operates at 2600°F maximum. Other versions of the F101 are the F101-100 and -101.

## Features

| | |
|---|---|
| Compressor | Combustion Chamber . . . . . . . . . . . . . . . . . . Annular |
|   LP Rotor (fan) . . . . . . . . . . . . . . . .2-stage, Var IGVs | Turbine |
|   HP Rotor (compressor . . . . . . . . . . . . . . . . 9-stage |   LP Rotor . . . . . . . . . . . . .2-stage, moderate loading |
| Max Design Pressure Ratio/SLS: |   HP Rotor. . . . . . . . . . . . . . . . . . . . . . . . . . . . 1-stage |
|   Fan . . . . . . . . . . . . . . . . . . . . . . . . . . . . . . 2.31:1 | Exhaust Nozzle . . . . . . . . . . ..Hinged flap, cammed link |
|   HP Rotor . . . . . . . . . . . . . . . . . . . . . . . . . . 11.0:1 | variable converging/diverging |
|   Overall . . . . . . . . . . . . . . . . . . . . . . . . . . . . 26.8:1 | Thrust to Weight ratio . . . . . . . . . . . . . . . . . . . . 7.1:1 |

## Performance

Performance Ratings at Standard Sea Level Static Conditions for F101-102

| RATING | THRUST (lb) | RPM (HP/LP) | SFC (lb/hr/lb) | AIRFLOW (lb/sec) |
|---|---|---|---|---|
| Maximum | 30,780 | 14,950/7,520 | 2.46 | 355 |
| Intermediate | 17,390 | 14,950/7,520 | 0.562 | 355 |
| 90% Intermediate | 15,650 | 14,030/7,150 | 0.540 | 340 |
| 75% Intermediate | 13,030 | 13,600/6,790 | 0.523 | 313 |
| Ground Idle | 1,050 | 10,210/3,090 | | |

## Size and Weight

| | |
|---|---|
| Length, Overall. . . . . . . . . . . . . . . . . . . . . . . . 180.7 in | Weight, Dry . . . . . . . . . . . . . . . . . . . . . . . . . 4,372 lb |
| Diameter, Nominal . . . . . . . . . . . . . . . . . . . . 55.2 in | Weight, Wet. . . . . . . . . . . . . . . . . . . . . . . . . 4,498 lb |
| Max Radial Projection. . . . . . . . . . . . . . . . . . 34.25 in | |

## Applications

Intended for use (4 engines each) in USAF B-1B.

**B-1B**

# F101

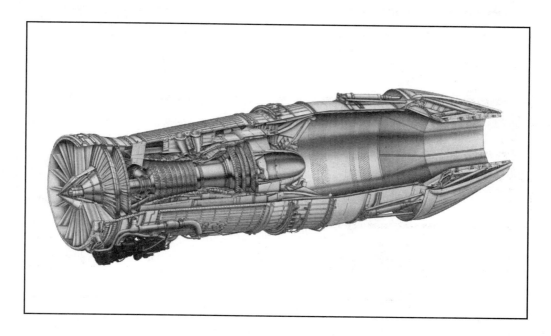

# F102

**Lycoming**

## Comments

The F102-LD-100 is a conventional, two-spool, high-bypass turbofan. The low-pressure compressor consists of a fan and F100 supercharging stages driven by the two-stage, low-pressure turbine through a fixed planetary gear assembly located in the front frame of the engine. Although the F102 was proposed for the A-X competition, the TF35 engine won the competition.

## Features

Compressor . . . . . . . . . . . . . . . . . . . . . . Dual Rotor,
   fixed geometry
LP Rotor, Fan. . . . . . . . . . . . . . . . . . . Axial, 3-stage
   (1 fan and 2 supercharging stages)
HP Rotor. . . . . . . . . . . . . . . . . . . Axial, 7-stage and
   centrifugal, 1-stage
Bypass Ratio . . . . . . . . . . . . . . . . . . . . . . . 5.40:1

Max Design Pressure Ratio/SLS:
   Fan . . . . . . . . . . . . . . . . . . . . . . . . . . . . . . . . 1.48:1
   LP Rotor . . . . . . . . . . . . . . . . . . . . . . . . . . . . 2.00:1
   HP Rotor . . . . . . . . . . . . . . . . . . . . . . . . . . . 6.95:1
   Overall . . . . . . . . . . . . . . . . . . . . . . . . . . . . . 14.0:1
Combustion Chamber. . . . . . . . . .Single, annular, reverse flow,
   with pressure atomizing injection nozzles

## Performance

### Performance Ratings at Standard Sea Level Static Conditions

| RATING | THRUST (lb) | RPM (HP/LP) | SFC (lb/hr/lb) | MEAS. EGT (°F) | AIRFLOW (lb/sec) |
|---|---|---|---|---|---|
| Max (5 min) | 7,652 | 20,270/7,390 | 0.412 | 1,600 | 272 |
| Intermediate (30 min) | 6,910 | 19,730/7,110 | 0.396 | 1,495 | 260 |
| Max Continuous | 6,246 | 19,280/6,850 | 0.386 | 1,405 | 248 |
| 90% Max Cont. | 5,620 | 18,880/6,570 | 0.379 | | 236 |
| 75% Max Cont. | 4,684 | 18,220/6,110 | 0.371 | | 217 |

## Size and Weight

Length, Overall. . . . . . . . . . . . . . . . . . . . . . . .65.57 in
Diameter, Nominal . . . . . . . . . . . . . . . . . . . . .42.40 in
Max Radial Projection. . . . . . . . . . . . . . . . . . .28.75 in

Weight, Dry . . . . . . . . . . . . . . . . . . . . . . . . . . . .1195 lb
Weight, Wet . . . . . . . . . . . . . . . . . . . . . . . . . . .1229 lb

## Applications

Originally proposed (2 engines each) for the Northrop A-9A (A-X) Attack Aircraft. Program terminated in Dec. '72 upon source selection in favor of the A-10A Aircraft.

**A-9A**

# F102

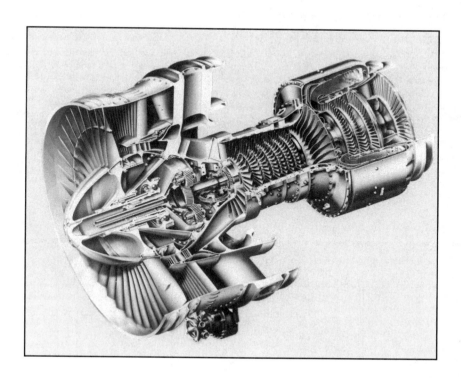

# F103

**General Electric**

## Comments

The F103-GE-100 is a dual-rotor, high-bypass-ratio turbofan with a single-stage front fan plus three booster stages. The booster stages supercharge the high-pressure compressor, giving an overall pressure ratio of 30:1. The first six stator rows of the 14-stage high-pressure compressor are variable. The combustor is annular with thirty fuel nozzles. A four-stage, low-pressure turbine drives the fan unit and a two-stage, air-cooled, high-pressure turbine drives the high pressure compressor. The primary exhaust nozzle is fixed. The engine is commercially certified.

## Features

Compressor . . . . . . . . . . . . . . . . . . . . . . . Dual rotor
   LP Rotor (fan) . . . . . . . . . . . . . . . . . . . . . . 3-stage
   HP Rotor . . . . . . . . . . . . . . . . . . . . Axial, 14-stage
Max Design Pressure Ratio/SLS:
   LP Rotor . . . . . . . . . . . . . . . . . . . . . . . . . . . 1.71:1
   HP Rotor . . . . . . . . . . . . . . . . . . . . . . . . . . 17.5:1
   Overall . . . . . . . . . . . . . . . . . . . . . . . . . . . 30.2:1

Combustion Chamber . . . . . . . . . . . . . Annular, single
Turbine
   LP Rotor . . . . . . . . . . . . . . . . . . . . . . Axial, 4-stage
   HP Rotor . . . . . . . . . . . . . . . . . . . . . . Axial, 2-stage
Thrust to Weight ratio . . . . . . . . . . . . . . . . . . . 6.3:1

## Performance

Performance Ratings at Standard Sea Level Static Conditions for F103-100

| RATING | THRUST (lb) | RPM (core/fan) | SFC (lb/hr/lb) | AIRFLOW (lb/sec) |
|---|---|---|---|---|
| Maximum | 28,000 | 14,780/8,214 | 2.063 | 263.3 |
| Intermediate | 16,760 | 14,788/8,214 | 0.675 | 263.3 |
| 90% Intermediate | 14,610 | 14,446/7,927 | 0.665 | 245.0 |
| 75% Intermediate | 12,170 | 14,052/7,572 | 0.665 | 220.0 |
| Ground Idle | 685 | 10,590/3,296 | | 83.3 |

## Size and Weight

Length, Overall . . . . . . . . . . . . . . . . . . . . . . . 190.0 in
Diameter, Nominal . . . . . . . . . . . . . . . . . . . . . 107.0 in
Max Radial Projection . . . . . . . . . . . . . . . . . . . . 60.0 in

Weight, Dry . . . . . . . . . . . . . . . . . . . . . . . . . . 8,325 lb
Weight, Wet . . . . . . . . . . . . . . . . . . . . . . . . . . 8,347 lb

## Applications

Used in the A300B (2 engines), DC-10-30 (3 engines), Boeing 747 (4 engines), and the McDonnell Douglas KC-10.

**DC-10**

**KC-10**

# F103

# F106

**Teledyne CAE**

## Comments

The F106-CA-100 is a two-spool, axial flow turbofan engine. Fuel is provided by a centrifugal (slinger) fuel injector. The oil system provides continuous lubrication to the shaft bearings and accessory drive pad. An engine mounted oil tank and fuel/oil coolers are included. Provisions are made for driving engine accessories and an air-vehicle-supplied alternator with power extracted from the high-pressure spool. Customer bleed air is delivered from the high-pressure compressor.

## Features

Compressor . . . . . . . . . . . . . . . . . . . . . . . Two-spool
   LP Rotor, Fan . . . . . . . . . . . . . . . . . Two axial stages
   HP Rotor. . . . . . . . . . . . . . . . . . . . Three axial stages
   plus one centrifugal
Max Design Pressure Ratio/SLS:
   LP Rotor (Fan) . . . . . . . . . . . . . . . . . . . . . . . . 2.1:1
   HP Rotor . . . . . . . . . . . . . . . . . . . . . . . . . . . . 6.6:1
   Overall . . . . . . . . . . . . . . . . . . . . . . . . . . . . 13.9:1

Bypass Airflow Ratio . . . . . . . . . . . . . . . . . . . . . . 1.0:1
Max Allowable Air Bleed . . . . . . . . . . . . . . . . . . 3.0%
Max Rated Airflow/SLS . . . . . . . . . . . . . . . . . 12.8 lb/sec
Combustion Chamber . . . . . . . . . . . . . Single, annular
Turbine . . . . . . . . . . . . . . . . . . . . . . . . . . . Two-spool
   LP Rotor . . . . . . . . . . . . . . . . . . . . . . Axial, 2-stage
   HP Rotor . . . . . . . . . . . . . . . . . . . . . . Axial, 2-stage

## Performance

Performance Ratings at Standard Sea Level Static Conditions for F106-100

| RATING | THRUST (lb) | RPM | SFC (lb/hr/lb) | TIT /TET (°F) | AIRFLOW (lb/sec) |
|---|---|---|---|---|---|
| Max and Intermediate | 614 | 53,580 | 0.613 | 1,795/980 | 12.6 |
| 90% Intermediate | 553 | 52,460 | 0.593 | 1,685/919 | 12.2 |
| 75% Intermediate | 460 | 50,450 | 0.577 | 1,550/844 | 11.3 |
| Idle, Max | 90 | 36,540 | | | |

## Size and Weight

Length, Overall. . . . . . . . . . . . . . . . . . . . . . . . . 29.0 in
Diameter, Nominal . . . . . . . . . . . . . . . . . . . . . . 12.6 in
Max Radial Projection. . . . . . . . . . . . . . . . . . . . 11.3 in

Weight, Dry. . . . . . . . . . . . . . . . . . . . . . . . . . . . 125 lb
Weight, Wet . . . . . . . . . . . . . . . . . . . . . . . . . . . 126 lb

## Applications

The F106-CA-100 was planned for the AGM-86A SCAD Program which has been terminated. A derivative is planned for the ZBGM-110 (SLCM) Program.

AIRCRAFT PHOTO
UNAVAILABLE

# F106

**ENGINE PHOTO
UNAVAILABLE**

# F107

**Williams International**

## Comments

The F107-WR-400 is a low-bypass-ratio turbofan with mixed exhaust. The low-pressure spool consists of a two-stage axial fan, followed by two additional axial compressor stages in the gas generator flow path, all driven by a two-stage axial turbine. The high-pressure spool consists of a single centrifugal stage driven by another two-stage axial turbine. The engine utilizes an annular burner with rotary fuel injection, and is started by impingement of solid propellant gases on the turbine blades. The lubrication system is self-contained. Other versions of the engine are F107-100, -101, -102, -103, -104, and the -402, an uprated version of the -400. Teledyne CAE serves as a second production source.

## Features

| | |
|---|---|
| Compressor. . . . . . . . . . . . . . . . . . . . . . . . . 2-spool, counter-rotating | Turbine . . . . . . . . . . . . . . . . . . . . . . . . . . . . . 2-spool, counter-rotating |
| Max Design Pressure Ratio/SLS | LP Rotor . . . . . . . . . . . . . . . . . . . . . .Axial, 2-stage |
| Fan . . . . . . . . . . . . . . . . . . . . . . . . . . . . 2.1:1 | HP Rotor . . . . . . . . . . . . . . . . . . . . . .Axial, 2-stage |
| Engine. . . . . . . . . . . . . . . . . . . . . . . . . . 13.8:1 | Exhaust Nozzle. . . . . . . . . . . . . . . . . . . Fixed, mixed |
| Combustion Chamber . . . . . . . . . . . . .Annular, single with slinger type injection | flow, convergent |

## Performance

Performance Ratings at Standard Sea Level Static Conditions F107-400

| RATING | THRUST (lb) | RPM (HP/LP) | SFC (lb/hr/lb) | AIRFLOW (lb/sec) |
|---|---|---|---|---|
| Max Continuous | 635 | 63,200/33,100 | 0.683 | 13.6 |
| 90% Max Continuous | 571 | 61,650/31,600 | 0.665 | 13.0 |
| 75% Max Continuous | 476 | 54,700/29,600 | 0.643 | 12.1 |
| Idle | 150 (max) | 48,645/20,040 | 1.04 | 7.07 |

## Size and Weight

| | |
|---|---|
| Length, Overall. . . . . . . . . . . . . . . . . . . . . . . .36.9 in | Weight, Dry. . . . . . . . . . . . . . . . . . . . . . . . . .139 lb |
| Diameter, Nominal . . . . . . . . . . . . . . . . . . . . 12.0 in | Weight, Wet . . . . . . . . . . . . . . . . . . . . . . . . .142 lb |
| Max Radial Projection. . . . . . . . . . . . . . . . . .10.73 in | |

## Applications

F107 engine variants are used in sea-, air- and ground-launched cruise missiles, including the Boeing AGM-86 and the Tomahawk.

**Boeing AGM-86**
*(Photo courtesy of U.S. Air Force Museum)*

# F107

# F108

**CFM International**

## Comments

Designed for long life, high reliability, ease of maintenance, high thrust-to-weight, low noise, low emissions and low SFC, the F108-CF-100 (CFM56) is a dual-rotor, high-bypass-ratio turbofan designed for subsonic service. The basic design utilizes a variable-stator compressor, an air-cooled high-pressure turbine, two frames and two sumps. The low-pressure system is designed and built by SNECMA (France) while the high-pressure system is designed and built by General Electric (USA). The core of the CFM56 engine is similar to that of the F101 engine.

## Features

Compressor . . . . . . . . . . . . . . . . . . . . . . . . Axial flow
 LP Rotor (fan) . . . . . . . . . . . . . . . . . . . . . . 4-stage
 HP Rotor (compressor) . . . . . . . . . . . . . . 9-stage
Max Design Pressure Ratio/SLS:
 Fan . . . . . . . . . . . . . . . . . . . . . . . . . . . . . . 1.5:1
 LP Rotor . . . . . . . . . . . . . . . . . . . . . . . . . . 2.2:1
 HP Rotor . . . . . . . . . . . . . . . . . . . . . . . . . . 10.5:1
Overall . . . . . . . . . . . . . . . . . . . . . . . . . . . . 23.7:1

Combustion Chamber . . . . . . . . . . . . . . . . . . . Annular
 . . . . . . . . . . . . . . . . (20 nozzles)
Turbine . . . . . . . . . . . . . . . . . . . . . . . . . . . . Axial flow
 LP Rotor . . . . . . . . . . . . . . . . . . . . . . . . . . 4-stage
 HP Rotor . . . . . . . . . . . . . . . . . . . . . . . . . . 1-stage
Exhaust Nozzle . . . . . . . . . . . . . . . . Convergent, fixed
Thrust to Weight Ratio . . . . . . . . . . . . . . . . . . . 4.8:1

## Performance

**Performance Ratings at Standard Sea Level Static Conditions for F108-100**

| RATING | THRUST (lb) | RPM (LP Rotor) | SFC (lb/hr/lb) | MEAN GAS TEMP (°F) | AIRFLOW (lb/sec) |
|---|---|---|---|---|---|
| Takeoff | 21,634 | 4,630 | 0.363 | 1,499 | 785 |
| Max continuous | 21,194 | 4,569 | 0.361 | 1,481 | 777 |
| Flight Idle (max) | 3,230 | | | | |
| Ground Idle (max) | 860 | | | | |

## Size and Weight

Length, Overall . . . . . . . . . . . . . . . . . . . . . . . 115.35 in
Diameter, Nominal . . . . . . . . . . . . . . . . . . . . 72.04 in
Max Radial Projection . . . . . . . . . . . . . . . . . . . 48.24 in

Weight, Dry . . . . . . . . . . . . . . . . . . . . . . . . . . . . 4610 lb
Weight, Wet . . . . . . . . . . . . . . . . . . . . . . . . . . . . 4632 lb

## Applications

Military: KC-135R, 4 engines, USAF; E-6A, 4 engines, USN; C-135F French AF, 4 engines; E-3A, 4 engines, Royal Saudi AF. Commercial: DC-8-70, 4 engines; Boeing 737-300, 2 engines; A-320, 2 engines.

**KC-135R**

**Boeing 737**

# F108

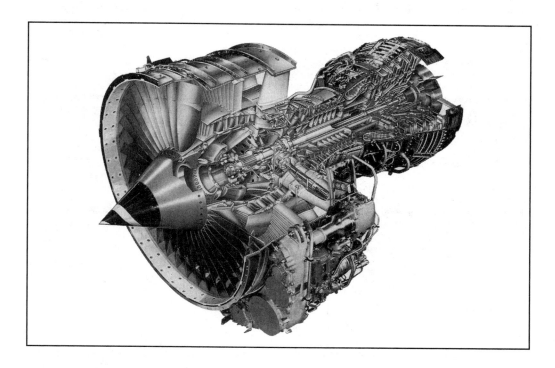

# F109

**Garrett**

## Comments

The F109-GA-100 turbofan is a scaled-down version of the larger Garrett commercial TFE731 engine. It is a two-spool, counter rotating, concentric-shaft, non-augmented, fixed-geometry engine of high bypass ratio. In addition, it is the first engine developed under the Air Force's strict Enhanced Structural Integrity Program (ENSIP) to produce engines more durable and tolerant to structural failure and damage.

## Features

Compressor................One fan + stator exit
  HP Rotor.............2 centrifugal compressors
Max Design Pressure Ratio/SLS:
  Fan...................................1.6:1
  HP Rotor...........................14.02:1
  Overall............................20.7:1

Bypass Airflow Ratio......................5.0:1
Max Allowable Air Bleed...................6.0%
Max Rated Airflow/SLS...............52.3 lb/sec
Combustion Chamber...........Annular, reverse

## Performance

Performance Ratings at Standard Sea Level Static Conditions for F109-100

| RATING | THRUST (lb) | RPM (LP/HP) | SFC (lb/hr/lb) | MEAS. GAS TEMP (°F) | AIRFLOW (lb/sec) |
|---|---|---|---|---|---|
| Max (Uninstalled) | 1,330 | 14,761/44,418 | 0.392 | 1,318 | 52.32 |
| Max Cont | 1,205 | 14,222/43,691 | 0.388 | 1,258 | 49.93 |
| 90% Max Cont (Uninst.) | 1,086 | 13,612/42,844 | 0.383 | | 47.60 |
| 75% Max Cont (Uninst.) | 905 | 12,599/41,417 | 0.380 | | 43.77 |
| Idle | 73 | 4,219/26,812 | 0.932 | | 9.46 |

## Size and Weight

Length, Overall........................43.17 in
Diameter, Nominal.....................23.16 in
Max Radial Projection..................17.30 in

Weight, Dry............................400 lb
Weight, Wet............................405 lb

## Applications

Used in the T-46A Squalus (TFE109).

**T-46A Squalus**

**T-46A Squalus**

# F109

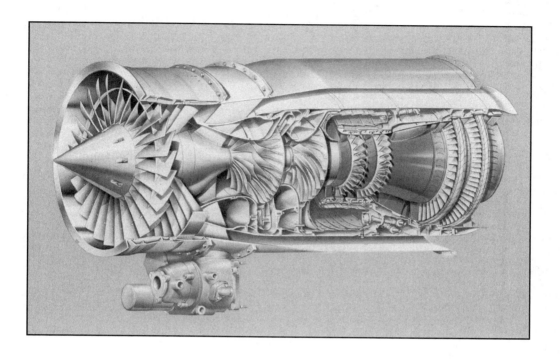

# F110

**General Electric**

## Comments

General Electric combined the proven technologies of the F101 core engine and the F404 fan and augmentor to produce the F110. An augmented mixed-flow, turbofan engine, the F110-GE-100 consists of a fixed-geometry fan with
variable inlet guide vanes, a high-stage-loading compressor, an annular combustor, single-stage high-pressure turbine,
and an integrated exhaust system with a converging-diverging nozzle.  Other versions of the engine are the F110-129
and the -400.

## Features

| | |
|---|---|
| Compressor | Combustion Chamber . . . . . . . . . . . . . . Annular scroll |
| LP Rotor (fan) . . . . . . . . . . . . . . . . . . . . . . . 3-stage | Turbine |
| HP Rotor (compressor) . . . . . . . . . . . . . . 9-stage | LP Rotor . . . . . . . . . . . . . . . . . . . . . . . . . . . 2-stage |
| Max Design Pressure Ratio/SLS: | HP Rotor. . . . . . . . . . . . . . . . . . . . . . . . . . . 1-stage |
| Fan . . . . . . . . . . . . . . . . . . . . . . . . . . . . . . 3.31:1 | Exhaust Nozzle . . . . . . . . . . . . . . . . . . . . Hinged flap, |
| HP Rotor . . . . . . . . . . . . . . . . . . . . . . . . . . 9.38:1 | cammed link, variable |
| Overall . . . . . . . . . . . . . . . . . . . . . . . . . . . 31.2:1 | converging-diverging |

## Performance

Performance Ratings at Standard Sea Level Static Conditions for F110-100

| RATING | THRUST (lb) | RPM (core/fan) | SFC (lb/hr/lb) | AIRFLOW (lb/sec) |
|---|---|---|---|---|
| Maximum | 28,000 | 14,780/8,214 | 2.063 | 263.3 |
| Intermediate | 16,760 | 14,788/8,214 | 0.675 | 263.3 |
| 90% Intermediate | 14,610 | 14,446/7,927 | 0.665 | 245.0 |
| 75% Intermediate | 12,170 | 14,052/7,572 | 0.665 | 220.0 |
| Ground Idle | 685 | 10,590/3,296 | | |

## Size and Weight

| | |
|---|---|
| Length, Overall. . . . . . . . . . . . . . . . . . . . . . 182.3 in | Weight, Dry . . . . . . . . . . . . . . . . . . . . . . . . . 3909.6 lb |
| Diameter Nominal . . . . . . . . . . . . . . . . . . . . 46.5 in | Weight, Wet. . . . . . . . . . . . . . . . . . . . . . . . . 3979.6 lb |
| Max Radial Projection. . . . . . . . . . . . . . . . . . 25.6 in | |

## Applications

Used in the F-15, 2 engines, and in the F-16, 1 engine.

**General Dynamics F-16 Fighting
Falcon**

**McDonnell Douglas F-15 Eagle**

# F110

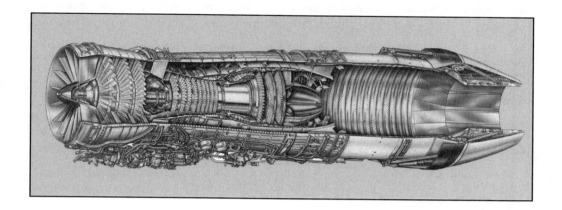

# F117

**Pratt & Whitney**

## Comments

A two-shaft, high-bypass-ratio turbofan engine, the F117-PW-100 incorporates such technology advancements as single crystal turbine blades, higher strength disc material, aerodynamically superior airfoils, and full authority digital controls. The single stage fan uses a moderate tip speed and no inlet guide vanes, and incorporates a wide axial separation between the blade and vane rows. Highly efficient design minimizes fuel burn, and rugged rotating components are designed for tolerance to foreign object ingestion.

## Features

Compressor
   LP . . . . . . . . . . . . . . . . . . . . . . . . . . . . . . . 4-stage,
   with controlled-diffusion airfoils
   HP . . . . . . . . . . . . . . . . . . . . . . . . . . . . . 12-stage,
   with controlled-diffusion airfoils
   Overall Cruise Pressure Ratio . . . . . . . . . . . . . .31:8

Combustion Chamber . . . . . . . . . . . . . . . . . . . Annular
Turbine
   LP . . . . . . . . . . . . . . . . . . . . . . . . . . . . . . . 5-stage,
   with active clearance control
   HP . . . . . . . . . . . . . . . . . . . . . . . . . . . . . . . 2-stage,
   with active clearance control

## Performance

Performance Ratings at Standard Sea Level Static Conditions for F117-100

RATING

Sea Level Takeoff . . . . . . . . . . . . .170.1 kN (38,250 lb)

## Size and Weight

Length . . . . . . . . . . . . . . . . . . . . .3,591 mm (141.1 in)
Fan case diameter . . . . . . . . . . . . .2,154 mm (84.8 in)

Weight, Dry . . . . . . . . . . . . . . . . . .3,248 kg (7,160 lb)

## Applications

The F117-PW-100 powers the McDonnell Douglas C-17 Globemaster III, four engines total.

**McDonnell Douglas
C-17 Globemaster III**

**McDonnell Douglas
C-17 Globemaster III**

# F117

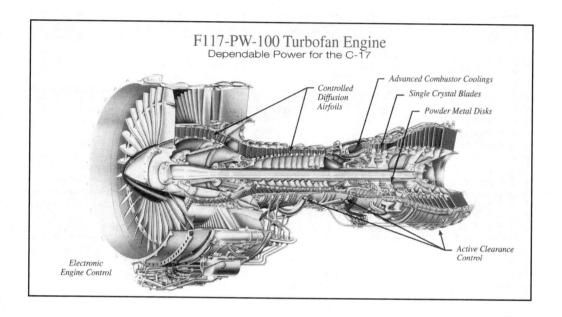

F117-PW-100 Turbofan Engine
Dependable Power for the C-17

Controlled Diffusion Airfoils

Advanced Combustor Coolings

Single Crystal Blades

Powder Metal Disks

Active Clearance Control

Electronic Engine Control

# F118

**General Electric**

## Comments

An unaugmented turbofan developed under USAF contract to meet the demanding propulsion requirements of the Northrop B-2A bomber, the F118-GE-100 combines new long-chord fan technology with the compressor and turbine used on the F110. Higher airflow and pressure ratio than the F110 result in higher thrust.

## Features

| | |
|---|---|
| Compressor . . . . . . . . . . . . . . . . . . . . . . . . . . . 9-stage, variable IGV on first three rows | Turbine |
| | High Pressure . . . . . . . . . . . . . . . . . 1-stage, cooled |
| Fan . . . . . . . . . . . . . . . . . . . . . . . .3-stage, variable IGV | Low Pressure . . . . . . . . . . . . . . . . . 2-stage, cooled |
| Bypass Ratio. . . . . . . . . . . . . . . . . . . . . . . . . . . . . . . 0.80 | Engine Controls . . . . . . . . . . Electro-hydromechanical |
| Combustion Chamber . . . . . . . . . . . . . . . . . Annular | Engine Monitoring System . . . . . . . . . . . . . .Electronic |

## Performance

Performance Ratings at Standard Sea Level Static Conditions for F118-100

RATING

Thrust Class . . . . . . . . . . . . . . . . . . . . . . . . . . 19,000 lb
Air Flow Class . . . . . . . . . . . . . . . . . . . . . . . 280 lb/sec

## Size and Weight

Length. . . . . . . . . . . . . . . . . . . . . . . . . . . . . . . 100.5 in
Max Diameter . . . . . . . . . . . . . . . . . . . . . . . . . 46.5 in

## Applications

The F118-GE-100 is used in the Northrop B-2 bomber.

B-2

B-2

# FI18

# F119

**Pratt & Whitney**

## Comments

The F119 is a two-shaft low bypass ratio augmented turbofan engine, designed using the Integrated Product Development approach to ensure a balance among performance, safety and reliability, maintainability and low life-cycle cost. It incorporates supercruise capability without afterburner and a two dimensional nozzle with limited thrust vectoring.

## Features

Fan . . . . . . . . . . . . . . . . . . . . . . . . . . . . . . . . . . 3 stages
snubberless wide-chord blades
Compressor . . . . . . . . . . . . . . . . . . . . . . . Multi-stage
Combustion Chamber . . . . . . . . . . . . . . . . . Annular

Turbine. . . . . . . . . . . . . . . . . . . . . . . . . . . . . . Single-stage
counterrotating HP and LP turbines

## Performance

Performance Ratings at Standard Sea Level Static Conditions for F119-100

RATING

S/L . . . . . . . . . . . . . . . . . . . . . . .155.6 kN (35000 lb st)

## Size and Weight

Generally similar to the PW1129

## Applications

The F119 engine is used in the Lockheed F-22A Advanced Tactical Fighter.

**Lockheed F-22A Raptor**

**Lockheed F-22A Raptor**

# FI19

# F401

**Pratt & Whitney**

## Comments

The F401-PW-400A and -401 are augmented twin-spool mixed-flow turbofan engines. The fan, consisting of three full stages and one stub stage, is driven by a two-stage turbine, and the 10-stage compressor is driven by an air-cooled two-stage turbine. The main burner is annular with air-assist spray nozzles. The control system is a combination of hydromechanical and digital electronic. The engine main gearbox and engine remote gearbox are both bottom mounted and driven by the high pressure rotor. The -401 is a designation change to the -400A modified by removal of the stub duct and accessory gearbox and power take-off shaft.

## Features

Compressor . . . . . . . . . . . . . . . Axial flow, twin-spool,
    variable geometry with interstage bleed
LP Rotor, Fan . . . . . . ..4 stages including 3-stage fan,
    variable fan inlet guide vanes
HP Rotor . . . . . .10 stages, variable inlet guide vanes,
    1st and 2nd stage stators, start air bleeds

Nominal Pressure Ratio (SLS)
    Fan . . . . . . . . . . . . . . . . . . . . . . . . . . . . . . 3.03:1
    Overall . . . . . . . . . . . . . . . . . . . . . . . . . . . 30.5:1
Bypass Ratio (SLS . . . . . . . . . . . . . . . . . . . . . . . 6.4:1

## Performance

Performance Ratings at Standard Sea Level Static Conditions for F401-400A, 401

| RATING | THRUST (lb) | RPM (LP/HP) | SFC (lb/hr/lb) | MEAS. GAS TEMP (°F) | AIRFLOW (lb/sec) |
|---|---|---|---|---|---|
| Max | 26,777 | 9,218/12,925 | 2.195 | 1,646 | 264 |
| Max Cont | 14,592 | 8,858/12,689 | 0.679 | 1,565 | 252 |
| 90% Max Cont | 13,143 | 8,614/12,479 | 0.669 | | 240 |
| 75% Max Cont | 10,947 | 8,236/12,140 | 0.657 | | 222 |
| Ground Idle (max) | 839 | 4,522/9,935 (min) | 1,136 pph | | 100 |

## Size and Weight

Afterburner Length . . . . . . . . . . . . . . . . . . . . . . 65.0 in
Overall Length . . . . . . . . . . . . . . . . . . . . . . . . 242.8 in
Maximum Width . . . . . . . . . . . . . . . . . . . . . . . . 50.5 in

Maximum Height . . . . . . . . . . . . . . . . . . . . . . . . 57.1 in
Weight, Dry . . . . . . . . . . . . . . . . . . . . . . . . . . 3,699 lb

## Applications

F-14B Flight Development Aircraft (two engines) and the XFV-12A Research Aircraft (one engine-non A/B).

**F-14B Tomcat**

**XFV-12A**

# F401

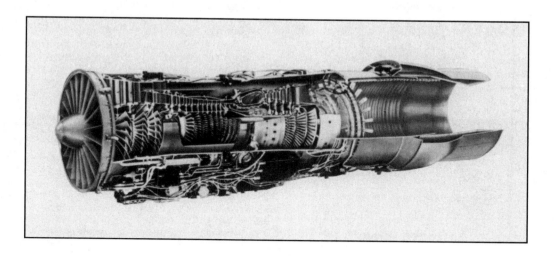

# F402

**Rolls-Royce**

## Comments

The F402-RR-402 engine is a vectored thrust turbofan engine with three fan stages on one spool and eight high-pressure compressor stages on a second spool, each spool being independently driven by separate two-stage turbines through counterrotating co-axial shafts. All lifting and propulsive thrust is delivered by four symmetrically positioned vectoring thrust nozzles, two at the front of the engine discharging a portion of the fan air, and two at the rear discharging all the turbine flow. Thrust augmentation is provided by water injection. Other versions are the F402-402A/B/C/S, -404, -406, -406A, -406, -408, and -408A

## Features

| | | | |
|---|---|---|---|
| Compressor | Axial, twin spool | Turbine | Axial, 4-stage |
| LP Rotor | 3-stage | LP Rotor | 2-stage |
| HP Rotor | 8-stage, var. IGV | HP Rotor | 2-stage |
| Max Design Comp. Ratio (SLS) | 14.75:1 | Turbine Cooling | Air |
| Combustion Chamber | Axial, annular | Exhaust Nozzle | Thrust vectoring |
| vaporizing type | | Thrust to Weight Ratio (SLS) | 5.57:1 |

## Performance

### Performance Ratings at Standard Sea Level Static Conditions

| RATING | THRUST (min) (lb) | RPM (HP/LP) | SFC (lb/hr/lb) | MEAS. EGT (°F/°C) | AIRFLOW (lb/sec) |
|---|---|---|---|---|---|
| Lift, wet | 20,400 | 10,753/6,747 | 0.742 | 1,220/660 | 441 |
| Lift | 19,030 | 10,634/6,500 | 0.689 | 1,202/650 | 432 |
| Maximum | 16,350 | 10,345/6,133 | 0.670 | 1,100/593 | 407 |
| Max Continuous | 13,090 | 9,962/5,700 | 0.659 | 988/531 | 370 |
| Idle | 1,000 | 5,210/1,690 | | | 92 |

## Size and Weight

| | |
|---|---|
| Length, Overall | 137.2 in |
| Compressor Inlet Diameter | 46.25 in |
| Weight, Dry | 3,765 lb |

## Applications

The F402 engine is used in the AV-8 Harrier VSTOL aircraft.

**AV-8 Harrier**

**AV-8 Harrier**

# F402

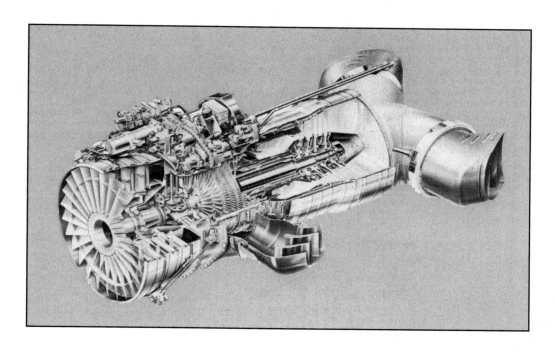

# F404

**General Electric**

## Comments

A mixed-flow, dual-spool, augmented turbofan, the F404-GE-400 incorporates a three-stage low-pressure compressor and a seven-stage high-pressure compressor, each driven by a single-stage turbine. Both compressors incorporate variable geometry. The combustor is a through-flow annular type, and the hinged-flap, cam-linked (HFCL) exhaust nozzle is hydraulically actuated. The lubrication system is self-contained. Other versions of the engine are the F404-100, -100A, -100D, -400D, and -402.

## Features

Compressor
LP Rotor . . . . . . . . . . . . . . . . . . . . . . . . . . . . . 3-stage
HP Rotor. . . . . . . . . . . . . . . . . . . . . . . . . . . . . . 7-stage
Max Design Pressure Ratio/SLS:
LP Rotor . . . . . . . . . . . . . . . . . . . . . . . . . . . . . . 3.9:1
HP Rotor . . . . . . . . . . . . . . . . . . . . . . . . . . . . . 6.2:1
Overall . . . . . . . . . . . . . . . . . . . . . . . . . . . . . . 24.0:1

Combustion Chamber . . . . . . . . . . . . . . . . . . . Annular
Turbine
LP Rotor . . . . . . . . . . . . . . . . . . . . . . . . . . . . . 1-stage
HP Rotor. . . . . . . . . . . . . . . . . . . . . . . . . . . . . . 1 Stage
Exhaust Nozzle . . . . . . . . . .Hinged flap, cammed link
Thrust to Weight Ratio . . . . . . . . . . . . . . . . . . . . 7.4:1

## Performance

Performance Ratings at Standard Sea Level Static Conditions

| RATING | THRUST (lb) | RPM (LP/HP) | SFC (lb/hr/lb) | MEAS. EGT (°F) | AIRFLOW (lb/sec) |
|---|---|---|---|---|---|
| Maximum | 16,016 | 13,688/16,464 | 1,851 | 1,466 | 141.5 |
| Intermediate | 10,608 | 13,688/16,479 | 0.813 | 1,466 | 141.5 |
| Max Cont. | 9,608 | 13,230/16,201 | 0.798 | 1,392 | 135.3 |
| 50% Intermediate | 5,304 | | 0.772 | | |
| Ground Idle | 320 | | | | |

## Size and Weight

Length, Overall. . . . . . . . . . . . . . . . . . . . . . . . .158.8 in
Diameter, Nominal . . . . . . . . . . . . . . . . . . . . . .27.9 in
Max Radial Projection. . . . . . . . . . . . . . . . . . . . .25.2 in

Weight, Dry . . . . . . . . . . . . . . . . . . . . . . . . . . . .2,180 lb
Weight, Wet. . . . . . . . . . . . . . . . . . . . . . . . . . . .2,237 lb

## Applications

Used in the F-18/A Hornet, two engines each.

**McDonnell Douglas F-18/A Hornet**

**McDonnell Douglas F-18/A Hornet**

# F404

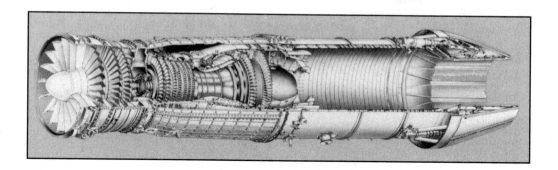

# F405

**Rolls-Royce**

## Comments

The F405-RR-401 is the U.S. version of the Rolls Royce Adour Mk 871. It is a two-shaft turbofan for subsonic aircraft.

## Features

| | |
|---|---|
| Fan. . . . . . . . . . . . . . . . . . . . . . . . . . . . . . . . . . . 2-stage | HP Turbine . . . . . . . . . . . . . . . . . . . . . . . . Single stage, |
| Compressor . . . . . . . . . . . . . . . . . . . . . . . . . . 5-stage | air-cooled |
| Bypass Ratio. . . . . . . . . . . . . . . . . . . . . . . . 0.75/0.80 | LP Turbine. . . . . . . . . . . . . . . . . . . . . . . . . Single stage, |
| Combustion Chamber . . . . . . . . . . . . . . . . . . Annular | squeeze-film bearings |

## Performance

Performance Ratings at Standard Sea Level Static Conditions for F405-401

RATING

Sea Level Takeoff . . . . . . . . . . . . . . .26.2 kN (5,900 lb)

## Size and Weight

| | |
|---|---|
| Length, Overall . . . . . . . . . . . . . . . . . . . . . . . . . . 77 in | Weight . . . . . . . . . . . . . . . . . . . . . . . . . . . . . . 1,330 lb |
| Inlet Diameter. . . . . . . . . . . . . . . . . . . . . . . . . . . 22 in | |
| Max Width. . . . . . . . . . . . . . . . . . . . . . . . . . . . . 30 in | |
| Max Height . . . . . . . . . . . . . . . . . . . . . . . . . . . . 41 in | |

## Applications

The F405-RR-401 is produced for use in the T-45A Goshawk.

**T-45A Goshawk**
*(Photo courtesy of Universal Technology Corporation)*

**T-45A Goshawk**
*(Photo courtesy of Universal Technology Corporation)*

# F405

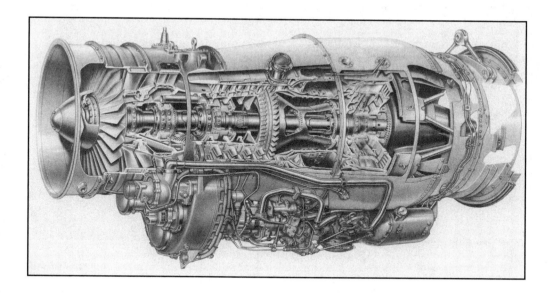

# GE4

**General Electric**

## Comments

The GE4/J5P is an axial-flow, augmented turbojet for the Boeing 2707 Supersonic Transport. It incorporates a nine-stage, variable-stator, axial compressor directly coupled to a two-stage, axial, air-cooled turbine. The design objectives are to provide a workhorse engine based on proven technology, long life, reliability, and ease of maintenance consistent with the high standards established by airlines. The engine is optimized for Mach 2.7 cruise.

## Features

Compressor . . . . . . . . . . . . . . . . . . . . . Axial, 9-stage, variable geometry
Max Design Pressure Ratio/SLS . . . . . . . . . . . . 12.7:1
Max Allowable Air Bleed . . . . . . . . . . . . . . . . . . 2.0%
Max Rated Airflow/SLS . . . . . . . . . . . . . . . 633 lb/sec

Combustion Chamber . . . . . . . . . . . . . Annular, single, through-flow
Turbine . . . . . . . . . . . . . . . . . . . . . . . . . . Axial, 2-stage
Turbine Cooling . . . . . . . . . . . . . . . . . . . . . . . . . . . . . Air
Max Rated Turb Inlet Temp/SLS . . . . . . . . . . . 2,280°F

## Performance

Performance Ratings at Standard Sea Level Static Conditions

| RATING | THRUST (lb) | RPM | SFC (lb/hr/lb) | TIT/TET (max, °F) | AIRFLOW (lb/sec) |
|---|---|---|---|---|---|
| Max (Augmented) | 68,600 | 5,200 | 1.770 | 2,280/1,700 | 633 |
| Max (Non-Augmented) | 51,500 | 5,200 | 1.040 | 2,280/1,700 | 633 |
| Normal Idle | | 3,170 | | | |

## Size and Weight

Length, Overall . . . . . . . . . . . . . . . . . . . . . . . . 296 in
Diameter, Max . . . . . . . . . . . . . . . . . . . . . . . . . 90 in

Weight, Dry . . . . . . . . . . . . . . . . . . . . . . . . 13,243 lb

## Applications

Originally planned (4 engines each) for the Boeing 2707 Mach 2.7 Supersonic Transport.

**Boeing 2707 SST**
*(Photo courtesy of National Air & Space Museum)*

# GE4

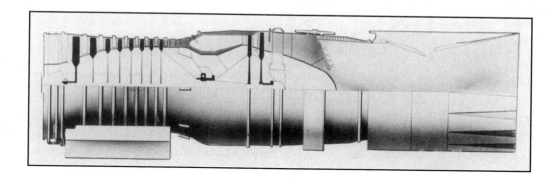

# I-A

**General Electric**

## Comments

Based on the Whittle engine, the I-A turbojet engine was the first turbojet engine built in the United States. The first test date was March 18, 1942, and about six months later, on October 2, two I-A engines powered the Bell XP-59, marking the first jet-powered flight in the United States.

## Features

Compressor . . . . . . . . . . . . . . . . . 1-stage, centrifugal
Cycle Pressure Ratio . . . . . . . . . . . . . . . . . . . . . . 3:1
Turbine . . . . . . . . . . . . . . . . . . . . . . . . . . . . 1-stage

## Performance

Performance Ratings at Standard Sea Level Static Conditions

| RATING | THRUST (lb) | RPM | SFC (lb/hr/lb) | TI TEMP (°F) | AIRFLOW (lb/sec) |
|--------|------------|--------|-----------------|---------------|-------------------|
|        | 1,250      | 16,500 | 1.1             | 1,400         | 30                |

## Size and Weight

Length, Overall. . . . . . . . . . . . . . . . . . . . . . . 70.5 in      Weight, Dry. . . . . . . . . . . . . . . . . . . . . . . . . . 780 lb
Diameter, Nominal . . . . . . . . . . . . . . . . . . . 44.0 in      Weight, Wet . . . . . . . . . . . . . . . . . . . . . . . . . 802 lb

## Applications

Two I-A engines powered the Bell XP-59 aircraft.

**Bell XP-59**

# I-A

# J30

**Westinghouse**

## Comments

The J30 is the military version of Westinghouse's WE19B, an improvement of the WE19A. The WE19A was the first wholly American-designed and -manufactured jet engine. It has a 10-stage axial compressor with one row of aluminum alloy inlet guide vanes and nine rows of steel guide vanes. The three-piece rotor consists of one aluminum alloy forging with eight rows of steel blades, and two separate forged steel discs with steel blades, bolted to the forging. The rotor shaft is supported in a combination sleeve-thrust bearing at the front end of the compressor.

## Features

| | |
|---|---|
| Compressor......................Axial, 10-stage | |
| Combustion Chamber..............Single, annular | |
| Turbine..........................Single, axial | |
| Exhaust Nozzle.................Fixed inner cone | |

## Performance

Performance Ratings at Standard Sea Level Static Conditions

| RATING | THRUST (lb) | RPM | SFC (lb/hr/lb) |
|---|---|---|---|
| Military Static | 1,600 | 17,000 | |
| Normal Static | 1,340 | 15,700 | 1.15 |
| Military Flight | 603 | 17,000 | |
| Normal Flight | 509 | 15,700 | 1.15 |

## Size and Weight

| | |
|---|---|
| Length, Overall.........................94.0 in | Weight................................718 lb |
| Diameter .............................19.0 in | |

## Applications

J30 variants were used in the FH-1, X-4, XP-79, and XF-92.

**McDonnell FH-1 Phantom**
*(Photo courtesy of National Air & Space Museum)*

**X-4**
*(Photo courtesy of National Air & Space Museum)*

# J30

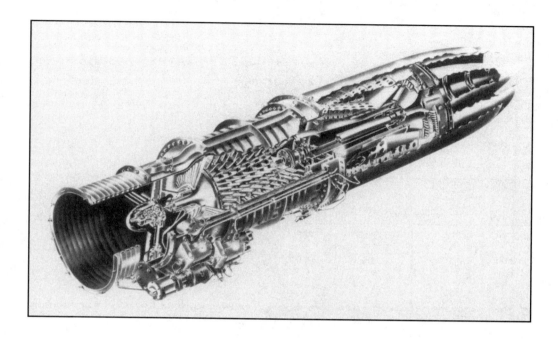

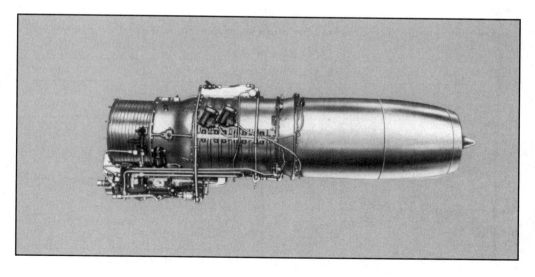

# J31

**General Electric**

## Comments

The J31 is a turbojet with a one-stage centrifugal compressor, 10 interconnected tubular stainless steel combustion chambers of reverse-flow type and a one-stage axial turbine. It is derived from the Whittle W1.

## Features

Compressor . . . . . . . . . . . . . . . . . . . . . . . Centrifugal
Turbine . . . . . . . . . . . . . . . . . . . . . . . . Axial, 1-stage
Turbine Cooling. . . . . . . . . . . . . . . . . . . . . . . . . Air
Combustion Chamber . . . . . . . . . . . . . Cannular with
                    10 through-flow inner chambers
Exhaust Nozzle. . . . . . . . . . . . . . . . . Inner/outer cones

## Performance

Performance Ratings at Standard Sea Level Static Conditions for J31/I-16

| RATING | THRUST (lb) | RPM | SFC (lb/hr/lb) | MEAS. EGT (°F) | AIRFLOW (lb/sec) |
|---|---|---|---|---|---|
| Takeoff | 1,600 | 16,500 | | 1,472 | |
| Military | 1,600 | 16,500 | | 1,472 | |
| Normal | 1,425 | 16,000 | 1.20 | | 33 |
| Idle | 70 | 5,000 | | | |

## Size and Weight

Length. . . . . . . . . . . . . . . . . . . . . . . . . . . . 72.0 in
Diameter . . . . . . . . . . . . . . . . . . . . . . . . . . 41.5 in

Frontal Area . . . . . . . . . . . . . . . . . . . . . . . . 9.39 sq ft
Weight. . . . . . . . . . . . . . . . . . . . . . . . . . . . . 850 lb

## Applications

Used in the first U.S. jet-powered production aircraft, the Bell P-59A.

**Bell P-59A**

**Bell P-59A**

# J31

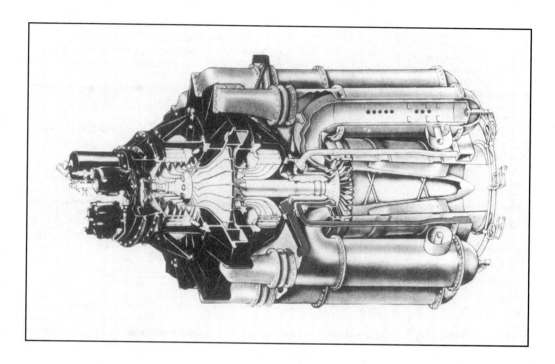

# J33

**General Electric**

## Comments

General Electric's first turbojet engine of its own design, the J33 consisted of a one-stage centrifugal compressor, 14 interconnected tapering stainless steel combustion chambers, and a single-stage axial turbine. Developed by General Electric as the I-40, it was installed in the Lockheed P-80. All production was later turned over to Allison, which produced thousands.

## Features

Compressor . . . . . . . . . . . . . . . . . . . . . . . Centrifugal
Turbine . . . . . . . . . . . . . . . . . . . . . . . Axial, 1-stage
Turbine Cooling . . . . . . . . . . . . . . . . . . . . . . . . Air
Weight/Thrust . . . . . . . . . . . . . . . . . . . . . . . 46 lb
Combustion Chamber . . . . . . . . . . . . . Cannular with
            14 through-flow inner chambers

Exhaust Nozzle . . . . . . . . . . . . . . . . Inner/outer cones

## Performance

Performance Ratings at Standard Sea Level Static Conditions for J33/I-40

| RATING | THRUST (lb) | RPM | SFC (lb/hr/lb) | MEAS. EGT (°F) | AIRFLOW (lb/sec) |
|---|---|---|---|---|---|
| Takeoff | 4,000 | 11,500 | | 1,472 | 79 |
| Military | 4,000 | 11,500 | | 1,472 | |
| Normal | 3,200 | 11,000 | 1.18 | | |
| Idle | 120 | 3,500 | | | |

## Size and Weight

Length . . . . . . . . . . . . . . . . . . . . . . . . . . . . . 103.0 in
Diameter . . . . . . . . . . . . . . . . . . . . . . . . . . . 52.0 in

Frontal Area . . . . . . . . . . . . . . . . . . . . . . . 14.7 sq ft
Weight . . . . . . . . . . . . . . . . . . . . . . . . . . . . 1850 lb

## Applications

J33 engines were used in several aircraft including the P-80, T-33, F-84, F-94, F9F, and F-89.

**P-80 Shooting Star**

**F-94**

*(Photo courtesy of U.S. Air Force Museum)*

# J33

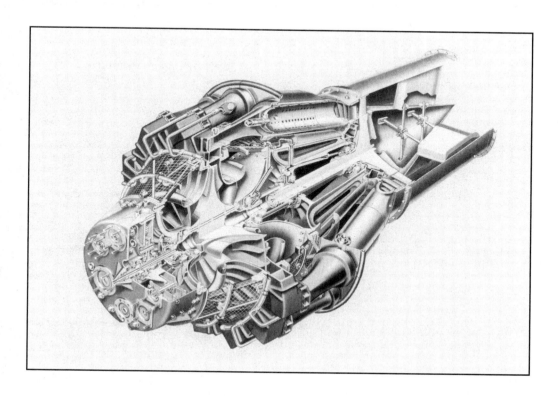

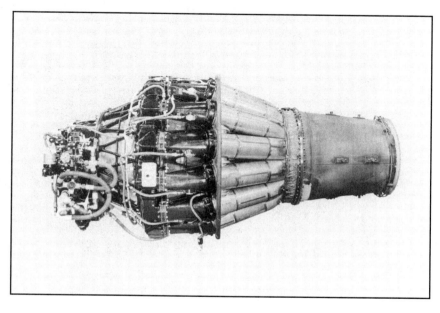

# J34

**Westinghouse**

## Comments

The J34-WE-34 engine has a single-spool, axial, 11-stage compressor, a double annular combustion chamber, a two-stage turbine, provisions for a fixed-area exhaust nozzle, and accessories mounted at the vertical centerline on the bottom of the engine. Other versions of the engine include the J34-22, -32, -34A, 36, -36A, and -46.

## Features

| | |
|---|---|
| Compressor . . . . . . . . . . . . . . . . . . . . . . . . Axial flow, single spool | Turbine . . . . . . . . . . . . . . . . . . . . . . . . . . Axial, 2-stage |
| | Turbine Cooling . . . . . . . . . . . . . . . . . . . . . . . . None |
| Max Design Pressure Ratio/SLS . . . . . . . . . . . . . 3.76:1 | Max Turb Inlet Temp/SLS . . . . . . . . . . . . . . . 1,435°F |
| Max Allowable Air Bleed . . . . . . . . . . . . . . . . . . 3.5% | MIL/MRP Oil Consumption . . . . . . . . . . . . . . 2.0 lb/hr |
| Max Rated Airflow/SLS . . . . . . . . . . . . . . . . 59 lb/sec | Rotor Speed Limit . . . . . . . . . . . . . . . . . . . 13,000 rpm |
| Combustion Chamber . . . . . . . . . . . . Double annular | |

## Performance

Performance Ratings at Standard Sea Level Static Conditions for J34-34

| RATING | THRUST (lb) | RPM | SFC (lb/hr/lb) | MEAS. GAS TEMP (°F) | AIRFLOW (lb/sec) |
|---|---|---|---|---|---|
| Max Cont (Normal) | 2,650 | 11,800 | 1.05 | 1,145 | 59 |
| 90% Max Cont | 1,750 | 10,500 | 1.14 | 1,035 | |
| 75% Max Cont | 1,400 | 9,900 | 1.23 | 1,000 | |
| Idle | 200 | 4,000 | 5.70 | 1,135 | |

## Size and Weight

| | |
|---|---|
| Length . . . . . . . . . . . . . . . . . . . . . . . . . . . . . 122 in | Height . . . . . . . . . . . . . . . . . . . . . . . . . . . . . . 35 in |
| Width . . . . . . . . . . . . . . . . . . . . . . . . . . . . . . . 28 in | Weight, Dry . . . . . . . . . . . . . . . . . . . . . . . . . 1,194 lb |

## Applications

Used in the P2H Director and the SP2E Neptune Anti-Submarine Aircraft (two auxiliary engines each).

**P2H**

# J34

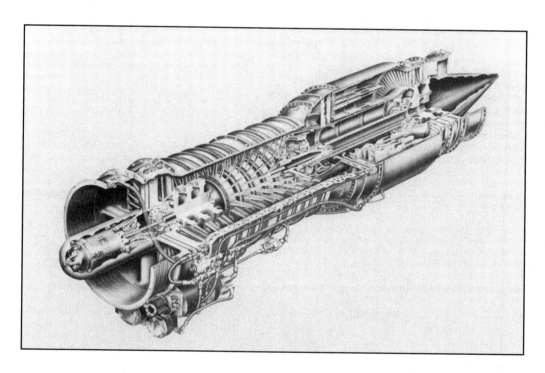

# J35

**General Electric**

## Comments

Development of axial flow compressors for the T31 turboprop led to the design of the J35 (TG-180) turbojet that became the powerplant for a host of experimental fighters and bombers, many later to become operational military aircraft. Versions of the engine include the J35-7, -17, -23, -35, -35A, and -35B. All design and production was turned over to the Allison Division of General Motors in 1947.

## Features

Compressor.....................Axial, 11-stage
Turbine.......................Axial, single-stage
Cycle Pressure Ratio.........................4:1
Combustion Chamber.............Cannular with
                8 through-flow inner chambers

Exhaust Nozzle....................Two position
Fuel System......................Dual manifold

## Performance

Performance Ratings at Standard Sea Level Static Conditions for J35/TG-180

| RATING | THRUST (lb) | RPM | SFC (lb/hr/lb) | MEAS. EGT (°F) | AIRFLOW (lb/sec) |
|--------|-------------|-----|----------------|----------------|------------------|
|        | 3,750/4,125 | 7,700 | 1.08 | 1,500 | 75 |

## Size and Weight

Length (with tail tube)...................166.0 in
Diameter...............................37.5 in

Frontal area..........................7.7 sq ft
Weight.............................2,400 lb

## Applications

J35 engine variants were used in various aircraft, including the Republic F-84, North American B-45, Boeing B-47, F-89D, H, and J fighters, and Douglas F4D (Prototype).

**F-84**

**B-45**

*(Photo courtesy of U.S. Air Force Museum)*

# J35

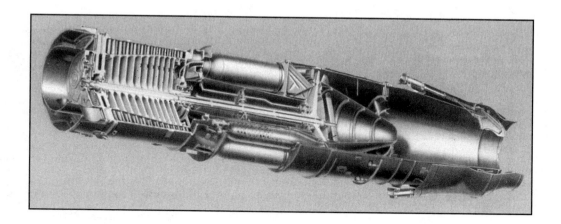

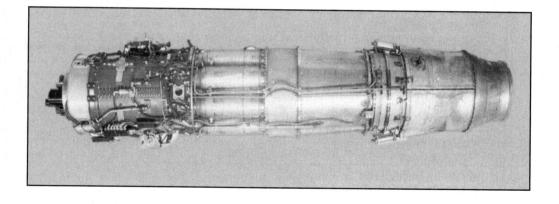

# J40

**Westinghouse**

## Comments

The J40-WE-22 was the largest turbojet engine manufactured by Westinghouse. It had a 10-stage axial compressor, an annular combustion chamber, a two-stage turbine, and a tubular detachable afterburner with downstream fuel injection. Other versions of the engine include the J40-1, -6, -8, and -12.

## Features

Compressor . . . . . . . . . . . . . . . . . . . . . Axial, 10-stage
Pressure Ratio . . . . . . . . . . . . . . . . . . . . . . . 5.0:1
Combustion Chamber . . . . . . . . . . . . . . . . . Annular
Turbine . . . . . . . . . . . . . . . . . . . . . . . Axial, 2-stage
Turbine Cooling . . . . . . . . . . . . . . . . . . . . Air-cooled
Exhaust Nozzle . . . . . . . . . . . . . . . . . . . Variable area,
                                                afterburner

## Performance

### Performance Ratings at Standard Sea Level Static Conditions

| RATING | THRUST (lb) | RPM | SFC (lb/hr/lb) | MEAS. EGT (°F) | AIRFLOW (lb/sec) |
|---|---|---|---|---|---|
| Take-off Static (dry) | 11,600 | 7,600 | 2.2 | | |

## Size and Weight

| | |
|---|---|
| Length, Overall . . . . . . . . . . . . . . . . . . . . . . 300.0 in | Weight . . . . . . . . . . . . . . . . . . . . . . . . . . . . . . 3,500 lb |
| Diameter . . . . . . . . . . . . . . . . . . . . . . . . . . 40.0 in | |

## Applications

J40 engine variants were used in the F3H, XF10F, XA3D, XF4D, and X-10.

**McDonnell F3H Demon**
*(Photo courtesy of National Air & Space Museum)*

**Douglas A3D Skywarrior**

# J40

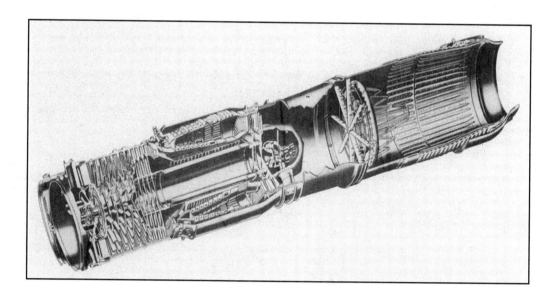

# J42

**Pratt & Whitney**

## Comments

The J42 Turbo-Wasp, as it was called, was Pratt & Whitney's first production jet engine. It had a single-stage centrifugal compressor with a two-piece magnesium alloy casing and nine tangential outlets and vaned elbows connecting with nine, straight-through, interconnected, elongated, conical, sheet steel combustion chambers.

## Features

Compressor . . . . . . . . . . . . . . . . . . Centrifugal, 1-stage
Combustion Chamber . . . . . . . . . . 9, straight-through
Turbine . . . . . . . . . . . . . . . . . . . . . . . . . . . Single, axial
Exhaust Nozzle . . . . . . . . . . . . . . . . . Fixed inner cone
Compression ratio . . . . . . . . . . . . . . . . . . . . . 4.3:1

Max Thrust-to-Weight . . . . . . . . . . . . . . . . . . . . . 3.36

## Performance

Performance Ratings at Standard Sea Level Static Conditions

| RATING | THRUST (lb) | RPM | SFC (lb/hr/lb) |
|---|---|---|---|
| Take-off (wet) | 5,750 | 12,300 | |
| Take-off (dry) | 5,000 | 12,300 | |
| Normal | 4,000 | 11,600 | |
| Cruise | 2,700 | 10,500 | 1.09 |

## Size and Weight

Length, Overall . . . . . . . . . . . . . . . . . . . . . . . 103.2 in
Diameter . . . . . . . . . . . . . . . . . . . . . . . . . . . . 49.5 in

Weight . . . . . . . . . . . . . . . . . . . . . . . . . . . . . 1,715 lb

## Applications

Used in Grumman F9Fs. Built under license from Rolls-Royce (Nene 2).

### Grumman F9F-Panther
*(Photo courtesy of National Air & Space Museum)*

# J42

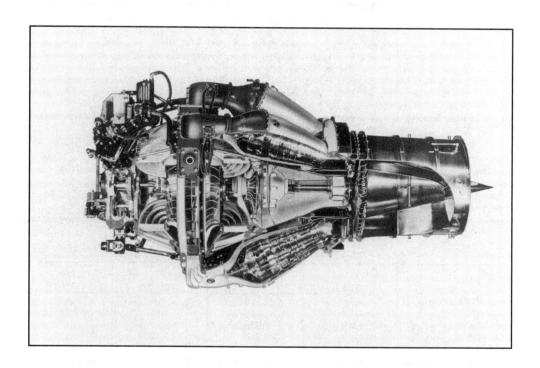

# J47

**General Electric**

## Comments

Credited with making General Electric a major world manufacturer, the J47 (TG-190) is an axial flow engine based on the J35 (TG-180). The compressor was developed to deliver higher pressure ratios and airflow and lower pattern factors than the J35. As a result, the J47 produces 20% more thrust and better specific fuel consumption than the J35 in the same frame size. J47 engine variants include the J47-1, -2, -3, -7, -9, -11, -13, -15, -17, -19, -23, -25, -25A, -27, and -33. Data that follow represent the J47-17, which incorporates afterburning, all-weather anti-icing, and four power take-off pads for customers' accessories.

## Features

| | |
|---|---|
| Compressor . . . . . . . . . . . . . . . . . . . . . . Axial, 12-stage | Max Rated Turb. Inlet Temp . . . . . . . . . . . . . . 1,600°F |
| Max Design Pressure Ratio/SLS . . . . . . . . . . . . 5.35:1 | Power Control . . . . . . . . . . . . . Motorized fuel valves |
| Combustion Chamber . . . . . . . . . . . Can-type, 8 cans | controlled by electronic amplifiers |
| Turbine . . . . . . . . . . . . . . . . . . . . . . . . Axial, 1-stage | Max Rated Airflow . . . . . . . . . . . . . . . . . . 101.5 lb/sec |
| Exhaust Nozzle. . . . . . . . . . . . . . . . . . . Variable area | |

## Performance

### Performance Ratings at Standard Sea Level Static Conditions for J47-17

| RATING | THRUST (lb) | RPM | SFC (lb/hr/lb) | MEAN GAS TEMP (°F) |
|---|---|---|---|---|
| Maximum AB (30 min) | 7,500 | 7,950 | 2.30 | 1,265 |
| Military (30 min) | 5,425 | 7,950 | 1.15 | 1,265 |
| Normal (continuous) | 4,990 | 7,950 | 1.13 | 1,175 |
| 90% Normal | 4,490 | 7,790 | 1.12 | 1,175 |
| Idle | 400 | 3,000 | | |

## Size and Weight

| | |
|---|---|
| Length . . . . . . . . . . . . . . . . . . . . . . . . . . . . . . 228 in | Weight, Dry. . . . . . . . . . . . . . . . . . . . . . . . . . . 3263 lb |
| Diameter. . . . . . . . . . . . . . . . . . . . . . . . . . . . . . 41 in | |

## Applications

J47 engine variants have been used in a number of aircraft including the B-36, B-45, B-47, FJ-2, and several versions of the F-86.

**Boeing B-47**

**North American F-86D Sabre Jet**

# J47

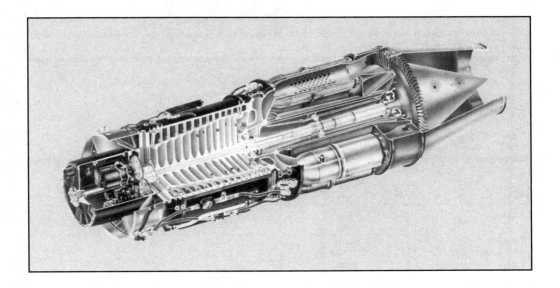

# J48

**Pratt & Whitney**

## Comments

The J48 is interchangeable with the Pratt & Whitney J42, but has water injection and an afterburner. It was produced under license from Rolls Royce (Tay).

## Features

Compressor. . . . . . . . . . . . . . . . . Centrifugal, 1-stage
Combustion Chamber. . . . . . . . . . 9, straight-through
Turbine . . . . . . . . . . . . . . . . . . . . . . . . . Single, axial
Exhaust Nozzle. . . . . . . . . . . . . . . . . Fixed inner cone
Max Thrust-to-Weight. . . . . . . . . . . . . . . . . . . . . 4.5

## Performance

Performance Ratings at Standard Sea Level Static Conditions

| RATING | THRUST (lb) | RPM | SFC (lb/hr/lb) |
|---|---|---|---|
| Take-off | 6,250 | 11,000 | |
| With Afterburner (wet) | 9,000 | 12,300 | |
| With Afterburner (dry) | 8,000 | 12,300 | |
| Normal | 7,000 | 11,600 | 1.0 |

## Size and Weight

Length, Overall. . . . . . . . . . . . . . . . . . . . . . . 106.7 in
Diameter . . . . . . . . . . . . . . . . . . . . . . . . . . . . 50.0 in

Weight . . . . . . . . . . . . . . . . . . . . . . . . . . . . . 2,000 lb

## Applications

Used in the FYF-93, F-94, and F9F-6.

**Lockheed F-94**
*(Photo courtesy of U.S. Air Force Museum)*

**Grumman F9F-6 Cougar**
*(Photo courtesy of National Air & Space Museum)*

# J48

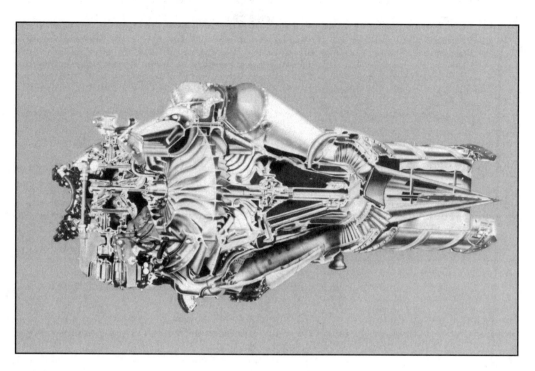

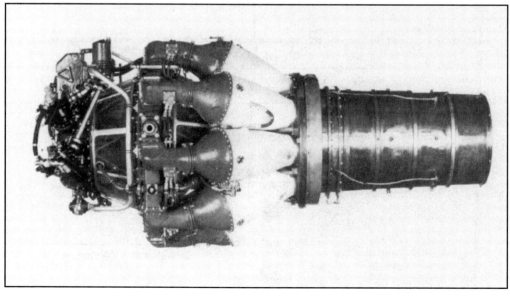

# J52

**Pratt & Whitney**

## Comments

The J52-P-3 incorporated a dual-spool, axial-flow compressor, nine through-flow combustion chambers arranged in an annular chamber and a two-stage axial turbine. The five-stage, low-pressure section of the compressor connects by a through shaft to the second turbine wheel and the seven-stage, high-pressure section connects independently by a hollow shaft to the first turbine wheel. The engine is equipped with a convergent-divergent exhaust nozzle suited for high Mach number operation. It is the same as the YJ52-P-1 except that it is 80 pounds lighter, does not incorporate titanium, and consumes less fuel.

## Features

Compressor . . . . . . . . . . . . . . . . . . . Axial, compound
Max Design Pressure Ratio/SLS . . . . . . . . . . . . . . 12:1
Turbine . . . . . . . . . . . . . . . . . . . . . . . . Axial, 2-stage
Combustion Chambers. . . . . . . . . . . . . Annular outer
Exhaust Nozzle. . . . . . . . . . . . . . . . . . . . . Plug type

## Performance

Performance Ratings at Standard Sea Level Static Conditions

| RATING | THRUST (lb) | RPM (LP/HP) | SFC (lb/hr/lb) |
|---|---|---|---|
| Take-Off (5 min) | 7,500 | 9,600/11,200 | 0.830 |
| Max continuous | 3,450 | 7,800/10,000 | 0.830 |
| Idle (min) | | 7,500 | |

## Size and Weight

Length. . . . . . . . . . . . . . . . . . . . . . . . . . . . . 149.5 in
Diameter . . . . . . . . . . . . . . . . . . . . . . . . . . . 31.5 in
Max Radial Projection. . . . . . . . . . . . . . . . . . . 26.3 in

Weight, Dry . . . . . . . . . . . . . . . . . . . . . . . . . 2,145 lb

## Applications

Used in the AGM-28A (formerly GAM-77) and AGM-28B (formerly GAM 77-A) Hound Dog (WS-131B) air-to-surface missiles, the Grumman A-6 Intruder, and the Douglas A-4 Skyhawk.

**Grumman A-6 Intruder**

**Douglas A-4 Skyhawk**

# J52

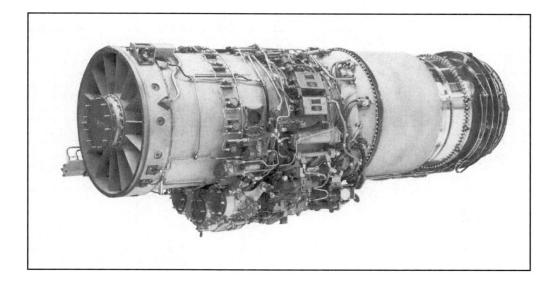

# J54

**Westinghouse**

## Comments

The J54 turbojet has a 16-stage axial-flow compressor, an annular combustor, and a two-stage axial-flow turbine with hollow nozzle blades and solid rotor blades

## Features

Compressor . . . . . . . . . . . . . . . . . . . . . Axial, 16-stage
Combustion Chamber . . . . . . . . . . . . . . . . . . annular
Turbine . . . . . . . . . . . . . . . . . . . . . . . . . 2-stage axial
Pressure Ratio . . . . . . . . . . . . . . . . . . . . . . . . . 9.0:1
Exhaust Nozzle . . . . . . . . . . . . . . . . . . . . . fixed area

## Performance

Performance Ratings at Standard Sea Level Static Conditions

| Takeoff Static | THRUST (lb) | RPM | SFC (lb/hr/lb) | MEAS. GAS TEMP (°F) | AIRFLOW (lb/sec) |
|---|---|---|---|---|---|
| | 6,500 | 11,000 | 0.85 | | |

## Size and Weight

Length, Overall . . . . . . . . . . . . . . . . . . . . . . . . 142.0 in
Diameter . . . . . . . . . . . . . . . . . . . . . . . . . . . . 35.0 in
Weight . . . . . . . . . . . . . . . . . . . . . . . . . . . . . 1,400 lb

None.

**No Application Developed**

# J54

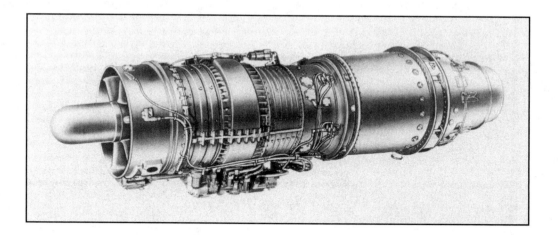

# J57

**Pratt & Whitney**

## Comments

The dual-spool-compressor, axial-flow J57 is one of Pratt & Whitney's most successful turbojet designs. More than 21,000 engines were delivered in almost twenty years of production. Its commercial version is the JT3. There are several variations of the J57. Data for the J57-P-420 are shown below.

## Features

| | |
|---|---|
| Compressor . . . . . . . . . . . . . . . . . . .Axial, twin spool | Max Primary Airflow/SLS . . . . . . . . . . . . . . 186 lb/sec |
|   LP Rotor . . . . . . . . . . . . . . . . . . . . . . . . . 9-stage | Combustion Chamber . . . . . . . . . . .8 unit, can-annular |
|   HP Rotor. . . . . . . . . . . . . . . . . . . . . . . . . . 7-stage | Turbine . . . . . . . . . . . . . . . . . . . . . . . . .Axial, 3-stage |
| Max Design Pressure Ratio/SLS . . . . . . . . . . . . . 12.9:1 |   LP Rotor . . . . . . . . . . . . . . . . . . . . . . . . . . 2-stage |
| Max Allowable Air Bleed 6.5% below max continuous, |   HP Rotor . . . . . . . . . . . . . . . . . . . . . . .Single stage |
|                  1.5% above max continuous | Turbine Cooling . . . . . . . . . . . . .Air-cooled first stage |

## Performance

Performance Ratings at Standard Sea Level Static Conditions for J57-P-420

| RATING | THRUST (lb) | RPM (HP/LP) | SFC (lb/hr/lb) | MEAS. GAS TEMP (°F) | AIRFLOW (lb/sec) |
|---|---|---|---|---|---|
| Max | 19,600 | 10,435/6,710 | 2.30 | 1,256 | 186 |
| Max Cont (Normal) 90% | 9,150 | 9,750/6,050 | 0.82 | | 163 |
| Max Cont | 8,250 | 9,580/5,850 | 0.82 | | 157 |
| 75% Max Cont | 6,850 | 9,310/5,550 | 0.82 | | 145 |
| Idle | 550 | 7,100/3,200 | 2.30 | | |

## Size and Weight

| | |
|---|---|
| Length, Overall. . . . . . . . . . . . . . . . . . . . . . . 266.92 in | Weight, Dry. . . . . . . . . . . . . . . . . . . . . . . . . . . 4840 lb |
| Maximum Width. . . . . . . . . . . . . . . . . . . . . . . 40.50 in | |
| Maximum Height . . . . . . . . . . . . . . . . . . . . . . 47.37 in | |

## Applications

J57 variants have been used in several different aircraft such as the F-100 Super Sabre, F-101 Voodoo, F4D Skyray, A3D Skywarrior, C-135, KC-135, F8U-2 Crusader, Lockheed U-2, Boeing 720, RF-8G, and the Northrop Snark intercontinental guided missile. The J57-P-420 is used in the Vought F-8E/-8H/-8J fighter.

**Vought F-8E**

**F-100 Super Sabre**

# J57

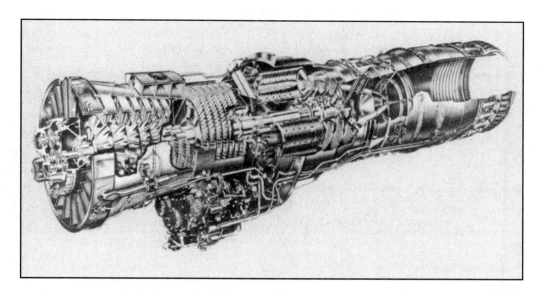

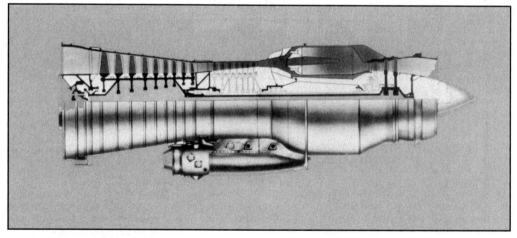

# J58

**Pratt & Whitney**

## Comments

The first turbojet to fly at Mach 3, the J58 has an eight-stage axial compressor, a cannular combustor, and a 2-stage turbine. The one-piece air intake casing incorporates 20 fixed steel inlet vanes with a de-icing system. The military version has an afterburner.

## Features

Compressor. . . . . . . . . . . . . . . . . . . . . .Axial, 8-stage
Max Design Pressure Ratio/SLS . . . . . . . . . . 6.0/8.0:1
Combustion Chamber. . . . . . . . . . . . . . . Can-annular
Turbine . . . . . . . . . . . . . . . . . . . . . . . . . . . 2-stage
Exhaust Nozzle . . . . . . . . . . . . . . . . .Fixed area, C-D
Thrust to weight . . . . . . . . . . . . . . . . . . . . . . . . 4.0

## Performance

Performance Ratings at Standard Sea Level Static Conditions

RATING                                    THRUST
Take-off with a/b . . . . . . . . . . . . . . . . . . . . . . 30,000
Take-off static (normal) . . . . . . . . . . . . . . . . 23,000

## Size and Weight

Length, Overall. . . . . . . . . . . . . . . . . . . . .225.0 in  Weight . . . . . . . . . . . . . . . . . . . . . . . . . . .7,000 lb
Max Diameter . . . . . . . . . . . . . . . . . . . . . . 45.0 in

## Applications

J58 engines are used in the Lockheed A-12 and SR-71 Blackbird.

**Lockheed A-12**
*(Photo courtesy of U.S. Air Force Museum)*

**Lockheed SR-71 Blackbird**
*(Photo courtesy of U.S. Air Force Museum)*

# J58

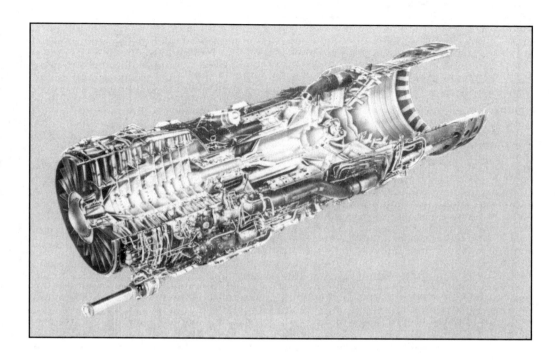

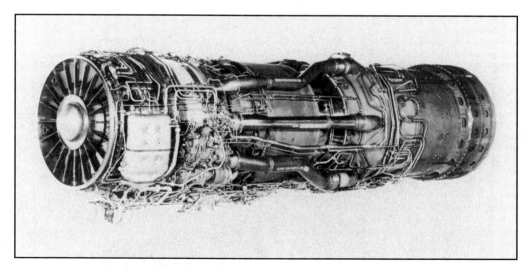

# J60

**Pratt & Whitney**

## Comments

Designed for easy maintenance and high operational reliability, the J60-P-9 is a small, light, axial-flow, medium-pressure-ratio, high-performance engine incorporating a fixed geometry single rotor. The -9 is the same as the -3A except for turbine rematching and the incorporation of a JFC46-6 Hamilton Standard Fuel Control. Other versions of the J60 are the J60-3, -3A, -5A, -5B, and -6.

## Features

| | |
|---|---|
| Compressor. . . . . . . . . . . . . . . . . . . . . . Axial, 9-stage | Max Rated Turb Inlet Temp . . . . . . . . . . . . . . . 1600°F |
| Max Design Pressure Ratio/SLS . . . . . . . . . . . . . . . 7:1 | Fuel . . . . . . . . . . . . . . . . . . . . . . . . . . . JP-4, MIL-T-5624 |
| Turbine . . . . . . . . . . . . . . . . . . . . . . Reaction, 2-stage | Ignition . . . . . . . . . . . . . . . . . . . . . . . . . . . . . . . Electrical |
| Combustion Chamber . . . . . . . . . . . . Cannular outer, | Power Control . . . . . . . . . . . . . . . . Hydromechanical |
| with 8 through-flow inner chambers | Max Rated Thrust Airflow. . . . . . . . . . . . . . 50 lb/sec |
| Exhaust Nozzle. . . . . . . . . . . . . . . . . . . . . Fixed area | |

## Performance

Performance Ratings at Standard Sea Level Static Conditions for J60-P-9

| RATING | THRUST (lb) | RPM | SFC (lb/hr/lb) |
|---|---|---|---|
| Max | 2,900 | 16,700 | 0.960 |
| Normal | 2,570 | 15,750 | 0.935 |
| 90% Normal | 2,310 | 15,300 | 0.925 |
| 75% Normal | 1,930 | 14,550 | 0.920 |
| Idle | 180 | 6,800 | 3.194 |

## Size and Weight

| | |
|---|---|
| Length. . . . . . . . . . . . . . . . . . . . . . . . . . . 77.92 in | Weight, Dry. . . . . . . . . . . . . . . . . . . . . . . . . . . 486 lb |
| Diameter . . . . . . . . . . . . . . . . . . . . . . . . . . 22.00 in | (Includes oil tank, cooler, continuous ignition system and |
| Max Radial Projection. . . . . . . . . . . . . . . . . . . 18.92 in | inlet nose cone) |

## Applications

Used (2 auxiliary engines each) on the WB-57F (formerly RB-57F) Reconnaissance Aircraft.

**WB-57F Canberra**

**WB-57F Canberra**

# J60

# J65-W-20, -420

**Curtiss-Wright**

## Comments

The J65-W-20 engine is a single-rotor turbojet having an annular intake, a 13-stage compressor coupled directly to a two-stage turbine, an annular vaporizing combustion chamber, and provisions for the attachment of a fixed-area exhaust nozzle. The J65-W-20 is similar to the J65-W-16A except for incorporation of parts required to permit higher intermediate and maximum continuous ratings. The J65-W-420 is identical in performance, construction, and weight to the J65-W-20 except that it features a reworked accessory gearbox to increase durability through the incorporation of new drive gears and shafts and improved lubrication of critical train components.

## Features

Compressor . . . . . . . . . . . . . . . . . . . . . Axial, 13 stages
   Max Design Pressure Ratio/SLS: . . . . . . . . . . 7.25:1
   Max Allowable Air Bleed . . . . . . . . . . . . . . . . 2.0%
   Max Airflow/SLS . . . . . . . . . . . . . . . . . . . . 130 lb/sec
Combustion Chamber . . . . . . . . . . Annular, vaporizing
Turbine . . . . . . . . . . . . . . . . . . . . . Axial flow, 2 stages
   Turbine Cooling . . . . . . . . . . . . . . . . . . . . . . None

Exhaust Nozzle . . . . . . . . . . . . . .Fixed area, 325 sq in
Power Control . . . . . . . . . . . . . . . . Hydromechanical
Oil Consumption . . . . . . . . . . . . . . . . . . . . 0.47 gal/hr

## Performance

### Performance Ratings at Standard Sea Level Static Conditions

| RATING | THRUST (lb) | RPM | SFC (lb/hr/lb) | MEAS. GAS Temp °F) | AIRFLOW (lb/sec) |
|---|---|---|---|---|---|
| Max Cont (Normal) | 7,400 | 8,300 | 0.930 | NA | NA |
| 90% Max Cont | 6,600 | 8,100 | 0.920 | | |
| 76% Max Cont | 5,550 | 7,800 | 0.905 | | |
| Idle | 460 | 3,500–4,000 | 1.250 (max) | | |

## Size and Weight

Length. . . . . . . . . . . . . . . . . . . . . . . . . . . . . 113.1 in
Maximum Width. . . . . . . . . . . . . . . . . . . . . . 40.0 in
Maximum Height . . . . . . . . . . . . . . . . . . . . . 40.6 in

Weight, Dry. . . . . . . . . . . . . . . . . . . . . . . . . 2797 lb

## Applications

A-4P (Argentina Air Force)/-4Q (Argentina Navy)/-4C/-4L/-4S (Singapore) Attack, NA-4C Skyhawk Special Test Aircraft (one engine each); F-11A Tiger Fighter Aircraft, and TA-4B Trainer (-20). B-57A, B, C, & E Series bombers.

**B-57**

# J65-W-20, -420

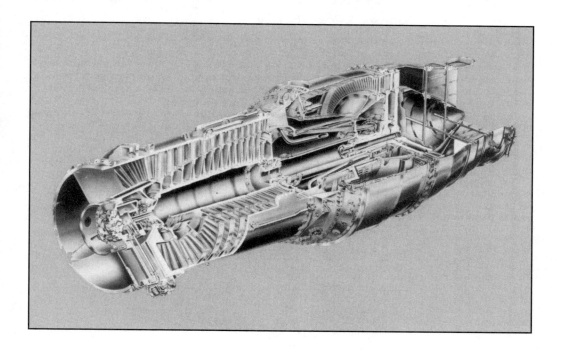

# J69

**Teledyne CAE**

## Comments

The J69-T-41A was developed as a short-life drone engine with a single-entry ram air inlet, a two-stage compressor section consisting of a transonic axial stage and a centrifugal stage, an annular , and a single-stage axial-flow turbine directly connected to the compressor. It is similar to the -29 except for design improvements to provide increased thrust. The -41A is a modification of the -41 and includes increased thrust, higher turbine inlet temperature, increased effective flow area of the turbine nozzle, and fuel control flow adjustments. Other versions are the YJ69-406 and the J69-25, 25A, 29, 41B.

## Features

Compressor . . . . . . . . . . . . . . . .Single Rotor, 2-stage
   Max Design Pressure Ratio/SLS . . . . . . . . . . 5.45:1
   Max Allowable Air Bleed. . . . . . . . . . . . . . . . None
   Max Rated Airflow/SLS . . . . . . . . . . . . . 29.8 lb/sec
Combustion Chamber. . . . . . . . . . . . . Annular, single

Turbine . . . . . . . . . . . . . . . . . . . . . . .Axial, single-stage
   Turbine Cooling . . . . . . . . . . . . . . . . . . . . . . . None
   Max Rated Turb Inlet Temp/SLS. . . . . . . . . 1750°F
Exhaust Nozzle . . . . . . . . . . . . . .Fixed area, 83.5 sq in

## Performance

Performance Ratings at Standard Sea Level Static Conditions for J69-41A

| RATING | THRUST (lb) | RPM | SFC (lb/hr/lb) | MEAS. EGT (max, °F) | AIRFLOW (lb/sec) |
|---|---|---|---|---|---|
| Max (30 min) | 1,920 | 22,000 | 1.100 | 1,400 | 29.8 |
| Normal (continuous) | 1,650 | 20,900 | 1.090 | 1,250 | 27.9 |
| 90% Normal | 1,485 | 20,400 | 1.090 | 1,180 | 26.6 |
| 75% Norma | 1,238 | 19,500 | 1.110 | 1,110 | 24.4 |
| Idle (estimated) | 160 | 11,000 | 2.406 | 1,025 | |

## Size and Weight

Length, Overall. . . . . . . . . . . . . . . . . . . . . . . . . 44.8 in
Diameter, Nominal . . . . . . . . . . . . . . . . . . . . . 22.3 in
Max Radial Projection. . . . . . . . . . . . . . . . . . . 14.5 in

Weight, Dry. . . . . . . . . . . . . . . . . . . . . . . . . . . 350 lb
Weight, Wet . . . . . . . . . . . . . . . . . . . . . . . . . . 352 lb

## Applications

Used (one engine each) in the Ryan AQM-34K, L, M and N Drone Aircraft.

**Ryan AQM-34**
*(Photo courtesy of Universal Technology Corporation)*

**Ryan AQM-34**
*(Photo courtesy of Universal Technology Corporation)*

# J69

# J71

**Allison**

## Comments

The J71-A-13 is an axial flow turbojet with ten through-flow combustion chambers, air inlet screens, and a 16-stage compressor directly connected to a three-stage turbine. The diameters of the compressor and turbine are approximately 33.5 inches. The -13 is same as the -11 except that it incorporates improved takeoff performance and lower idle thrust, and has 16th stage bleeds to eliminate low-RPM surge.

## Features

| | | | |
|---|---|---|---|
| Compressor . . . . . . . . . . . . . . . . . . Axial, single rotor | Turbine. . . . . . . . . . . . . . . . . . . . . . .Axial, single rotor |
| Max Design Pressure Ratio/SLS . . . . . . . . . . 8.25:1 | Turbine Cooling . . . . . . . . . . . . . . . . . . . . . . None |
| Max Allowable Air Bleed. . . . . . . . . . . . .5% of total | Max Rated Turb Outlet Temp/SLS . . . . . . . 1230°F |
| Max Rated Airflow/SLS . . . . . . . . . . . . . 157.8 lb/sec | Max Allowable Turb Outlet Temp . . . . . . . . 1240°F |
| Combustion Chamber . . . . . . . Cannular, 10 thru-flow | Exhaust Nozzle. . . . . . . . . . . . . . . . . . . .Variable area |

## Performance

### Performance Ratings at Standard Sea Level Static Conditions

| RATING (estimated) | THRUST (lb) | RPM | SFC (lb/hr/lb) | MEAS. EGT (° F) | AIRFLOW (lb/sec) |
|---|---|---|---|---|---|
| Max (5 min.) | 10,200 | 6,175 | 0.920 | 1,230 | 157.8 |
| Normal (continuous) | 8,090 | 5,950 | 0.885 | 990 | 153.1 |
| 90% Normal | 7,280 | 5,865 | 0.845 | | 150.9 |
| 75% Normal | 6,070 | 5,760 | 0.845 | | 148.2 |
| Idle | 582 | 3,350 min. | 3.093 est. | | |

## Size and Weight

| | |
|---|---|
| Length, Overall. . . . . . . . . . . . . . . . . . . . . . . . 191.4 in | Weight, Dry . . . . . . . . . . . . . . . . . . . . . . . . . . 4,090 lb |
| Diameter, Nominal . . . . . . . . . . . . . . . . . . . . . 39.5 in | |
| Height (across gearbox . . . . . . . . . . . . . . . . . 47.7 in | |

## Applications

Used (2 engines each) in the B-66A, B, C, and D Series Bomber Aircraft.

**B-66**
*(Photo courtesy of U.S. Air Force Museum)*

**B-66**
*(Photo courtesy of U.S. Air Force Museum)*

# J71

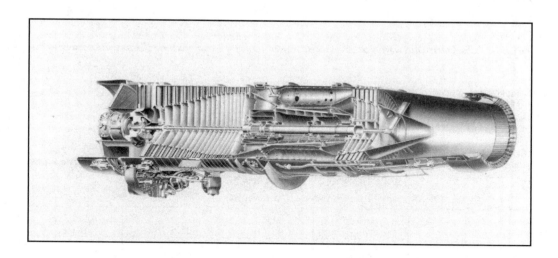

# J73

**General Electric**

## Comments

The J73 turbojet engine was a post-Korean conflict improvement of the J47, providing almost 50 percent more thrust.

## Features

Compressor . . . . . . . . . . . . . . . . . . . . . . Axial, 12-stage
   Max Des Pressure Ratio/SLS . . . . . . . . . . . . . . . 7:1
Combustion Chamber . . . . . . . . . . Annular walls with
   10 cylindrical inner liners
Turbine . . . . . . . . . . . . . . . . . . . . . . . . . Axial, 2-stage
Exhaust Nozzle . . . . . . . . . . . . . . . . . . . . . Fixed area

## Performance

Performance Ratings at Standard Sea Level Static Conditions for J73-3E

| RATING | THRUST (lb) | RPM | SFC (lb/hr/lb) | AIRFLOW (lb/sec) |
|---|---|---|---|---|
| Maximum (5 min) | 8,920 | 7,950 | 0.917 | |
| Military (30 min) | 8,920 | 7,950 | 0.917 | |
| Normal (continuous) | 7,820 | 7,650 | 0.884 | |
| Normal | 5,865 | 7,150 | 0.858 | |
| Idle | 600 | 3,600 | | 83.3 |

## Size and Weight

Length, Overall . . . . . . . . . . . . . . . . . . . . . . . 147.2 in     Weight, Dry . . . . . . . . . . . . . . . . . . . . . . . . . 3,650 lb
Diameter Nominal . . . . . . . . . . . . . . . . . . . . . 36.8 in
Max Radial Projection . . . . . . . . . . . . . . . . . . . 29.0 in

## Applications

Used in the F-86H fighter.

**North American F-86H Sabre**

**North American F-86H Sabre**

# J73

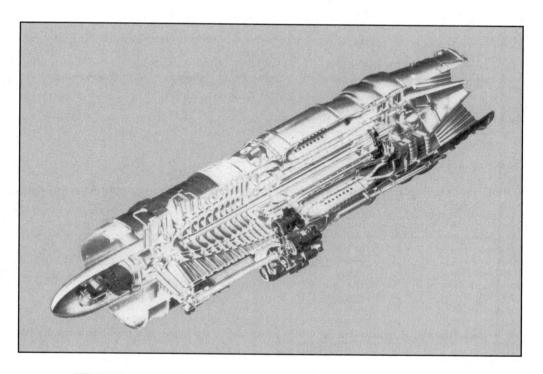

# J75

**Pratt & Whitney**

## Comments

The J75-P-19W is the same as the J75-P-19 except that it incorporates a standard water injection system for takeoff at air temperatures above 40° F. Like the J75-P-19, the low-pressure compressor contains some titanium alloy parts. Other versions include the J75-5, -9, and -17.

## Features

Compressor . . . . . . . . . . Compound, two-spool axial
   Max Design Pressure Ratio/SLS . . . . . . . . . . . 11.9:1
   Max Rated Airflow . . . . . . . . . . . . . . . . . 252 lb/sec
Turbine . . . . . . . . . . . . . . . . . . . . . . . . . Axial, 3-stage
   Max Rated Turb Inlet Temp . . . . . . . . . . . 1,610° F
Exhaust Nozzle . . . . . . . . . Two position, convergent

Fuel . . . . . . . . . . . . . . . . . . . . . . . . . . . JP-4, MIL-J-5624
Oil . . . . . . . . . . . . . . . . . . . . . Synthetic, MIL-L-7808
Ignition . . . . . . . . . . . . . . . .High energy, capacitor type
Power Control . . . . . . . . . . . . . . . . Hydromechanical

## Performance

Performance Ratings at Standard Sea Level Static Conditions for J75-19W

| RATING | THRUST (lb) | RPM (LP/HP) | SFC (lb/hr/lb) | AIRFLOW (lb/sec) |
|---|---|---|---|---|
| Maximum (5 min) | 24,500 | 6,400/8,990 | 2.150 | |
| Normal | 14,300 | 6,080/8,750 | 0.790 | |
| 90% Normal | 12,900 | 5,830/8,575 | 0.770 | |
| 75% Normal | 10,700 | 5,470/8,300 | 0.760 | |
| Idle | 1,150 | 2,750/5,950 | 1.800 | 83.3 |

## Size and Weight

Length. . . . . . . . . . . . . . . . . . . . . . . . . . . . . . 259.3 in
Diameter . . . . . . . . . . . . . . . . . . . . . . . . . . . 43.0 in
Max Radial Projection. . . . . . . . . . . . . . . . . . . 29.3 in

Weight, Dry . . . . . . . . . . . . . . . . . . . . . . . . . . 5,950 lb

## Applications

Used in the F-105D and F fighter.

**F-105**

# J75

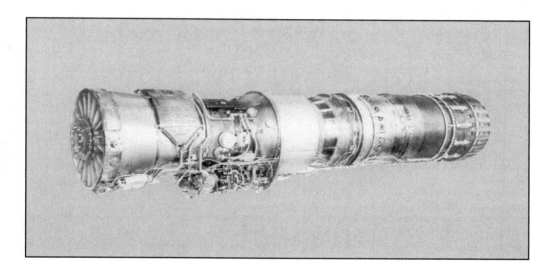

# J79

**General Electric**

## Comments

The J79 was America's first Mach 2 jet engine. It features a high-pressure-ratio, single-rotor compressor with variable inlet guide vanes and six stages of variable stator vanes, a cannular combustor, a high-inlet-temperature three-stage turbine, a third-stage turbine blade guard over the upper half of the turbine casing, and a high-augmentation-ratio afterburner with a variable-area, guided-expansion, convergent-divergent jet exhaust nozzle. Data that follow represent the J79-17. Other versions include the J79-1, -3, -3A, -5, -5A, -7, -8B-D, -10, -10A, -10B, -17A, and -17C.

## Features

Compressor . . . . . . . . . . . . . . . . . . . . . . . . . . . . Axial
   Max Design Pressure Ratio/SLS . . . . . . . . . . 13.5:1
Combustion Chamber . . . . . . . . . . . . . . Annular outer
Turbine . . . . . . . . . . . . . . . . . . . . . . . . . . Axial, 3-stage
Exhaust Nozzle . . . . . Variable, 39.06 in. diameter, C-D
Thrust to Weight ratio . . . . . . . . . . . . . . . . . . . . 4.67:1

## Performance

Performance Ratings at Standard Sea Level Static Conditions

| RATING | THRUST (lb) | RPM | SFC (lb/hr/lb) | MEAS. EGT (°F) | AIRFLOW (lb/sec) |
|---|---|---|---|---|---|
| Maximum AB (30 min) | 17,820 | 7,460 | 1.965 | 1,240 | 170.0 |
| Military (30 min) | 11,810 | 7,460 | 1.240 | 1,240 | 170.0 |
| Normal (continuous) | 11,100 | 7,385 est | 0.810 | | 169.0 |
| 75% Normal | 8,330 | 6,900 est | 0.760 | | |
| Idle | 390 max | 5,000 est | | | 83.3 |

## Size and Weight

Length, Overall. . . . . . . . . . . . . . . . . . . . . . . 208.69 in
Diameter, Nominal . . . . . . . . . . . . . . . . . . . . 39.06 in
Max Radial Projection. . . . . . . . . . . . . . . . . . . 28.16 in

Weight, Dry . . . . . . . . . . . . . . . . . . . . . . . . . . 3,835 lb
Weight, Wet. . . . . . . . . . . . . . . . . . . . . . . . . . 3,850 lb

## Applications

Used in the A-5, B-58, F-4, and F-104.

**B-58 Hustler**

**McDonnell Douglas F-4E Phantom**

# J79

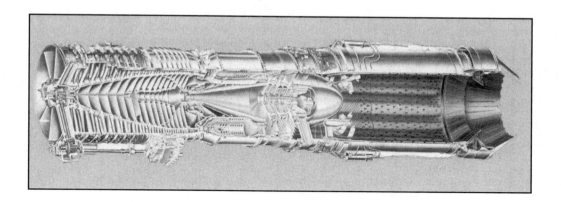

# J85

**General Electric**

## Comments

The J85-GE-21 is a compact, high thrust, lightweight, afterburning turbojet comprised of a nine-stage, lightweight, axial compressor coupled directly to a high-performance two-state turbine. It incorporates variable inlet guide vanes plue three variable stator stages, a through-flow, annular combustion system, and an afterburner with a variable-area exhaust nozzle. The -21A designation is assigned to engines whose configuration meets the requirements of 400-hour periodic inspection intervals. Other versions of the engine include the J85-4, -4A, -4B, -5A-K, 7, -13A-D, -15, -17, -17A, -17B, and -21B.

## Features

Compressor . . . . . . . . . . . .Axial, single rotor, 9-stage
  Max Design Pressure Ratio/SLS . . . . . . . . . . .8.3:1
Combustion Chamber. . . . . . . . . .Annular, thru-flow
                                      single chamber
Turbine. . . . . . . . . . . . . . .Axial, single rotor, 2-stage

Exhaust Nozzle . . . . . . . . . . . . . .Convergent, variable
Thrust to Weight ratio . . . . . . . . . . . . . . . . . . . . .7.3:1

## Performance

### Performance Ratings at Standard Sea Level Static Conditions

| RATING | THRUST (lb) | RPM | SFC (lb/hr/lb) | MEAS. EGT (°F) | AIRFLOW (lb/sec) |
|---|---|---|---|---|---|
| Maximum (Reheat) | 5,000 | 16,600 | 2.13 | 1,345 | 53.0 |
| Intermediate (military) | 3,500 | 16,600 | 1.00 | 1,345 | 53.0 |
| Max Cont (Normal) | 3,280 | 16,400 | 0.99 | 1,295 | 52.3 |
| 75% Normal | 2.46 | | 0.96 | | |
| Idle | 210 max | | 575 lb/hr | | |

## Size and Weight

Length, Overall. . . . . . . . . . . . . . . . . . . . . . . . . .115.7 in
Diameter, Nominal . . . . . . . . . . . . . . . . . . . . . .20.2 in
Max Radial Projection. . . . . . . . . . . . . . . . . . . .15.7 in

Weight, Dry. . . . . . . . . . . . . . . . . . . . . . . . . . . . . .684 lb
Weight, Wet . . . . . . . . . . . . . . . . . . . . . . . . . . . . .692 lb

## Applications

Used in the F-5A through F-5F, and the T-38.

**F-5B**

*(Photo courtesy of U.S. Air Force Museum)*

**F-5E**

*(Photo courtesy of U.S. Air Force Museum)*

# J85

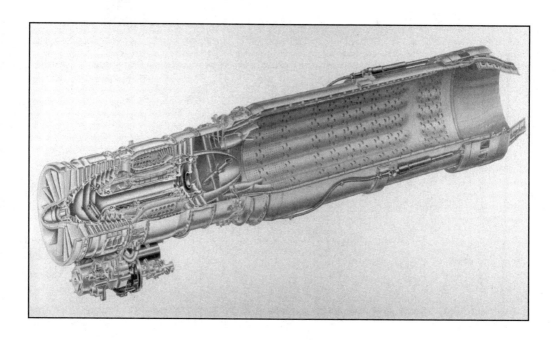

# J93

**General Electric**

## Comments

The J93, capable of continuous Mach 3 cruise and continuous afterburning, carries forward the proven high Mach concept of variable compressor stators and simple, three-main-bearing design.

## Features

Compressor.......................Axial, 11-stage
   Max Des Pressure Ratio/SLS: ..............8.7:1
Combustion Chamber ...................Annular
Turbine .........................Axial, 2-stage
Exhaust Nozzle.............Convergent-Divergent

## Performance

Performance Ratings at Standard Sea Level Static Conditions

| RATING | THRUST (lb) | | RPM | SFC (lb/hr/lb) |
|---|---|---|---|---|
| Maximum (continuous) | 28,000 (A/B) | | 6,825 | 2.00 |
| Military (continuous) | 19,900 | | 6,825 | 1.08 |
| Normal (continuous) | 17,700 | | 6,825 | 1.03 |
| 75% Normal | 13,200 | | | 0.96 |
| Idle | | 1,250 | 4,160 | |

## Size and Weight

Length, Overall.........................236.3 in
Diameter Nominal .......................54.2 in
Max Radial Projection....................32.4 in

Weight, Dry.............................5220 lb

## Applications

Used to power the North American XB-70 Valkyrie supersonic bomber.

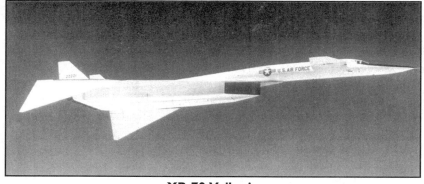

**XB-70 Valkyrie**

# J93

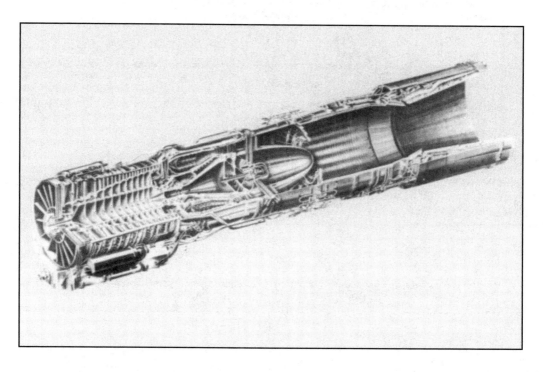

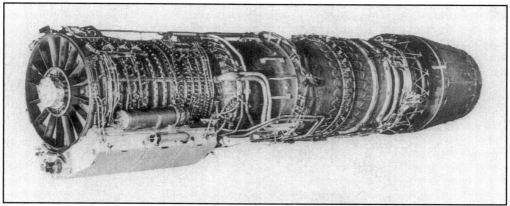

# J97

**General Electric**

## Comments

A derivative of the GE1 "core engine," the J97-GE-100 is an advanced, lightweight, high thrust-to-weight-ratio turbo-jet offering low specific fuel consumption.

## Features

| | |
|---|---|
| Compressor . . . . . . . . . . . . . . . . . . . . . Axial, 14-stage | Turbine Entry Gas Temp . . . . . . . . . . . . . . . . 2,000°F |
| Max Mass Flow . . . . . . . . . . . . . . . . . . . . . . . 70 lb/sec | Jet Pipe . . . . . . . . . . . . . . . . . . . . . . . . . . . . . Fixed area |
| Combustion Chamber . . . . .Annular, straight-through, 16 vaporizing burners | |
| Turbine . . . . . . . . . . . . . . . . . . . . . . .Axial, 2-stage, air-cooled guide vanes | |

## Performance

Performance Ratings at Standard Sea Level Static Conditions for J97-100

RATING

Unaugmented. . . . . . . . . . . . . . . . . . . . . . . . . . 5,270 lb
Augmented . . . . . . . . . . . . . . . . . . . . . 7,000-10,000 lb

## Size and Weight

| | |
|---|---|
| Length. . . . . . . . . . . . . . . . . . . . . . . . . . . . . 109.5 in | Weight, Dry. . . . . . . . . . . . . . . . . . . . . . . . . . . 694 lb |
| Diameter . . . . . . . . . . . . . . . . . . . . . . . . . . 24.4 in | |

## Applications

The J97-GE-100 engine powers the Boeing YQM-94A Compass Cope RPV.

**YQM-94A Compass Cope**

# J97

ENGINE PHOTO UNAVAILABLE

# J400

**Williams International**

## Comments

The J400-WR-404 turbojet incorporates an axial-flow inlet, an axial-centrifugal two-stage compressor, an annular combustor and a single-stage, axial-flow turbine. The YJ400-400, -401, -402, and -403 are other versions of the engine.

## Features

| | |
|---|---|
| Compressor. . . . . . . . . . . . . . . . . . . . . . . Single-spool | Max Allowable Air Bleed . . . . . . . . . . . . . . . . . . . < 0.1 |
|   LP Rotor . . . . . . . . . . . . . . . . . . . . . . . . . . 2-stage | Max Rated Airflow/SLS. . . . . . . . . . . . . . . . 4.1 lb/sec |
| Max Design Pressure Ratio/SLS: | Combustion Chamber . . . . . . . . . . . . . . . . . Annular |
|   LP Rotor. . . . . . . . . . . . . . . . . . . . . . . . . . . . 1.5:1 | Turbine . . . . . . . . . . . . . . . . . . . . . . . . . . Single-rotor |
|   Overall . . . . . . . . . . . . . . . . . . . . . . . . . . . . 5.8:1 | Turbine Cooling. . . . . . . . . . . . . . . . . . . . . . . . None |

## Performance

Performance Ratings at Standard Sea Level Static Conditions

| RATING | THRUST (lb) | RPM | SFC (lb/hr/lb) | MEAS. EGT (°F) | AIRFLOW (lb/sec) |
|---|---|---|---|---|---|
| Maximum Continuous | 240 | 52,000 | 1.20 | 1,390 | 4.1 |
| Idle | 95 | 42,000 | 1.38 | 980 | |

## Size and Weight

| | |
|---|---|
| Length, Overall. . . . . . . . . . . . . . . . . . . . . . . . . 37.4 in | Weight, Dry. . . . . . . . . . . . . . . . . . . . . . . . . . . 46 lb |
| Diameter, Nominal . . . . . . . . . . . . . . . . . . . . 11.8 in | Weight, Wet. . . . . . . . . . . . . . . . . . . . . . . . . 46.5 lb |
| Max Radial Projection. . . . . . . . . . . . . . . . . . . . 9.2 in | |

## Applications

Used in the Northrop Target BQM-74C.

**BQM-74C**

# J400

# J402

**Teledyne CAE**

## Comments

The J402-CA-400 has a single-entry inlet, a two-stage compressor section consisting of a transonic axial stage and a centrifugal stage, an annular combustor, and a single-stage, axial turbine. This engine features a minimum frontal profile, compactness of components and accessories, high reliability, low cost and unusually high tolerance for distorted inlet air flows. The J402-700 is another version.

## Features

Compressor............Single axial plus centrifugal
Max Design Pressure Ratio.................. 5.3:1
Combustion Chamber ................... Annular
Turbine .......................... Axial, 1-stage
Turbine Cooling......................... None
Exhaust Nozzle ................... Straight, fixed
Thrust to Weight Ratio .................... 6.5:1

## Performance

Performance Ratings at Standard Sea Level Static Conditions

| RATING | THRUST (lb) | RPM | SFC (lb/hr/lb) | MEAS. EGT (°F) | AIRFLOW (lb/sec) |
|---|---|---|---|---|---|
| Max | 660 | 41,200 | 1.20 | 1,550 | 9.6 ± 3% |
| Cruise | 471 | 40,025 | 1.52 | | |

## Size and Weight

Length, Overall......................... 29.4 in
Diameter, Nominal ..................... 12.5 in
Max Radial Projection.................... 12.5 in

Weight, Dry ........................... 100.5 lb

## Applications

J402 engine variants are used in the Navy Harpoon Missile (J402-400) and the Beech MQM-107 (J402-700).

**Harpoon**

**MQM-107**

# J402

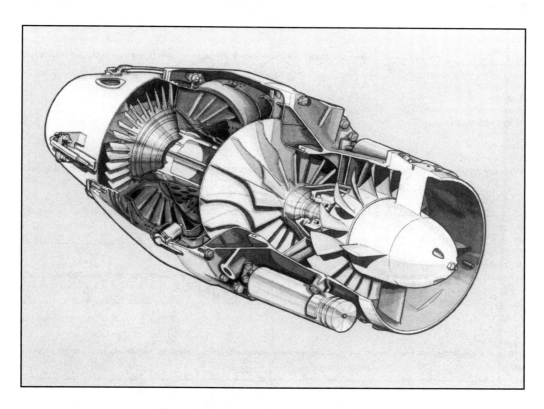

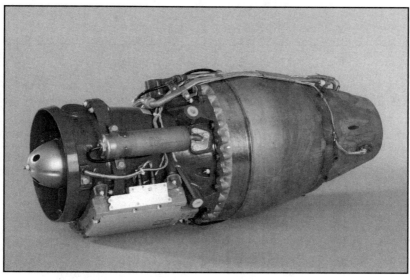

# T31

**General Electric**

## Comments

The T31 (TG-100A) was America's first turboprop engine.

## Features

Compressor . . . . . . . . . . . . . . . . . . . . . Axial, 14-stage
Max Des Pressure Ratio/SLS . . . . . . . . . . . . . . . . . 6:1
Combustion Chamber . . . . . . . . . . . . . . . 9-chamber,
external-annular
Turbine . . . . . . . . . . . . . . . . . . . . . . . . Axial, 1-stage
Exhaust Nozzle . . . . . . . . . . . . . . . . Outer/fixed inner

## Performance

### Performance Ratings at Standard Sea Level Static Conditions

| RATING | THRUST (lb) | RPM (lb/hr) | SHP |
|---|---|---|---|
| Take-Off (static) | 600 | 13,000 | 2,200 |
| Military (static) | | 13,000 | 2,430 ehp |

## Size and Weight

Length . . . . . . . . . . . . . . . . . . . . . . . . . . . . . 113.0 in
Diameter . . . . . . . . . . . . . . . . . . . . . . . . . . . 37.0 in
Frontal Area . . . . . . . . . . . . . . . . . . . . . . . . 7.5 sq ft

Weight, Dry . . . . . . . . . . . . . . . . . . . . . . . . . . 2,000 lb

## Applications

Used in the OV-1A and -1C Army Fixed Wing Aircraft, XP-81 (+J33), XC-113, and XF2R.

**Ryan XF2R-1**

**Consolidated Vultee XP-81**
*(Photo courtesy of U.S. Air Force Museum)*

# T31

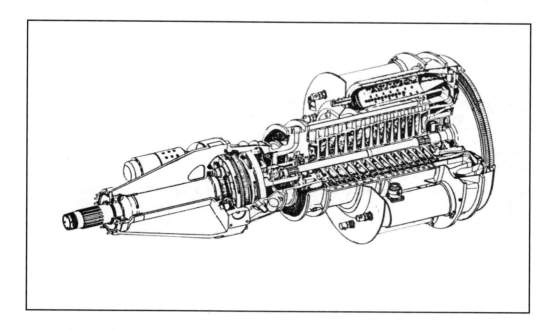

# T34

**Pratt & Whitney**

## Comments

The T34-P-7WA is a single-unit, high-pressure, axial-flow turboprop engine. The propeller reduction gear is flexibly coupled to the front of the compressor shaft and the compressor and turbine are rigidly coupled at the rear of the compressor case. The T34-P-7WA differs from other T34 versions in that it has an increased-capacity thrust bearing and, like the -7W, features a wide-chord turbine enabling better altitude performance, and coolant injection to maintain standard day takeoff rating up to 100°F ambient temperature. The T34-9W is another version of the engine.

## Features

Compressor. . . . . . . . . .Axial, 13-stage, constant I.D.
Turbine . . . . . . . . . . . . . . . . . . . . . . . . . Axial, 3-stage
Exhaust Nozzle. . . . . . . . . . . . . . . . . . . . . Fixed area
Max Design Pressure Ratio/SLS . . . . . . . . . . . . . 6.7:1

## Performance

Performance Ratings at Standard Sea Level Static Conditions for T34-7WA

| RATING | RPM | SHP | JET THRUST (lb) | FUEL CONS. (lb/hr) |
|---|---|---|---|---|
| Take-Off (5 min) | 11,000 | 6,500 | 1,250 | 4,130 |
| Military (30 min) | 11,000 | 5,300 | 1,250 | 3,685 |
| Normal (continuous) | 10,750 | 4,750 | 1,125 | 3,405 |
| Cruise (80% normal) | 10,500 | 3,800 | 1,000 | 2,940 |
| Cruise (60% normal) | 10,400 | 2,850 | 875 | |

## Size and Weight

Length. . . . . . . . . . . . . . . . . . . . . . . . . . . . . . . . . 156.8 in
Max Diameter . . . . . . . . . . . . . . . . . . . . . . . . 33.75 in

Weight, Dry . . . . . . . . . . . . . . . . . . . . . . . . . . . . 2,670 lb

## Applications

Used in the C-133A Cargo Aircraft.

**Douglas C-133A**

**Douglas C-133A**

# T34

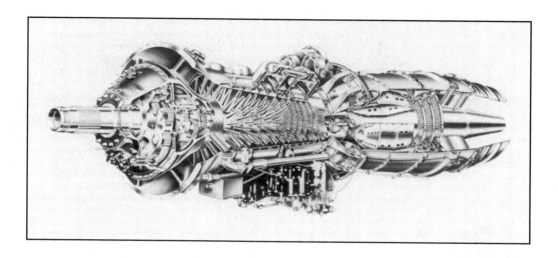

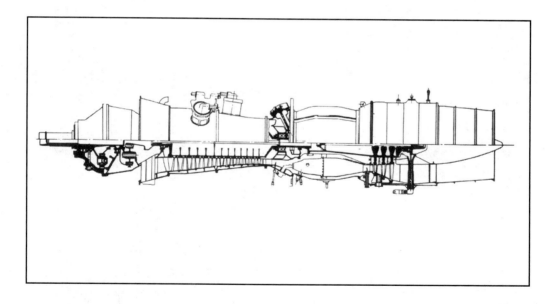

# T53

**Lycoming**

## Comments

The T53-L-11D is a turboshaft engine comprised of a single-stage free type power turbine, a single-stage gas generator turbine driving a combination axial-centrifugal compressor with interstage bleed and an external annular vaporizing combustion chamber. The reduction gear is housed with the air inlet housing and reduces power turbine speed to output shaft speed. The T53-L-11D incorporates an improved reduction gear assembly and larger output shaft spline. Other versions include the T53-1A, 1B, 3, 5, 7, 9, 9A, 9B, 11, 11A, 13, 13A, and 13B.

## Features

| | |
|---|---|
| Compressor . . . . . . . . . . . . . . Combination, 6-stage | Combustion Chamber . . . . . . . . Annular, reverse-flow |
| (axial, 5-stage; centrifugal, 1-stage) | Turbine . . . . . . . . . . . . . . . . . . . . . . . . Axial, 2-stage |
| Max Design Pressure Ratio/SLS . . . . . . . . . . . . . 6.0:1 | Turbine Cooling. . . . . . . . . . . . . . . . . . . . . . . None |
| Max Allowable Airbleed. . . . . . . . . . . . . . . . . . 4.0% | Exhaust Nozzle . . . . . . . . . . . . . .Fixed area, 203 sq in |
| Maximum Airflow . . . . . . . . . . . . . . . . . . . 12.0 lb/sec | Power Control . . . . . . . . . . . . . . . . Hydromechanical |

## Performance

Performance Ratings at Standard Sea Level Static Conditions for T53-11D

| RATING | THRUST (lb) | RPM (Engine) | SHP | MEAS. GAS TEMP (°F) | SFC (lb/hr/shp) |
|---|---|---|---|---|---|
| Maximum Cont Intermediate (Military) 90% Maximum Cont | 115 | 24,220 | 1,000 | 1,110 | 0.690 |
| | 124 | 24,770 | 1,100 | | 0.682 |
| | 107 | 23,670 | 900 | | 0.702 |
| 75% Maximum Cont | 93 | 22,900 | 750 | | 0.738 |
| Ground Idle (max) | 15 | 11,110 | 35 | | 140 lb/hr |

## Size and Weight

| | |
|---|---|
| Length, Overall. . . . . . . . . . . . . . . . . . . . . . . . . 47.6 in | Weight, Dry. . . . . . . . . . . . . . . . . . . . . . . . . .502 lb |
| Diameter . . . . . . . . . . . . . . . . . . . . . . . . . . . . 23.7 in | |
| Max Radial Projection. . . . . . . . . . . . . . . . . . . .13.3 in | |

## Applications

Used in the Army UH-1/-1E Utility and the NUH-1E Iroquois Special Test Helicopter.

**Army UH-1 Utility**

**NUH-1E Iroquois**

# T53

# T55

**Lycoming**

## Comments

The T55-L-7 incorporates a 2-stage, free-type power turbine, a combination axial-centrifugal compressor driven by a single stage turbine, and an external-annular reverse flow vaporizing combustion chamber. The power turbine shaft is located concentrically inside the compressor shaft and the power output shaft is located at the compressor inlet plane. The output speed is equal to the power turbine speed. Same as the T55-L-5 except for refinements and improved performance.

## Features

Compressor. . . . . . . . . . . . . . . Combination, 8-stage,
(axial, 7-stage; centrifugal, 1-stage)
Max Design Pressure Ratio/SLS . . . . . . . . . . . . . 6.6:1
Combustion Chamber . . . . . . . . . . . . Single chamber,
external-annular

Turbine . . . . . . . . . . . . . . . . . . . . . . . . Axial, 3-stage
(1st stage drives compressor;
2nd and 3rd stages drive output shaft)
Exhaust Nozzle. . . . . . . . . . . . . .Fixed Area, 384 sq in

## Performance

Performance Ratings at Standard Sea Level Static Conditions for T55-7

| RATING | RPM | THRUST (lb) | SHP | FUEL CONS (lb/hr) |
|---|---|---|---|---|
| Maximum (10 min) | 19,280 | 237 | 2,650 | 1,631 |
| Military (30 min) | 18,910 | 225 | 2,500 | 1,538 |
| Normal (cont.) | 18,160 | 200 | 2,200 | 1,368 |
| Cruise (90% norm shp) | 17,600 | 182 | 1,980 | 1,271 |
| Cruise (75% norm shp) | 16,750 | 158 | 1,650 | 1,119 |

## Size and Weight

Length. . . . . . . . . . . . . . . . . . . . . . . . . . . . . . .44.03 in
Diameter . . . . . . . . . . . . . . . . . . . . . . . . . . .24.25 in
Max Radial Projection. . . . . . . . . . . . . . . . . .14.16 in

Weight, Dry. . . . . . . . . . . . . . . . . . . . . . . . . . .580 lb

## Applications

Used in the Army CH-47A Helicopter.

**CH-47 Chinook**

**CH-47 Chinook**

# T55

# T56

**Allison**

## Comments

The T56-A-15 consists of an internal combustion gas turbine power section connected by extension shafting and a supporting structure to a single reduction gear assembly having a single shaft offset above the power section center-line. The power section has six thru-flow combustion chambers assembled within a single annular chamber, and in-corporates a 14-stage axial flow compressor directly coupled to a 4-stage axial turbine. The -15 is basically a -7 incorporating an air-cooled turbine assembly for improved performance. Higher turbine inlet temperature and stalk type turbine blade improve endurance. Other versions include the T56-7, 8, 8A, 8B, 9B-D, 10W, 10WA, 14, 16, 423, 425A, 426, and 427.

## Features

Compressor . . . . . . . . . . . . . . . . . . . . .Axial, 14-stage
Max Design Comp. Ratio (SLS). . . . . . . . . . . . .9.55:1
Combustion Chamber . . Annular, single 6 inner liners

Turbine . . . . . . . . . . . . . . . . . . . . . . . . .Axial, 4-stage
Turbine Cooling. . . . . . . . . . . . . . . . .1st stage vanes
   and blades
Exhaust Nozzle. . . . . . . . . . . . . . . . . . . . .Fixed area
SHP to Weight Ratio. . . . . . . . . . . . . . . . . . .2.49:1

## Performance

Performance Ratings at Standard Sea Level Static Conditions for T56-15

| RATING (SLS) | THRUST (lb) | RPM (rotor/output) | SFC (lb/hr/shp) | MEAS. GAS TIT °F/°C | AIRFLOW (lb/sec) |
|---|---|---|---|---|---|
| Take-off (5 min.) Military | 797 | 13,820/1,021 | 0.501 | 1,970/1,077 | 32.5 |
| (30 min.) Normal (cont) | 781 | 13,820/1,021 | 0.507 | 1,920/1,049 | 32.5 |
| 90% SHP | 760 | 13,820/1,021 | 0.517 | 1,850/1,010 | 32.5 |
| 75% SHP | 730 | 13,820/1,021 | 0.533 | 1,754/957 | 32.5 |
| | 686 | 13,820/1,021 | 0.565 | 1,610/877 | 32.5 |

## Size and Weight

Length, Overall. . . . . . . . . . . . . . . . . . . . . .145.979 in
Width . . . . . . . . . . . . . . . . . . . . . . . . . . . . .27.250 in
Height. . . . . . . . . . . . . . . . . . . . . . . . . . . . .41.380 in

Weight, Dry . . . . . . . . . . . . . . . . . . . . . . . . .1,844 lb

## Applications

The T56-15 is used in variations of the C-130 aircraft.

**Lockheed C-130 Hercules**

**Lockheed C-130 Hercules**

# T56

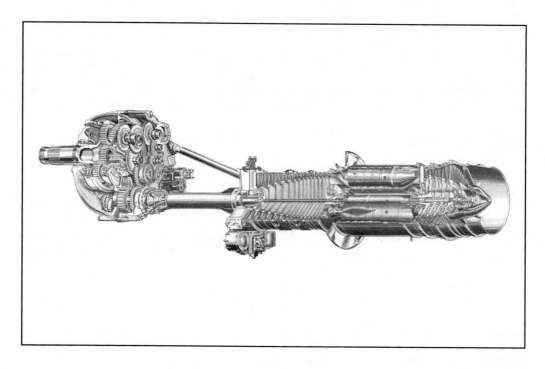

# T58

**General Electric**

## Comments

The T58-GE-402 turboshaft is converted from the T58-GE-10 model. It features an axial flow compressor, a free-type turbine, high power-to-weight ratio, small size, integrated controls tailored for helicopter application, turbine bucket guard, a safety shield, shrouded fuel and oil lines, a three position exhaust, and spray shields. Versions of the engine include the T58-1, 5, 8B, 8C, 8E, 8F, 10, 16, 100, 400, and 400B.

## Features

Compressor . . . . . . . . . . . . . . . . . . . . . . Axial, 10-stage
Max Des Pressure Ratio/SLS . . . . . . . . . . . . . . . 8.4:1
Combustion Chamber . . . . . . . . . . . . . Annular, single
Turbine . . . . . . . . . . . . . . . . . . . . . . . . . Axial, 3-stage
Turbine Cooling . . . . . . . . . . . . . . . . . . . . . . . Partial
Exhaust Nozzle . . . . . . . . . . . . . . . . . . . . . Fixed area

## Performance

Performance Ratings at Standard Sea Level Static Conditions for T58-402

| RATING | OUTPUT (lb-ft) | RPM (lb) | SHP | SFC (lb/hr/shp) | AIRFLOW (lb/sec) |
|---|---|---|---|---|---|
| Maximum (10 min) | 404.0 | 27,200 | 1,500 | 0.61 | 14.0 |
| Military (30 min) Normal | 404.0 | 27,200 | 1,500 | 0.61 | 13.7 |
| (cont) | 366.3 | 26,700 | 1,500 | 0.61 | 13.5 |
| Idle | 37 (max) | 15,400 | | | 13.2 |

## Size and Weight

Length . . . . . . . . . . . . . . . . . . . . . . . . . . . . . 58.51
Maximum Width . . . . . . . . . . . . . . . . . . . . . . . 18.7 in
Maximum Height . . . . . . . . . . . . . . . . . . . . . 20.23 in

Weight, Dry . . . . . . . . . . . . . . . . . . . . . . . . . . . . 345 lb

## Applications

The T58-402 has several applications including the CH-46D/-46F Cargo/Transport, UH-46D Sea Knight Utility, SH-3D/-3H Sea King Anti-Submarine Helicopter, and the VH-3D Sea King Staff Helicopter.

**Boeing Vertol CH-46**

**Sikorsky VH-3 Presidential**

# T58

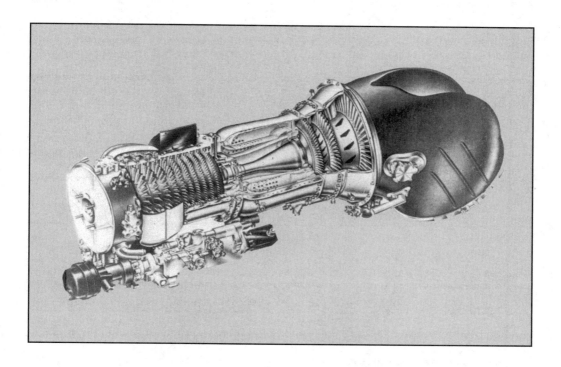

# T60

**Boeing**

## Comments

The T60 (520-6), one of the few engines manufactured by Boeing, is a turboshaft with a single-stage centrifugal compressor, two combustion chambers, single-stage gas generator turbine, and a single-stage free power turbine. Accessories include an electric starter-generator. Other versions of the T60 are the 520-2A, 520-4, and 520-8.

## Features

| | |
|---|---|
| Compressor . . . . . . . . . .2-piece aluminum alloy casing | Control System . . . . . . . . . . . . . . . . . . . . . Mechanical |
| Max Design Pressure Ratio. . . . . . . . . . . . . . . . . 6.5:1 | Fuel Specification . . . . . . . . . . . . . . . . . . . . MIL-J-5616 |
| Air Mass Flow . . . . . . . . . . . . . . . . . . . . . . . . 5.3 lb/sec | Fuel Consumption . . . . . . . . . . . . . . . . . . . 65 lb/shp/hr |
| Turbine . . . . . . . . . . . . . . . . . . . . . . . . . . . . . . . . Axial | Oil Specification . . . . . . . . . . . . . . . . . . . . . MIL-L-7808 |
| Exhaust. . . . . . . . . . . . . . . . . . . . . . . . . . . Fixed area | Oil Consumption . . . . . . . . . . . . . . . . . . . . . .20 lb/hr |

## Performance

Performance Ratings at Standard Sea Level Static Conditions for T60 (520-6)

RATING

| | |
|---|---|
| Military | 550 shp + 35 lbt (11 kgp)/26,000 power turbine rpm/static |
| Max Cont | 500 shp + 32 lbt (10 kgp)/26,000 power turbine rpm/static |

## Size and Weight

| | |
|---|---|
| Length. . . . . . . . . . . . . . . . . . . . . . . . . . . . . . . .55.0 in | Weight. . . . . . . . . . . . . . . . . . . . . . . . . . . . . . . .250 lb |
| Diameter . . . . . . . . . . . . . . . . . . . . . . . . . . . . 25.0 in | Power/Weight Ratio . . . . . . . . . . . . . . . . . 2.20 shp/lb |
| Frontal Area. . . . . . . . . . . . . . . . . . . . . . . . . . 3.4 ft$^2$ | |

## Applications

The T60 is used as a shaft power unit for helicopters.

**AIRCRAFT PHOTO
UNAVAILABLE**

# T60

# T63

**Allison**

## Comments

The T63-A-5A (Allison 250) is an internal combustion turboshaft engine of the free turbine type. The gas producer section is composed of a combination six-stage axial and single-stage centrifugal flow compressor directly coupled to a two-stage gas producer turbine. The power turbine section is composed of a two-stage free turbine which is gas coupled to the gas producer turbine. The engine has a single combustion chamber, and has an air bleed valve at the fifth compressor stage to insure surge free accelerations. The -5A is basically same as the -5 except incorporates design and production type improvements resulting in increased performance.

## Features

Compressor . . . . . . . . . . . . . . . . . . . . . Axial, 6- stage
                                    Centrifugal, 1-stage
Max Design Pressure Ratio/SLS . . . . . . . . . . . . 6.25:1
Combustion Chamber . . . . . . . . . . . . Single chamber
Turbine . . . . . . . . . . . . . . . . . . . . . . . . . . . . . . Axial
            (one 2-stage gas producer turb and
            one 2-stage free-type power turb)

Turbine Cooling. . . . . . . . . . . . . . . . . . . . . . . . None
Exhaust Nozzle . . . . . . . . . . . . . . . . . . . . . Fixed area,
                                    facing upward

## Performance

### Performance Ratings at Standard Sea Level Static Conditions for T63-5A

| RATING | SHP | RPM rotor/output | SFC (lb/hr/hp) | GAS PROD TOT (°F) | AIRFLOW (lb/sec) |
|--------|-----|------------------|----------------|-------------------|------------------|
| Take-Off (30 min.) | 317 | 51,600/6,000 | 0.697 | 1,380 | 3.17 |
| Military (30 min.) | 315 | 51,600/6,000 | 0.697 | 1,380 | 3.17 |
| Normal (cont) | 270 | 49,760/6,000 | 0.706 | 1,280 | 3.04 |
| 90% normal SHP | 243 | 48,650/6,000 | 0.725 | 1,226 | 2.95 |
| 75% normal SHP | 202 | 46,950/6,000 | 0.762 | 1,148 | 2.82 |

## Size and Weight

Length, Overall. . . . . . . . . . . . . . . . . . . . . . . 40.402 in
Height. . . . . . . . . . . . . . . . . . . . . . . . . . . . . 22.500 in
Width . . . . . . . . . . . . . . . . . . . . . . . . . . . . . 19.006 in

Weight, Dry. . . . . . . . . . . . . . . . . . . . . . . . . 136.0 lb.
Weight, Wet . . . . . . . . . . . . . . . . . . . . . . . . 136.5 lb.

## Applications

Used (1 engine each) in the Army OH-6A (Hughes) Light Observation Helicopter.

**OH-6A Helicopter**

# T63

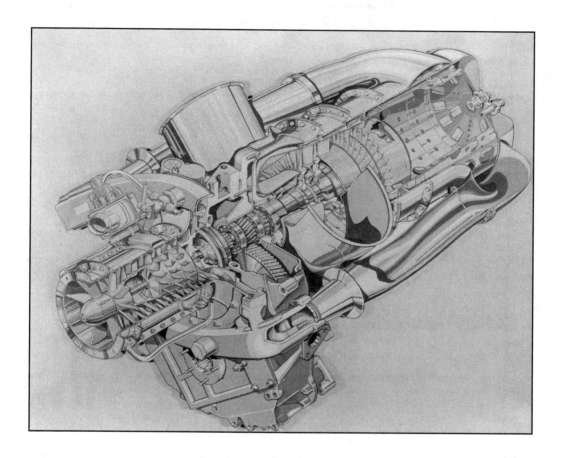

# T64

**General Electric**

## Comments

The T64 production engine family includes both turboshaft and turboprop engines that power both helicopter and fixed-wing aircraft. The compressor is based on J93 technology while the combustor is based on technology derived from the T58. T64 engine versions include the T64-1, 3, 6B, 7, 7A, 10, 14, 413, 413A, 415, 416, 416A, and 419. The following data represents T64-419.

## Features

Compressor . . . . . . . . . . . . . . . . . . . . Axial, 14-stage
Max Des Pressure Ratio/SLS . . . . . . . . . . . . . . . . 14.0
Combustion Chamber . . . . . . . . Annular, through-flow
Turbine . . . . . . . . . . . . . . . . . . . . . . . . Axial, 2-stage
        gas generator, 2-stage power turbine
Turbine Cooling . . . . . . . . . . . . . Air-cooled, 1st-stage
        blades and 1st 2-stage vanes
Exhaust Nozzle . . . . . . . . . . . . . . .Fixed area, 450 sq in

Max Allowable Airbleed . . . . . . . . . 6.5% (Idle-Inter.)
    3% (Inter.-Max.)
Max Gas Generator Airflow (SLS) . . . . . . . 29.4 lb/sec
Max Allow. Pwr Turb Inlet Temp. . . . . . . . (SS) 1525°F
    (Trans) 1540°F
SHP (SLS) to Weight (Dry) Ratio . . . . . . . . . . . . 6.3:1

## Performance

Performance Ratings at Standard Sea Level Static Conditions for T64-419

| RATING | RPM (g.g.) | SHP | SFC (lb/shp-hr) | TORQUE (lb-ft) | OUTPUT (RPM) | MEAS. GAS TEMP (°C) |
|---|---|---|---|---|---|---|
| Maximum (10 min) | 18,370 | 4,750 | 0.474 | 1,747 | 14,280 | 821 |
| Military (30 min) | 18,200 | 4,560 | 0.470 | 1,677 | 14,280 | 801 |
| Maximum Cont | 17,000 | 4,230 | 0.472 | 1,555 | 14,280 | 761 |
| 90% Max Cont  75% Max | | 3,810 | 0.480 | 1,401 | 14,280 | |
| Cont | | 3,170 | 0.500 | 1,166 | 14,280 | |

## Size and Weight

Length. . . . . . . . . . . . . . . . . . . . . . . . . . . . . . 78.8 in
Maximum Height . . . . . . . . . . . . . . . . . . . . . . 32.5 in
Maximum Width. . . . . . . . . . . . . . . . . . . . . . . 26.1 in

Weight, Dry. . . . . . . . . . . . . . . . . . . . . . . . . . .755 lb

## Applications

Used in the CH-53E, MH-53E, Super Sea Stallion Helicopter, Minesweeping, Cargo/Transport (3 engines).

**CH-53E**

**MH-53E**

# T64

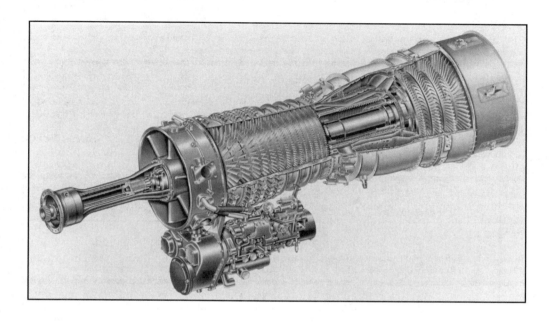

# T65

**Teledyne CAE**

## Comments

The T65-T-1 is a two-shaft turboshaft featuring a hot bleed air anti-icing system and a compressor with an automatic interstage air bleed valve for unloading axial compressor at intermediate speeds.

## Features

| | |
|---|---|
| Compressor . . . . . . . . . . . . . . . . . . . . . . . Axial, 1-stage Centrifugal, 1-stage | Turbine (Gas Generator) . . . . . . . . 1-piece, Air-cooled |
| Pressure Ratio . . . . . . . . . . . . . . . . . . . . . . . . . 6.0:1 | Turbine (Power) . . . . . . . . . . . . . . . 1-piece, 3rd-stage free wheel |
| Air Mass Flow . . . . . . . . . . . . . . . . . . . . . . 3.3 lb/sec | Exhaust . . . . . . . . . . . . . . . . . . . . . . . Fixed, dual ducts |
| Combustion Chamber . . . . . . . . . . . . . . . . . Annular | Reduction Gearbox Ratio . . . . . . . . . . . . . . . . . 6.48:1 |
| | Control System . . . . . . . . . . . . . . . Hydro-mechanical |

## Performance

Performance Ratings at Standard Sea Level Static Conditions for T65-1

RATING

Take-off    335 shp/39,000 power turbine rpm/static
Military    250 shp/39,000 power turbine rpm/SL to 10000 ft. (3050 m)

## Size and Weight

| | |
|---|---|
| Length . . . . . . . . . . . . . . . . . . . . . . . . . . . . 38.7 in | Height . . . . . . . . . . . . . . . . . . . . . . . . . . . . . 19.1 in |
| Frontal Area . . . . . . . . . . . . . . . . . . . . . . . . . 2.2 ft$^2$ | Weight . . . . . . . . . . . . . . . . . . . . . . . . . . . . . 130 lb |
| Width . . . . . . . . . . . . . . . . . . . . . . . . . . . . . 18.2 in | |

## Applications

The T65 is suitable for use in small military and commercial helicopters.

AIRCRAFT PHOTO
UNAVAILABLE

# T65

# T67

**Teledyne CAE**

## Comments

The T67-T-1 is a twin turboshaft comprised of two single-shaft 217-10B engine. Each engine unit is started independently. Overriding clutch enables either one or both engine units to drive the coupling gearbox and common output shaft.

## Features

Compressor . . . . . . . .2-stage axial, 1-stage centrifugal
Pressure Ratio. . . . . . . . . . . . . . . . . . . . . . . . . . . 7.85:1
Air Flow . . . . . . . . . . . . . . . . . . . . . . . . . . . 7.2 lb/sec
Combustion Chamber . . . . . . . . . . . . . . . . . Annular

Turbine (Gas Generator). . . . . . . . . 2-stage, air-cooled
Turbine (Power) . . . . . . . . . . . . . . . . . . . . . . . . 1-stage
Exhaust . . . . . . . . . . . . . . . . . . . . . . . . . . . Fixed area
Power Outlet Ratio. . . . . . . . . . . . . . . . . . . . . . 4.91:1
Control System . . . . . . . . . . . . . . . Hydro-mechanical

## Performance

Performance Ratings at Standard Sea Level Static Conditions for T67-1

RATING
Normal      1,700 shp + 75 lbt (34 kgp)/32,400 power turbine rpm/static
Military    1,540 shp + 63 lbt (28 kgp)/32,400 power turbine rpm/SL to 10,000 ft. (3,050 m)

## Size and Weight

Length. . . . . . . . . . . . . . . . . . . . . . . . . . . . . . . 52.5 in
Frontal area . . . . . . . . . . . . . . . . . . . . . . . . . . 4.6 ft$^2$
Width . . . . . . . . . . . . . . . . . . . . . . . . . . . . . . . 38.0 in

Height. . . . . . . . . . . . . . . . . . . . . . . . . . . . . . . 20.8 in
Weight. . . . . . . . . . . . . . . . . . . . . . . . . . . . . . . 552 lb

## Applications

Used in the Bell 208 (UH-1D) Iroquois helicopter (flight test).

**Bell 208**

# T67

# T72

**Teledyne CAE**

## Comments

The T72-T-2 is a free-turbine turboshaft featuring single-entry ram intake and a hot bleed air anti-icing system.

## Features

| | |
|---|---|
| Compressor . . . . . . . . . . . . . . . . . . . . .Axial, 1-stage | Turbine (Compressor) . . . . . . . . . . . . . . .Axial, 2-stage |
|    Centrifugal, 1-stage | Turbine (Free) . . . . . . . . . . . . . . . . . . . . .Axial, 1-stage |
| Pressure Ratio. . . . . . . . . . . . . . . . . . . . . . . . 6.0:1 | Gas Temperature Before Turbine . . . . . . . . 375°F max |
| Air Mass Flow . . . . . . . . . . . . . . . . . . . . . 5.3 lb/sec | Exhaust . . . . . . . . . . . . . . . . . . . . . . . . . . . Fixed area |
| Combustion Chamber . . . . . . . . . . . . . . . . . Annular | Control System . . . . . . . . . . . . . . . Hydro-mechanical |

## Performance

Performance Ratings at Standard Sea Level Static Conditions for T67-2

RATING

Take-off    500 shp + 50 lbt/35,000 power turbine rpm/static
Military     450 shp + 50 lbt/34,800 power turbine rpm/static

## Size and Weight

| | |
|---|---|
| Length. . . . . . . . . . . . . . . . . . . . . . . . . . . . . 42.5 in | Weight. . . . . . . . . . . . . . . . . . . . . . . . . . . . . . .210 lb |
| Frontal area . . . . . . . . . . . . . . . . . . . . . . . . . 2.0 ft$^2$ | |
| Diameter . . . . . . . . . . . . . . . . . . . . . . . . . . 19.4 in | |

## Applications

Tested in a Republic Lark (Alouette II) helicopter.

**Republic Lark (Alouette II)**

# T72

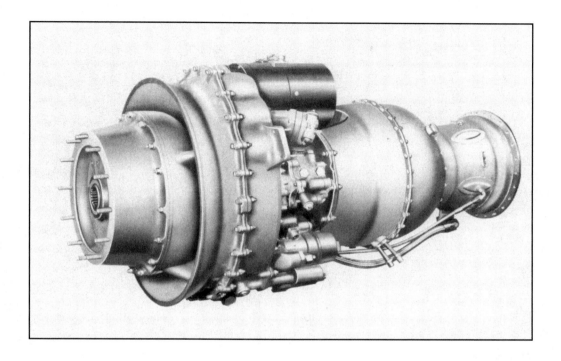

# T76

**Garrett**

## Comments

The (TPE331) T76-G-420 and -421 are single-shaft turboprop engines. Fuel is introduced into a single annular combustion chamber through atomizing fuel nozzles. The combustion products drive a three-stage axial turbine which is shaft coupled to a two-stage centrifugal compressor. The turbine drives an integral reduction gearbox located at the forward end of the engine. The gearbox provides a propeller shaft, a pad for the starter or a starter-generator, and pads for other accessories. The -420 has a clockwise propeller shaft rotation while that of the -421 is counterclockwise when viewed from the rear of the engine. Other versions of the T76 are the T76-410, 410A, 411A, 412, 413, 414, 415, 416, 417, 418, and 419.

## Features

| | | | |
|---|---|---|---|
| Compressor........Centrifugal, 2-stage, Single spool | SHP to Weight Ratio........................ 2.60:1 |
| Max Design Comp. Ratio (SLS)............. 10.7:1 | Max Cont Oil Consumption............ 0.01 gal/hr |
| Combustion Chamber ........Annular, reverse flow | Torquemeter ........................ Electronic |
| Turbine ..........................Axial, 3-stage | Maximum Airflow (SLS)................. 7.7 lb/sec |
| Turbine Cooling..................... Air-cooled | Reduction Gear Ratio .................. 20.865:1 |
|                  1st-stage rotor and stator | Max Allow Calc. Turb In. Temp ............ 2047°F |
| Exhaust Nozzle...................... Fixed area | Max Allow Comp. Turb In. Temp.......... 2027°F |

## Performance

Performance Ratings at Standard Sea Level Static Conditions for T76-421, 421

| RATING | SHP | OUTPUT (LB/FT) | RPM | SFC (lb/hr/shp) | CALC GAS TEMP (°F) |
|---|---|---|---|---|---|
| Military (30 min) | 1,040 | 2,731 | 2,000 | 0.558 | 2,027 |
| Max Cont. (Norm) | 813 | 2,135 | 2,000 | 0.607 | 1,830 |
| 90% Max Cont. | 732 | 1,922 | 2,000 | 0.635 | 1,763 |
| 75% Max Cont. | 609 | 1,600 | 2,000 | 0.691 | 1,663 |
| Idle (Ground) | 123 | 470 | 1,374 | 187 lb/hr | 1,548 |

## Size and Weight

| | |
|---|---|
| Length, Overall......................... 43.21 in | Weight, Dry............................ 400 lb |
| Width ................................ 20.52 in | |
| Height................................ 26.05 in | |

## Applications

The T76 engine is used in variations of the OV-10D Bronco Observation Aircraft.

**OV-10D Bronco**
*(Photo courtesy of U.S. Air Force Museum)*

**OV-10D Bronco**
*(Photo courtesy of U.S. Air Force Museum)*

# T76

# T400

**United Aircraft of Canada**

## Comments

The (PT6T-4) T400-WV-402 is identical in construction and design to the -400 with the exception of changed material for the compressor turbine blades, incorporation of dual orifice fuel nozzles, integral T5 thermocouple harnesses, addition of power turbine overspeed limiters, provision of electrical torque sensor signals, provision for ducting compressor bleed air overboard, replacement of overtemperature limiters by overtemperature indicator signals, deleting of torque sharing controls, and deletion of provision for remote oil quantity indicators. Maximum gas temperature is increased, gearbox torque limits are unchanged and all components are identical compared to the -400 engine. The T400-401 is another version of the engine.

## Features

| | | | |
|---|---|---|---|
| Compressor | Single spool | Power Control | Hydromechanical |
| Max Design Pressure Ratio/SLS | 7.7:1 | Fuel | MIL-T-5624, JP-4/5 |
| Max Allowable Air Bleed | 5.25% | Oil | MIL-L-23699/7808 |
| Max Rated Airflow/SLS | 7.0 lb/sec | Max Cont Oil Consumption | 0.04 gal/hr |
| Combustion Chamber | Annular, reverse | Reduction Gear Ratio | 5.0:1 |
| Turbine | Axial | Torquemeter | Hydraulic |
| Max Rated Pwr Turb Inlet Temp | 2020°F | | |

## Performance

Performance Ratings at Standard Sea Level Static Conditions for T400-402

| RATING | THRUST (lb) | RPM Gen./Output | SFC (lb/hr/shp) | MEAS. GAS TEMP (°F) | AIRFLOW (lb/sec) |
|---|---|---|---|---|---|
| Intermediate | 1,568 | 38,400/6,600 | 0.591 | 1,512 | 7.00 |
| Max Cont | 1,331 | 37,400/6,600 | 0.604 | 1,406 | 6.71 |
| 75% Max Cont | 999 | 35,770/6,600 | 0.661 | 1,261 | 6.18 |
| 50% Max Cont | 666 | 33,920/6,600 | 0.792 | 1,132 | 5.64 |
| Idle | 0 | 21,140/6,600 | 288 lb/hr | 815 | 2.89 |

## Size and Weight

| | | | |
|---|---|---|---|
| Length, Overall | 66.26 in | Maximum Height | 32.61 in |
| Inlet Area (Engine) | 3.6 sq ft | Weight, Dry | 750 lb |
| Maximum Width | 43.47 in | | |

## Applications

The T400-402 is used in U.S. Marine AH-IJ and AH-IT attack helicopters and the USAF UH-IN.

**AH-1J Seacobra**

**UH-1N**

*(Photo courtesy of Universal Technology Corporation)*

# T400

# T406

**Allison**

## Comments

The T406-AD-400 is a 6,000 shaft horsepower class free turbine engine. A fourteen-stage axial flow compressor which includes variable-geometry stators on the first six stages is directly coupled to an air-cooled, two-stage turbine. The combustion section includes an annular, convection-film cooled combustor and piloted air-blast fuel nozzles. Forward shaft power is available directly from the two-stage power turbine. An accessory gearbox provides drives for the fuel pump, starter, alternator and pumps. There are four main bearings within the system. The primary lubrication system provides regulated oil pressure, filtering and cooling, dry sump scavenge and low pressure pump venting.

## Features

Compressor . . . . . . . . . . . . . . . . . . . . . Axial, 14-stage
   Max Design Pressure Ratio (SLS) . . . . . . . . . . 14.0
   Max Allowable Airbleed . . . . . . . . . . . . . . . . 8.0%
Max Gas Gen. Airflow (SLS) . . . . . . . . . . 35.50 lb/sec
Combustion Chamber . . . . . . . . . . . . . . . . . Annular

Turbine . . . . . . . . . . . . . . . . . . . . . Axial, Dual Rotor
   Turbine Cooling . . . . . . . . . . . . . . . . . . . . . . . Air
Exhaust Nozzle . . . . . . . . . . . . . . . . . . . . . . . None
Power to Weight Ratio . . . . . . . . . . . . . . . . . . 7.0

## Performance

Performance Ratings at Standard Sea Level Static Conditions for T406-400

| RATING | RPM | SHP | SFC (lb/shp-hr) | TORQUE (lb-ft) | AIRFLOW (lb/sec) | MEAS. GAS Temp (°C) |
|---|---|---|---|---|---|---|
| Maximum Intermediate | 15,114 | 6,150 | 0.405 | 2,153 | 36.7 | 772.9 |
| Max Cont | 15,114 | 6,150 | 0.405 | 2,153 | 36.7 | 772.9 |
| 75% Max Cont | 15,110 | 6,135 | 0.406 | 2,148 | 36.7 | 772.0 |
| 50% Max Cont | 14,571 | 4,504 | 0.433 | 1,855 | 32.9 | 690.0 |
|  | 13,942 | 2,953 | 0.477 | 1,216 | 28.0 | 601.7 |

## Size and Weight

Length, Overall . . . . . . . . . . . . . . . . . . . . . . . 77.06 in
Diameter, Nominal . . . . . . . . . . . . . . . . . . . . 28.00 in
Max Radial Projection . . . . . . . . . . . . . . . . . . 21.90 in

Weight, Dry . . . . . . . . . . . . . . . . . . . . . . . . . 970.5 lb
Weight, Wet . . . . . . . . . . . . . . . . . . . . . . . . . 995.9 lb

## Applications

The T406 is used in the Navy V-22 Osprey.

**V-22 Osprey**

**V-22 Osprey**

# T406

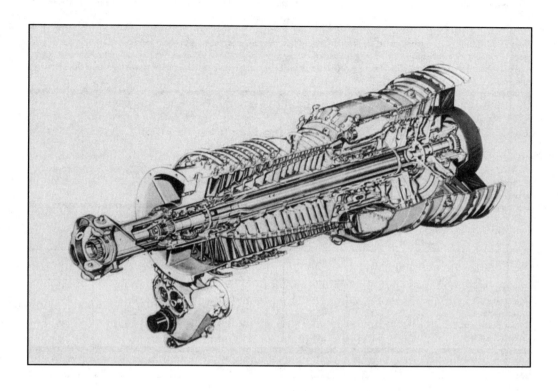

# T700

**General Electric**

## Comments

The T700-GE-401C is a front-drive turboshaft engine featuring an integral inlet particle separator, a single-spool gas generator section consisting of a five-stage axial single-stage centrifugal flow compressor, a through flow annular combustion chamber, a two-stage axial flow gas generator turbine and a free or independent two-stage axial flow power turbine.

## Features

| | |
|---|---|
| Compressor . . . . . . . . . . . . . . . . . . . . . . . Axial, 5-stage | Max Rated Turb In. Temp (SLS) . . . . . . . . . . . 1354°C |
| 1-stage centrifugal, single spool | Turbine . . . . . . . . . . . . . . . . . . . . . . . . . . Axial, 2-stage |
| Max Des Pressure Ratio/SLS . . . . . . . . . . . . . . . . 17.9 | Exhaust Nozzle . . . . . . . . . . . . . . . . . . Fixed area, div |
| Max Allowable Airbleed . . . . . . . . . . . . . . . . . . . . 6.5% | Turbine Cooling . . . . . . . . . . . . . . . . . . . . . Air cooled |
| Combustion Chamber . . . . . . . . . . Annular, thru-flow | SHP (SLS) to Weight . . . . . . . . . . . . . . . . . . . . . 4.24:1 |
| Max Allow SS Turb In. Temp . . . . . . . . . . . . . 1385°C | |

## Performance

Performance Ratings at Standard Sea Level Static Conditions for T700-401C

| RATING | SHP | TORQUE (lb-ft) | RPM (g.g./output) | AIR FLOW (lb/sec) | SFC (lb/shp-hr) | MEAS. GAS TEMP °F |
|---|---|---|---|---|---|---|
| Contingency | 1,940 | 488 | 45,100 | 11.9 | 0.462 | 880 |
| Maximum | 1,890 | 475 | 44,617 | 11.8 | 0.460 | 856 |
| Intermediate | 1,800 | 452 | 44,079 | 11.5 | 0.459 | 828 |
| Maximum Cont | 1,662 | 418 | 43,517 | | 0.459 | 786 |
| 50% Max Cont | 831 | 209 | | | 0.552 | |

## Size and Weight

| | |
|---|---|
| Length . . . . . . . . . . . . . . . . . . . . . . . . . . . . . 46.12 in | Weight, Dry . . . . . . . . . . . . . . . . . . . . . . . . . . . 458 lb |
| Diameter . . . . . . . . . . . . . . . . . . . . . . . . . . . 15.55 in | Weight, Wet . . . . . . . . . . . . . . . . . . . . . . . . . . 478 lb |
| Max Radius . . . . . . . . . . . . . . . . . . . . . . . . . 17.10 in | |

## Applications

Used in the SH-60B Seahawk, LAMPS MARK III (U.S. Navy), SH-60F, CV-HELO, HH-60J Jayhawk, HH-60H, HCS Spanish Navy Seahawk, and SH-60B in Japan and Austria.

**Sikorsky SH-60B
Seahawk**

**Sikorsky HH-60J Jayhawk**

# T700

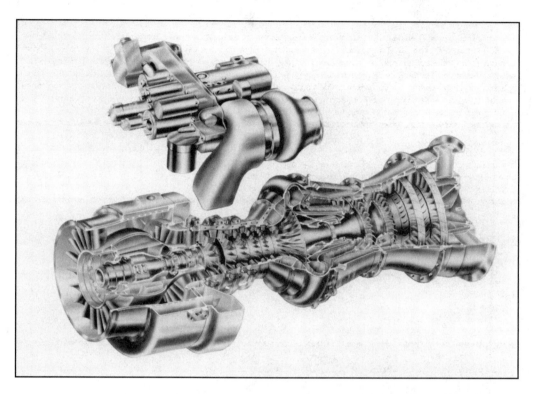

# T800

**LHTEC (Allison and Garrett)**

## Comments

The Light Helicopter Turbine Engine Company is a partnership between Allison and Garrett structured specifically for the T800 program. The T800 turboshaft engine was designed to be the most supportable and maintainable propulsion engine introduced into military/commercial service. Its technology stems from both Garrett's F109 engine and Allison's Advanced Technology Demonstrator Engine (ATDE), and provides unprecedented reliability, tilt-rotor compatibility, and low specific fuel consumption (SFC). In addition, the T800 boasts high power density and performance capability without life or durability sacrifice due to proper selection of materials, cooling techniques, and state-of-the-art electronic control system.

## Features

Compressor . . . . . . . . . . . . . . . . . Centrifugal, 2-stage
Combustion Chamber . . . . . . . . Annular, reverse-flow
Compressor Turbine . . . . . . . . . . . . . . Axial, 2-stage

Turbine Cooling . . . . . . . . . . . . . . . . . . . . . Single-pass
Power Turbine . . . . . . . . . . . . . . . . . . . . Axial, 2-stage
Inlet . . . . . . . . . . . . . . . . . . . . . . . . . . . . . . . . Annular

## Performance

Performance Ratings at Standard Sea Level Static Conditions

| RATING | SHP | FUEL FLOW |
|---|---|---|
| Contingency (2 min.) | 1,399 | 627 lb/h |
| T-O (5 min.) | 1,334 | 600 lb/h |
| Continuous | 1,239 | 563 lb/h |
| T-O  (30 min.) | 1,038 | 486 lb/h |

## Size and Weight

Length . . . . . . . . . . . . . . . . . . . . . . . . . . . . . 33.2 in
Width . . . . . . . . . . . . . . . . . . . . . . . . . . . . . . 21.7 in
Height . . . . . . . . . . . . . . . . . . . . . . . . . . . . . 26.1 in

Weight, Dry . . . . . . . . . . . . . . . . . . . . . . . . . . . . . 315 lb

## Applications

Helicopters – RAH-66 and UH-1H.

**RAH-66 Helicopter**

**UH-1H Helicopter**

# T800

# TF30

**Pratt & Whitney**

## Comments

The TF30 was the world's first afterburning turbofan engine and the first gas turbine qualified for supersonic operation at sea level. Versions include the TF30-P-1, 1A, 3, 6, 6C, 6E, 7, 8, 9, 12, 12A, 100, 408, and 414/414A. Data that follows represents the TF30-P-414/414A.

## Features

| | |
|---|---|
| Compressor . . . . . . . . . . . . . . . . . . . . . . . Dual Rotor | Exhaust Nozzle . . . . . . . . . . . . . . . . . . . . Variable area, |
| LP Rotor . . . . . . . . . . . . . . . . . . . . . Axial, 9-stage, | C-D iris type |
| includes 3 fan stage | Thrust to Weight Ratio . . . . . . . . . . . . . . . . . . . 5.26:1 |
| HP Rotor . . . . . . . . . . . . . . . . . . . . . . Axial, 7-stage | Max Design Pressure Ratio/SLS: |
| Bypass Airflow Ratio . . . . . . . . . . . . . . . . . . . . 0.878:1 | Fan . . . . . . . . . . . . . . . . . . . . . . . . . . . . . . . . . 2.14:1 |
| Combustion Chamber . . . . . . . . . . . . . . Can-annular, | Overall . . . . . . . . . . . . . . . . . . . . . . . . . . . . . . 19.8:1 |
| 8 unit, through-flow | Turbine . . . . . . . . . . . . . . . . . . . . . . . . Axial, 4-stage |
| Power Control . . . . . . . . . . . Hydromechanical main | Turbine Cooling. . . . . . . . . . . . . . . . . . . . Air-cooled |

## Performance

### Performance Ratings at Standard Sea Level Static Conditions

| RATING | THRUST (lb) | RPM (LP/HP Rotor) | SFC (lb/hr/lb) | MEAS. EGT (°F) | AIRFLOW (lb/sec) |
|---|---|---|---|---|---|
| Maximum | 18,800 | 14,780/10,000 | 2.78 | 2,040 | 242.0 |
| Military | 12,350 | 14,800/9,950 | 0.689 | 2,040 | 242.0 |
| Normal (Cont.) | 10,800 | 14,300/9,375 | 0.631 | 1,845 | 234.0 |
| 75% Max Cont. | 8,090 | 13,650/8,550 | 0.574 | 1,640 | 211.5 |
| Idle | 740 max | 8,550/3,650 (min) | 980 lb/hr max | | |

## Size and Weight

| | |
|---|---|
| Length, Overall. . . . . . . . . . . . . . . . . . . . . . 235.48 in | Weight, Dry. . . . . . . . . . . . . . . . . . . . . . . . . . 4176 lb |
| Maximum Diameter . . . . . . . . . . . . . . . . . . . . 51.42 in | |
| Maximum Height . . . . . . . . . . . . . . . . . . . . . 51.78 in | |

## Applications

TF30 versions power the F-14A fighter, JF-14A Tomcat Special Test Aircraft, and various models of the General Dynamics F-111 and the Navy/Vought A-7.

**EF-111A Raven**

**F-14 Tomcat**

# TF30

# TF33

**Pratt & Whitney**

## Comments

Derived from the J57 (JT3C) turbojet, the TF33 (JT3D civil designation) is Pratt & Whitney's first production turbofan engine.. Versions include the TF33-P-3, 3B, 5, 7, 7A, 9, 11, 11A, 100, 100A, 102, and 103. Data that follows represents the TF33-P-103 which is actually the original -3 configuration reidentified.

## Features

Compressor . . . . . . . . . . . . .Compound, 2-spool axial
(LP unit, 8-stage; HP unit, 7-stage)
Max Design Pressure Ratio/SLS:
    Engine. . . . . . . . . . . . . . . . . . . . . . . . . . . . . 1.7:1
    Fan. . . . . . . . . . . . . . . . . . . . . . . . . . . . . . . . 13:1

Turbine . . . . . . . . . . . . . . . . . . . . . . . . .Axial, 4-stage
(1st stage drives HP compressor;
2, 3, and 4 stages drive LP compressor & fan)
Exhaust Nozzle . . . . . . . . . . . . . . . . . . . . .Fixed area
Combustion Chamber . . . . . . . . . . . . .Annular outer,
8-thru flow inner chambers

## Performance

Performance Ratings at Standard Sea Level Static Conditions

| RATING | THRUST (lb) | RPM (LP/HP Rotor) | SFC (lb/hr/lb) | AIRFLOW (lb/sec) |
|---|---|---|---|---|
| Max (5 min) | 17,000 | 6,550/10,050 | 0.520 | 450 |
| Military (30 min) | 16,500 | 6,470/10,000 | 0.520 | 444 |
| Normal (cont) | 14,500 | 6,150/9,750 | 0.505 | 419 |
| 75% Normal Thrust | 10,875 | 5,550/9,310 | 0.495 | 376 |
| Idle | 1,050 (max) | 1,940/5,665(min) | 1.124 | |

## Size and Weight

Length. . . . . . . . . . . . . . . . . . . . . . . . . . . . . 136.32 in
Diameter . . . . . . . . . . . . . . . . . . . . . . . . . . . 53.14 in
Max Radial Projection . . . . . . . . . . . . . . . . . . . . 29.52

Weight, Dry . . . . . . . . . . . . . . . . . . . . . . . . .3,905 lb

## Applications

TF33 versions powers the B-52H bomber, WB-57F reconnaissance aircraft, and various models of C-135, VC-137, C-141, and E-3 aircraft. The JT3D civil engine powers the Boeing 707 and McDonnell Douglas DC-8.

**C-141 Starlifter**

**B-52H Stratofortress**

# TF33

# TF34

**General Electric**

## Comments

The TF34 (CF34 civil designation) is a high bypass turbofan engine with low specific fuel consumption suited for aircraft with extended subsonic cruise mission requirements. Engine versions include the TF34-GE-(AWACS), 2, 2A, 100, 400/400A (converted from TF34-2/2A), and 400B (converted from TF34-400). Data that follows represents the TF34-GE-100.

## Features

| | |
|---|---|
| Compressor . . . . . . . . . . . . . . . . . . . . . . . Dual rotor | Combustion Chamber . . . . . . . . . . . . . . Axial. annular single chamber |
|    LP Rotor . . . . . . . . . . . . . . . . . . . . . Axial, 1-stage | Turbine . . . . . . . . . . . . . . . . . . . . . . . . . Dual Rotor |
|    HP Rotor . . . . . . . . . . . . . . . . . . . . Axial, 14-stage |    LP Rotor . . . . . . . . . . . . . . . . . . . . Axial, 4-stage |
| Max Design Pressure Ratio/SLS: |    HP Rotor . . . . . . . . . . . . . . . . . . . . Axial, 2-stage |
|    Fan . . . . . . . . . . . . . . . . . . . . . . . . . . . . . 1.5:1 | Turbine Cooling . . . . . . . . . . . . . . . . . . . . Air cooled |
|    Compressor . . . . . . . . . . . . . . . . . . . . . . . . 14.5:1 | Exhaust Nozzle. . . . . . . . . . . . . . . . . . . Converg., fixed area, 695 sq.in. cold, 233 sq.in. hot |
|    Overall . . . . . . . . . . . . . . . . . . . . . . . . . . . 19.8:1 | Thrust to Weight Ratio . . . . . . . . . . . . . . . . . . 6.35:1 |
| Bypass Airflow Ratio . . . . . . . . . . . . . . . . . . . . . 6.22:1 | |

## Performance

Performance Ratings at Standard Sea Level Static Conditions for TF34-100

| RATING | THRUST (lb) | RPM (Gas Gen/Fan) | SFC (lb/hr/lb) | MEAS TIT (°F) | AIRFLOW (lb/sec) |
|---|---|---|---|---|---|
| Maximum (5 min) | 9,065 | 17,600/7,110 | 0.371 | 1,495 | 333 |
| Intermediate (30 min) | 7,990 | 17,180/6,720 | 0.369 | 1,405 | 314 |
| Max continuous | 7,335 | 16,910/6,490 | 0.355 | 1,350 | 301 |
| 75% Max Continuous | 5,501 | | 0.347 | 257 | 417 |
| Ground Idle | 550 | | 420 (max) | | |

## Size and Weight

| | |
|---|---|
| Length, Overall. . . . . . . . . . . . . . . . . . . . . . . . 100.0 in | Weight, Dry. . . . . . . . . . . . . . . . . . . . . . . . . . . 1427 lb |
| Diameter, Nominal . . . . . . . . . . . . . . . . . . . . 48.5 in | Weight, Wet . . . . . . . . . . . . . . . . . . . . . . . . . . 1443 lb |
| Max Radial Projection. . . . . . . . . . . . . . . . . . 24.25 in | |

## Applications

The TF34-100 powers the Republic A-10A. Other TF34 engine models power E-3A AWACS, S-3A Anti-submarine, and KS-3A Tanker aircraft. The CF34 commercial version powers the Canadair Challenger 601.

**Republic A-10A**
*(Photo courtesy of U.S. Air Force Museum)*

**Lockheed S-3A Viking**
*(Photo courtesy of U.S. Navy)*

# TF34

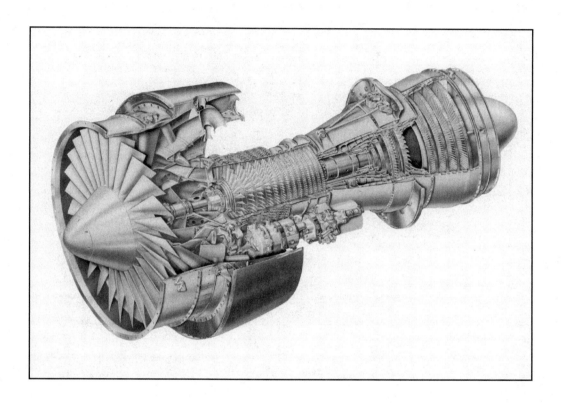

# TF35

**General Electric**

## Comments

The TF35 turbofan is the military version of the CJ-805 turbofan engine. General Electric became the first American engine manufacturer to test fly an all-turbofan-powered aircraft when two CJ-805-23 engines powered a modified Douglas RB-66. These aft-fan engines were converted from the basic J79 engines used in earlier turbojet flight test programs. Other versions of the CJ-805 include the CJ-805-1, -2, -3, -3A, -3B, -11, -13, -21, -23A, and -41.

## Features

Compressor.....................Axial, 17-stage
Pressure ratio ........................ 12.01:1
Air mass flow  ....................... 180 lb/sec
Combustion Chamber ................. Cannular
Turbine ........................ Axial, 3-stage

## Performance

Performance Ratings at Standard Sea Level Static Conditions

RATING
(take-off)

15,000 lb (6,800 kg) at 7,460 rpm

## Size and Weight

Length, Overall........................ 144.0 in
Diameter............... 32.0 in (with fan 53.0 in)

Weight ............................... 3,800 lb

## Applications

Used in the Douglas RB-66 and Convair 990.

**Douglas RB-66**

**Convair 990**

# TF35

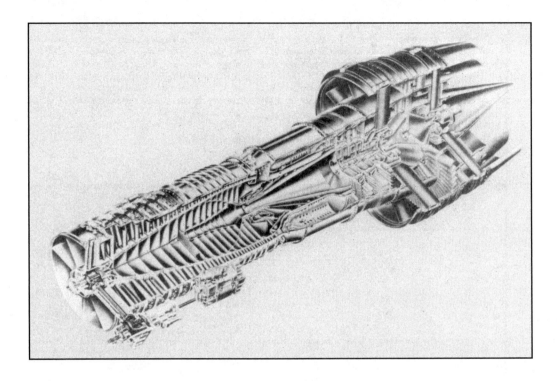

# TF37

**General Electric**

## Comments

The TF37 is a turbofan engine utilizing the J85 gas generator and an aft mounted fan for high takeoff thrust and relatively low fuel consumption. It incorporates a single-stage aft fan aerodynamically coupled to the gas generator, a fixed area concentric exhaust section, and an integrated hydromechanical control system. Provision is made for allotting separate inlet ducts to the gas generator and fan. Provision is also made for attaching a confluent tailpipe to the exhaust system.

## Features

| | |
|---|---|
| Compressor.......................Axial, 8-stage | Max Design Pressure Ratio/SLS: |
| Combustion Chamber.............Single, Annular, | Fan...................................1.91:1 |
| Thru-flow | Engine...............................6.7:1 |
| Turbine........................Axial, 2-stage | Exhaust Nozzle.....................Fixed Area |

## Performance

Performance Ratings at Standard Sea Level Static Conditions for TF37-1

| RATING | THRUST (lb) | RPM (LP/HP) | SFC (lb/hr/lb) | TIT (°F) | AIRFLOW (lb/sec. Core/Fan) |
|---|---|---|---|---|---|
| Maximum (15 min) | 4,200 | 16,500/8,610 | 0.690 | 1,700 | 43.7/84.0 |
| Military (30 min) | 4,000 | 16,250/8,400 | 0.680 | | 43.1/82.4 |
| Normal (cont.) | 3,500 | 15,680/8,160 | 0.670 | | 40.7/77.0 |
| 90% Normal thrust | 3,150 | | 0.680 | | |
| 75% normal thrust | 2,625 | | 0.700 | | 36.0/66.1 |
| Idle | 360 | 7,760/2,500 min | 1.389 | | |

## Size and Weight

| | |
|---|---|
| Length.................................74.0 in | Max Radial Projection...................16.2 in |
| Diameter..............................33.2 in | Weight, Dry............................670 lb. |

## Applications

Used in the Dassault Falcon (French) and the Sabre 75 aircraft

**Dassault Falcon**

**Sabre 75**

# TF37

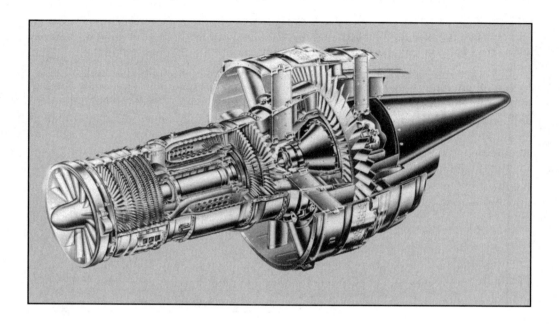

# TF39

**General Electric**

## Comments

The TF39-GE-1 is an 8:1 bypass, high-pressure ratio, dual rotor turbofan engine. The fan consists of a two-stage inner annulus flow-path and a single stage outer annulus flow-path. The high-pressure compressor is a 16-stage axial flow configuration with variable stators in the forward stages. The engine has an annular combustion system followed by a two-stage high-pressure turbine with film cooled blades in the first stage. The six-stage low-pressure turbine is coupled to the fan through coaxial shafting independent of the high-pressure turbine and compressor. Approximately 2200 lb of titanium is utilized in the engine construction. The fan and basic engine utilize separate nozzle exhaust systems.

## Features

Compressor (HPR) . . . . . . . . . . . . .Axial, single rotor
16-stage, w/variable fwd stator stages
Combustion Chamber . . . . . . . . . . . . .Annular, single
Turbine. . . . . . . . . . . . . . . . . . . . . . . . . . . .Dual rotor
   LP Rotor . . . . . . . . . . . . . . . . . . . . . .Axial, 6-stage
   HP Rotor . . . . . . . . . . . . . . . . . . . . . .Axial, 2-stage
with film cooled 1st-stage blades

Thrust to Weight Ratio . . . . . . . . . . . . . . . . . . . . 5.7:1
Max Design Pressure Ratio/SLS:
   Fan (LPR) . . . . . . . . . . . . . . . . . . . . . . . . . . . 1.45:1
   Compressor (HPR). . . . . . . . . . . . . . . . . . . . 15.55:1
   Overall . . . . . . . . . . . . . . . . . . . . . . . . . . . . 22.08:1
Fan Exhaust Nozzle. . . . . . . . . .Fixed Area, 3195 sq in.
Engine Exhaust Nozzle . . . . . . . .Fixed Area, 841 sq in.

## Performance

Performance Ratings at Standard Sea Level Static Conditions for TF39-1

| RATING | THRUST (lb) | RPM (LP/HP Rotor) | SFC (lb/hr/lb) | TIT LPR/HPR (°F) | AIRFLOW (lb/sec) |
|---|---|---|---|---|---|
| Take-Off (5 min) | 40,805 | 3,276/9,394 | 0.315 | 1,463/2,225 | 1,536 |
| Military (30 min) | 40,805 | 3,276/9,394 | 0.315 | 1,463/2,225 | 1,536 |
| Normal (cont) | 39,767 | 3,242/9,329 | 0.313 | 1,445/2,201 | 1,517 |
| 75% normal thrust | 29,824 | 2,842/8,866 | 0.304 | 1,268/1,968 | 1,320 |
| Idle | 2,404 | 9,37/6,469 | 1,198 lb/hr | 738/1,067 | 378 |

## Size and Weight

Length, Overall. . . . . . . . . . . . . . . . . . . . . . .203.11 in
Diameter, Nominal (Fan) . . . . . . . . . . . . . . .100.00 in
Max Radial Projection. . . . . . . . . . . . . . . . . . 54.64 in

Weight, Dry. . . . . . . . . . . . . . . . . . . . . . . . . .7475 lb
Weight, Wet . . . . . . . . . . . . . . . . . . . . . . . . .7499 lb

## Applications

Used (4 engines) in the USAF C-5A Heavy Logistics Transport Aircraft.

**USAF C-5A Galaxy**

# TF39

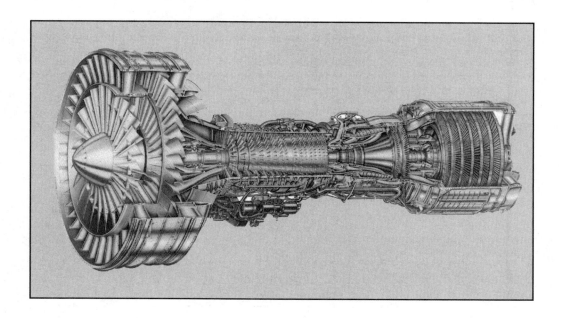

# TF41

**Allison**

## Comments

The TF41-A-1 is a flat-rated non-afterburning turbofan engine developed and produced as a joint United King-dom-United States effort. It incorporates a round fixed geometry inlet, a multi-stage low and high pressure compressor driven by low and high pressure turbines through coaxial shafts. It has an annular outer combustion chamber with ten thru flow can-annular inner chambers. It utilizes a bypass duct between the low pressure compressor discharge and the engine outlet which forces air at an 0.76:1 ratio to the high pressure compressor at the intermediate rating. It has an annular mixer for blending bypass air with the turbine exhaust gases. The direction of rotation for both rotors is counter-clockwise.

## Features

| | |
|---|---|
| Compressor . . . . . . . . . . . . . . . . . . . . . . . . Dual rotor | Bypass Airflow Ratio . . . . . . . . . . . . . . . . . . . . . . 0.76:1 |
|    LP Rotor . . . . . . . . . . . . . . . . . . . . . . Axial, 5-stage | Max Allowable Air Bleed . . . . . . . . . . . . . . . . . . 6.0% |
|    HP Rotor . . . . . . . . . . . . . . . . . . . . . . Axial, 11-stage | Max Rated Airflow/SLS . . . . . . . . . . . . . . . . 260 lb/sec |
| Max Design Pressure Ratio/SLS: | Combustion Chamber . . . . . . . . . . . . . . . . . . . Annular |
|    Fan . . . . . . . . . . . . . . . . . . . . . . . . . . . . . . . . . . 2.45:1 | Turbine Cooling . . . . . . . . . . . . . . . . . . . . . . . . . . . . Air |
|    LP Rotor (Intermediate . . . . . . . . . . . . . . . . 1.40:1 | Exhaust Nozzle . . . . . . . . . . . . . . . . Convergent, fixed |
|    HP Rotor . . . . . . . . . . . . . . . . . . . . . . . . . . . 6.13:1 | |
|    Overall . . . . . . . . . . . . . . . . . . . . . . . . . . . . . . 21.0:1 | |

## Performance

Performance Ratings at Standard Sea Level Static Conditions for TF41-1

| RATING | THRUST | RPM | SFC | MEAS EGT | AIRFLOW |
|---|---|---|---|---|---|
| Max Cont | (lb) | | (lb/hr/lb) | TEMP (°F) | (lb/sec) |
| Intermediate (30 min) | 13,200 | 8,600/12,550 | 0.629 | 1,008 | 251 |
| 90% Max Cont | 14,500 | 8,940/12,840 | 0.647 | 1,044 | 260 |
| 75% Max Cont | 11,880 | 8,270/12,270 | 0.615 | 975 | 240 |
| Ground Idle | 9,900 | 7,770/11,850 | 0.600 | 921 | 221 |
| | 680 max | 2,558/7,000 est | 1,132 est | | |

## Size and Weight

| | |
|---|---|
| Length, Overall . . . . . . . . . . . . . . . . . . . . . . . 114.17 in | Weight, Dry . . . . . . . . . . . . . . . . . . . . . . . . . . 3,175 lb |
| Diameter, Nominal . . . . . . . . . . . . . . . . . . . . 39.54 in | Weight, Wet . . . . . . . . . . . . . . . . . . . . . . . . . . 3,190 lb |
| Max Radial Projection . . . . . . . . . . . . . . . . . . 31.00 in | |

## Applications

TF41 engine versions are used in various models of A-7 aircraft.

**A-7**

**A-7**

# TF41

# TFE731

**Garrett AiResearch**

## Comments

The first turbofan engine in the TFE731 family, the TFE731-2 was prompted by the demand for a quiet, yet high performing fan jet engine for the executive jet market of the 1970's and 1980's.

## Features

Compressor . . . . . . . . . . . . . . . . . . . . . . Three-spool
    Fan . . . . . . . . . . . . . .Axial, one stage, gear-driven
    LP Rotor . . . . . . . . . . . . . . . . . . . . .Axial, 4 stages
    HP Rotor . . . . . . . . . . . . . . .Centrifugal, one stage
Max Design Pressure Ratio/SLS:
    Fan . . . . . . . . . . . . . . . . . . . . . . . . . . . . . . 1.54:1
    Overall . . . . . . . . . . . . . . . . . . . . . . . . . . . 15.0:1

Bypass Ratio . . . . . . . . . . . . . . . . . . . . . . . . . 2.67:1
Max Rated Airflow/SLS. . . . . . . . . . . . . . . 113 lb./sec
Combustion Chamber . . . . . . . .Annular, reverse flow
Turbine . . . . . . . . . . . . . . . . . . . . . . . . . . . . Two-spool
    LP . . . . . . . . . . . . . . . . . . . . . . . . . . .Axial, 3 stages
    HP . . . . . . . . . . . . . Axial, one stage, air-cooled IGV

## Performance

Performance Ratings at Standard Conditions for TFE731-2

| RATING | THRUST (lb) | RPM (HP/LP) | SFC (lb/hr/lb) | TIT (°F) | AIRFLOW (lb/sec) |
|---|---|---|---|---|---|
| Max SLS | 3,500 | 28,942/10,967 | 0.493 | 1,850 | 113 |
| Cruise (M 0.8, 40K ft) | 755 | | 0.815 | | |

## Size and Weight

Length, Overall. . . . . . . . . . . . . . . . . . . . . . . . 49.7 in
Diameter, Nominal . . . . . . . . . . . . . . . . . . . . 28.2 in
Frontal Area. . . . . . . . . . . . . . . . . . . . . . . . . .5.2 ft²

Weight, Dry. . . . . . . . . . . . . . . . . . . . . . . . . .625 lb
Thrust to Weight . . . . . . . . . . . . . . . . . . . . . . . 5.60

## Applications

Used (two engines each) in the French Dassault Falcon, the Learjet 26, and the Sabre 75 aircraft.

**Dassault Falcon**

**Learjet 26 / Air Force C-21**

# TFE731

# Acronyms and Abbreviations not in the Index

| | | | | |
|---|---|---|---|---|
| A/C | Aircraft | | CMC | Ceramic Matrix Composite |
| AAF | Army Air Forces | | CO | Carbon Monoxide |
| ACE | Advanced Chinook Engine | | Comm | Commercial |
| ACP | Airborne Command Post | | CT | Combat Talon |
| AEBG | Aircraft Engine Business Group | | CVI | Chemical Vapor Infiltration |
| | | | Dem/Val | Demonstration/Validation |
| AFSC | Air Force Systems Command | | DFRT | Demonstration Flight Rating Test |
| AGT | Aircraft Gas Turbine | | | |
| AGTE | Aircraft Gas Turbine Engine | | DIANE | Digital Integrated Attack Navigation Equipment |
| AIAA | American Institute of Aeronautics and Astronautics | | DOD | Department of Defense |
| APNASA | Average Passage NASA Computer Code | | DOE | Department of Energy |
| | | | DSARC | Defense System Acquisition Review Committee |
| APU | Auxiliary Power Unit | | | |
| ARPA | Advanced Research Projects Agency | | EGT | Exhaust Gas Temperature (°F or °C) |
| ARV | Army of the Republic of Vietnam | | EHI | E.H. Industries |
| | | | Eng | Engine |
| ASD | Aeronautical Systems Division | | EPA | Environmental Protection Agency |
| ASME | American Society of Mechanical Engineers, The | | EPM | Enabling Propulsion Materials |
| ASTOVL | Advanced Short Takeoff and Vertical landing | | ER&D | Engine Research and Development |
| ASW | Antisubmarine Warfare | | FN/WA | Specific Thrust or Thrust per Pound of Airflow |
| ATTAP | Advanced Turbine Technology Applications Program | | | |
| | | | FOI | Foreign Object Ingestion |
| AWACS | Airborne Warning and Control System | | FQT | Formal Qualification Test |
| | | | FSD | Full Scale Development |
| BAEL | Bristol Aero Engine Limited | | GFE | Government Furnished Equipment |
| BLISK | Blade & Disk | | | |
| BMW | Bavarian Motor Works | | GLCM | Ground-Launched Cruise Missiles |
| CADS | Cushion Augmentation Devices | | GM | General Motors |
| CAE | Continental Aviation Engines | | GOR | General Operational Requirement |
| C-D | Convergent-Divergent | | | |
| CIT | Combustor Inlet Temperature | | GPS | Global Positioning System |

| | | | | |
|---|---|---|---|---|
| GRC | Glenn Research Center | | MOS | Ministry of Supply |
| GTC | Gas Turbine Compressor | | MOU | Memorandum of Understanding |
| GTP | Gas Turbine Power | | MPH | Miles per Hour |
| He S | He (Heinkel), S (Strahl, or jet) | | MQT | Military Qualification Test |
| HEF | High Energy Fuel | | NAA | North American Aircraft |
| HIP | Hot Iso-static Pressed | | NAF | Naval Air Factory |
| HOST | Hot Section Technology | | NARDET | Naval Air Reserve Detachment |
| HPCC | High Performance Computing and Communications | | NAS | Naval Air Station |
| HPT | High Pressure Turbine | | NATC | Naval Air Training Center |
| HPTET | High Performance Turbine Engine Technology | | NATO | North Atlantic Treaty Organization |
| HSCT | High Speed Civil Transport | | NBMR | National Basic Military Requirement |
| HSR | High Speed Research | | NiAl | Nickel Aluminide |
| HTTB | High Technology Test Bed | | NOx | Oxides of Nitrogen |
| ICBM | Intercontinental Ballistic Missile | | ODS | Oxide Dispersion Strengthened |
| IGTI | International Gas Turbine Institute | | OMC | Organic Matrix Composites |
| IGV | Inlet Guide Vane | | P&W | Pratt & Whitney |
| IIR | Imaging Infrared | | PFRT | Preliminary Flight Ratings Test |
| IOC | Initial Operational Capability | | R&D | Research & Development |
| JATO | Jet Assisted Takeoff | | RAF | Royal Air Force |
| JSF | Joint Strike Fighter | | RBSN | Reaction Bonded Silicon Nitride |
| LEAP | Lockheed Electra Achievement Program | | RFI | Request For Information |
| LeRC | Lewis Research Center | | RFP | Request For Proposal |
| LIDS | Lift Improvement Devices | | RPM | Revolutions per Minute |
| LZ | Landing Zone | | RR | Rolls-Royce |
| M*A*S*H | Mobile Army Surgical Hospital | | S&T | Science and Technology |
| MAP | Military Assistance Program | | SAE | Society of Automotive Engineers |
| MAW | Military Airlift Wing | | SAS | Stability Augmentation System |
| Mil | Military | | SFC | Specific Fuel Consumption |
| MIT | Massachusetts Institute of Technology | | SGI | Silicon Graphics Incorporated |
| | | | SHP/WT | Shaft Horsepower-to-Weight |
| MMC | Metal Matrix Composite | | SiC | Silicon Carbide |

| | | | | |
|---|---|---|---|---|
| SLAM | Supersonic Low Altitude Missile | | U.S. | United States |
| | | | UAV | Uninhabited Air Vehicle |
| SOR | Specific Operational Requirement | | UK | United Kingdom |
| SRBSN | Sintered Reaction Bonded Silicon Nitride | | USAF | United States Air Force |
| | | | USMC | United States Marine Corps |
| SSME | Space Shuttle Main Engine | | USN | United States Navy |
| STOVL | Short Takeoff and Vertical Landing | | UTTAS | Utility Tactical Transport Aircraft System |
| T/W | Thrust-to-Weight | | UTTCO | Utility Tactical Transport Helicopter Company |
| TBC | Thermal Barrier Coatings | | VIFF | Vectoring in Forward Flight |
| TBO | Time Between Overhaul | | VL | Vertical Landing |
| THC | Total Unburned Hydrocarbons | | VSTT | Variable Speed Training Target |
| TiAl | Titanium Aluminides | | VTOL | Vertical Takeoff and Landing |
| TIT | Turbine Inlet Temperature | | W.U. | Whittle Unit |
| TMP | Technical Modernization Program | | WASP | Williams Aerial Systems Program |
| TOW | Takeoff Weight | | WESAG | Weapons Systems Advisory Group |
| TOW | Tube-launched Optically-tracked, Wire-guided | | WPAFB | Wright-Patterson Air Force Base |
| TPE | Turboprop Engine | | | |
| TPP | Total Package Procurement | | | |
| TSE | Turboshaft Engine | | | |

# Index

## Numeric Designations
9.5A (Westinghouse) 133, 136
19A (Westinghouse) 79, 133-136, 137, 230
19B (Westinghouse) 133-136
47 (Bell) 199, 201
208 (Bell) 538
240 (Convair) 231
304 (Pratt & Whitney) 267-268
501 (Allison) 233, 235, 239-241
580 (Convair) 235
707 (Boeing) 181, 183-186, 190, 241,
    332-333, 398, 554
720 (Boeing) 190, 490
727 (Boeing) 189-192
737 (Boeing) 186, 190-192, 444
747 (Boeing) 257, 327, 331-334, 338-339,
    438
767 (Boeing) 339
777 (Boeing) 398
880 (Convair) 184, 286
990 (Convair) 184, 558
2707 SST (Boeing) 464

## A
A-3 123-124, 151, 235, 237
A3D Skywarrior 138-139, 182, 478, 490
A3J Vigilante 283, 285
A-4 Skyhawk 124, 187-189, 232, 237, 244,
    351, 373, 486, 496
A-5 150, 237, 283, 359-360, 506
A-6 Intruder 187-189, 237, 324, 374, 486
A-7 237-238, 312, 373-374, 552, 564
A-9 436
A-10 Thunderbolt 233, 239, 243, 289-290,
    293, 360, 436, 556
A-12 265-267, 492
A-20 Havoc 64, 311
A-28 Hudson 64, 89
A300 338-339, 438
A310 335, 339
A320 257
A330 339
AAF. See Army Air Force
AAFSS. See Advanced Aerial Fire Support
    System
AAH. See Advanced Attack Helicopter

Aardvark. See F-111
acoustic fatigue 282
Adamson, Art 303
Adenstedt, Dr. Heinrich 202
Advanced Aerial Fire Support System
    (AAFSS) 208
Advanced Attack Helicopter (AAH) 222,
    224
Advanced Combustor Technology 400
Advanced Compressor Technology 399
Advanced Manned Strategic Aircraft
    (AMSA) 318
Advanced Materials Technology 412
Advanced Tactical Fighter 386-387, 424,
    454
Advanced Technology Demonstrator Engine
    (ATDE) 221, 550
Advanced Technology Engine (ATE) 313.
    See also Joint Engine Development
    Program
Advanced Technology Transition
    Demonstrations (ATTD) 394
Advanced Turbine Aerothermal Research
    Rig (ATARR) 390
Advanced Turbine Engine Gas Generator
    (ATEGG) 313, 371, 390, 393, 411, 413
Advanced Turbine Technology 403, 417
AEDC. See Arnold Engineering
    Development Center
Aero Propulsion and Power Directorate
    306, 384, 426
Aero Propulsion Laboratory 171, 173, 194,
    313, 327, 329, 383
Aerospatiale 191, 338
AFE. See Alternate Fighter Engine
afterburner 32, 76-78, 123-124, 147, 151,
    154-155, 163, 165-168, 178-181, 260-261,
    264, 267-273, 280-282, 284, 296,
    298-301, 304-305, 309, 311-312, 315-316,
    323-324, 371, 454, 478, 482, 484, 492,
    506, 508, 510, 552, 564
afterburner overpressure 168
afterburner roughness 168
AGM-28 486
AGM-86 379, 440, 442. See also Subsonic
    Cruise Armed Decoy (SCAD)

AH-1 Cobra 201, 208-209, 225, 544

AH-64 Apache 224-225, 386-387

Air-cooled Axial Turbine 55

air-cooled turbine engine 262

Air France 338

Air Launched Cruise Missile (ALCM) 378-379

Air Materiel Command (AMC) 73-74, 94-95, 97-98, 100, 123, 162, 168, 258, 260-261, 281

Air Parts Ltd. 251

Air Research & Development Command (ARDC) 258, 260-261

Air Turbine Starter (ATS) 245

Airbus 327. *See also* A300, A310, A320, A330

AiResearch 84, 244, 246-249, 251, 254, 566. *See also* ATF3, ATS35, F109, GTC43/44, GTCP85-91, GTP50, GTP70, GTP85, T76, T76/TPE331, TFE731, TPE331

airflow distortion 311

ALCM. *See* Air Launched Cruise Missile

Alitalia 338

Allen, Sidney 136

AlliedSignal 84, 200, 245, 250, 385, 393-394. *See also* AiResearch

Allis-Chalmers 71, 78-81, 143-144

Allison 70, 84, 122-125, 147, 149-151, 173, 200, 227-244, 259-260, 313, 384-385, 394, 418, 426, 472, 476, 550. *See also* J33, J35, J71, T38, T40, T56, T63, T406, TF41, YC-131, 501

All-Nickel Compressor 414

Alouette II. *See* Lark

Alternate Fighter Engine (AFE) 322

AMC. *See* Air Materiel Command

American Airlines 184, 240-241, 336

AMSA. *See* Advanced Manned Strategic Aircraft

Analysis and Design Technology 419

Andrew Willgoos Laboratory 161, 174

Andrews Air Force Base 236, 358

annular combustor 133, 137, 170, 203,214, 263, 280, 287, 295, 301, 314, 318, 333, 336-337, 356, 370, 400, 419, 448, 488, 492, 506, 514, 516

Apache. *See* AH-64

AQM-34 379, 498

Arado Ar 234 53

ARDC. *See* Air Research & Development Command

Armstrong Siddeley 5, 18-19, 136

Army Air Force (AAF) 33, 89, 92-103, 111-114, 116, 119-120, 122, 124-126, 143-145, 147-149, 152-153, 161, 170, 175, 197, 202, 208, 229-230, 245, 344, 368

Army Aviation Center 200

Army Aviation Directorate 201-202

Army Materiel Development and Readiness Command 223

Army Tactical Mobility Requirements Board 201

Arnold, General Henry H. "Hap" 32-33, 60, 67, 78, 83, 96, 111-113, 143

Arnold Engineering Development Center (AEDC) 90-92, 95, 101-107, 262, 300, 306, 330, 421

Artouste turboshaft 369

Aspin ducted turbofan 369

AST 410, 420

Astroloy 288

ATARR. *See* Advanced Turbine Aerothermal Research Rig

ATDE. *See* Advanced Technology Demonstrator Engine

ATE. *See* Advanced Technology Engine

ATEGG. *See* Advanced Technology Engine Gas Generator

ATF. *See* Advanced Tactical Fighter

ATF3 engine 430-431

ATLAS 338.

atomized fuel injection 18

ATS35 starter (AiResearch) 245

ATTD. *See* Advanced Technology Transition Demonstrations

Attinello, Dr. John 359

Austenal Laboratories 66-67

Autogyro Schools 197

AV-8 Harrier 342-363, 458

Avco-Lycoming 202, 205, 210, 225, 227. *See also* Lycoming, Textron Lycoming

Aviation Gas Turbine Division 131, 134, 138

Avro Lancaster Bomber 161

AWACS 244, 290, 556. *See also* E-3A

axial compressor 42, 47-48, 50, 54, 63, 73, 78, 94-95, 143, 145, 149, 187, 191, 202,

210, 245, 371, 376, 399, 442, 464, 468, 478, 492, 508, 536
axial turbine 4, 211, 247, 370, 375, 377-378, 442, 470, 472, 486, 516, 526, 542
axial turbojet 4, 34, 48, 50, 53, 63, 71, 93, 120, 131, 135, 138, 144, 147, 162, 164, 183, 280, 343
axial-centrifugal compressor 202, 210, 222, 522, 524
axial-flow turboprop 76, 144, 170, 243, 520
Axi-Nozzle 409

# B

B.23 engine 115, 117
B.26 engine 26-27, 30
B-1 bomber 318, 320, 379, 434
B-2 bomber 452
B-17 Flying Fortress 64, 68, 89, 170, 231-233, 235
B-24 Liberator 64, 68
B-25 Mitchell 64
B-26 Marauder 64, 248
B-29 Superfortress 64, 68, 149, 153, 180
B-36 bomber 75, 153, 155-156, 180, 281, 482
B-45 bomber 149, 153, 187-188, 190, 280, 476, 482
B-47 Stratojet 142, 149, 154, 156, 174, 288, 476, 482
B-50 bomber 178
B-52 Stratofortress 74, 172, 174-175, 177-179, 181, 183-184, 295, 298, 330, 333, 373, 377, 554
B-57 Canberra 343, 494, 496, 554
B-58 Hustler 258, 278, 280-282, 284, 506
B-61 missile 124
B-66 Skywarrior 182, 500, 558
B-70 Valkyrie 258, 260-264, 267, 275, 292, 510
BAC 111 190
Bachem Ba 349 47
Bachle, Carl F. 368-370
Bader, Paul 52
BAe 146 aircraft 213.
BAEL. *See* Bristol Aero Engine Limited
Baker, Lieutenant Colonel Bud 357, 359
Baldwin, Sir John 4
Banks, Air Commodore Francis Rodwell 368

Banshee. *See* F2H
Barney, Joe 235
Bartels & Becker Repair Shop 42
Barthelemy, Dr. Robert 383
Barton, B. 25
Baseler, Richard 170
Baumann, K. 36
BE.26 Orpheus engine 343
BE.53 engine 346-347, 351-352
Beardsley, Guy Jr. 165
bearing failure 21, 135, 151, 168
Beaverbrook, Lord 18
Beck, General A. J. 42-43, 359
Bedford, A. W. 352, 357
Beech 250-251. *See also* MQM-107
Belitz, Friedrich 203
Bell, Lawrence D. 113
Bell Aircraft 34, 93-94, 113-114, 199-201, 208, 222, 224, 302. *See also* 47, 208, AH-1, H-40, HH-1K, NUH-1E, OH-13, P-59, TH-1F, TH-L, UH-1, X-14, XH-40, XP-59, YH-40, YUH-1
Bell/ARPA 377
Bendix speed density control 150, 163
Benson, John 114-115, 127
Bentele, Dr. Max 54-55
Berkey, Don 328
Berkner, Hans 202
Berlin Airlift 229
Betz, Albert 48
Betz, Stanley 237
Bf 109 47
Bielitz, Dr. Friedrich 202
Birmann, Rudolph 79-81
Black Hawk. *See* UH-60A
Blackbird. *See* SR-71
bleed bypass cycle 270-272
blisk. *See* integral blade and disk
Blohm und Voss 55
Blue Angels 189
BMW 003 52-53,55
Boeing 64, 68, 74, 89, 149, 154, 158, 170, 174-175, 178-179, 182-186, 189-194, 201, 205, 208, 211-213, 215-217, 222, 224, 226-227, 234, 237, 241, 257-260, 280-281, 290, 292, 310, 327, 331-334, 338-340, 378-379, 398. *See also* 707, 720, 727, 737, 747, 767, 777, 2707, AGM-86, B-17, B-29, B-47, B-50, B-52,

C-135, E-3A, E-4, KC-135, SST, T60, XB-52, XB-55
Boeing Vertol 201, 205, 208, 212, 217. *See also* CH-21, CH-46, CH-47, H-21, UH-46D, V-107, VZ-2
Bowers, Peter M. 178, 186
Bozzoni, G. B. 33, 113
BQM-74C drone 514
Bramson, M. L. 6, 12, 18
Brandt, Maj Carl 33, 112
Braniff Airlines 241
Brayton Cycle 173
Bristol Aero Engine Limited (BAEL) 5, 36, 343-347, 349-356, 362. *See also* BE.26, BE.53, Olympus, Orion, Orpheus, Pegasus
Bristol Siddeley Engines 350-351
British Aerospace (BAe) 351, 355, 361-362. *See also* AV-8, Harrier
British Air Commission 33
British Air Ministry 4, 6, 8, 12, 18-19, 36, 112-113, 368
British Aircraft 19, 5, 7, 9, 11, 13, 15, 17, 21, 23, 27, 29, 31, 33, 37-39, 126
British Institution of Mechanical Engineers 12
British Thomson-Houston (BTH) 5-11, 13, 16-20, 22-25, 36, 44
Bronco. *See* OV-10
Broughton, Colonel J. M. 359
Brown, W. H. 85
Brown-Boveri 12, 79
Browne, Sam 35
Bruckmann, Bruno 56
brush seals 405
BTH. *See* British Thomson-Houston
BuAe. *See* Bureau of Aeronautics
Buckingham Study 76
Buckner, Howard 249
Buechel, Joe 296
Buffalo 220, 375
Bulman, G. P. 16, 23, 25
Bureau of Aeronautics 61, 78, 131-132, 138-141, 162, 174, 218, 233, 246
Bureau of Standards (U.S.) 77-78, 330
Burgess, Neil 152, 155, 279, 283
Burke, Woodward 135
Bush, Dr. Vannevar 78, 111-112
bypass duct 315, 410, 416, 564

# C

C-5 Galaxy 190, 193, 326, 330-332, 334, 562
C-9A Nightingale 191
C-9B Skytrain 191
C-17 Globemaster 450
C-21 transport 566
C-97 transport 241
C-119 transport 236
C-123 transport 301
C-130 Hercules 193, 200, 228-229, 235-241, 243-244, 526
C-131 transport 235-236, 240
C-133 Cargomaster 170, 520
C-135 transport 178, 320, 444, 490, 554
C-137 transport 554
C-141 Starlifter 193, 554
C355 metal alloy 373
CAA. *See* Civil Aviation Administration
CAESAR. *See* Component and Engine Structural Assessment Research
Cambridge University 6, 8
Camm, Sir Sidney 346-347, 350
Campbell, Kenneth 69
Campini, Secondo 77
Campini ducted fan 77
can-annular burners 191
Canadair 301. *See also* Challenger 600, Challenger 601, CL89
Canberra. *See* B-57
Caproni-Campini aircraft 77
Cargo Experimental-Heavy Logistics System (CX-HLS) 193, 327, 333
Cargomaster. *See* C-133
Caribou. *See* CV-2
Carroll, Brigadier General Frank 93-94, 96
Carter, George 14, 33, 112
casualty evacuation (CASEVAC) 198-199, 207
Central Intelligence Agency (CIA) 265-266
centrifugal compressor 4, 7, 42, 50, 70, 78, 89, 91, 94, 117, 119-120, 143, 202, 222, 225, 246, 250, 345-346, 370, 373, 375-376, 378, 399-400, 446, 470, 472, 480, 522, 524, 530, 542
centrifugal turbojet 63, 94, 117, 120, 125, 148-149, 162, 164, 168-170
Century-Series fighters 178
Ceramic Matrix Composite 401, 416, 417, 427

Cessna Aircraft 369-370. *See also* T-37
CF6 engine 301, 327, 331, 334-340, 336-339
CF700 engine 301-302, 331
CFB. *See* Chemical Fuel Bomber
CFD. *See* Computational Fluid Dynamics
CFM International. *See* F108 engine
CH-21 Shawnee 200
CH-34 Choctaw 200
CH-37 Mojave 200
CH-46 Sea Knight 215-216, 360, 528
CH-47 Chinook 208, 211-213, 226, 524
CH-53 Jolly Green Giant/Sea Stallion 220-221, 360, 534
Challenger 600 213
Challenger 601 556
Chamberlin, Steven J. 289-290, 293, 426
Chance Vought. *See* F7U, F8U, Vought
Chaplin, Roy 350
Chapman, Colonel Willis 345-346, 351
Charles, Robert H. 193
Charles Plan 193. *See also* total package procurement
Chemical Fuel Bomber (CFB) 184
Chenoweth, Opie 176
Chidlaw, General Benjamin W. 83, 112, 114, 116
Chinook. *See* CH-47
Choctaw. *See* CH-34
CIA. *See* Central Intelligence Agency
CIP. *See* Component Improvement Program
Civil Aviation Administration (CAA) 216, 240
CJ610 engine 301-302, 331
CJ805 engine 184, 286, 301-302, 327, 331, 335
CL89 drone 375
Clark, Eugene 202
Coar, Richard 161-163, 165, 174-176, 178, 183
Cobra. *See* AH-1
Cohu, LaMotte T. 72
COIN. *See* Counter-insurgency Aircraft
Cold War 257
Collier Trophy 181, 266, 379
Collingham 6
Combustion Panel 28
Combustor Diffuser 415
Combustor Dome 402
Comet 183-185

Commercial Engine Projects 301, 331
Component and Engine Structural Assessment Research (CAESAR) 394
Component Improvement Program, Air Force (CIP) 303, 314, 319, 337
composites 50, 224, 396, 401, 406-407, 409, 413, 415-418, 427
compressor disks and blades failure 203
Compressor Research Facility, Air Force (CRF) 390, 422
computational fluid dynamics 386, 396, 398, 420, 425
Connolly, Vice Admiral Tom 357
Consolidated *See* B24 Liberator
Consolidated Vultee Aircraft Corporation 145-146, 280. *See also* Convair; XP-81
Constant, Edward 59, 143, 164
Constant, Dr. Hayne 11, 13-14, 27, 30, 35
Continental Motors 84, 90, 239, 368-371, 373, 395. *See also* Marbore, Teledyne CAE
Convair 180, 232-235, 280-282, 284, 378. *See also* 240, 580, 880, 990, B-36, C-131, F-102, F-106, R3Y-1, Super 580, T-29, Turboliner, VC-131H, XFY-1, XP5Y
convection cooling 272, 336
Conway engines 184
core-driven fan 397, 399
Cornell, W. G. 277, 291
Corsair 64, 132, 312
Cougar. *See* F9F-6
Counter-insurgency Aircraft (COIN) 247-248, 250
Cox, Dr. Roxbee 18-19, 23-24, 27, 29, 33, 36, 112
Craft, Albert 73, 213
Craigie, Brigadier General L. C. 98, 100
Crater, Bill 73
Crawford, Brigadier General A. R. 100
CRF. *See* Compressor Research Facility
Cripps, Sir Stafford 30-31, 34
Crites, Sherman 296
Cronidor 15 406
cruise missile 226, 242, 366-369, 371-373, 375, 377-379, 381, 386-387, 390, 442
Crusader. *See* F8U
CT7-6 engine 225
CT58-100 engine 216
CTF39 engine 331

Curtiss-Wright 113, 145, 154, 173, 176, 222, 284. *See also* J65, P-40
Cutlass. *See* F7U
CV-2 Caribou 202, 220
CV-HELO 548
CX-HLS. *See* Cargo Experimental-Heavy Logistics System
CXX 327-328, 331-332. *See also* Cargo Experimental-Heavy Logistics System

**D**

D17 Project 155
Daimler-Benz 47, 55
DARPA. *See* Defense Advanced Research Projects Agency
Dassault 560, 566. *See also* Falcon 10, Falcon 200, Mercure
DC-3 190
DC-5 190
DC-7 186, 190
DC-8 181, 184-185, 190, 332, 398, 444, 554
DC-9 186, 190-192
DC-10 334, 336-339, 438
Decher, Dr. Siegfried 202-203
decoupling 233
decoy 295-296, 377
Dees, W. Stanley 272, 275
Defense Advanced Research Projects Agency (DARPA) 384-385, 389-390
Defense Plant Corporation 80
DeLaval blade 20
DeLaval Steam Turbine Company 80
Delta Airlines 190-192, 241
Delta Dagger. *See* F-102
Delta Dart. *See* F-106
Demon. *See* F3H
Department of Defense Appropriation Act 321
Derivative Fighter Engine (DFE) 312, 318, 320. *See also* F101
Derwent engines 17, 26, 70, 162
Desert Storm *See* Gulf War
Detroit Diesel Allison. *See* Allison
Deutsche Versuchsanstalt für Luftfahrt (DVL) 47
DFE. *See* Derivative Fighter Engine
Dibble, Charles 73
divergent phugoid (porpoising) sequence 233

Dix, Dr. Donald 384
Doll, Walt 65, 184
Donovan, Al 267
Douglas Aircraft Corporation 72, 138, 182-195, 234, 237. *See also* A-3, A-4, A-20, A3D, B-66, C-133, DC-3, DC-5, DC-7, DC-8, DC-9, DC-10, F3D, F3H, F4D, F5D, KC-10, XB-43, McDonnell Douglas
Drewes, Robert 313, 316, 320-321, 325
Drinkwater, Fred 362
Driscoll, Colonel Johnnie 344
drone aircraft 133, 299, 367, 369-371, 374-376, 498
dual-spool compression 174-175, 186, 333, 486, 490
dual-spool turbofan 460
dual-use technology 424-425
Duppstadt, J. P. 208
Durand, Dr. William 78, 93, 111, 131, 143-144
Durand Committee 61, 71, 78-79, 93, 131, 143-144
DVL. *See* Deutsche Versuchsanstalt für Luftfahrt

**E**

E. H. Industries. *See* EH 101
E.28 18, 13, 15-16, 19-21, 23, 27, 32-33, 52, 112
E.28/39 18, 13, 15, 19, 21, 33, 52, 112
E-2 Hawkeye 237-239, 243-244
E³ *See* Energy Efficient Engine Project
E-3A AWACS aircraft 290, 444, 556
E-4 aircraft 338-339
E-6A aircraft 444
EA-6B Prowler 189
Eagle. *See* F-15
Eastern Airlines 190, 240-241, 246, 336
ECCP. *See* Experimental Clean Combustor Program
Echols, General Oliver P. 83, 112
EF-111A Raven 552
Effusion-Cooled Liner 402
Egbert, Harry T. 279
EH 101 225
Electra 89, 235, 239-241, 243, 246.
EMDP. *See* Engine Model Derivative Program
Emergency Fighter Requirement 55

Encke, Walter  47-48

Energy Efficient Engine Project (E³)  398, 402

Engine Materials  412-418. *See also* Astroloy, C355, Ceramic Matrix Composite, Cronidor 15, Hastelloy, high-nickel alloy, Inconel, IN100, K-42-B, magnesium alloy, Metal Matrix Composite, Monolithic ceramics, nickel-chrome alloy, Nimonic, Organic Matrix Composite, PMR polyimides, Pyrowear 675, RR.56, Rex 78, SAE 6150, Silchrome No. 1, silicon nitride, single-crystal nickel aluminides, Stayblade, Stellite, Structural Ceramics, Timken, Tinidur, titanium, Titanium Matrix Composite, Udimet 700, Vitallium, Waspaloy, X-40

Engine Model Derivative Program (EMDP)  239, 244, 317, 319-320

engine problems. *See* acoustic fatigue, afterburner overpressure, afterburner roughness, bearing failure, compressor disks and blades failure, erosion, flutter, fatigue, Foreign Object Damage, foreign object ingestion, fuel nozzle failure, sand ingestion, stall, surge, throttle creep, turbine failures, unstart, vibration, yawing

English Electric Team  343

enhanced-flow compressor  399-400

erosion  206, 250, 348, 354

European airline consortium  337-338. *See also* KSSU, ATLAS

Evans, Howard  283

exhaust system technologies  409

Experimental Clean Combustor Program (ECCP)  402, 426

**F**

F.9/40 Meteor  18, 28, 112

F2H Banshee  137, 166

F3D Skyknight  137, 139

F3H Demon  138-140, 478

F-4 Phantom II  276, 285, 309, 416, 506

F4D Skyray  138-139, 182-183, 282, 304, 476, 490

F4U Corsair  64, 132

F-5 Freedom Fighter and Tiger II  168-169, 294, 303-305, 508

F5D Skylancer  182

F7U Cutlass  137, 139-140

F8U Crusader  181-182, 490

F9F Panther  160-164, 166, 168-169, 234, 472, 480

F9F-6 Cougar  484

F-11A Tiger  496

F-14 Tomcat  312-314, 319-320, 322-323, 372, 456, 552

F-15 Eagle  308, 312-319, 321-323, 372, 409, 424, 432, 448

F-16 Fighting Falcon  312, 315-323, 372, 409, 424, 432, 448

F-18 Hornet  324, 372, 409, 460

F-22A Raptor  454

F-80 Shooting Star  63, 94-95, 122-123, 166-167

F-84 Thunderjet  149-151, 154-155, 257, 472, 476

F-86 Sabre  153, 155-156, 166, 180, 257, 482, 502

F-89 Scorpion  151, 472, 476

F-93 fighter  166, 169

F-94 Starfire  123-124, 166-168, 472, 484

F100 engine  104-105, 308-309, 312-322, 325, 394, 424, 432-433

F-100 Super Sabre  179-180, 267, 416, 490

F101 engine  105, 309, 312, 318-320, 434, 435, 444, 448

F-101A Voodoo  180-181, 490

F102 engine  436-437

F-102 Delta Dagger  180, 267

F103 engine  438-439

F-104 Starfighter  263, 280, 282, 284-285, 506

F-105 Thunderchief  267, 504

F106 engine  440-441

F-106 Delta Dart  180, 267

F107 engine  366-368, 375, 377-380, 442-443

F108 engine  444-445

F-108 Rapier  261-262, 266

F109 engine  446-447, 550

F110 engine  105, 309, 312, 317-318, 320, 322-323, 394, 424, 448-449, 552

F-111 Aardvark  310-313, 552

F112 engine  366, 368, 379

F117 engine  450-451

F118 engine  452-453

F119 engine  394, 418, 422, 424, 454-455

F401 engine  313-314, 456-457

F402 engine 342-343, 356-357, 361, 458-459

F404 engine 305, 309, 318, 323-324, 460-461

F405 engine 462-463

FAA. *See* Federal Aviation Administration

FADEC. *See* full authority digital electronic control

FADF. *See* Fleet Air Defense Fighter

Fairchild 237, 296, 370. *See also* C-119, C-123

Fairchild-Hiller Heli Porter 251

Fairchild Republic. *See* A-10

Falcon 10 302

Falcon 200 430

Falk and Partners 6, 9, 239

Fang. *See* N-102

Farren, W. S. 10, 13, 16

fatigue 31, 181, 186, 273, 316, 329, 403, 406, 421-422

Federal Aviation Administration (FAA) 186, 190-192, 201, 240-241, 251-252, 298-302, 333-334, 336-339, 398

Fernberger, John M. 219, 253

Fetters, Jack 235

FH-1 Phantom 82, 134, 468

Fiat 220, 225, 339. *See also* G91

Fielding, G. B. R. 23

Fighting Falcon. *See* F-16

Finnair 190

Fireball. *See* FR-1

Firebee drone 369-372

Firth Vickers 8, 13

Fischer, Lee 303, 328

FJ-2 aircraft 482

Fleet Air Defense Fighter (FADF) 309

Fleet Life Extension Program (FLEX) 209

Floatwall 400-401

Flock, Art 237

Flugsport 12

flutter 314

Flying Fortress. *See* B-17

Flying Wing. *See* YB-49

Focke-Wulf 55

FOD. *See* foreign object damage

Folland. *See* Gnat

foreign object damage (FOD) 324, 330

foreign object ingestion 249, 450

Fottinger, Professor Hermann 44

Fozard, John 350, 355-357

FR-1 Fireball 82, 146

Francillon, Rene 162, 193-194, 237

Franz, Dr. Anselm 56, 202-203

Fraser & Chalmers 19

Freedom Fighter. *See* F-5

Freeman, Sir Wilfred 18-19, 29

Friedrich, Dr. Rudolph 53, 202-203

Fritz, John 52, 304

fuel nozzle failure 168

full authority digital electronic control (FADEC) 407

FYF-93 aircraft 484

# G

G91 fighter 344

Galaxy. *See* C-5

GAM-72 Green Quail decoy 295-296, 298, 300

Garrett, Cliff 245-246

Garrett 84, 244-252, 384, 550. *See also* AiResearch, AlliedSignal, ATF3, T76, F109

Gas Turbine Collaboration Committee 24, 28-29, 83, 116

Gas Turbine Technical Advisory and Co-Ordinating Committee (GTTACC) 35-36

Gasser, Lieutenant Colonel C. D. 97, 100

Gaubatz, Art 231

GE. *See* General Electric

GE1 engine 512

GE1/6 engine 193, 328

GE1/10 engine 318

GE4 engine 464-465

GE9 engine 318

GE12 engine 221-222

GEBO. *See* Generalized Bomber Study

General Dynamics 180, 311, 317, 323-324, 379. *See also* B-58, F-16, F-102, F-111

General Dynamics/Convair. *See* Tomahawk

General Dynamics/Grumman. *See* F-111

General Electric (GE). 28, 33-34, 66-69, 71-82, 84, 90, 94, 111-126, 138, 143-156, 161-162, 173, 176, 184, 193, 200, 213-225, 230-231, 258-264, 278-291, 295-305, 313, 318-324, 327-332, 335-339, 384-385, 394, 398, 402, 417-418. *See also* CF6, CF700, CJ610, CJ805, CT58, CT7, CTF39, F101, F103, F108, F110, F118, F404, GE1, GE1/6, GE1/10, GE4,

GE9, GE12, GOL-1590, I-14, I-16, I-18, I-20, I-40, I-A, J31, J33, J35, J47, J73, J75, J79, J85, J93, J97, LM1500, MX2118, T31, T58, T64, T700, TF34, TF35, TF37, TF39, TG-100, TG-180, TG-190, X104, X24A, X30, X35, XJ101, XJ53, XJ93, XT58, YJ85, YTF39
Generalized Bomber Study (GEBO) 280-281
German Air Ministry. *See* Reichsluftfahrtministerium
GLCM. *See* ground launched cruise missile
Glenn, Maj. John 125, 143, 181, 383
Globemaster. *See* C-17
Gloster Aircraft 13-15, 18-22, 25, 28, 31-33, 111-112. *See also* E.28, E.28/39, F.9/40 Meteor
Gnat 343-344
Gnome engine. *See* T58
GOL-1590 engine 277-279, 286
Goldsbury, J. 117, 119-120
Goshawk. *See* T-45A
Gorton, Bill 162, 165, 184
Gotaverken 62, 75
Gotthold, Peter 55
Great Engine War 312-313, 320, 324-325
Green Quail. *See* GAM-72
Griffith, A. A. 4, 8, 30, 164
Griffith engine 26
Groom Lake 265-266
Gross, Robert E. 100
ground launched cruise missile (GLCM) 379
Grumman 161-162, 164, 166, 168-169, 187, 189, 205-206, 234, 244, 286-287, 310, 312. *See also* A-6, E-2, EA-6B, F9F, F9F-6, F-14, OV-1, S-2E Tracker, W2F, XF9F
GTC43/44 compressor 245-246
GTCP85-91 power unit 246
GTP50 engine 245
GTP70 engine 245-246
GTP85 turbine 246
GTTACC. *See* Gas Turbine Technical Advisory and Co-Ordinating Committee
Guenther, Siegfried 44, 48
Guenther, Walter 44, 46
Gulf War (Desert Storm) 213, 367, 374, 425
Gundermann, Wilhelm 44-46, 50, 57

Gunston, Bill 164, 175, 181, 183, 189, 279, 312
Gyroptere 345

# H
H-1 engine 94-96, 132
H-19 helicopter 198-200
H-21 helicopter 201, 205
H-34 helicopter 200-201
H-40 helicopter 201, 204
H-43 Huskie 204
Hague, F. T. 131, 136, 141
Hahn, Max 42, 44-46, 50
Halford, Maj H. 24, 36, 94-95, 132
Hall, A. A. 8, 90, 92, 108
Hall, Russ 125, 278
Hallion 275, 374, 379
Hamm, J. R. 136, 141
Hansa. *See* HFB320
Harland Ltd. 251
Harpoon missile 89, 368, 371, 373-374, 516
Harrier 342-363. *See also* AV-8
Harrison, Admiral 161, 174, 340
Hastelloy 66-67, 71, 114-115, 118, 121, 133, 287
Havoc. *See* A-20
Hawker Aircraft 346-347, 350. *See also* AV-8, Hunter, Kestrel, P1127, P1154, Sea Hawk
Hawker Siddeley 351, 355, 357-358, 361
Hawkeye. *See* E-2
Hawkins, Willis 90, 95, 237
Haynes Stellite 66-67, 71, 114
He 011 54
He 111 47
He 118 48
He 162 Salamander 47, 55
He 178 40, 46, 48-50
He 280 49-52, 54
He 343 53
He 500 55
He S 001 52
He S 006 53
He S 011 54-56
He S 1 44-46
He S 2A 45-46
He S 3 40, 48-50
He S 8 50-53
He S 30 48, 50, 53-54
Heenan, Major J. 33

HEF. *See* High Energy Fuel
Heineman, Ed  182, 187, 351
Heinkel, Ernst  43-45, 47, 53-54, 56
Heinkel Aircraft  44-56. *See also* He 011,
    He 111, He 118, He 162, He 178, He 280,
    He 343, He 500, He S 001, He S 006, He
    S 011, He S 1, He S 2A, He S 3, He S 8,
    He S 30
Heinkel-Hirth  52-55
Hemsworth, Marty  122, 328
Henderson, Dr. John  383
Hercules. *See* C-130
HFB320 aircraft  302
HH-1K helicopter  209
HH-60J Jayhawk.  548
Hibbard, Hall  90, 92, 94
Hicks, Bob  231, 235
high-bypass engine  193, 213, 287, 291, 320,
    327, 329, 331, 332, 334, 335, 337, 339,
    341, 398, 436, 438, 444, 450. *See also*
    BAe 146
High Duty Alloys Limited  8
High Energy Fuel (HEF)  262
high-energy fuels  259
high-nickel alloy  314, 333
High-Temperature Bearing Rig  405
High Temperature Materials Research
    Committee  24
High-Work Turbine  403-404
Hill, Homer S.  358
Hill, Richard  384, 386, 388, 390, 394, 412,
    424
Hiller, Stanley  197, 251
Hirth Aviation  52-55
Hives, E. W.  16, 19, 23, 26, 28-30, 36, 164
HMR-161 helicopter squadron  198
Hobbs, Leonard S.  75, 161, 165, 173-175,
    181
Hoffman Company  7
Hokanson, Harold T.  297
Holbrook, Gordon  235
hollow bladed fan  396
Holman, Jim  232-233
honeycomb construction  205
Hood, Ed  301, 331
Hooker, Sir Stanley  16, 19, 30, 164,
    343-347, 350, 352
Hooper, Ralph S.  346-347, 350-351, 355,
    357
Horn, Edward  329-331

Hornet. *See* F-18
Houdry  79
Hound Dog missile. *See* WS-131B
Howard, Alan  43, 143-144, 249, 283
Howmet Manufacturing  173
Howze, General Hamilton  201
HR2S-1 helicopter  198
Hudson. *See* A-28
Huey. *See* UH-1
Hughes  43, 224, 371. *See also* AH-64,
    OH-6A
Hun  179-180. *See also* F-100
Hunsaker, Gene  73-74
Hunsaker, J. C.  75
Hunter  351
Huskie. *See* H-43
Hustler. *See* B-58
hydrogen combustor  45

**I**

I-14 engine  68, 111, 117, 120, 122
I-16 engine  33, 68, 73, 82, 111, 117-122,
    148, 470
I-18 engine  68, 119-120
I-20 engine  68, 111, 119-120
I-40 engine  67, 71-72, 86, 111, 119-122,
    127, 148-149, 472
I-A engine  33-34, 68, 72, 110-111,
    113-118, 122, 466-467
IBR. *See* Integrally Bladed Rotor
ICE. *See* Increased Capability Engine
IEDP. *See* Initial Engine Development
    Program
IHPTET. *See* Integrated High Performance
    Turbine Engine Technology
IHPTET Consortium  389
IHPTET Goals  386
IHPTET Organizational Structure  384
IHPTET Phase I  388-389, 411
IHPTET Phase II  388-389
IHPTET Phase III  389
IHPTET Time Phases  385
Imperial College of Science and Technology
    28
Improved Performance Engine (IPE)  317,
    322-323
IN100  273
Inconel  118, 121, 177
Increased Capability Engine (ICE)  317, 404
Ingells, Douglas J.  171, 275

Initial Engine Development Program (IEDP) 313
inlet particle separator 223, 548
Innovative Structures Technology 407-409
integral blade and disk 222
Integrally Bladed Rotor (IBR) 397, 413
Integrated High Performance Turbine Engine Technology (IHPTET) 213, 382-426
intercontinental bomber 257-258, 260, 278, 284, 292
Intruder. See A-6
IPE. See Improved Performance Engine
Iroquois. See NUH-1E, UH-1
Irvine, Major Bill 112, 184, 261

# J

J30 engine 81-82, 130-135, 137, 161, 230, 468-469
J31 engine 82, 117, 119, 470-471
J32 engine 133
J33 engine 67, 71-72, 111, 119-125, 127, 148-150, 161-162, 167-168, 230, 472-473
J34 engine 136-137, 139-140, 162, 474-475
J35 engine 74, 120, 124-125, 139, 143, 147-152, 155, 162, 176, 230, 476-477, 482
J40 engine 136, 138-141, 174-175, 182-183, 367-368, 371-374, 478-479
J42 engine 161-166, 169-170, 177,183, 480-481, 484
J46 engine 136, 139-140
J47 engine 142-143, 147, 149-156, 158, 174, 177, 214, 277, 280, 482-483, 502
J48 engine 160-161, 163-171, 177, 183, 484-485
J52 engine 186-193, 339, 486-487
J54 engine 140, 488-489
J57 engine 104, 139, 170, 173-183, 267-268, 281, 309, 330, 333, 490-491, 554
J58 engine 163, 256-258, 264-269, 271, 273-274, 334, 432, 492-493
J60 engine 494-495
J65 engine 188, 284, 496-497
J69 engine 367-368, 370-372, 498-499
J71 engine 139-140, 176, 500-501
J73 engine 213, 279, 502-503
J75 engine 104, 183-184, 265, 267-268, 504-505

J79 engine 176, 184, 259, 263, 276-286, 291, 298, 300, 304, 323-324, 327, 506-507, 558
J85 engine 294-307, 327, 508-509, 560
J91 engine 184-185, 267
J93 engine 219, 257-258, 260-264, 292, 510-511, 534
J97 engine 512-513
J400 engine 514-515
J402 engine 367-368, 371-374, 516-517
Jacobs, Eastman N. 77-78
JAS 39 Gripen aircraft 324
Jayhawk. See HH-60J
JEDP. See Joint Engine Development Program
JEPO. See Joint Engine Program Office
JETEC. See Joint Expendable Turbine Engine Concept
Johnson, Clarence L. "Kelly" 90, 95-96, 357
Johnson, Harold K. 201
Johnson, Louis 137
Johnson, W. E. P. 4, 26-27, 30
Johnson, Wilfred E. 122
Joint Cruise Missile Project Office 378-379
Joint Engine Development Program (JEDP) 312-314
Joint Engine Program Office (JEPO) 314
Joint Expendable Turbine Engine Concept (JETEC) 390, 393-395
Joint Technology Demonstrator Engine (JTDE) 390-393, 416
Joint Turbine Advanced Gas Generator (JTAGG) 390, 392-394, 401
Jolly Green Giant. See CH-53
Jones, B. M. 6, 427
JT3 engine 173-178, 181-186, 189-190, 192, 267, 327, 334, 490, 554
JT4 engine 183-185, 267, 327
JT8 engine 186-193, 339
JT9D 193, 327, 332-335, 339
JT11 engine 265, 267-273
JTAGG. See Joint Turbine Advanced Gas Generator
JTDE. See Joint Technology Demonstrator Engine
JTF-14E engine design 193, 327, 332. See also JT90
JTF-22 engine design 313. See also F100
Jumo 004 52, 202

Junkers 47-48, 52, 55, 60-61, 202

# K
K-42-B alloy 67
K600-1. *See* H-43
Kalitinsky, Andrew 75-76, 78, 170
Kaman 197. *See also* H-43, K600-1, UH-2
KC-10 transport 338-339, 438
KC-130F-LM transport 238
KC-135 transport 178, 320, 444, 490
Keirn, Major Donald J. 33, 112-113, 116, 120
Kelsey, Harold D. 125-126, 154
Kestell, J. A. 25
Kestrel aircraft 349, 351, 353-356, 359, 362. *See also* Tripartite Squadron
King, RAF Flight Sergeant J. A. 33, 113
KLM 337-338
Knaack, Marcelle Size 258-259, 280-281
Knott, Jim 234
Kohn, Art 296
Krebs, Jim 328
Kroon, Reinout P. 131, 135
KS-3A tanker 556
KSSU 337-338

# L
L-100 aircraft 239, 241
L-133 fighter 62, 88, 90-95
L-188. *See* Electra
L-1000 engine 62, 73-74, 81-82, 84, 88-103, 105, 107
L-1011 Tristar 336
Laidlaw, A. B. S. 7-9
LAMPS MARK III helicopter 548
Lander, Professor 28
Landing Craft Air Cushion (LCAC) 213
LaPierre, C. W. "Jim" 125, 278
Lark helicopter 246-247, 540
Laser Doppler Velocimeter (LDV) 410-411
Lasley Turbine Motor Company 71
Lawson, G. W. 154, 298
LCAC. *See* Landing Craft Air Cushion
LDV. *See* Laser Doppler Velocimeter
LEAP. *See* Lockheed Electra Achievement Program
Learjet 301-302, 566
Lechthaler, Louis 295
Lee, John 184, 303, 328

Lehman, John F. 322-324
LeMay, General Curtis 258, 261, 281
Lenherr, Frank 296, 303
Lewis, Gordon 132, 346, 350
LHTEC (Allison and Garrett). *See* T800
Liberator. *See* B-24
Lightning. *See* P-38
Linnell, Air Marshal 24-25, 27-29, 33
Lippencott, Harvey H. 173
Lippisch, Alexander M. 280
LM1500 engine 286
Lock, C. N. H. 9, 154, 156, 213
Lockheed 84, 89-107, 167, 193, 236-244, 264-266, 280. *See also* A-12, A-28, C-130, C-141, C-5, C-97, CX-HLS, Electra, F-104, F-22A, F-80, F-94, KC-130F-LM, L-100, L-1000, L-1011, L-133, P2, P-3, P-38, P-49, P-80, RF-80, S-3A, SC-130B, SR-71, T-33, U-2, XF-90, XFV-1, XJ37, XP-49, XP-80, XT35, YF-12A, YC-130, YC-131, YF-22, YF-94C, YP-3V-1
Lockheed Electra Achievement Program (LEAP) 241
long chord compressor 262
Long Range Aircraft Propulsion Development Program 97
Lovett, Robert A. 112-113, 199
LTC1 engine 202
LTC4 engine 210-212
LTE4 engine 210
LT-X engine 202
Lubbock, I. 18
lubricants 269, 405
Lucas 19, 25, 28, 163
Ludwig Prandtl Institute 47
Lufthansa 338
Luftwaffe 47-48, 55-57, 63, 85, 354
Lunar Landing Training Vehicle 302
Lycoming 84, 200-207. *See also* F102, LTC1, LTC4, LTE4, LT-X, PLF1A-2, T53, T55, TF40, Avco-Lycoming, Textron Lycoming
Lyon, Colonel A. J. 33, 112

# M
MacFee, Fred 298
MACV. *See* Military Assistance Command, Vietnam
magnesium alloy 210, 480

Mandle, Richard J. 376

Manufacturing Technology 418

Marauder. *See* B-56

Marbore 343, 369-370

marine propulsion 134, 136, 143

Mars aircraft 234

Marsh, Bob 351

Martin. *See* B-26, B-57, Mars, Matador

Massey, Bernard 344

Matador missile 368

Materiel Air Transport Service (MATS) 199, 202

MATS. *See* Materiel Air Transport Service, Military Air Transport Service

Mauch, Hans 47, 60

May, Major Paul F. 94

McConnell, General John P. 201

McCutcheon, Major General Keith B. 356-357

McDermott, Jack 163

McDonnell Aircraft Corporation 82, 85, 134-135, 137, 139-140, 166, 180-181, 295. *See also* F-101A, F2H, F3H, FH-1, GAM-72, Harpoon, XF-88, XFD-1, McDonnell Douglas

McDonnell Douglas 224, 338, 358, 361-362. *See also* C-9A/B, C-17, DC-8, DC-10, DC-9, F-4, F-15, F-18, Harrier, KC-10, MD-11, MD-80, MD-82, T-45, YAV-8B, McDonnell Aircraft Corporation

McKinney, Marion "Mack" 351

McNamara, Robert 201, 264, 284, 309-310

McReynolds, J. H. 5

MD-11 aircraft 257, 339

MD-80 aircraft 192

MD-82 aircraft 192

Me 109 aircraft 63

Me 110 aircraft 63

Me 163 aircraft 47

Me 262 aircraft 47, 53-54, 57, 62-63, 82, 96, 372

Mechanical Systems Technology 405

Menasco Manufacturing Company 74, 81, 98-103, 108-109, 230

Mercure aircraft 192

Merlin engine 26, 69, 84, 251, 370

Mesko, Jim 205

Messerschmitt 47-56, 62-63. *See also* Bf 109, Me 109, Me 110, Me 163, Me 262

metal matrix composite 407, 413

Meteor 18, 20, 28-33, 47, 96, 112, 116, 119, 372

Metropolitan Vickers 15, 34, 36, 84, 132.

Meyer, Dr. Adolph 12

MH-53E Super Sea Stallion 534

MiG-15 aircraft 163, 166, 169, 180, 257, 372

Military Air Transport Service (MATS) 193, 202, 238

Military Assistance Command, Vietnam (MACV) 206

Miller, Colonel Tom 357-359

Ministry of Aircraft Production 13, 17-20, 22-36

Minty, Russ 100, 176

Mitchell. *See* B-25

Mitsubishi 63

Moellmann, Heinz 202

Mohawk. *See* OV-1

Mojave. *See* CH-37

Mondey, David 113

monolithic ceramics 415, 417

Mooney-Mitsubishi 250

Morre, Joseph 268

Moss, Sanford 71, 113, 143

MQM-74 376

MQM-107 373-374, 516

MTU 338-339

Mueller, Max Adolph 48, 50, 53

Muir, Roy C. 112

Mulready, Richard 268

Mustang. *See* P-51

Mutual Weapons Development Program (MWDP) 344-346, 350-353, 362

MX2118 engine 279

Myles, Bruce 357


**N**

N-102 Fang 298

N-156 aircraft 298-299, 303

NA-180 aircraft. *See* F-100

NACA. *See* National Advisory Committee for Aeronautics

NASA. *See* National Aeronautics and Space Administration

National Advisory Committee for Aeronautics (NACA) 61, 70-71, 75-79, 81-83, 93, 111, 116, 143-145, 167, 180, 400

National Aeronautics and Space
   Administration (NASA) 263, 274, 296,
   298, 351-352, 362, 383-385, 389-390,
   396, 398-399, 402-403, 410, 416-427
National Physical Laboratory Bearings 19
Naval Air Materiel Command 162
Naval Industrial Reserve Aircraft Plant 137
Navy (U.S.) 34, 56, 61, 71, 73-74, 76,
   78-83, 86, 93, 101, 116, 119, 122, 126,
   130-141, 143-146, 149, 160-163, 165-166,
   169, 174, 180-183, 187-189, 191,
   197-199, 209, 213-221, 224-225, 227,
   229-234, 236-239, 242-248, 251-254,
   258-259, 265, 267, 276, 282-283,
   285-291, 293, 309-310, 312-314, 318-319,
   321-324, 343, 354, 357-359, 361,
   367-368, 370-371, 373-374, 376-379,
   383-385, 389, 396, 422, 496, 516, 546,
   548, 552, 556
Neitzel, R. E. 277
Nene 161-164, 166, 343, 347, 480. *See also*
   J42
Neptune. *See* P2
Nerad, Tony 117-118
Nernst turbine 42
Neumann, Gerhard 277-278, 280, 328
Newill, Ed 123
nickel-chrome alloy 13
Nightingale. *See* C-9A
Nimonic 25, 27, 67, 115, 356
Nix, Major Tack 319
North American Aircraft (NAA) 64, 140,
   153, 155, 166, 179, 248-249, 258-263,
   266-267, 283, 292, 368, 371. *See also*
   A3J, A-5, B-25, B-45, B-70, F-86, F-93,
   F-100, F-108, NA-180, OV-10, P-51,
   P-86, RA-5C, XB-70, XF-86
North American Rockwell. *See* B-1
Northrop, Jack 72
Northrop 68, 72-74, 76, 81-82, 84, 89, 94,
   100, 289, 298-299, 303-304, 318, 368,
   374-376. *See also* A-9, B-2, BQM-74C,
   F-5, F-89, MQM-74, N-102, N-156,
   Snark, T-38, Turbodyne, XT37, YB-49,
   YF-17
Northwest Airlines 241, 334
NUH-1E Iroquois 204, 522
Numerical Propulsion System Simulation
   (NPSS) 420-421

**O**
Office of Air Armament 50
OH-6A helicopter 532
OH-13 helicopter 201
Olympus 176, 343, 346
Operation Bumblebee 198
Operation Forecast 327-328
Operation Hourglass 240
Operation Paperclip 63, 245
Optical Diagnostic System 411
organic matrix composite 396, 407, 415
Orion aircraft 89, 238-239, 242-244. *See
   also* P-3
Orion engine 345-346. *See also* Bristol
   Aero
Orpheus 343-348. *See also* Bristol Aero
Orr, Verne 322
Osprey. *See* V-22
OV-1 Mohawk 205-206, 248-250, 356, 518
OV-10 Bronco 248-250, 356, 542

**P**
P.1073 aircraft 55
P2 Neptune 220, 243
P-3 Orion 238-239, 242-244
P-38 Lightning 64, 68, 89-90, 96
P-40 Warhawk 63, 188-189
P-47 Thunderbolt 64, 68
P-49 interceptor 90
P-51 Mustang 64, 96, 118
P-59 aircraft 34, 83, 96, 118-119, 372, 470
P-80 Shooting Star 161, 245, 472
P-86 Sabre 166
P1127 aircraft 350-356, 362
P1154 aircraft 353, 355
Packard, David 360
Packard Motors 156. *See also* J47
Page, Colonel Edward R. 93-94
Palouste compressed air generator 369
Pan American Airways 161, 184, 302,
   331-332
Panther. *See* F9F
Parker, Jack S. 213, 260, 280, 295, 327-328
Parkins, Wright 184
Patterson Field 197. *See also*
   Wright-Patterson Air Force Base
Pavlecka, Vladimir 72-73, 84
Peach, John 249
Pederson, Gerard 283

Pegasus engine  342-343, 346-357, 361-363
Pennell, Maynard  184
people's fighter.  *See* Volksjaeger
Perkins, Kendall  135
Peterson, Victor  235
Petter, W. E. W.  343
Petty, Dr. James  383-384
Phantom.  *See* F-4, FH-1
Phelan, Art  73
Philippine Sea aircraft carrier 163
Piasecki, Frank  197, 222
"pin-type" blade fastener  298
PLF1A-2 engine  327
PMR polyimides  416
Pohl, Professor Robert W.  41-43
Power Jets Limited  6-36, 44, 47, 61, 76,
    112-113, 117. *See also* W.1, W.1.X, W.2,
    W.2 Mark IV, W.2/500, W.2/700, W.3.X,
    W.B23, W.B26;  Whittle, Sir Frank
Power Plant Laboratory (Army Air
    Force/Air Force) 68, 93-94, 98-100, 116,
    122, 175-176, 184, 200, 259
Powers, Francis Gary  264
Pracher, O. P.  231
Prandtl, Dr. Ludwig  42
Pratt, Perry  165, 170, 175, 184
Pratt & Whitney  70, 75-76, 113, 160-170,
    173-193, 231, 266-268, 327, 367-368,
    384-385, 390-391, 394, 402, 417. *See
    also* 304, F100, F117, F119, F401, J42,
    J48, J51, J52, J57, J58, J60, J75, J91,
    JT11, JT3, JT4, JT8, JT9D, PT-1, PT-2,
    PT6, PW4052, PW4084, ST9, T34, T45,
    TF30, TF33, XJ52, XJTF10A, YJ52,
    YJ57, YTF30, United Technologies
    Corporation
pregnant worm  203
Preliminary Flight Ratings Test (PFRT)
    187, 248, 260, 262, 280, 282-283
Price, Nathan C.  34, 84, 89-107, 174, 230
Prince, D. C.  277
Project Forecast  327-328
Project Red Baron  359
Project Zoom.  *See* high-energy fuels
Propulsion Directorate  173. *See also* Power
    Plant Laboratory
Pryor, Roy  155, 304
PT-1 engine  62, 75-76, 81, 170
PT-2 engine  76, 170
PT6 engine  248, 544

Puffer, Sam  112, 125
Putt  261
PW4052 engine  335
PW4084 engine  398
Pye, Dr.  10, 13-14, 17, 112
Pyestock  35
Pyrowear 675  406

# Q
Quesada, Elwood  241
Quiet Clean Short-Haul Experimental
    Engine (QCSEE)  398

# R
R3Y-1 Tradewind  233-234
RA-5C Vigilante  283
RAH-66 helicopter  550
ramjet-turbojet  50
Randles, W. A.  8
Ransome and Marles Bearings  19
Rapier.  *See* F-108
Raptor.  *See* F-22A
Rawlings  261
RB.37 engine  30-32
RB211 engine  334, 336, 339
reconnaissance  89, 169, 180-181, 220, 230,
    258-259, 264-266, 274, 281, 285, 351,
    354, 358, 367, 374-375, 494, 554
Reeder, Jack  362
Reichsluftfahrtministerium (RLM)  43,
    47-57, 60
Remotely Piloted Vehicle (RPV)  367, 374,
    512. *See also* YQM-94A
Rentschler, Frederick B.  161, 184
Republic Aviation  180, 345, 354. *See also*
    A-10, F-105, F-84, Lark, P-47
Rex 78  13, 25, 67
Reynolds, N. B.  5, 14, 112, 114-115
RF-8G aircraft  490
RF-80 aircraft  122
Ricardo Engineering Company  19, 23-24
ring rotor  413, 414
RLM.  *See* Reichsluftfahrtministerium
RM8 aircraft  189
Robey, Colonel Pearl H.  98
Robinson, M. G.  116
Rockwell Corporation  301-302, 318
Rogers, Ole  131, 201

Rolls-Royce 5, 11-24, 26-32, 35-36, 44, 62, 84, 139, 161-162, 164-165, 200, 244, 351, 426. *See also* Derwent, F402, F405, Merlin, Nene, RB211, Tay
Rosenthal, Sherman 296
Ross, A. A. 25, 27
Rotor Spin Facility, Navy 422
Rover 6, 13, 16-29, 33, 35, 44, 113, 115, 117
Rowbotham 36
Rowe, Brian 300, 303, 331
Royal Aircraft Establishment 8, 10-11, 13, 15-16, 18-19, 24, 27-28, 30, 34, 62
RPV. *See* Remotely Piloted Vehicle
RR.56 aluminum 8
Ryan, Claude 370
Ryan Aircraft Corporation 82, 145-146, 205, 252, 358, 369-371, 374, 385. *See also* AQM-34, Fireball, Firebee, FR-1, Scarab, XF2R, XFR-1, XQ-2A

## S

S-2E Tracker 286-287
S-3A Viking 288-289, 293, 375, 556
S-51 helicopter 352
S-61 Sea King 208, 215, 217, 528
S-62 helicopter 217
Sabena Airlines 338
Sabre 179, 267, 302. *See also* F-86, P-86
Sabre 75 560, 566
SAC. *See* Strategic Air Command
SAE 6150 66
Salamander. *See* He 162
Samuelson 6
sand ingestion 206
SAS. *See* Scandinavian Air Services, Stability Augmentation System
Sayer, Gerry 14, 21-22
SC-130B aircraft 238
SCAD. *See* Subsonic Cruise Armed Decoy
Scandinavian Air Services (SAS) 191, 337
Scarab 374
Schafer, Fritz 52
Schalk, Louis W. 266
Schelp, Dr. Helmut 47-48, 51, 53-54, 60, 245
Schlaifer, Robert 4, 59-63, 67, 71, 75, 78, 81-86, 89-90, 94, 116, 120, 131
Schmidt, Heinz 56
Schmidt, Marvin 297, 305

Schoneberger, William A. 241
Schriever, General Bernard A. 327
Scorpion. *See* F-89
Scott, Sir Harold 34
Scrimgeour, David 354
Sea Harrier 361, 364
Sea Hawk 347
Sea King. *See* S-61, SH-3, VH-3
Sea Knight. *See* CH-46, UH-46D
Sea Sprite. *See* UH-2
Sea Stallion. *See* CH-53, MH-53E
Seahawk. *See* SH-60B
Sens, W. H. 174
Setze, Paul 303
SH-3 Sea King 215, 216, 360, 528
SH-60B Seahawk LAMPS MARK III 225, 548
Shannon 232
Shaped Tube Electrolytic Machining (STEM) 259, 263
Shaw, Dave 200, 328
Shawnee. *See* CH-21
Shell Petroleum 18-19
Shooting Star. *See* F-80, P-80
Short Brothers 251
short-takeoff-and-landing (STOL) 206, 239, 248-250
Shoults, D. Roy 33, 112-114
Sidgreaves 26, 28, 30
Sikorsky, Igor 197
Sikorsky 197-201. *See also* CH-34, CH-37, CH-53, H-19, H-34, HH-60J, HR2S-1, MH-53E, S-51, S-61, S-62, SH-3, SH-60, UH-60A, VH-3
Silchrome No. 1 66
silicon nitride 406, 417
Simpson, Ernest C. "Cliff" 173, 175-176, 327
Sims, Tom 384
single-crystal blade 334-335
single-crystal nickel aluminides 415
Singleton, Dr. Henry 371
Siuru, Bill 209, 225
Six Day War 360, 372
Skanze, General 320, 384
Skunk Works 90
Skyhawk. *See* A-4
Skylancer. *See* F5D
Skyray. *See* F4D
Skytrain. *See* C-9B

Skyvan aircraft  251

Skywarrior. *See* A3D

Slay, General Alton D.  319

Small, R. E.  283

Smith, Arthur  165, 184

Smith, James H. Jr.  140

Smith, Lewis  132

Smith, R. G.  174

Smithson Tester  155

Snark missile  368, 490

solar afterburner  151, 166-167

Sondertriebwerke (Special Propulsion
  Systems)  47

Sonnenburg, Paul  241

South Philadelphia Works  134, 136, 141

Spaatz, Major General Carl  112

Spangler, Admiral Selden  132, 246

Sparkman, Captain James L.  122

Special Operations Forces  213

Speer, Ivan  246, 251

Spherical Convergent Flap Nozzle  410

splittered rotor  397

Sporborg, H. N.  17, 36

Squalus. *See* T-46A

SR-71 Blackbird  256, 258, 264, 266-270,
  272-275, 492

SST aircraft. *See* 2707 SST, supersonic
  transport

SST engine  301, 331

ST9  222

Stability Augmentation System (SAS)
  269-270

Stack  351

stall  31, 176-177, 207, 222, 263, 270-271,
  277, 297, 311, 314-315, 318

Standerwick  114

Stanley, Robert  116

Starfighter. *See* F-104

Starfire. *See* F-94

Stark  362

Starlifter. *See* C-141

Staurohr-Turbine-Luftstrahl (STL)  50

Stayblade  8, 13, 67

Steam Turbine Division (GE)  71, 78-79, 81,
  143-145

Stein  202

Stellite  66-67, 71, 114, 121, 133

STEM. *See* Shaped Tube Electrolytic
  Machining

STL. *See* Staurohr-Turbine-Luftstrahl

Stodola, Professor A.  79

Stoeckly  122, 125-126, 278

Stokes  136

STOL. *See* short-takeoff-and-landing

Strategic Air Command (SAC)  180, 258,
  260, 281-282

strategic bomber  75, 154, 178, 182, 257,
  318, 377-378

Stratofortress. *See* B-52

Stratojet  154

Streaker  373-374

Streid  120-121, 259

Structural Ceramics  417

Studebaker  156

Styx  372

Subsonic Cruise Armed Decoy (SCAD)
  Program  377-378. *See also* AGM-86A

Super 63  332

Super 580  241

Super Sabre. *See* F-100

Super Sixty  190

superalloys  415-416

supercharger  5, 7, 65-72, 79-81, 84, 89-90,
  112-114, 118, 120-121, 125, 145, 204,
  213

Superfortress  64, 68

supersonic transport (SST)  264, 309, 464

surge  22, 114-115, 118, 168, 206, 223, 247,
  269-272, 297, 306, 348, 356, 360, 376,
  500, 532

Swearingen Aircraft  251

Sweetman, Bill  334, 340

SwissAir  192, 335, 337

Swofford, Colonel Ralph  94, 114

Szydlowski, Josef  368

## T

T-29 transport  231

T30 engine  232

T31 engine  79, 82, 143-145, 147, 476,
  518-519

T-33 trainer  123, 298, 472

T34 engine  76, 161, 170, 520-521

T-37 trainer  369-370

T38 engine  229-233, 235

T-38 Talon  298-300, 508

T40 engine  229-235, 239

T45 engine  175-176, 178

T-45A Goshawk  462

T-46A Squalus  446

T53 engine 196-197, 200-210, 213, 216, 225, 227, 522-523

T55 engine 197, 210-213, 225-226, 524-525

T56 engine 228-231, 235-244, 252-253, 526-527

T58 engine 147, 197, 207, 213-219, 222, 226-227, 286, 289, 295, 298, 528-529, 534

T60 engine 530-531

T63 engine 532-533

T64 engine 147, 197, 217-221, 227, 287, 289, 295, 534-535

T65 engine 536-537

T67 engine 538-540

T72 engine 540-541

T76 engine 229, 244-245, 247-252, 254, 542-543

T76/TPE331 engine 244-245, 249

T400 engine 544-545

T406 engine 546-547

T700 engine 197, 221-225, 227, 548-549

T800 engine 550-551

TA-4B trainer 496

Tacit Blue 430

Taft, Undersecretary of Defense 384

Talon aircraft. *See* T-38

Tay engine 343, 484

Taylor, Phil 161

Taylor Turbine Corporation 162-163

T-cane design 203

Technical Policy Committee 36

Tedder, Air Marshal 17-18, 24

Teledyne CAE 368, 371-374, 379, 384, 442. *See also* F106, J402, J69, Marbore, T65, T67, T72

Textron Lycoming 200, 209, 384-385, 392

TF30 engine 309-312, 317, 319, 323, 552-553

TF33 engine 172, 178, 183-186, 290, 554-555

TF34 engine 277, 286-293, 556-557

TF35 engine 436, 558-559

TF37 engine 560-561

TF39 engine 193, 286-287, 326-331, 335-337, 339-340, 562-563

TF40 engine 213

TF41 engine 317, 564-565

TFE731 engine 446, 566-567

TFX Program 310, 312-313. *See also* Joint Engine Development Program

TG-100 engine 67, 71, 79, 81, 93, 144-147, 157, 518

TG-180 engine 71, 120, 147-150, 476, 482

TG-190 engine 149, 152-153, 155, 482

TH-1F helicopter 216

Thompson 114

throttle creep 273

thrust vectoring 359, 363, 409-410, 425, 454

Thunderbolt. *See* A-10A, P-47

Tiger. *See* F-11A

Tiger II. *See* F-5

Timken 133, 144

Tinidur 67

Tinling, J. C. B. 6, 23-25, 29, 34-35

titanium 115, 164, 177, 179, 181, 183, 187, 202, 219-220, 247, 250, 263, 314, 333, 336, 338, 347, 349, 353-356, 394, 396, 406-407, 486, 504, 562

Titanium Matrix Composite 406

Tizard, Henry 8, 20-22

Tobin, D. G. 18

Todd, D. M. 278

Tomahawk missile 366, 368, 378-379, 386-387, 442

Tomcat. *See* F-14

total package procurement (TPP) 193

Townsend, Guy 177

TPE331 engine 244-247, 249-252, 254, 542

TPP. *See* total package procurement

Tracker. *See* S-2E

Tradewind. *See* R3Y-1

Tramm, Pete 244

Trans World Airlines 68, 336

transpiration cooling 272

Travers, William R. 113-114, 121-122, 145-146, 153-156, 214, 218-220, 222, 259, 261, 264, 278-279, 286, 296-297, 301-303, 336

Tripartite Agreement 354

Tripartite Squadron 354. *See also* Kestrel

tri-passage diffuser 400-401

Trippe, Juan 184, 331-332

Tri-Wall Air Swirler 401

Tuffen, Harry 350

Turbine Engine Division 173, 175, 306, 327, 383-384, 426. *See also* Aero Propulsion Laboratory

turbine failures 314, 316, 334
Turbo Engineering Corporation 70, 79-80, 83
Turbodyne 72-74, 81, 84, 94, 100
Turboliner 230, 233, 235, 239, 251
Turbomeca 368-370
turbosupercharger 5, 65-69, 70-72, 79-81, 84, 89-90, 112-114, 118, 120-121, 125, 145, 213
Tweedie, W. L. 4, 17-18
twin-spool axial compressor 175, 191, 339, 456

# U

U-2 264-265, 490
Udet, Ernst 50, 52
Udimet 700 263
UH-1 (model 204) Huey 196, 201, 204-210, 216, 225, 522, 538, 544, 550
UH-2 Sea Sprite 209, 215
UH-46D Sea Knight 216, 528
UH-60A Black Hawk 224-225
Union Carbide and Carbon Corporation 66
United Aircraft Corporation 170, 174, 184, 194-195, 324
United Aircraft of Canada 544
United Airlines 336
United Technologies Corporation 171, 174, 194, 275. *See also* Pratt & Whitney
Universal Cyclops Corporation 66
University of Goettingen 41
Unmanned Air Vehicle (UAV) 386
unstart 263, 269-270, 274
Utility Tactical Transport Aircraft System (UTTAS) 222, 224
Utility Tactical Transport Helicopter Company (UTTCO) 205

# V

V-22 Osprey 546
V-107 helicopter 217
Valkyrie. *See* B-70, XB-70
Valli, Kurt 345
Vanderpool, Colonel J. 200
variable compressor 277, 279, 281, 285, 287, 291, 293, 510
variable stator experimental engine (VSXE) 263, 271, 277-280, 314

variable stator 214, 223, 286, 291, 304, 338-339, 444, 464, 506, 508, 562
Vauxhall Engines 19-20
VC-131H transport 236
VC-137 aircraft 554
vectored-thrust 343, 345, 347, 350-351, 353-354, 361-362
Vectoring in Forward Flight (VIFF) 357-358, 363
Verkamp, Frank 244
Vertical Take-Off (VTO) aircraft 211, 234, 348, 353
Vertical/Short Takeoff and Landing (VSTOL) 343-363, 432, 458
very-high-bypass turbofan engines 291-339
VFX program 310. *See also* Joint Engine Development Program, Advanced Technology Engine
VH-3 Sea King 528
vibration 28, 31, 42, 54, 72, 146, 176, 203, 231-232, 241, 252, 272, 282, 297, 306, 349, 411
VIFF. *See* Vectoring in Forward Flight
Vigilante. *See* A3J, RA-5C
Viking. *See* S-3A
Vitallium 67, 144-145
Volksjaeger (people's fighter) 55
Volpar 250-251
Volvo Flygmotor 189, 324, 339. *See also* JAS 39 Grippin, RM8
von der Nuell, Dr. W. T. 245
von Karman, Theodore 344
von Ohain, Dr. Hans Pabst Joachim 41-57, 59, 61, 84, 173
Voodoo. *See* F-101A, XF-88
vortex theory 9-10
Vought 64, 137, 139-140, 181-182. *See also* A-7, F4U, F7U, F8U
VSTOL. *See* Vertical/Short Takeoff and Landing
VSXE. *See* variable stator experimental engine
VTO. *See* Vertical Take-Off aircraft
VZ-2 experimental tilt-wing aircraft 205

# W

W.1 engine 18, 13-16, 19-23, 25, 27-28, 33, 113
W.1.X engine 18-23, 33, 113

W.2 engine  15-33, 35, 113, 115-118, 120, 132, 161
W.2 Mark IV engine  20, 23-24
W.2/500 engine  27-33, 35, 115, 117, 132
W.2/700 engine  31-32
W.3.X engine  26
W.B23 engine  17-18
W.B26 engine  17
W.U.  *See* Whittle Unit
W2F aircraft  243-244
W19 engine  67, 468
Wagner, Herbert  41, 47-48, 61
Wagner, Ray  187
Wagner, William  368
Walker, Chap  278
Walker, D. N.  23, 26, 33, 113
Walsh, E. P.  136
Warhawk.  *See* P-40
Warnemuende (Germany)  43-44
Warner, Donald F.  33, 113, 116, 118
Warren, Glenn  125, 143-144
Warsitz, Erich  49
Waspaloy  273
Watt, Wing Commander G. E.  33
Way, Dr. Stewart  131, 133, 241
Weapons System Advisory Group (WESAG)  360
Wegg, John  233
Weidhuner, Donald  202
WESAG.  *See* Weapons System Advisory Group
Westinghouse  34, 63, 67, 78-79, 81-84, 93, 116, 130-140, 143-144, 161-162, 173-176, 202, 232.  *See also* 9.5A, 19A/B, J30, J32, J34, J40, J46, J54, T30, W19
Westwind aircraft  302
Wetzel, Harry  246
Wheatley, John  235
Whetstone test facility  27, 29, 35
Whitcomb, Richard  180
Whittle, Sir Frank  4-36, 41-42, 44, 47, 56, 60-61, 67-68, 70, 72-73, 76, 81-84, 93, 96, 111-113, 115-118, 122, 124-125, 132, 143, 145, 161, 164, 170, 173, 203, 230, 343, 466, 470.  *See also* Power Jets Limited
Whittle Unit (W.U.)  6-11, 20
Whyte  15, 17-18
Wibault, Michel  345-346
Wilks, Maurice  16-17, 22, 29

Willgoos, Andrew  175.  *See also* Andrew Willgoos Laboratory
Williams, R. Dudley  6
Williams, Dr. Sam  375
Williams International  84, 226, 366, 368, 375-380, 384-385.  *See also* F107, F108, F112, J400, WR1, WR2, WR-5, WR-6, WR9-7, WR19, WR24, WR27-1
Williams Research.  *See* Williams International
Wilson, Al  141, 244
Wilson, Eugene  161
Wimmer, Roy  237
Wimperis, H. E.  8
Wolff , Harold  54
Woll, Edward  278, 295, 298-299, 303
Wood, Homer  134, 246
WR1 engine  375
WR2 engine  375-376
WR-5 engine  375
WR-6 engine  375
WR9-7 engine  375
WR19 engine  377-378
WR24 engine  375-377, 379
WR27-1 engine  375
Wragg, David  225
Wright Aeronautical Corporation (Wright Aero)  61-62, 69, 76, 84, 102-103, 106, 154, 180
Wright Field  61, 66, 68-69, 71, 73, 83, 92-100, 102, 108-109, 116, 120, 123, 145, 148, 174, 178, 202, 302.  *See also* Wright-Patterson Air Force Base
Wright-Patterson Air Force Base  122, 127, 157, 168, 171, 175, 194, 259, 261, 306, 316, 328, 383, 421-422, 426
WS-110A  184.  *See also* Chemical Fuel Bomber
WS-131B  187, 368, 486
Wuertembergische-Metall  54

# X

X-4 aircraft  468
X-10 aircraft  478
X-14 aircraft  351-352
X24A engine  278
X30 engine  278
X35 engine  278
X-40  288
X104 engine  295

XA3D aircraft 478
XB-43 aircraft 148
XB-52 aircraft 175, 178
XB-55 aircraft 280
XB-70 aircraft 260, 262-264, 267, 275, 510
XC-113 aircraft 518
XF2R aircraft 145, 518
XF4D aircraft 282, 304, 478
XF9F-1 aircraft 161-162
XF9F-2 aircraft 162-163
XF10F aircraft 478
XF-86 aircraft 153
XF-88 Voodoo 137
XF-90 aircraft 137
XF-92 aircraft 123, 468
XFD-1 Phantom 130, 134-135
XFR-1 Fireball 82, 146
XFV-1 aircraft 234
XFV-12A aircraft 456
XFY-1 aircraft 234
XH-40 helicopter 201, 204
XJ37 engine 92, 100-103
XJ52-P-1 engine 187
XJ53 engine 278
XJ93 engine 261
XJ101 engine 318
XJTF10A engine 311
XP5Y (Model 117) aircraft 232-233
XP-49 interceptor 90
XP-59 aircraft 93, 110, 113, 116-117, 466
XP-79 aircraft 468
XP-80 aircraft 96, 121-122
XP-81 aircraft 145-146, 518
XQ-2A drone 370

XT35 engine 82, 102
XT37 engine 103
XT58 engine 213

## Y

Yaffee, Michael 287, 292, 340
Yankee axial turbojet program 93
Yankee series engine 84, 131, 133-135, 230. *See also* J30
YAV-8B aircraft 361
yawing 282
YB-49 Flying Wing 72, 74
YC-130 aircraft 229, 235, 237, 239
YC-131 aircraft 235, 240
Yenne, Bill 85, 158, 190, 194-195, 227
YF-12A aircraft 265
YF-17 aircraft 318
YF-22 aircraft 386-387
YF-94C aircraft 167
YH-40 (model 204) helicopter 201, 204
YJ52 engine 187-188, 486
YJ57-P-3 engine 175
YJ85 engine 296, 298-299
YJ101 engine 305, 318
Young, Roger 165
YP-3V-1 aircraft 243
YQM-94A Compass Cope 512
YTF30 engine 311
YTF39 engine 329-330
YUH-1B helicopter 205
YUH-1D helicopter 207

## Z

Zimmerman, Don 235

## The History of Aircraft Gas Turbi
### ... A Trad

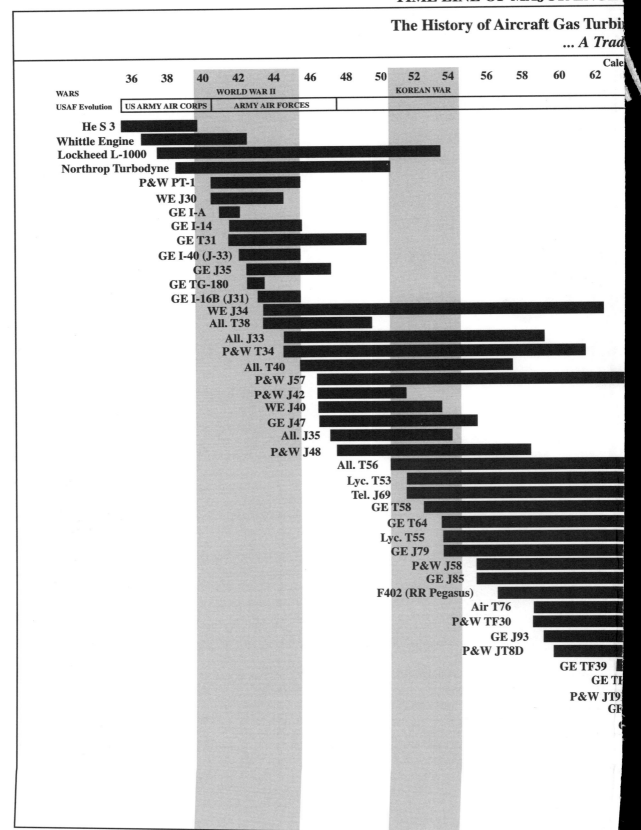